Source Books in the History of the Sciences
GREGORY D. WALCOTT, *General Editor*

A Source Book in Chemistry

Source Books in the History of the Sciences
GREGORY D. WALCOTT · *General Editor*

A Source Book in Astronomy
HARLOW SHAPLEY · *Director, Harvard Observatory*
Harvard University AND
HELEN E. HOWARTH · *Harvard University*

A Source Book in Mathematics
DAVID EUGENE SMITH · *Columbia University*

A Source Book in Physics
W. F. MAGIE · *Princeton University*

A Source Book in Geology
KIRTLEY F. MATHER · *Harvard University*
AND SHIRLEY L. MASON

A Source Book in Greek Science
MORRIS R. COHEN · *College of the City of New*
York and University of Chicago AND
I. E. DRABKIN · *College of the City of New York*

A Source Book in Animal Biology
THOMAS S. HALL · *Washington University*

A Source Book in Chemistry
HENRY M. LEICESTER · *College of Physicians and*
Surgeons of San Francisco AND
HERBERT S. KLICKSTEIN · *University of Pennsylvania*

Endorsed by the American Philosophical Association, the American Association for the Advancement of Science, and the History of Science Society. Also by the American Anthropological Association, the Mathematical Association of America, the American Mathematical Society, and the American Astronomical Society in their respective fields.

A SOURCE BOOK
IN CHEMISTRY
1400–1900

Henry M. Leicester

College of Physicians and Surgeons of San Francisco

AND

Herbert S. Klickstein

Edgar Fahs Smith Library in the History of Chemistry
University of Pennsylvania

FIRST EDITION

New York   Toronto   London
McGRAW-HILL BOOK COMPANY, INC.
1952

A SOURCE BOOK IN CHEMISTRY

THE MAPLE PRESS COMPANY, YORK PA.

Source Books in the History of the Sciences

GENERAL EDITOR'S PREFACE

This series of Source Books, conceived by the General Editor in the spring of 1924, has aimed, and still aims, to present the most significant passages from the works of the most important contributors to the major sciences during the last three or four hundred years. Source books in philosophy have been in use for at least half a century, while carefully selected source material, bearing about the same designation, has long been utilized in the fields of history, economics, ethics, psychology, and sociology. This series deals in a similar way with mathematics and the leading physical and biological sciences.

The general plan, as originally mapped, was to treat each major science in a single volume with as much finality of scholarship as possible from the Renaissance to the end of the nineteenth century. Eight or ten volumes were projected to appear as rapidly as might be consistent with sound scholarship.

In June, 1924, the General Editor began to organize an Advisory Board, which, when completed, was composed of the following members:

HAROLD C. BROWN	*Philosophy*	Stanford University
MORRIS R. COHEN	*Philosophy*	College of the City of N.Y.
ARTHUR O. LOVEJOY	*Philosophy*	John Hopkins University
GEORGE H. MEAD	*Philosophy*	University of Chicago
WILLIAM P. MONTAGUE	*Philosophy*	Columbia University
WILMON H. SHELDON	*Philosophy*	Yale University
EDWARD G. SPAULDING	*Philosophy*	Princeton University
JOSEPH S. AMES	*Physics*	John Hopkins University
FREDERICK BARRY	*Chemistry*	Columbia University
R. T. CHAMBERLIN	*Geology*	University of Chicago
EDWIN G. CONKLIN	*Zoology*	Princeton University
HARLOW SHAPLEY	*Astronomy*	Harvard University
DAVID EUGENE SMITH	*Mathematics*	Columbia University
ALFRED M. TOZZER	*Anthropology*	Harvard University

The advice and suggestions given by the members of this Board, several of whom are now deceased, have been of inestimable value.

In December, 1925, the General Editor presented this project to the Eastern Division of the American Philosophical Association, and it was turned over immediately to the Executive Committee with power to act. In the spring of 1926 the desired approval was forthcoming, and somewhat later the Association named the philosophers of the Board to serve as the committee, with the General Editor as chairman, in charge of this undertaking. In November, 1927, the Carnegie Corporation of New York granted $10,000 to the American Philosophical Association as a revolving fund to help finance the series. In December, 1927, the American Association for the Advancement of Science approved the project and appointed a committee consisting of Professor Edwin G. Conklin, Professor Harlow Shapley, and the General Editor as chairman to represent that Association in cooperation with the Advisory Board. In February, 1928, the History of Science Society officially indorsed the enterprise. Indorsements have also been given by the American Anthropological Association, the Mathematical Association of America, the American Mathematical Society, and the American Astronomical Society within their respective fields.

The General Editor wishes to thank again the members of the Advisory Board for their assistance while this undertaking was being launched and throughout its devious developments; the late Dr. J. McKeen Cattell for helpful advice in the early days of the project and later; the late Dr. William S. Learned for many valuable suggestions; the several societies and associations that gave their indorsements; and the Carnegie Corporation for the necessary initial financial assistance.

Two volumes, the *Source Book in Astronomy* and the *Source Book in Mathematics*, have been on the market for twenty years. The reception accorded these two and the subsequent volumes has been very gratifying. The usefulness of these books has been demonstrated.

Several years after the series got under way, the plan was extended to include *A Source Book in Greek Science* and *A Source Book in Medieval Science*. The former, edited by the late Morris R. Cohen and Dr. Israel E. Drabkin, was published late in 1948; the latter is in preparation. *A Source Book in Twentieth Century Science* (1900–1950) is projected, while a similar volume will appear, it is hoped, each half century thereafter indefinitely.

GREGORY D. WALCOTT

LONG ISLAND UNIVERSITY
BROOKLYN, N.Y.
August, 1950

Preface

THE task of tracing the development of modern chemistry in the actual words of the men whose work led to its growth is fascinating but formidable. This is true largely because of the difficulty of selecting a limited number of contributions important to the evolution of chemistry. It is true that certain names are usually associated with the major advances, but a close study almost always reveals that these men were in reality expanding the work of predecessors who are often relatively unknown. The choice of selections for a source book in chemistry is therefore not easy.

It is probable that no two historians of chemistry, working separately, would ever choose exactly the same selections for a book of this sort. We have, however, sought to make our selections as representative as possible. The original list of citations which we drew up was submitted to historians of chemistry throughout the world. We owe our thanks to the scholars whose names are listed below, for their suggestions were of great assistance to us in compiling our final list. We are, of course, responsible for its imperfections.

As in the other volumes of this series of source books, the selections are representative of the development of the science between the years 1400 and 1900. The final selection, which is taken from the thesis of Marie Curie, although published in 1903, actually represents work done before 1900. Forthcoming volumes will cover the period of medieval and recent science.

In order to keep the volume within reasonable bounds, certain standards had to be set up to guide our selection. The chief of these was the decision to restrict ourselves to material which illustrates the development of chemical theory only. Descriptions of the discovery of individual elements, compounds, or processes were therefore excluded, unless some contribution to the theoretical development of chemistry resulted from such discovery. Thus, the discoveries of phosphorus and glycogen were omitted, but the first description of chlorine and the urea synthesis were included because of the changes which they effected in the thinking of contemporary chemists. We made our selections, also, because of their importance to further developments, rather than because they represented the very first investigations in their field. For example,

vii

catalysis was discovered before Berzelius proposed a name for the phenomenon, but it was his authority which brought about the recognition of catalysis as a fact, and it was on the basis of his paper that further studies were made in this field. Thus it is that the writings of the better known chemists predominate in this book, since these were the men who chiefly influenced the development of chemistry. The possibility was also considered of separating the selections for the nineteenth century into the various branches of chemistry which had then developed; inorganic, organic, and physical, but we found that such a classification offered no advantage.

The prefatory remarks to each selection did not provide sufficient space for adequate biographical treatment of the authors quoted. It was therefore felt that an indication of the life span of the author would place him in his time, and this space could better be employed to show the significance of the work quoted. In these remarks, an attempt has been made by the use of cross references to show what previous work led to the study selected and how this investigation in turn influenced later progress. In this manner it is hoped that the unity and sequence of chemical development have been emphasized. To complete the story, a brief introduction to the selections as a whole has been added to illustrate the development of the ideas on which the earliest citations given are based.

In order that adequate biographical material might be obtained by anyone interested, we have included at the end of the selections a bibliography of biographical papers and books on each author. The aim has been, wherever possible, to give references which will not be too difficult to locate. No claim is made to completeness.

It has also seemed desirable to include complete references to the sources from which each citation is taken. We have therefore given the full titles of books and complete page references for all selections. We have cited reprints of the articles wherever possible; these are frequently more easily obtained than the originals. For articles in languages other than English, especially those of the older authors, we have preferred to present English translations made by contemporary chemists, since we feel that a translation of a seventeenth-century chemist, for example, by another seventeenth-century chemist will always be more faithful to the meaning of the original than a translation made in the twentieth century.

The preparation of the source book was subject to unforeseen delay. The work was originally begun by Prof. Frederick Barry of Columbia University. After his death, the task was taken up by Dr. Tenney L. Davis, but lack of time prevented his continuation of the project. Dr. Hewitt G. Fletcher, Jr., then began active preparation of the manuscript. A number of citations for the earlier period were prepared by him. The advent of World War II again interrupted the work, and at the conclusion of the war Dr. Fletcher was unable to resume his task. The present editors took over the work in 1948.

We wish to express our gratitude to the many scholars who have made it possible to bring this volume to completion. In particular we wish to thank Eva V. Armstrong and Robert F. Sutton of the Edgar Fahs Smith Collection in the History of Chemistry of the University of Pennsylvania. Without the facilities which they extended to us, this book could not have been completed. We are grateful to the American Institute of Mining and Metallurgical Engineers for permission to quote from the translation of Biringuccio's "De la Pirotechnia" by Cyril Stanley Smith and Martha Teach Gnudi, and to Herbert Hoover and the Dover Publishing Company for permission to quote from the translation of Agricola's "De Re Metallica" by H. C. Hoover and L. H. Hoover. We are indebted to Denis I. Duveen for giving us access to his unpublished studies on Lavoisier and to his extensive library, and to the Rev. Charles H. Herkert for assistance in translations from the medieval Latin. Thanks are extended to Hans Burkhard for his excellent photographic work, and to the Edgar Fahs Smith Collection and the libraries of Stanford University, Yale University, and the American Philosophical Society for assistance in obtaining illustrations. We are especially grateful to the following scholars and historians of chemistry who have given us valued advice during the course of our work: Virginia Bartow, R. D. Billinger, Earle R. Caley, Maurice Daumas, Tenney L. Davis, Claude K. Deischer, Clara de Milt, V. Deulofeu, Sidney M. Edelstein, Eduard Färber, H. E. Fierz-David, R. J. Forbes, Sidney J. French, Josué Gollan, Mildred Grafflin, Harrison Hale, Williams Haynes, Arne Holmberg, R. Hooykaas, Willem P. Jorrisen, Moritz Kohn, P. Lemay, Shiao-ping Li, Douglas McKie, Wyndham Miles, Alwin Mittasch, Ralph E. Oesper, J. R. Partington, V. F. Payne, W. Prandtl, N. W. Rakestraw, John Read, Herbert Reichner, Desmond Reilly, F. Sherwood Taylor, Umberto Tergolini, George Urdang, H. S. van Klooster, A. E. Vitolo, Paul Walden, Florence E. Wall, Mary Elvira Weeks, Rudolf Winderlich, and William J. Wiswesser.

HENRY M. LEICESTER
HERBERT S. KLICKSTEIN

SAN FRANCISCO, CALIF.
PHILADELPHIA, PA.
September, 1951

Contents

Introduction

BY THE sixteenth century, when men such as Biringuccio, Agricola, and Paracelsus were active in fields which we now term chemical, the theories of chemical transformation which were current had behind them a long history. For nearly two thousand years men had speculated on the changes which they saw going on around them and had built up a reasonably consistent explanation, based on observable facts. The original theories were evolved by the Greek philosophers from about 600 to 300 B.C. Upon this foundation, a small group of practical chemists in Alexandria had made additions which led to the theory accepted even in 1500. In order to understand the ideas of the authors of the earliest selections given in the following pages, it is desirable to trace briefly the development of the chemical speculations upon which these ideas were based. The selections themselves, as they follow one another, show how these ideas were gradually modified until the chemistry of today resulted.

The Greek thinkers, beginning with Thales of Miletus about 600 B.C., were primarily interested in explaining the working of the whole cosmos around them. In the course of their speculations, which involved geometry, astronomy, and an elementary physics, they became especially interested in what we should call the states of matter. They conceived the elements as ideal embodiments of these states of matter. Thus earth, water, and air stood for solid, liquid, and gas. To these was added fire, the principle of heat, or motion, the element of which the heavenly bodies were composed. Thus any solid body was an earth, any liquid, a water. Moreover, water (liquid) could be converted to air (gas) by boiling, or to earth (solid) by freezing. Thus the elements were mutually interconvertible. These basic ideas were modified in different ways by various philosophers, but all the concepts were finally brought together by Aristotle (384–323 B.C.) in a synthesis to which his established position in later centuries gave an authority that was not shaken even at the time the first selections quoted here were written.

Aristotle assumed a prime matter of which everything was composed. This matter, however, was entirely without form and had no distinctive properties until form was impressed on it. Everything material was produced by the interaction of matter and form. By changing the form, new substances were produced. This theory was made concrete by the further idea of the opposing qualities: heat, cold, moisture, and dryness. These qualities could be combined in any way, so long as the direct contraries

1

did not unite. In this way the four elements resulted. The ideal earth consisted of cold and dryness, water of cold and moisture, air of heat and moisture, and fire of heat and dryness. The actual substances earth, water, air, and fire approached these in composition, but the theoretical ideal balance was slightly disturbed by an excess of one quality over another. If one quality was removed, or another added in excess, a new substance would be produced. Thus everything could theoretically be transformed into anything else, especially since the four elements could combine into *homoeomeria*, or compound atoms, of which all material objects actually consisted. Substances were classified in terms of their predominant element, which gave to them their chief properties. Thus a substance which could be melted was called a *water*, since it partook of the nature of water. Like water, however, it could be congealed by replacing the quality of moisture with that of dryness, while cold remained; thus it was changed to an earth. Metals were therefore waters, and their oxides, or calces, were earths. These ideas of Aristotle formed the basis for all scientific thought in succeeding centuries.

In Alexandria in the first and second centuries A.D., a group of practical chemists, trained in the metallurgical arts of Egypt and Babylon and well acquainted with the ideas of Aristotle, used his ideas to explain the changes which they actually saw occurring in the metals with which they worked. Metals could be reduced to their calces and then regenerated by suitable treatment. Obviously this was a change of form, and it implied that any metal could be converted to any other. Furthermore, influenced by the philosophical ideas which flourished in Alexandria, these men believed in the growth and perfection of all things. Since gold was the most perfect metal, it followed that its existence in the earth was due to the perfection of the baser metals into gold. These Alexandrian chemists, the first alchemists, believed they should be able to carry out this growth more rapidly in their workshops. They relied on repeated oxidations and reductions, on long periods of gentle heat, and on various simple reagents, such as sulfur water. The striking changes produced by this substance gave to their minds a strong feeling of the importance of sulfur.

Only during the first two or three centuries of our era did practical chemists work on this problem. Then, as the mystical philosophies of the East became dominant in Alexandria, philosophers and mystics took up the speculations of the chemists, and alchemy, in the sense in which the term is now used, first came into true existence. The changes of metals and salts were considered symbolic of deeper secrets, and the search for perfection in gold symbolized the search for perfection everywhere. The complex speculations of the alchemists and the strange symbolic language in which they expressed themselves have confused students of the history of chemistry ever since. Fundamentally, however, alchemical ideas were

Aristotelian, and the modifications which were gradually introduced were still firmly grounded in the theories of the great Greek philosopher.

With the decline of Alexandrian culture, the learning of the Greeks passed by way of Syria to the Arabs, where it found a ready welcome. The Arabs received ideas not only from the West but also from India and China. A Chinese form of alchemy had existed from almost the same period as the Greek, and the Chinese sages sought to prepare a medicine from which gold could be formed. This may have been the origin of the idea of the philosopher's stone, which is not mentioned among the Greeks. The Arabs, better acquainted with the properties of mercury than the early alchemists had been, saw in it the ultimate example of the watery nature of metals. The peculiar properties of sulfur, its effect on metals, and its combustibility were also well known to them. Thus among the Arabian alchemists arose the theory that the ultimate constituents of all things were mercury and sulfur. These in turn consisted of the four Aristotelian elements, but the idealized mercury and sulfur (not, of course, the grosser physical substances also known by these names) were the materials with which the alchemist sought to work. The basic theories of medieval chemistry were now fully formed.

In the twelfth and thirteenth centuries, the science of the Arabs passed at an increasing rate back to western Europe. Translators in Spain and Italy conveyed these theories to Western scholars, and a series of great schoolmen (Albertus Magnus, Raymond Lully, Roger Bacon, and others) collected the ideas and made them generally known. They were taken up enthusiastically, and alchemy became exceedingly popular. Some alchemists actually sought to make gold, some were mere charlatans, and some were absorbed only in the mystic symbolism of the art. Gradually the excesses of many of the alchemists began to discredit alchemy among the clearer thinkers, though many truly intelligent men believed in it. Its theories of the nature of matter and of chemical transformation were, however, accepted everywhere.

Such was the chemical background of the sixteenth century. It remains now to trace, in the words of the men themselves, how these ideas were modified, at first timidly and with many returns to the older concepts, but then with more and more boldness, until, in the mind of Lavoisier, modern chemistry was born.

Vannuccio Biringuccio

(1480–1539)

THE art of printing was but a hundred years old when the first work on metallurgy appeared. Few of the thirty thousand books issued in the fifteenth century dealt with science and none with metallurgy. It was a period of new intellectual movements and revolts against all authority. Chemistry was gradually throwing off the ill repute of alchemy and assuming a more useful role. It was in the early technological treatises that the first practical aspects of this new science were to be found. "De la Pirotechnia" by Vannuccio Biringuccio was first printed in 1540 in Venice and was the earliest classic of metallurgy. It anticipated by sixteen years Agricola's "De re metallica." It describes casting, glassmaking, smelting, ores and minerals, assaying, and chemical processes.

Biringuccio acquired his knowledge of mining and metallurgy by extensive travels through Italy and Germany. His written work reveals a man amazingly devoid of superstition. The scorn he felt for alchemy and its delusions mark him as one of the first real chemists. He was primarily concerned with experimental results. The state of chemistry at this period provided him with few working hypotheses.

Book I of the "Pirotechnia" discusses the treatment of the ores of gold and silver, copper, lead, tin, and iron. It describes their location, surface markings, and recovery. Book II is devoted to mercury, sulfur, antimony, alum, arsenic, salts, and borax. In Book III cupellation, roasting, and testing are treated. The preparation and use of aqua fortis in parting is found in Book IV. Alloys, casting, furnaces, and molds are the subjects of Books V through VIII. The last two books are of chemical interest, containing details on sublimation, distillation, pyrotechny, and allied subjects. The first description of the recovery of silver by amalgamation is found in Book X. The method for the preparation of saltpeter in the Book X is the earliest complete account. Agricola's process was taken from this source, as was his description of the distillation of mercury and sulfur, glass and steel manufacture, and the preparation of alum and vitriol.

It is surprising that, although the "Pirotechnia" appeared in six Italian and three French editions and was used widely, it was overshadowed by the "De re metallica." This has been attributed largely to the unattractive format and poor illustrations, as well as to a crude literary style. It was written in Italian and not in the scholarly Latin. Its influence has been mainly through later metallurgical publications.

The first English edition of this classic appeared just four hundred and two years after its initial publication. It is in this work[1] that the following selections

---

[1] "The Pirotechnia of Vannuccio Biringuccio. Translated from the Italian with an Introduction and Notes by Cyril Stanley Smith and Martha Teach Gnudi," The

appear. Biringuccio in discussing alchemy protests against the waste of time and money that is consumed in its deceptions.[2]

The more I look into this art of theirs, so highly praised and so greatly desired by men, the more it seems a vain wish and fanciful dream that it is impossible to realize unless someone should find some angelic spirit as patron or should operate through his own divinity. Granted the obscurity of its beginnings and the infinite processes and concordances that it needs in order to reach its destined maturity, I do not understand how anyone can reasonably believe that such artists can ever do what they say and promise. That this is true is shown by considering how many philosophers there have been in the world through many centuries who were most learned, informed, and experienced in things of Nature; and also how many great princes who with money and authority have had the power to have this work done and to aid all skillful men who work in this art. These men in order to arrive at such a port have equipped their vessels with sails and hard-working oarsmen and have sailed with guiding stars, trying every possible course, and, finally, submerged in the impossible (according to my belief) not one of them to my knowledge has yet come to port. . . .

. . . I must tell you that with diligent study I have looked at many books containing such things and not only have I had discussions with many experienced men, but I have not refrained from attempting to make some experiments myself in order to understand it better. I have also taken care to listen to the opinion of wise and experienced persons, as I have heard them subtly arguing whether such things are true or only fantastic dreams. And finally, taking all the alchemistic principles and comparing them with the processes of Nature, and pondering on the procedure of the one and of the other, it seems to me that there is no proportion between their powers, granting that Nature operates in things from within and causes all of her basic substances to pass wholly one into the other; while art, very weak in comparison, follows Nature in an effort to imitate her, but operates in external and superficial ways, and it is very difficult, even impossible, for her to penetrate things. And presupposing that through this it were granted to men to have those basic and particular materials from which Nature composes metals, I would like to be told

American Institute of Mining and Metallurgical Engineers, New York, 1942. This is a translation of the first edition, "De la Pirotechnia. Libri X. dove ampiamente si tratta non solo di ogni sorte & diversita di Miniere, ma anchora quanto si ricerca intorno à la prattica di quelle cose di quel che si appartiene a l' arte de la fusione ouer gitto de metalli come d' ogni altra cosa simile à questa. Composti per il. S. Vanocio Biringuccio Sennese. . . . Stampata in Venetia per Venturino Roffinelo. Ad instantia di Curtio Navo & Fratelli," 1540.

[2] *Ibid.*, pp. 35–37, 40–42.

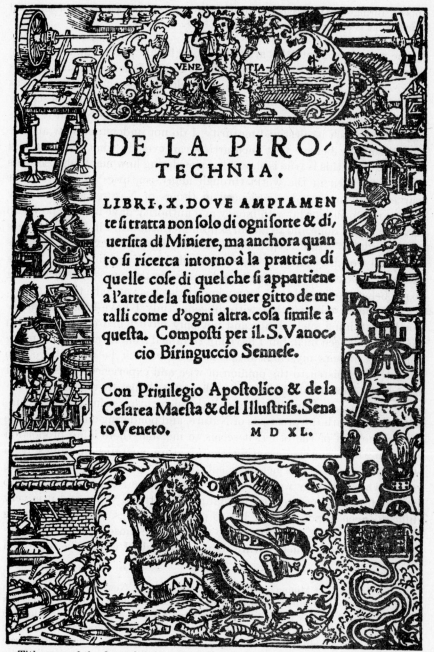

Title page of the first edition of Biringuccio's "De la Pirotechnia," Venice, 1540.

how they can receive at will the influence of the heavens, on which are dependent all inferior things on this convex of the world, and also how men ever know by this art how to purify those elemental substances or how to proportion necessary quantities one to the other, or finally how to carry these substances to perfection as Nature does and make metals of them. I do not believe that anyone could accomplish all this unless men were not only geniuses but also angels upon earth, and therefore I believe that those err who expend their energies on this art, standing with long and continuous vigil always ardent in their desire and in the conduct of their operations, more inflamed than the very coals in their furnaces in the effort to see whether they can bring the adamantine hardness of such fruit to ripeness. God's aid would be needed to do this, and those who knew how to do such things would be called not men but gods, for they would extinguish the insatiable thirst of avarice in this world and in the extraordinary excellence of their knowledge would by far outstrip the power of Nature (she who is mother and minister of all things created, daughter of God, and soul of the world) if they should use methods that perhaps she does not possess, or, if she does have, does not employ them to such ends. . . .

. . . Now in having spoken and in speaking thus I have no thought of wishing to detract from or decrease the virtues of this art, if it has any, but I have only given my opinion, based on the facts of the matter. I could still discourse profusely concerning this the art of transmutation, or alchemy as it is called, yet neither through my own efforts nor through those of others (although I have sought with great dilligence) have I ever had the fortune to see anything worthy of being approved by good men, or that it was not necessary to abandon as imperfect for one cause or another even before it was half finished. For this reason I surely deserve to be excused, all the more because I know that I am drawn by more powerful reasons, or perhaps by natural inclination, to follow the path of mining more willingly than that of alchemy, even though mining is a harder task, both physical and mental, is more expensive, and promises less at first sight and in words than does alchemy; and it has as its scope the observation of Nature's powers rather than those of art—or indeed of seeing what really exists rather than what one thinks exists. . . .

For this reason I tell and advise you that I believe the best thing to do is turn to the natural gold and silver that is extracted from ores rather than that of alchemy, which I believe not only does not exist but also, in truth, has never been seen by anyone, although many claim to have seen it. For it is a thing whose principles are unknown, as I have told you; and whoever does not know the first principles of things is even less able to understand the end.

The manufacture of saltpeter for use in fireworks is described in the first chapter of Book X.[3]

CONCERNING THE NATURE OF SALTPETER AND THE METHOD FOLLOWED IN MAKING IT

As I told you in the chapter on salts, saltpeter is a mixture composed of many substances extracted with fire and water from arid and manurial soils, from that growth which exudes from new walls or from that loosened soil that is found in tombs or uninhabited caves where the rain cannot enter. It is my belief that it is engendered in these soils from an airy moisture that is drunk in and absorbed by the earthy dryness. . . .

Now, as I told you above, this saltpeter is extracted from the above mentioned manurial soils and from dark places that have stood turned over and loosened for a long time, provided the rains have not been able to quench the earthy dryness. . . .

Then, having tested the earth that you wish to work, either by taste or in some other way to assure yourself that it contains saltpeter, make a great heap of it in the middle of the room where you are to work. Near that heap, make another less than half its size which is composed of two parts of quicklime and three of cerris or oak ashes, or some other ashes that give a sharp, strong taste. Then mix these two heaps together very well and with this composition fill the tubs that you put astraddle up to within a *palmo* of the mouth. Or, if you do not wish to mix the earth, ashes, and lime together, first put a *palmo* of earth in the bottom of the tubs, and then another layer of a *dito* or two of ashes and lime. In this way, putting the two things in layer by layer, fill all the casks, tubs, and other vessels that you have prepared up to within a *palmo* or half a *braccio* of the top, as I told you above. Then, through a conduit, fill the rest of the space that you left with water. Let this penetrate through all the earth gradually and drain down into the receptacles, or into the channel or channels which conduct it into one or more large tubs, or wherever you wish. You will see all the water that you put over the earth run down and pass through the holes in the bottom. This now carries with it all the substance and virtue of the saltpeter that was in that earth. Taste it by placing some of it on the tongue, and when you find it to be sharp and strongly salt it will be good, and you will have made it well. Otherwise put it again on the same earth, or on new. When the first water is sufficiently saturated with substance, it is well to pour in water again in order to wash the remaining earth better. This second water is collected in another vessel, and after these a third could also be made in order to have perfectly every final bit of this substance. Do not mix this second water, and even less the third, with the first, unless perchance it should have the same flavor, (which I

[3] *Ibid.*, pp. 404–409.

do not believe possible), but place them separately in other vessels, for they are good to pour on the second working of subsequent earths. In this way continue to make and to collect a goodly quantity of these waters, taking care that they are well saturated with this saltpetery substance. When this does not seem to be of the perfection you wish, pour it again over the same earth or on other new earths until it satisfies you and until you know that it is saturated with a great quantity of saltpeter.

After you have done this, a furnace is made with one or two large copper kettles like those used in dyeing, bricked in at the top. These are filled two-thirds full with the aforesaid saltpetery water as saturated as possible. It is boiled very slowly until it is reduced to about a third. Then it is removed and put to settle in a large covered vat that is closed and fitted with iron bands, tightened so that it does not leak. When this water has settled and is very clear, an earthy thick sediment that it contained is removed, and it is put to boil again in the same or in a different kettle. Each time it boils, it forms a foam and swells up so much that if one is not watchful it sometimes runs over and spills, and much that is good is carried away. If you wish to prevent this, make a strong lye of three-quarters of soda, or ashes of cerris or oak, or of olive-bush ashes (which are perfect), and one-quarter of lime. Further, for every hundred pounds of water dissolve four pounds of rock alum. When the kettle boils, proceed to throw in one or two jugfuls of this lye at a time, especially when you see that the saltpeter water rises in foam. When this has been in but a short time you will see the water subside and become clear and beautiful and of a bluish color. Boil this until the fine watery parts evaporate and the saltpetery parts become thick so that the water congeals when taken out and put in chests or vats to cool. When the water has been brought to a lesser quantity, this is done better by removing it and putting it in a smaller kettle where it is made disposed to congeal. Having tested this water and seen that it is reduced to the point where it congeals, take it out and put it in vessels of wood or rough ones of earthenware that are crossed inside with some sticks of wood for congealing on. Let it cool and rest well for three or four days. By decantation, that is by tilting the vessel, or by a little tube put in the bottom, pour out all the water that has not congealed and save it to cook again. The saltpeter that you find congealed will be of a quantity depending on the virtue present in the water or in the earth, but its clarity and beauty will come from the virtue of the magistery of lye which is added as it boils and which has the power of cleansing it and causing it to come out refined at the first cooking. Now, when this has been removed with a chisel from the sides of the vessel where it congealed, and has been washed with its own water, it is put on boards to drain and to dry out well from the water.

If it seems necessary to you, or if for some of your processes you wish to have it purer than usual and completely without gross earthiness, without fatness, and without salt (which it must be for making very fine gunpowder and aqua fortis for parting), or for whatever reason you wish to make it come out well like this, do it in one of two ways that I shall now teach you. The first, and the one most pleasing to me, is with water, and the second is with fire.

The chapter concludes with a description of these methods.

Georg Agricola

(1494–1555)

"De re metallica," which was the standard work on mining and metallurgy of its time, was published at Basel in 1556. Its author, George Bauer (à name which was Latinized to Agricola) was a physician. Born in Saxony, he later settled in Joachmistaal, a mining center which is still active. There he had the opportunity to study mining, metallurgy, and technology. He studied so assiduously that he began to be sought as an expert. In later years he moved to Chemnitz, where he continued his investigations.

Agricola's major contribution was the "De re metallica," which was published posthumously. In this work he describes in a very lucid manner the various metallurgical and mining procedures of his time. Although he borrowed liberally from earlier authors (such as Biringuccio), sometimes with little acknowledgement, he also added much from his own rich experiences. Because of its complete and detailed accounts, its profuse woodcuts, and its admirable style, it was for more than a century the standard work in its field. The Latin edition was issued in 1556 and was followed by a German edition in 1557 and an Italian in 1563. The first English translation was published by the Hoovers in 1912.[1] This volume, like the "Pirotechnia," contains sections on assaying, salt preparation, niter,

[1] "Georgius Agricola, De Re Metallica, translated from the first Latin edition of 1556 with Biographical Introduction, Annotations and Appendices upon the Development of Mining Methods, Metallurgical Processes, Geology, Mineralogy and Mining Law from the earliest times to the 16th century, by H. C. Hoover and L. H. Hoover . . . ," London, 1912, reissued in a reduced facsimile edition, 1950. This is a translation of "De Re Metallica Libri XII. Quibus Officia, Instrumenta, Machinae, ac omnia denique ad Metallicam spectantia non modo luculentissime describuntur, sed & per effigies, suis locis insertas, adiunctis Latinis, Germanicisque appellationibus ita ob oculus ponuntur, ut clarius tradi non possint. Ejusdem De Animantibus Subterraneis Liber, ab auctore recognitus: cum Indicibus diversis, quicquid in opere tractatum est, pulchre demonstrantibus," Basel, Froeben, 1556.

and related subjects, in addition to the metallurgy. Throughout, Agricola maintains a high discriminatory standard.[2]

His chemical contributions were of lesser importance and are largely found in Book XII of "De re metallica." It is undeniable, however, that the clarity and practicality of his accounts had a salutary effect upon the development of chemistry. There is little doubt that his clear treatment paved the way for the "Alchymia" of Libavius.

Of his other published works, the "De natura fossilium"[3] is the most important. It was published in 1546, some ten years before the "De re metallica." It is in this book that the earliest attempt to classify minerals is to be found. Agricola's basis of classification is physical: fusibility, solubility, color, odor, taste. He explains his system in the following.[4]

The subterranean inanimate bodies are divided into two classes, one of which, because it is a fluid or exhalation, is called by those names, and the other class is called the minerals. Mineral bodies are solidified from particles of the same substance, such as pure gold, each particle of which is gold, or they are of different substances such as lumps which consist of earth, stone, and metal; these latter may be separated into earth, stone and metal, and therefore the first is not a mixture while the last is called a mixture. The first are again divided into simple and compound minerals. The simple minerals are of four classes, namely, earths, solidified juices, stones and metals, while the mineral compounds are of many sorts, as I shall explain later.

Earth is a simple mineral body which may be kneaded in the hands when moistened, or from which lute is made when it has been wetted. Earth, properly so called, is found enclosed in veins or veinlets, or frequently on the surface in fields and meadows. This definition is a general one. The harder earth, although moistened by water, does not at once become lute, but does turn into lute if it remains in water for some time. There are many species of earths, some of which have names but others are unnamed.

Solidified juices are dry and somewhat hard (*subdurus*) mineral bodies which when moistened with water do not soften but liquefy instead; or if they do soften, they differ greatly from the earths by their unctuousness (*pingue*) or by the material of which they consist. Although occasionally they have the hardness of stone, yet because they preserve the form and

[2] For some of Agricola's geological contributions, see K. F. Mather and S. L. Mason, "A Source Book in Geology," New York, 1939, pp. 7–11.

[3] "De ortu et causis subterraneorum Lib. V. De natura eorum quae effluunt ex terra Lib. IIII. De natura fossilium Lib. X. De veteribus et novis metallis, Lib. II. Bermannus, sive de re metallica Dialogus. Interpretatio Germanica vocum rei metallicae," Basel, Froeben, 1546.

[4] The translation is taken from the Hoover edition of "De re metallica," where it appears as footnote 4 to Book I, pp. 1 to 3.

nature which they had when less hard, they can easily be distinguished from the stones. The juices are divided into "meager" and unctuous (*macer et pinguis*). The "meager" juices, since they originate from three different substances, are of three species. They are formed from a liquid mixed with earth, or with metal, or with a mineral compound. To the first species belong salt and *Nitrum* [soda]; to the second, chrysocolla, verdigris, iron-rust, and azure; to the third, vitriol, alum, and an acrid juice which is unnamed. The first two of these latter are obtained from pyrites, which is numbered amongst the compound minerals. The third of these comes from *Cadmia* [in this case the cobalt-zinc-arsenic minerals; the acrid juice is probably zinc sulfate]. To the unctuous juices belong these species: sulphur, bitumen, realgar and orpiment. Vitriol and alum, although they are somewhat unctuous yet do not burn, and they differ in their origin from the unctuous juices, for the latter are forced out from the earth by heat, whereas the former are produced when pyrites is softened by moisture.

Stone is a dry and hard mineral body which may either be softened by remaining for a long time in water and be reduced to powder by a fierce fire; or else it does not soften with water, but the heat of a great fire liquefies it. To the first species belong those stones which have been solidified by heat, to the second those solidified [literally "congealed"] by cold. These two species of stones are constituted from their own material. However, writers on natural subjects who take into consideration the quantity and quality of stones and their value, divide them into four classes. The first of these has no name of its own but is called in common parlance "stone": to this class belong loadstone, jasper (or bloodstone) and *Aetites* [geodes?]. The second class comprises hard stones, either pellucid or ornamental, with very beautiful and varied colours which sparkle marvellously; they are called gems. The third comprises stones which are only brilliant after they have been polished, and are usually called marble. The fourth are called rocks; they are found in quarries, from which they are hewn out for use in building, and they are cut into various shapes. None of the rocks show colour or take a polish. Few of the stones sparkle; fewer still are transparent. Marble is sometimes only distinguishable from opaque gems by its volume; rock is always distinguishable from stones properly so called by its volume. Both the stones and the gems are usually to be found in veins and veinlets which traverse the rocks and marble. These four classes, as I have already stated, are divided into many species, which I will explain in their proper place.

Metal is a mineral body, by nature either liquid or somewhat hard. The latter may be melted by the heat of the fire, but when it has cooled down again and lost all heat, it becomes hard again and resumes its proper form.

In this respect it differs from the stone which melts in the fire, for although the latter regains its hardness, yet it loses its pristine form and properties. Traditionally there are six different kinds of metals, namely gold, silver, copper, iron, tin and lead. There are really others, for quicksilver is a metal, although the Alchemists disagree with us on this subject, and bismuth is also. The ancient Greek writers seem to have been ignorant of bismuth, wherefore Ammonius rightly states that there are many species of metals, animals, and plants which are unknown to us. *Stibium* when smelted in the crucible and refined has as much right to be regarded as a proper metal as is accorded to lead by writers. If when smelted, a certain portion be added to tin, a bookseller's alloy is produced from which the type is made that is used by those who print books on paper. Each metal has its own form which it preserves when separated from those metals which were mixed with it. Therefore neither electrum nor *Stannum* is of itself a real metal, but rather an alloy of two metals. Electrum is an alloy of gold and silver, *Stannum* of lead and silver. And yet if silver be parted from the electrum, then gold remains and not electrum; if silver be taken away from *Stannum*, then lead remains and not *Stannum*. Whether brass, however, is found as a native metal or not, cannot be ascertained with any surety. We only know of the artificial brass, which consists of copper tinted with the colour of the mineral calamine. And yet if any should be dug up, it would be a proper metal. Black and white copper seem to be different from the red kind. Metal, therefore, is by nature either solid, as I have stated, or fluid, as in the unique case of quicksilver. But enough now concerning the simple kinds.

I will now speak of the compounds which are composed of the simple minerals cemented together by nature, and under the word "compound" I now discuss those mineral bodies which consist of two or three simple minerals. They are likewise mineral substances, but so thoroughly mixed and alloyed that even in the smallest part there is not wanting any substance that is contained in the whole. Only by force of the fire is it possible to separate one of the simple mineral substances from another: either the third from the other two, or two from the third, if there were three in the same compound. These two, three or more bodies are so completely mixed into one new species that the pristine form of none of them is recognizable.

The "mixed" minerals, which are composed of those same simple minerals, differ from the "compounds," in that the simple minerals each preserves its own form so that they can be separated one from the other not only by fire but sometimes by water and sometimes by hand. As these two classes differ so greatly from one another I usually use two different words in order to distinguish one from the other. I am well aware that Galen calls the metallic earth a compound which is really a mixture, but he who wishes to instruct others should bestow upon each separate thing a definite name.

"De re metallica" is divided into twelve books. The preparation of soluble salts, alum, vitriol, sulfur, bitumens, and glass are recorded in Book XII. An example of this section is given in the passage below, describing the manufacture of vitriol.[5]

The fourth method of making vitriol is from vitriolous earth or stones. Such ore is at first carried and heaped up, and is then left for five or six months exposed to the rain of spring and autumn, to the heat of summer, and to the rime and frost of winter. It must be turned over several times with shovels, so that the part at the bottom may be brought to the top, and it is thus ventilated and cooled; by this means the earth crumbles up and loosens, and the stone changes from hard to soft. Then the ore is covered with a roof, or else it is taken away and placed under a roof, and remains in that place six, seven, or eight months. Afterward as large a portion as is required is thrown into a vat, which is half-filled with water; this vat is one hundred feet long, twenty-four feet wide, eight feet deep. It has an opening at the bottom, so that when it is opened the dregs of the ore from which the vitriol comes may be drawn off, and it has, at the height of one foot from the bottom, three or four little holes, so that, when closed, the water may be retained, and when opened the solution flows out. Thus the ore is mixed with water, stirred with poles and left in the tank until the earthy portions sink to the bottom and the water absorbs the juices. Then the little holes are opened, the solution flows out of the vat, and is caught in a vat below it; this vat is of the same length as the other, but twelve feet wide and four feet deep. If the solution is not sufficiently vitriolous it is mixed with fresh ore; but if it contains enough vitriol, and yet has not exhausted all of the ore rich in vitriol, it is well to dissolve the ore again with fresh water. As soon as the solution becomes clear, it is poured into the rectangular leaden cauldron through launders, and is boiled until the water is evaporated. Afterward as many thin strips of iron as the nature of the solution requires, are thrown in, and then it is boiled again until it is thick enough, when cold, to congeal into vitriol. Then it is poured into tanks or vats, or any other receptacle, in which all of it that is apt to congeal does so within two or three days. The solution which does not congeal is either poured back into the cauldron to be boiled again, or it is put aside for dissolving the new ore, for it is far preferable to fresh water. The solidified vitriol is hewn out, and having once more been thrown into the caldron, is re-heated until it liquefies; when liquid, it is poured into moulds that it may be made into cakes. If

[5] *Ibid.*, pp. 576–578.

the solution first poured out is not satisfactorily thickened, it is condensed two or three times, and each time liquefied in the caldron and re-poured into the moulds, in which manner pure cakes, beautiful to look at, are made from it.

Woodcut from Agricola's "De re metallica," Basel, 1556, page 464.

The vitriolous pyrites, which are to be numbered among the mixtures (*mistura*), are roasted as in the case of alum, and dissolved with water, and the solution is boiled in leaden caldrons until it condenses into vitriol. Both alum and vitriol are often made out of these, and it is no wonder, for these juices are cognate, and only differ in the one point,—that the former is less, the latter more, earthy. That pyrites which contains metal must be smelted in the furnace. In the same manner, from other mixtures of vitriolic and metalliferous material are made vitriol and metal. Indeed, if ores of vitriolous pyrites abound, the miners split small logs down the centre and cut them off in lengths as long as the drifts and tunnels are wide, in which they lay them down transversely; but, that they may be stable, they are laid on the ground with the wide side down and the round side up, and they touch each other at the bottom, but not at the top. The intermediate space is filled with pyrites, and the same crushed are scattered over the wood, so that coming in or going out, the road is flat and even. Since the drifts or tunnels drip with water, these pyrites are soaked, and from them are freed the vitriol and cognate things. If the water ceases to drip, these dry and harden, and then they are raised from the shafts, together with the pyrites not yet dissolved in the water, or they are carried out from the tunnels; then they are thrown into vats or tanks, and boiling water having been poured over them, the vitriol is freed and the pyrites are dissolved. This green solution is transferred to other vats or tanks, that it may be made clear and pure; it is then boiled in the lead caldrons until it thickens; afterward it is poured into wooden tubs, where it condenses on rods, or reeds, or twigs, into green vitriol.

Theophrastus Bombastus von Hohenheim (Paracelsus)

(1493–1541)

ONE of the most forceful men of the Renaissance was Philip Theophrastus Bombast von Hohenheim, who later called himself Paracelsus.[1] He was the founder of a new school of chemistry, iatrochemistry, which applied chemistry to medicine. It turned away from alchemy and held sway throughout the sixteenth and seventeenth centuries. Because of his doctrines, which opposed the teachings of Galen and Avicenna, and his boastful manner, Paracelsus wandered throughout Europe remaining in few places for long. These wanderings widened his observations and experiences.

The works of Paracelsus were published after his death. They are difficult to understand because of an obscure style and contradictory manner. Paracelsus believed in some of the alchemical concepts and embodied mysticism in his writing. The direct contributions he made to chemistry are small, for he was essentially a reformer of medicine. Yet it was his stimulation that induced many of his followers to refute age-old learnings and think for themselves. One of the

[1] For a complete bibliography of Paracelsus, see K. Sudhoff, "Versuch einer Kritik der Echtheit der Paracelsischen Schriften. I: Druckschriften. II: Handschriften," Berlin, 1894–1899.

greatest results of the work of this iconoclast was his emphasis on chemistry and its value to medicine and on the necessity for experimentation and observation.

The following passages taken from the "Hermetic and Alchemical Writings"[2] illustrate his style and attitude.[3]

We had decided to write our Archidoxies, as also other books concerning Medicine, with especial clearness and lucidity, inasmuch as all the highest medical arcana cannot be prepared without true chemical encheiries (undertakings), nor yet can they be speedily exalted in grade, and it is notorious that almost the whole world, through its devotion to riches and earthly wealth, zealously pursues tinctures only and transmutations of metals in order to amass the greatest possible amount of gold and silver, to obtain which they stand in the greatest need of chemical preparations, which also they would like to find in concise form and easily in our Archidoxies. Notwithstanding, it was in consideration of the very great evil which might thence arise, and at the same time to oppose their malice, that we have concealed our doctrine, according to ancient philosophic method and cabalistic practice. I shew this, my doctrine, clearly to the upright and the perfect, yet leave it none the less dark to contemptuous and impious men.

Chemistry is indebted to Paracelsus for his emphasis on the importance of experimentation. He compares the hard-working medical chemists with physicians.[4]

I praise alchemy, which compounds secret medicines, whereby all hopeless maladies are cured. They who are ignorant of this deserve neither to be called chemists nor physicians. For these remedies lie either in the power of the alchemists or in that of the physicians. If they reside with the latter, the former are ignorant of them. If with the former, the latter have not learnt them. How, therefore, shall those men deserve any praise? I, for my part, have rather judged that such a man shall be highly extolled who is able to bring Nature to such a point that she will lend help, that is, who shall know how after the extraction of the health-giving parts what is useless is to be rejected; who is also acquainted with the efficacy, for he must see that it is impossible that the preparation and the science—in other words, the chemia and the medicine—can be separated from one another, because should anyone attempt to separate them he will introduce more obscurities into medicine, and the result will be absolute folly. By this distinction all the fundamental principles of medicine will be overthrown. I do not think I need labour very hard in order that you may recognise the

[2] A. E. Waite (Editor), "The Hermetic and Alchemical Writings of Aureolus Philippus Theophrastus Bombast, of Hohenheim, called Paracelsus the Great: Now for the first time faithfully translated into English," London, 1894, 2 vols.

[3] *Ibid.*, vol. 2, p. 81.

[4] *Ibid.*, vol. 2, p. 95; vol. 1, p. 167.

certainty of my reasons. I give you this one piece of advice: Have regard
to the effect of quack remedies. They first destroy wounds which are already aggravated by a succession of processes, miserably torture the pa-
tients, and having after all accomplished no good, but removed all chance
of recovery, they do the unfortunate to death. . . . I who am an iatro-
chemist, that is, one who knows both chemistry and medicine, am in virtue hereof in a position to point out errors and to profitably reject all
pestiferous remedies, relegating them to their own place. My ardent desires and ready will to be of use prompt me to this. . . .

. . . The separation of those things which grow out of the earth and are
combustible, such as fruits, herbs, flowers, leaves, grasses, roots, woods,
etc., is also arranged in many ways. By distillation is separated from them
first the phlegma, afterwards the Mercury, after this the oil, fourthly their
sulphur, lastly their salt. When all these separations are made according
to Spagyric Art, remarkable and excellent medicaments are the result,
both for internal and external use.

But when laziness has grown to such an extent among physicians, and
all work and every pursuit are turned only to insolence, I do not wonder,
indeed, that preparations of this kind are everywhere neglected, and that
coals stand at so low a price. If smiths could do without coals for forging
and fashioning metals as easily as these physicians do without them in preparing their medicines, there is no doubt that all the coal merchants would
have been before now reduced to extreme beggery. In the meantime, I ex-
tol and adorn, with the eulogium rightly due to them, the Spagyric physicians. These do not give themselves up to ease and idleness, strutting
about with a haughty gait, dressed in silk, with rings ostentatiously dis-
played on their fingers, or silvered poignards fixed on their loins, and sleek
gloves on their hands. But they devote themselves diligently to their
labours, sweating whole nights and days over fiery furnaces. These do not
kill the time with empty talk, but find their delight in their laboratory.
They are clad in leathern garments, and wear a girdle to wipe their hands
upon. They put their fingers among the coals, the lute, and the dung, not
into gold rings. Like blacksmiths and coal merchants, they are sooty
and dirty, and do not look proudly with sleek countenance. In presence of
the sick they do not chatter and vaunt their own medicines. They perceive
that the work should glorify the workman, not the workman the work,
and that fine words go a very little way towards curing sick folks. Passing
by all these vanities, therefore, they rejoice to be occupied at the fire and
to learn the steps of alchemical knowledge. Of this class are: Distillation,
Resolution, Putrefaction, Extraction, Calcination, Reverberation, Sublimation, Fixation, Separation, Reduction, Coagulation, Tincture, and the
like.

Paracelsus believed in the four elements but held that they were present in substances as three principles: mercury, sulfur, and salt. Mercury was the principle of volatility and fusibility, sulfur of inflammability, and salt of incombustibility. The last principle, salt, seems to have been an addition by Paracelsus himself to the other two, which had long been familiar to the alchemist. In the following selection he discusses the elements and the principles.[5]

TEXT VI

As to the manner in which God created the world, take the following account. He originally reduced it to one body, while the elements were developing. This body He made up of three ingredients, Mercury, Sulphur, and Salt, so that these three should constitute one body. Of these three are composed all the things which are, or are produced, in the four elements. These three have in themselves the force and the power of all perishable things. In them lie hidden the mineral, day, night, heat, cold, the stone, the fruit, and everything else, even while not yet formed. It is even as with wood which is thrown away and is only wood, yet in it are hidden all forms of animals, of plants, of instruments, which any one who can carve what else would be useless, invents and produces. So the body of Iliaster [primitive chaos] was a mere trunk, but in it lay hidden all herbs, waters, gems, minerals, stones, and chaos itself, which things the supreme Creator alone carved and fashioned most subtly, having removed and cast away all that was extraneous. First of all He produced and separated the air. This being formed, from the remainder issued forth the other three elements, fire, water, earth. From these He afterwards took away the fire, while the other two remained, and so on in due succession. . . .

TEXT XII

Now, as to the philosophy of the three prime elements, it must be seen how these flourish in the element of air. Mercury, Sulphur, and Salt are so prepared as the element of air that they constitute the air, and make up that element. Originally the sky is nothing but white Sulphur coagulated with the spirit of Salt and clarified by Mercury, and the hardness of this element is in this pellicle and shell thus formed from it. Then, secondly, from the three primal parts it is changed into two—one part being air and the other chaos—in the following way. The Sulphur resolves itself by the spirit of Salt in the liquor of Mercury, which of itself is a liquid distributed from heaven to earth, and is the albumen of the heaven, and the mid space. It is clear, a chaos, subtle, and diaphanous. All density, dryness, and all its subtle nature, are resolved, nor is it any longer the same as it was before. Such is the air. The third remanant of the three primals has

[5] *Ibid.*, vol. 1, pp. 204–205, 208–209.

passed into air, thus; If wood is burnt it passes into smoke. So this passes into air, remains in its air to the end of its elements, and becomes Sulphur, Mercury, and Salt, which are substantially consumed and turned into air, just as the wood which becomes smoke. It is, in fact, nothing but the smoke of the three primal elements of the air. So, then, nothing further arises from the element of air beyond what has been mentioned. Many of the ancients and later writers, nay, even some now living, ascribe wind to the air, making out its cause to be the mobility of the sky. That is all nothing. It never reaches the sky; and the air is by itself, coming forth from its element as smoke from wood. Whoever wishes to understand more clearly about it, and what its motion is, let him read about the properties of fire, where more is set down than can be here comprised.

Paracelsus also writes of salt at some length.[6]

CONCERNING SALT AND SUBSTANCES COMPREHENDED UNDER SALT.

God has driven and reduced man to such a pitch of necessity and want that he is unable in any way to live without salt, but has most urgent need thereof for his food and eatables. This is man's need and condition of compulsion. The causes of this compulsion I will briefly explain.

Man consists of three things: sulphur, mercury, and salt. Of these consists also whatever anywhere exists, and of neither more nor fewer constituents. These are the body of every single thing, whether endowed with sense or deprived thereof. Now, since man is divided into species, he is therefore subject to decay, nor can he escape it except in so far as God has endowed him with a congenital balsam which also itself consists of three ingredients. This is salt, preserving man from decay; where salt is deficient, there that part which is without salt decays. For as the flesh of cattle which is salted is made free from decay, so also salt naturally infused into us by God preserves our body from putrefaction. Let that theory stand, then, that man consists of three bodies, and that one of these is salt, as the conservative element which prevents the body born with it from decaying. As, therefore, all created things, all substances, consist of these three, it is necessary that they should be sustained and conserved by their nutriments each according to its kind. . . .

Hence by parity of reasoning it is clear that man himself also must be nourished in the same way: that is to say, that his sulphur must receive nutrimental sulphur, mercury its nutrimental mercury, and the congenital salt its nutrimental salt, whereby, from these three, man may be sustained and conserved in his species. Whatever burns is sulphur, whatever is humid is mercury, and that which is the balsam of these two is salt.

[6] *Ibid.*, vol. 1, pp. 257–258.

Andreas Libavius

(1540–1616)

THE first textbook of chemistry, "Alchemia," appeared in 1597.[1] Its author, Andreas Libavius (Andreas Libau) was a teacher and physician of the later iatrochemical school. He was not a disciple of Paracelsus and vigorously denounced many of the latter's doctrines. Libavius contributed little original material to chemical theory, but his practical approach was an innovation. His volume was for many decades the most important chemical work of its type. It embodies a complete survey of the chemistry of the period, and is written in clear language with no attempt at obscurity. "Alchemia" is systematically arranged and includes some of Libavius's own discoveries. Such are the preparation of zinc, lead nitrate, and anhydrous stannic chloride ("fuming liquor of Libavius"). He has been credited with planning the first true chemical laboratory. His description of chemical apparatus is the most complete of its time.

In many respects, his intelligible and practical discussions are modeled after the form of Agricola's "De re metallica." The contents are a mixture of alchemical and chemical learning. They illustrate a transitional phase of chemical science. Although Libavius presents much rational material, he also admits the possibility of the transmutation of base metals.

In his attempt to systematize chemistry, Libavius uses a terminology which sounds strange today, though in its own setting it is clear and logical. He uses the word *alchemia* in the sense in which we now use the word *chemistry*. He subdivides the science into *encheria*, which deals with chemical methods, and *chymia*, which concerns substances and their properties. *Magisteria* is a term which implies not only chemical substances but also their properties and the forces which they produce. The following selections illustrate how Libavius attempted to define and systematize the materials of chemistry.[2]

CHAPTER I

WHAT IS ALCHEMY.

Alchemy is the art of producing *magisteria* and of extracting pure essences by separating bodies from mixtures.

[1] "Alchemia . . . opera e dispersis passim optimorum autorum, veterum & recentium exemplis potissimum, tum etiam praeceptis quibusdam operose collecta, adhibitisque ratione & experientia, quanta potuit esse, methodo accurata explicata, & in Intergrum corpus redacta. Accesserunt Tractatus nonnulli Physici Chymici, item methodice ab eodem autore explicati, quorum titulos versa pagella exhibet. Sunt etiam in Chymicis ejusdem D. Libavii epistolis, jam ante impressis, multa huic operi lucem allatura . . . ," Frankfurt, 1597.

[2] *Ibid.*, Book 1, Cap. 1–2, pp. 1–2.

Because these two functions are commonly embraced in the word *work*, it happens that it can also be called the art of working well, or of separating the pure from the impure by means of a water, or by a kind of fusion or solution; because of the excellence of this part, the name is judged to be fitting to this art.

In origin it had by nature what the first craftsmen desired to imitate by their industry, especially at first in exacting mineral juices from the veins and purifying them, as nature itself causes pure metals and juices to flow from mines so that at times they may be seen to be taken from the veins. Therefore, formerly, it had greater value in metallurgy. Now it is of greater importance in medicine, and is not only valuable for minerals, but also for animals and vegetables, for human use, and for safeguarding health. It is even useful for many of the adornments of life. . . .

There are two parts of alchemy: encheria and chymia.

Encheria is the first part of alchemy, concerning the methods of operation.

Therefore, this part in general describes the kinds of operations which are suitable for working on each magisterium and essence. And because the hand is very important in this work, and also has the name, by chance ἐγχείρησις, it is as if the name of the hands were brought artificially into the description, even though the work is carried on not only by the hands, but also by the shrewdness of all the senses, attention, and a keen ingenuity.

Encheria is served by ergalia[3] and pyronomia,[4] of whose use there is such a necessity in alchemy that the man who has a perfect knowledge and use of these is thought to be an absolute craftsman . . . since nothing can be done accurately without instruments and fire. . . .

Chymia[5] is the second part of alchemy, and concerns the combining of chemical substances.

A chemical substance is that which is produced by the operations described under encheria. . . .

Magisterium is a chemical substance before any extraction, carefully worked upon and brought to the ultimate, provided the external impurities are removed.

There are magisteria either of quality or of substance.

Magisteria of quality are found when a thing is worked upon and raised to the ultimate and are of two kinds, either of hidden or of manifest qualities.

[3] [Ergalia is the explanation of the instruments of alchemy. Book 1, Cap. 3, p. 2.]

[4] [Pyronomia is the knowledge of how to use heat and how to guide fire in its work. Book 1, Cap. 14, p. 23.]

[5] "Alchemia . . . ," Book 2, Cap. 1, pp. 85–90, 130.

Magisteria of hidden quality occur when the base of the entire substance is preserved in them, and their exaltation is perfected only when their effects are made evident through experience.

Magisteria of manifest quality are found when a substance is worked up in visible form. . . .

There are also magisteria of substance, in which the material which exists in itself, at least after crudities have been removed, is totally changed without any notable loss of quantity, as far as is possible.

Jan Baptist Van Helmont

(1577–1644)

ONE of the most prominent disciples of Paracelsus was Jan Baptist Van Helmont. After studying several sciences, he finally chose medicine and became an ardent follower of Paracelsus. An extended trip through Europe impressed him with the importance of chemistry. He gave up his medical interests and devoted the remainder of his life to chemical investigations. As a chemist, Van Helmont has been said to represent the transition from alchemy to chemistry.

Van Helmont had little use for philosophical reasoning and was an active exponent of experimental work. The true elements he asserted to be air and water. Many experiments were performed to support his views. His work on gases has earned him the title of "the real founder of pneumatic chemistry." It was he who first coined the name *gas* and recognized carbon dioxide (*gas sylvestre*) as a product of combustion and fermentation. Although he believed in magic and alchemy, he represents a definite advance over Paracelsus in the clarity of his many ideas and in his emphasis on the use of the balance. With it he demonstrated, in many instances, the indestructibility of matter in chemical changes. He was the first to use quantitative methods in chemical experiments.

As one of the early students of physiological chemistry, Van Helmont had an extensive knowledge of bile, gastric juice, and stomach acids. What today we term *enzymes* resemble in many ways his ferments. He had some understanding of wound infection and serum immunity. The gravimetric analysis of urine is to his credit. On Van Helmont's death, his son, Franz Mercurius (1614–1699) collected and edited his manuscripts, some of which had previously been printed separately. They were published in 1648.[1] An English translation, "Oriatricke,

[1] "Ortus medicinae, Id est, initia physicae inavdita. Progressus medicinae novus, in morborum, ultionem, ad vitam longam . . . ," Elzevir, Amsterdam, 1648. Other editions followed: 2d ed. Venice, 1651; 3d ed., Elzevir, Amsterdam, 1652; Lyons, 1655 and 1667; Frankfurt, 1682; Frankfurt, 1707.

or Physick Refined," appeared in 1662.[2] It is from this volume (edition of 1662) that the following passages are taken.

Van Helmont rejected the elements and principles of Paracelsus as well as the doctrines of Aristotle. He believed the true elements to be air and water.

I have said, that there are two primary Elements; the Air, and the Water; because they do not turn into each other: but, that the Earth is as it were born of water; because it may be reduced into water. But if water be changed into an Earthy Body, that happens by the force or virtue of the Seed, and so it hath then put off the simpleness of an Element. For a flint is of water, which is broken asunder into Sand. But surely, that Sand doth lesse resist in its reducing into water, than the Sand, which is the Virgin-Earth. Therefore the Sand of Marble, of a Gemme, or Flint, do disclose the presence of the Seed. But if the Virgin-Earth, may at length, by much labour be brought into water, and if it was in the beginning created as an Element; yet it seemes then to have come down to something that is more simple than it selfe; and therefore I have called those two, Primary ones. I have denied the fire to be an Element and Substance; but to be death in the hand of the Artificer, given for great uses. I say, an artificial Death for Arts, which the Almighty hath created; but not a natural one.[3]

The doctrine does not allow the interconvertibility of the two "elements" nor their reduction to a simpler state. Fire and earth are not elements. Van Helmont's famous "tree experiment" was supposed to prove that all plants are derived from water alone.

But I have learned by this handicraft-operation, that all Vegetables do immediately, and materially proceed out of the Element of water onely. For I took an Earthen Vessel, in which I put 200 pounds of Earth that had been dried in a Furnace, which I moystened with Rain-water, and I implanted therein the Trunk or Stem of a Willow Tree, weighing five pounds; and at length, five years being finished, the Tree sprung from thence, did weigh 169 pounds, and about three ounces: But I moystened the Earthen Vessel with Rain-water or distilled water (alwayes when there was need) and it was large, and implanted into the Earth, and least the dust that flew about should be co-mingled with the Earth, I covered

---

[2] "Oriatricke, or Physick Refined, the common Errors therein Refuted, and the whole Art reformed and rectified: being a new Rise and Progress of Phylosophy and Medicine, for the Destruction of Diseases and Prolongation of Life. Written by that most Learned, Famous, Profound, and Acute Phylosopher, and chemical Physitian, John Baptista Van Helmont, and now faithfully rendered into English, in tendency to a common good, and the increase of true Science; by J[ohn] C[handler], sometime of M[erton] H[all] Oxon.," London, 1662; reissued with new title page and introductory matter in 1664.

[3] Ibid., p. 104.

the lip or mouth of the Vessel, with an Iron-Plate covered with Tin, and easily passable with many holes. I computed not the weight of the leaves that fell off in the four Autumnes. At length, I again dried the Earth of the Vessel, and there were found the same 200 pounds, wanting about two ounces. Therefore 164 pounds of Wood, Barks, and Roots, arose out of water onely.[4]

His reasoning is not completely erroneous, for willow wood is about half water. Van Helmont did not recognize the role of carbon dioxide in this process. The first use of the word *gas* and some of Helmont's concepts on fermentation and chemistry are contained in the following passage.[5] It is not difficult to understand how experiments such as the one cited here on the burning of charcoal should have given rise to the phlogiston theory.

Moreover, every coal which is made of the co-melting of Sulphur and Salt (working among themselves in time of burning) although it be roasted even to its last day in a bright burning Furnace, the Vessel being shut, it is fired indeed; but there is true fire in the Vessel, no otherwise than in the coal not being shut up; yet nothing of it is wasted, it not being able to be consumed, through the hindering of its efflux. Therefore the live coal, and generally whatsoever bodies do not immediately depart into water, nor yet are fixed, do necessarily belch forth a wild spirit or breath. Suppose thou, that of 62 pounds of Oaken coal, one pound of ashes is composed: Therefore the 61 remaining pounds, are the wild spirit, which also being fired, cannot depart, the Vessel being shut.

I call this Spirit, unknown hitherto, by the new name of Gas, which can neither be contained by Vessels, nor reduced into a visible body, unless the seed being first extinguished. But Bodies do contain this Spirit, and do sometimes wholly depart into such a Spirit, not indeed, because it is actually in those very bodies (for truly it could not be detained, yea the whole composed body should flie away at once) but it is a Spirit grown together, coagulated after the manner of a body, and is stirred up by an attained ferment, as in Wine, the juyce of unripe Grapes, bread, hydromel or water and Honey, &c. Or by a strange addition, as I shall sometime shew concerning *Sal Armoniack:* or at length, by some alterative disposition, such as is roasting in respect of an Apple: For the Grape is kept and dried, being unhurt; but its skin being once burst, and wounded, it straightway conceiveth a ferment of boyling up, and from hence the beginning of a transmutation. Therefore the Wines of Grapes, Apples, berries, Honey, and likewise flowers and leaves being once pounced, a ferment being snatched to them, they begin to boyle and be hot, whence ariseth a Gas; but from Raysins bruised, and used, for want of a ferment, a Gas is not presently granted.

[4] *Ibid.*, p. 109.

[5] *Ibid.*, pp. 106–107.

The Gas of *Wines*, if it be constrained by much force within Hogs-heads, makes Wines furious, mute, and hurtfull: Wherefore also, the Grape being abundantly eaten, hath many times bought forth a diseasie Gas. For truly the spirit of the ferment is much disturbed, and seeing it is disobedient to our digestion, it associates it selfe to the vitall spirit by force; yea, if anything be prepared to be expelled in manner of a Sweat, that thing, through the stubborn sharpness or soureness of the ferment, waxeth clotty, and brings forth notable troubles, torments, or wringings of the bowels, Fluxes, and the Bloudy-flux. I being some-times in my young beginnings deluded by the authority of ignorant writers, have believed the Gas of Grapes to be the spirit of *Wine* in new *Wine*. But vain tryalls have taught me, that the Gas of Grapes and new Wine are in the way to *Wine* but not the spirit of Wine, for the juyce of Grapes differs from *Wine*, no otherwise than the pulse of water and meal, do from Ale or Beer: For a fermentall disposition coming between both, disposeth the fore-going matter into the transmutation of it self, that thereby another Being may be made. For truly, I will at sometimes teach, that every formall transmutation doth presuppose a corruptive ferment. Other more refined *Writers* have thought, that *Gas* is a winde or air inclosed in things, which had flowen unto that generation, for an Elementary co-mixture: And so *Paracelsus* supposed, that the air doth invisibly lurk under the three other Elements, in every body; but in time onely, that the Air is visible: but his own unconstancy reproveth himself, because, seeing that he sheweth in many places else-where, that bodies are mixed of the three first things; but that the Elements are not Bodies, but the meer wombs of things.

But he observed not a two-fold Sulphur in Tin (and therefore is it lighter than other Mettalls:) whereof one onely is co-agulable by reason of the strange or forreign property of its Salt, whereby *Jupiter* or Tin maketh every Mettall frangible or capable of breaking, and brickle, it being but a little defiled with its odour onely: but that the other Sulphur is Oily. For Gun-powder doth the most neerly express the History of *Gas:* For it consisteth of Salt-peter (which they rashly think to be the Nitre of the Antients, and the which is at this day plentifully brought to us, being dried up from the inundation of *Nilus*) of Sulphur, and a Coal, because they being joyned, if they are enflamed, there is not a Vessel in nature, which being close shut up, doth not burst by reason of the *Gas*. For if the Coal be kindled, the Vessel being shut, nothing of it perisheth: but the Sulphur, if (the Glasse being shut) it be sublimed, wholly ascends from the bottom, without the changing of its Species or kinde. Saltpeter also being melted in a shut Vessel, as to one part of it, gives a sharp Liquor that is watery; but as to the other part, it is changed into a fixed *Alcali*.

Therefore fire sends forth an Air, or rather a Gas, out of all of them singly, which else, if the air were within, it would send forth from the three things being connexed. Therefore those things being applied together, do mutually convert themselves into Gas, through destruction. But there is that un-sufferance of Sulphur and Salt-peter, not indeed by the wedlock of cold with hot, as of powerfull qualities (as is believed) but by reason of the un-cosufferable flowing of boyling Oil and Wine, no lesse than of water; or of Copper and Tin, being melted with Wine. For in so great heat, when they co-touch each other throughout their least parts, they are either turned into a Gas, or do leap asunder.

Van Helmont's identification of the gas obtained in fermentation with that produced by burning charcoal is one of the first important generalizations in agricultural chemistry.

Basil Valentine (Johann Thölde)

(Fl. 1604)

BASIL Valentine, Benedictine monk of St. Peter of Erfurt, seems never to have existed. The many works which bear his name were probably written by Johann Thölde or Thölden of Hesse, who published them during the early years of the seventeenth century. He claimed to have found manuscripts which had been written by Basil Valentine in the first decades of the sixteenth century. The contents of the works discredit this, for they contain many chemical processes that were definitely of a hundred years later. Nor has any search in the records of the monasteries in Germany and the archives at Rome revealed a monk of that name. The name Basil Valentine, or the "mighty king," has the suggestive ring of a pseudonym. But why should Thölde want to publish under another name especially works of some importance? It has been suggested that this was done to secure prestige for publication. In this he was successful, for the writings of the Benedictine monk became well known.

The works of Basil Valentine give clear evidence of the influence of Paracelsus and contain no chemistry which was not known to Thölde's contemporaries. Many are expositions in the symbolic and imaginative language of alchemy. The "Triumph-Wagen des Antimonii," one of the most important books from the pen of Thölde, first appeared in Leipzig in 1604. Most of Thölde's genuine chemical knowledge is contained in this volume. It makes extravagant claims for the efficacy of antimonial remedies but gives clear and accurate directions for the preparation of many of the compounds. It has been regarded as the first scientific monograph on the compounds of a single metal. A study of the "Pirotechnia" of Vannuccio Biringuccio shows that this claim is not completely valid, for antimony was well described in this work half a century before the publication of "The Triumphal Chariot of Antimony." There is little doubt that other sources were also used. But it was nevertheless an important work, in that it disseminated a great deal of useful chemistry to a wide audience. It was translated into Latin and other languages and was for many years the authoritative work on the subject.

The following passages are selected from the Waite translation of the "Triumph-Wagen des Antimonii" and are illustrative of the directions for the preparation of antimony compounds.[1]

[PREPARATION OF ANTIMONY OXIDE]

Take best Hungarian Antimony [stibnite, antimony sulfide], or any kind you can get, pulverize it as finely as possible, spread thinly on an earthenware dish, (round or square) provided with a low margin; place the dish on a calcinatory furnace over a coal fire, which should at first be moderate. As soon as you see smoke rise from the Antimony, stir it about with an iron spoon, and continue doing so till there is no more smoke, and the Antimony sticks together in the shape of small globules. Remove it from the fire, pulverize again into a fine powder, place it on fire, and calcine, as before, till there is no more smoke. This calcination must be repeated not only till the Antimony gives out no more smoke, but does not conglomerate into globules, and has the appearance of pure white ashes. Then has the calcination of Antimony been successfully completed.

Place this calcined Antimony in a crucible, such as goldsmiths use for melting gold and silver, and set it over a violent fire, either lighted in a wind furnace or increased by means of the bellows, till the Antimony becomes liquid like pure water. To test whether Antimony has acquired its proper glassy transparency, dip in it an oblong piece of cold iron, and examine the Antimony which clings to it carefully. If it be clear, pure, and transparent, it is all right, and has attained its due maturity. The tyro, or beginner, should know (these remarks are addressed to beginners who are students of the Spagyric Art) that glass, whether prepared from metals, minerals, or any other substance, must be subjected to heat, till it has attained to maturity, and exhibits a clear and pellucid transparency. . . .

When Antimony has become vitrified in the way described, heat a flat, broad, copper dish over the fire, pour into it the Antimony in as clear and thin a state as possible, and you will have pure, yellow, pellucid glass of Antimony. This preparation of what I call the glass of Antimony

[1] A. E. Waite (Editor), "The Triumphal Chariot of Antimony, with the Commentary of Theodore Kerckringius M.D.: being the Latin Version published at Amsterdam, 1685," London, 1893.

is the simplest, best, and most efficacious with which I am acquainted.
. . .

Common glass of Antimony is pulverized; six grains or more are absolved in warm wine overnight; in the morning the wine is drunk without the sediment, and purges, both by laxation and vomiting, on account of the poisonous crudeness which still remains in glass of Antimony.[2]

[ANTIMONY CHLORIDE AND OXYCHLORIDE]

Take one part of finely pulverized Antimony and pulverized salt-armoniac [ammonium chloride], so called because it comes from Armenia: mix these together, place in a retort, and distil together. On the product of this distillation pour hot distilled (common) rain water, removing thereby every salt and acrid taste [washing thoroughly]. Then the Antimony will be of a pure, brilliant, and feathery white. . . . [3]

Pound together one pound of Antimony, half a pound of common salt, and five pounds of broken bricks; place in a retort and distil a yellow oil, when all the spirits will pass away. Pour into a fresh vessel, and remove its oiliness [by washing with water]; there remains a powder, which, spread on a stone in a humid place, and you will have a humid balm which is of great efficacy against foul wounds.[4]

[POTASSIUM PYROANTIMONATE]

Pulverize pure Hungarian Antimony, and an equal quantity of thrice-purified saltpeter; burn this composition all together in a new glazed pot, which is free from grease, over a circulatory fire, but not all at once. (This operation the ancients called detonation.) Then pulverize the hard matter which remains in the pot; pour over it moderately hot ordinary water, and when the powder has settled to the bottom, add more water, till all the saltpeter is extracted. Dry the substance, and again add to it its own weight of saltpeter; burn again, and repeat this operation three times.[5]

[ANTIMONY OXYSULFIDE]

Sulfur of Antimony may also be prepared in the following manner: Pulverize the Antimony, and digest for two hours, or longer, in strong lye made of the ashes of beechwood. Strain, add vinegar, and the sulfur will be of a red color, and sink to the bottom; pour off the liquid, and dry the powder gently.[6]

[2] *Ibid.*, pp. 93–96, 108.
[3] *Ibid.*, p. 113.
[4] *Ibid.*, p. 166.
[5] *Ibid.*, pp. 138–139.
[6] *Ibid.*, pp. 169–170.

[ANTIMONY METAL]

Take equal parts of the best Hungarian Antimony and crude tartar [potassium hydrogen tartarate], and half the quantity of saltpeter; pound together, melt over a wind fire, pour into a copper dish, allow to cool, and you will find the Regulus. The Regulus is thrice, or oftener, purified with tartar and saltpeter till it become of a brilliant silvery white. . . .

Take two parts of Hungarian Antimony, and one part of steel; melt with four parts of burnt tartar [potassium carbonate] in an iron basin, such as those in which goldsmiths refine gold. Cool, take out the Regulus, remove all impurities and scoriae, pulverize finely, add to it, after ascertaining its weight, three times as much burnt tartar; melt, and pour into a basin as before. Repeat a third time, and the Regulus becomes highly refined and brilliant. If you have performed the fusion properly—which is the point of greatest importance—you will have a beautiful star of a brilliant white. The Star is as distinct as if a draftsman had traced it with a pair of compasses.[7]

Johann Rudolf Glauber

(1604–1670)[1]

ONE of the last great members of the iatrochemical school was Johann Rudolf Glauber. His importance has been underestimated. Though he was without any formal training, he can justly be called one of the first chemical engineers. He was essentially a practical chemist, a fact that is reflected in his thirty publications. Nevertheless, he was an ardent follower of Paracelsus, whom he resembled in manner, mode of life, and philosophy. Indeed, some have called him the Paracelsus of the seventeenth century. The works of Glauber, like those of Paracelsus and Van Helmont, are filled with mysticism and superstition. His chemical philosophy was based on the three principles of salt, sulfur, and mercury, although he held salt to be the most important.

Glauber's first book, sometimes called the most remarkable work on chemistry of the seventeenth century, was his "Furni novi philosophici," published at Amsterdam in 1648. It is an extensive treatise, not only on furnaces, but on

---

[7] *Ibid.*, pp. 142, 175–176.

[1] Most historians give the year of his death as 1668, but it has been positively shown by Jorissen to be 1670. See *Chem. Weekblad*, **11**: 1076 (1914); **15**: 268 (1918); *Chem. Ztg.*, **51**: 17 (1927).

methods of distillation and on oils and spirits, with their sources and uses. His many activities, discussed in this and the works which soon followed, covered a wide range. He devised improved methods for the preparation of sulfuric, nitric, acetic, and hydrochloric acids. To the latter he gave the name *muriatic* acid from *muria*, or brine, which was used in his method of manufacture. Glauber made extensive studies of the medicinal properties of metals dissolved in his muriatic acid. It was while preparing these chlorides and other salts that Glauber realized some of the fundamentals of chemical affinity. He had a firm grasp of the nature of several chemical reactions, in spite of the mystic terms he used in some of his definitions. His interests included explosives, poison gases, and wines. In one of his later books, he predicted chemical warfare. In his book, "Teutschlands Wohlfahrt" (Amsterdam, 1656), he set forth a program for the development of Germany's natural resources. Here he advanced ideas on chemical engineering and political economy far in advance of his time.

Paracelsus, Agricola, and Van Helmont had all recognized the method which should be followed in chemical research, but Glauber first applied it in a practical manner. He was a pioneer experimental chemist, who paved the way for the man generally regarded as the father of experimental chemistry, Robert Boyle.

The first collected edition of Glauber's works was published in 1658.[2] An English edition by Christopher Packe appeared in 1689.[3] It is from this folio volume that the selections given below are taken.

Prior to Glauber's time, hydrochloric acid was made by distilling a mixture of ferrous sulfate and salt. Glauber used salt and sulfuric acid and prepared sodium sulfate at the same time. He was the first to describe crystalline sodium sulfate, or Glauber's salt. It seemed to him such a remarkable substance that he called it *sal mirabile* (also *sal mirabilis*). The following extract concerns this method.[4]

A MOST EASIE WAY OF ACQUIRING SPIRIT OF SALT TOGETHER WITH THE SALT MIRABILE.

R. of common salt two parts, dissolve it in a sufficient quantity of common water; pour A[5] upon the solution; put the mixture into a glass

[2] "Opera Chymica, Bücher und Schrifften, so viel deren von ihme bisshero an Tag gegeben worden. Jetzo von neuem mit Fleiss übersehen, auch mit etlichen neuen Tractaten vermehret," Franckfurt, 1658–1659, 2 vols.

[3] "The works of the Highly Experienced and Famous Chymist, John Rudolph Glauber: Containing, Great Variety of Choice Secrets in Medicine and Alchymy in the Working of Metallik Mines, and the Separation of Metals: also, Various Cheap and Easie Ways of making Salt-petre, and Improving of Barren-Land, and the Fruits of the Earth. Together with many other things very profitable for all the Lovers of Art and Industry. Translated into English, and Published for Publick Good by the Labour, Care, and charge of Christopher Packe, Philo-chymico-Medicus. London, Printed by Thomas Milbourn, for the Author, and are to be sold at his House next door to the Gun in Little-Moorfields; by D. Newman at the King's-Arms in the Poultry, and W. Cooper at the Pelican in Little Britain," 1689. This edition was reissued with a new title page in 1694.

[4] *Ibid.*, second part of "Miraculum mundi," p. 225.

[5] [A is evidently sulfuric acid (spirit of vitriol). Glauber here obscures his otherwise clear directions because he fears he is on the point of disclosing a valuable sceret. This was a common practice in texts of his period.]

Body, or a glass Retort well coated, or else into an earthen Body or Retort. If a Body, set on an Head, and begin to destil with Fire of sand, encreasing your Fire gradually; with the first heat comes off the unsavoury Phlegm, which gather apart; when the Liquor comes forth sowrish, change your Receiver, and receive the sowre spirit: Continue the operation till no more spirits will arise, then let out the Fire, and permit the Vessel to stand in sand till all is cooled, when cold, take it out, and if it be unbroke, fill it again with the aforesaid matter, and proceed as we taught: The Phlegm is not to be cast away, but must be kept, that in it may be dissolved Salt (because it is better than common Water) for another destillation. Thus from every pound of salt you will have lb. 1. of the best and most pure spirit. Dissolve the salt remaining in the Body or Retort (if neither be broke) in Water, filter and evaporate the Water, let it crystallize, the Crystals will be white, endowed with wonderful Virtues, to be declared here following.

Note, If the Glass be broke, there will be no necessity of dissolving the Salt, it will be enough to take out the dried *Sal Mirabile,* and reserve it for Use. . . .

OF THE EXTERNAL FIGURE, COLOUR, TASTE, AND SMELL OF SAL MIRABILIS.[6]

This *Sal Mirabilis* being rightly prepared, looketh like Water congealed or frozen into Ice; it appeareth like the Crystals of Salt-petre, which shoot into a long Figure; also it is clear and transparent, and being put to the Tongue, melts like Ice. It tasteth neither sharp, nor very salt, but leaveth a little astringency upon the Tongue. Being put upon burning Coals, it doth not leap and crackle after the manner of common salt, neither conceiveth flame like Salt-petre, nor being red hot, sends forth any smell; which gifts or endowments no other salt possesseth.

OF THE EXTERNAL AND INTERNAL USE OF MY SAL MIRABILIS.

In the first place it is to be known, that my *Sal Mirabilis* containeth many great and hidden Virtues, inasmuch as it is not so sharp and acute as other salts, and therefore its internal as well as external use, is easily admitted in Medicine. Externally adhibited, it cleanseth all fresh wounds, and open Ulcers, and healeth them; neither doth it corrode or excite pain, as other salts are wont to do. Within the body it exerciseth admirable Virtues, especially being associated with such things whose Virtues it encreaseth, and which it conducteth to those places to which it is necessary they should arrive: For Salt is the Conducter and Rector both of good and evil Powers or Virtues, and carrieth them along with it self, according as they shall be joined with it.

[6] Packe translation, *op. cit.* "A Treatise of the Nature of Salts . . . ," pp. 261–262.

One of the properties of the *sal mirabile* which Glauber considered remarkable was its ability, when molten, to "dissolve" charcoal, organic substances, and metals. Its action on charcoal was described as follows:

LX. THE MANNER OF REDUCING ANY CHAR-COAL
IN HALF AN HOURS SPACE TO ITS FIRST MATTER, THAT IS, INTO A
SULPHUREOUS SALT, BY THE SAL MIRABILIS.[7]

Melt two or three ounces of *Sal Mirabilis* in some Pot or Crucible, and throw in a peice [*sic*] of Wood-coal or Char-coal, and cover the Pot with its Cover, and let it flow for one half hour, that so the salt may dissolve as much of that Coal as it can, and may leave the rest of it which it cannot dissolve, undissolved. Then pour out your matter and you shall find a red Stone of Salt, which being tasted upon the Tongue burns it like Fire, as all Alkaly Salts do. For the corrosive force is inverted by the Vegetable Sulphur, and changed into an Alkaly.

This red Carbuncle being dissolved in Water yields a green Solution, which being filtered, and let stand still for some hours, appears of a white colour, and being let alone quiet longer, acquireth a yellow colour. One drop thereof gilds over an imperial as Sulphur does, if it be therein put. For the Char-coal is no other thing but a Sulphur of the same nature as the mineral Sulphur is of, and penetrating all the Metals, suffers it self to be fixed with them, and doth after another manner perform all those things that the mineral Sulphur is wont to do.

Robert Boyle

(1627–1691)

ROBERT Boyle is a familiar name to the historian of science, for he contributed to many of its fields. In all he wrote more than twenty scientific works.[1] Although

---

[7] Packe translation, *op. cit.*, "The second century of Glauber's wealthy store-house of Treasures . . . ," p. 48.

[1] For collected English editions of Boyle's works see the following two sources: Thomas Birch, "The Works of the Honourable Robert Boyle. In Five Volumes . . . ," London, 1744; 2d ed., 6 vols., 1772 (with added unpublished material); and Peter Shaw, "The Philosophical Works of the Honourable Robert Boyle, Esq; Abridged, methodized, and disposed under the General Heads of Physics, Statics, Pneumatics, Natural History, Chymistry, and Medicine. The whole illustrated with Notes, containing the Improvements made in the several Parts of natural and experi-

his favorite science was chemistry, his important discoveries were chiefly in physics, *e.g.*, Boyle's law.[2] He is best known to chemistry for his speculative reasoning. Through his efforts the true value of experimental investigation was first realized, although Van Helmont and Glauber had set forth a few such ideas. He encouraged groups to work together and discuss their research, an innovation in chemistry. Perhaps his most important work for chemistry lay in demolishing the doctrine of the four elements and the three principles. This and other of his chemical theories are to be found in his famous work, "The Sceptical Chymist," first published in 1661.[3] The book is written in dialogue form. Carneades is the skeptical chemist; Philoponus the exponent of the three elements of Paracelsus; Themistius the defender of the Aristotelian or Peripatetic elements; and Eleutherius an independent participant. Boyle shows by experiment that the three chemical principles and the four elements are not true elements. Carneades presents his side in opening the discussion.

Notwithstanding the subtle reasonings I have met with in the books of the Peripateticks, and the pretty experiments that have been shew'd me in the Laboratories of Chymists, I am of so diffident, or dull a Nature,

---

mental knowledge since his time," London, 1725, 3 vols.; 2d ed., 1738 (contains fewer plates than edition of 1725).

The works of Robert Boyle are best discussed in J. F. Fulton, "A Bibliography of the Honourable Robert Boyle, Fellow of the Royal Society," *Oxford Bibilographical Soc. Proc. Papers*, **3** (Pt. 1): 1–172 (1932); Addenda, *ibid.*, **3** (Pt. 3): 339–365 (1933); Second addenda, *ibid.*, n.s., **1**: 33–38 (1947).

[2] W. F. Magie, "A Source Book in Physics," New York, 1935, pp. 84–87. K. F. Mather, and S. L. Mason, "A Source Book in Geology," New York, 1939, p. 27.

[3] "The Sceptical Chymist: or Chymico-Physical Doubts and Paradoxes, touching the Spagyrist's Principles commonly call'd Hypostatical, as they are wont to be Propos'd and Defended by the Generality of Alchymists, where unto is praemis'd Part of another Discourse relating to the same Subject. By the Honorable Robert Boyle, Esq; London, Printed by J. Caldwell for J. Crooke, and are to be Sold at the Ship in St. Paul's Church-Yard," 1661. There is a second title page in this edition; they are not duplicates, and only the first bears Boyle's name. This may be the cause of the misconception that the first edition was published anonymously.

The second English edition also has two title pages, but both are without the author's name. The only reference to Boyle is in the "Publisher's Advertisement," which is indicative of the author's rise to fame between the two editions (1661–1680). "The Sceptical Chymist: Or Chymico-Physical Doubts and Paradoxes, Touching the Experiments Whereby Vulgar Spagirists are wont to Endeavour to Evince their Salt, Sulphur and Mercury; To Be The True Principles of Things. To which in this Edition are subjoyn'd divers Experiments and Notes about the Producibleness of Chymical Principles. Oxford, Printed by Henry Hall for Ric. Davis, and B. Took at the Ship in St. Pauls Church-Yard," 1680.

See paper of Tenny L. Davis [*Isis*, **8**: 71 (1926)] for the best account of the first edition of "The Sceptical Chymist." The second edition is the source of the citations made here. A reprint is accessible in the Everyman's Edition (London, 1911, and New York, 1937) and in Ostwald's *Klassiker*, No. 229, "Der Skeptische Chemiker von Robert Boyle. Verkürzt herausgegeben und übersetzt von Eduard Färber und Moritz Färber," Leipzig, 1929.

as to think that if neither of them can bring more cogent arguments to evince the truth of their assertion than are wont to be brought; a Man may rationally enough retain some doubts concerning the very number of those materiall Ingredients of mixt bodies, which some would have us call Elements, and others Principles. Indeed when I considered, that the Tenents concerning the Elements, are as considerable amongst the Doctrines of natural Philosophy, as the Elements themselves are among the bodies of the Universe, I expected to find those Opinions solidly establish'd, upon which so many others are superstructured. But when I took the pains impartially to examine the bodies themselves that are said to result from the blended Elements, and to torture them into a confession of their constituent Principles, I was quickly induc'd to think that the number of the Elements has been contended about by Philosophers with more earnestness, than success. This unsatisfiedness of mine has been much wonder'd at, by these two Gentlemen (at which words he pointed at *Themistius* and *Philoponus*) who though they differ almost as much betwixt themselves about the question we are to consider, as I do from either of them, yet they both agree very well in this, that there is a determinate number of such ingredients as I was just now speaking of, and that what that number is, I say not, may be (for what may not such as they perswade?) but is wont to be clearly enough demonstrated both by Reason and Experience. This has occasion'd our present Conference.[4]

He shows that, contrary to earlier opinions, destructive distillation will not resolve a material into its elements.

But, before I enter any further into this Disquisition, I cannot but here take notice, that it were to be wish'd our Chymists had clearly inform'd us what kind of Division of Bodies by Fire must determine the number of the Elements: For it is nothing near so easy as many seem to think, to determine distinctly the Effects of Heat, as I could easily manifest, if I had leasure to shew you how much the Operations of Fire may be diversify'd by Circumstances. But not wholly to pass by a matter of this Importance, I will first take notice to you that *Guajacum* (for instance) burnt with an open Fire in a Chimney, is sequestred into Ashes and Soot, whereas the same Wood distill'd in a Retort does yield far other Heterogeneities, (to use the *Helmontian* expression) and is resolv'd into Oyl, Spirit, Vinegar, Water and Charcoal; the last of which to be reduc'd into Ashes, requires the being farther calcin'd than it can be in a close Vessel: Besides having kindled Amber, and held a clean Silver Spoon, or some other Concave and smooth Vessel, over the Smoak of its Flame, I observ'd the Soot into which that Fume condens'd to be very differing from everything that I had observ'd to proceed from the steam

[4] "The Sceptical Chymist," 2d ed., pp. 9–11.

of Amber purposely (for that is not usual) distilled *per se* in close Vessels. Thus having, for tryals sake, kindled Camphire and catcht the Smoak that copiously ascended out of the Flame, it condens'd into a Black and unctuous Soot, which would not have been guess'd by the Smell

THE
SCEPTICAL CHYMIST:
OR
CHYMICO-PHYSICAL
Doubts & Paradoxes,
Touching the
SPAGYRIST'S PRINCIPLES
Commonly call'd
HYPOSTATICAL,
As they are wont to be Propos'd and
Defended by the Generality of
ALCHYMISTS.
Whereunto is præmis'd Part of another Discourse
relating to the same Subject.

BY
The Honourable *ROBERT BOYLE*, Esq;

LONDON,
Printed by *J. Cadwell* for *J. Crooke*, and are to be
Sold at the *Ship* in St. *Paul's* Church-Yard.
MDCLXI.

Title page of the first edition of Boyle's "The Sceptical Chymist," London, 1661. (*Courtesy of the Historical Library, Yale Medical Library.*)

or other Properties to have proceeded from Camphire: whereas having (as I shall otherwise more fully declare) expos'd a quantity of that Fugitive Concrete to a gentle heat in a close Glass-Vessel, it sublim'd up without seeming to have lost anything of its whiteness, or its Nature, both which it retain'd, though afterwards I so encreased the Fire as to bring it to Fusion. And, besides Camphire, there are divers other Bodies (that I elsewhere name) in which the heat in close Vessels is not wont to make any separation of Heterogeneities, but only a comminution of Parts, those that rise first being Homogeal with the others, though subdivided into smaller Particles: whence Sublimations have been stiled, *The Pestles of the Chymists.* But not here to mention what I elsewhere take notice of, concerning common Brimstone once or twice sublim'd, that expos'd to a moderate Fire in Subliming-Pots, it rises into dry, and almost tastless, Flowers; Whereas being expos'd to a naked Fire it affords store of a Saline and Fretting Liquor: Not to mention this, I say, I will further observe to you, that as it is considerable in the *Analysis* of mixt Bodies, whether the Fire act on them when they are expos'd to the open Air, or shut up in close Vessels, so is the degree of Fire, by which the *analysis* is attempted, of no small moment. For a milde *Balneum* will sever unfermented Blood (for instance) but into Phlegme and *Caput mortuum*, the latter whereof (which I have sometimes had) hard, brittle, and of divers Colours (transparent almost like Tortoise-shell) press'd by a good Fire in a Retort yields a Spirit, an Oyl or two, and a volatile Salt, besides another *Caput mortuum*. It may be also pertinent to our present Designe, to take notice of what happens in the making and distilling of Sope; for by one degree of Fire the Salt, the Water, and the Oyl or Grease, whereof that factitious Concrete is made up, being boyl'd up together are easily brought to mingle and incorporate into one Mass; but by another and further degree of Heat the same Mass may be again divided into an oleagenous, an aqueous, a Saline, and an Earthy part. And so we may observe that impure Silver and Lead being expos'd together to a moderate Fire will thereby be colliquated into one Mass, and mingle *per minima*, as they speak; whereas a much vehementer Fire will drive or carry off the baser Metals (I mean the Lead, and the Copper or other Alloy) from the Silver, though not, for ought appears, separate them from one another. Besides, when a Vegetable abounding in fixt Salt is analyz'd by a naked Fire, as one degree of Heat will reduce it into Ashes, (as the Chymists themselves teach us) so, by only a further degree of Fire, those Ashes may be vitrified and turn'd into Glass. I will not stay to examine how far a meere Chymist might on this occasion demand, If it be lawful for an *Aristotelian* to make Ashes, (which he mistakes for meere Earth) pass for an Element, because by one degree of Fire it may be produc'd, why a Chymist may not upon the like Principle argue, that Glass is one of the Elements of many Bodies, because that also may be obtain'd from them, barely by the fire? I will not, I say, lose time to examine this, but observe, that by a Method of applying the Fire, such similar Bodies may be obtain'd from a Concrete, as Chymists have not been able to separate; either by barely burning it in an open Fire, or by barely distilling it in close Vessels. For to me it seems very considerable, and I wonder that men have taken so little notice of it, that I have not by any of the common wayes of Distillation in close Vessels, seen any separation made of such a volatile Salt as is afforded us by Wood, when that is first by an open Fire divided into Ashes and Soot, and that Soot is afterwards plac'd in a strong Retort, and compell'd by an urgent Fire to part with its Spirit, Oyl, and Salt; for though I dare not peremptorily deny, that in the Liquors of *Guajacum* and other Woods distill'd in Retorts after the common manner, there may be Saline parts, which by reason of the Analogy may pretend to the name of some kinde of volatile Salts; yet questionless there is a great disparity betwixt such Salts and that which we have sometimes obtain'd upon the first Distillation of Soot (though for the most part it has not been separated from the first or second Rectification, and sometimes not till the third). For we could never yet see separated from Woods analyz'd only the vulgar way in close vessels any volatile Salt in a dry and Saline form, as that of Soot, which we have often had very Chrystalline and Geometrically figur'd. And then, whereas the Saline parts of the Spirits of *Guajacum*, &c. appear upon distillation sluggish enough, the Salt of Soot seems to be one of the most volatile Bodies in all Nature; and if it be well made will readily ascend with the milde heat of a Furnace, warm'd only by the singled Wieck of a Lamp, to the top of the highest Glass Vessels that are commonly made use of for Distillation: and besides all this, the taste and smell of the Salt of Soot are exceeding differing from those of the Spirits of *Guajacum*, &c. and the former not only smells & tastes much less like a vegetable Salt, than that of Harts-horn, and other Animal Concretes; but in divers other Properties seems more of Kinne to the Family of Animals, than to that of vegetable Salts, as I may elsewhere (God permitting) have an occasion more particularly to declare. I might likewise by some other Examples manifest, That the Chymists, to have dealt clearly, ought to have more explicitly and particularly declar'd by what Degree of Fire, and in what manner of Application of it, they would have us Judge a Division made by the Fire to be a true *Analysis* into their Principles, and the Productions of it to deserve the name of Elementary Bodies. But it is time that I proceed to mention the particular Reasons that incline me to Doubt, whether the Fire be the true and universal Analyzer of mixt Bodies; of which Reasons what has been already objected may pass for one.

In the next place I observe, That there are some mixt Bodies from which it has not been yet made appear, that any degree of Fire can separate either Salt or Sulphur or Mercury, much less all the Three. The most obvious Instance of this Truth is Gold, which is a body so fix'd, and wherein the Elementary Ingredients (if it have any) are so firmly united to each other, that we finde not in the operations wherein Gold is expos'd to the Fire, how violent soever, that it does discernably so much as lose of its fixedness or weight, so far is it from being dissipated into those Principles, whereof one at least is acknowledged to be Fugitive enough; and so justly did the Spagyricall Poet somewhere exclaim,

> *Cuncta adeo miris illic compagibus haerent.*

And I must not omit on this occasion to mention to you, *Eleutherius*, the memorable Experiment that I remember I met with in *Gasto Claveus*, who, though a Lawyer by Profession, seems to have had no small Curiosity and Experience in Chymical affairs; He relates then, that having put into one small Earthen Vessel an Ounce of the most pure Gold, and into another the like weight of pure Silver, he placed them both in that part of a Glass-house Furnace wherein the Workmen keep their Metal (as our English Artificers call their Liquid Glass) continually melted, and that having there kept both the Gold and the Silver in constant Fusion for two Moneths together, he afterwards took them out of the Furnace and the Vessels, and weighing both of them again, found that the Silver had not lost above a 12th part of its weight, but the Gold had not of his lost anything at all. And though our Author endeavours to give us of this a Scholastick Reason, which I suppose you would be as little satisfied with, as I was when I read it; yet for the matter of Fact, which will serve our present turne, he assures us, that though it be strange, yet Experience it self taught it him to be most true.

And though there be not perhaps any other Body to be found so perfectly fix'd as Gold, yet there are divers other so fix'd or compos'd, at least of so strictly united parts, that I have not yet observ'd the Fire to separate from them any one of the Chymists Principles. I need not tell you what Complaints the more Candid and Judicious of the Chymists themselves are wont to make of those Boasters that confidently pretend, that they have extracted the Salt or Sulphur of Quicksilver, when they have disguis'd it by Additaments, wherewith it resembles the Concretes whose Names are given it; whereas by a skilful and rigid *Examen*, it may be easily enough stript of its Disguises, and made to appear again in the pristine form of running Mercury. The pretended Salts and Sulphurs being so far from being Elementary parts extracted out of the Bodie of Mercurie, that they are rather (to borrow a terme of the Grammarians) De-compound Bodies, made up of the whole Metal and the *Menstruum*, or other Additaments imploy'd to disguise it. And as for Silver, I never could see any degree of Fire make it part with any of its three Principles. And though the Experiment lately mentioned from *Claveus* may beget a suspition that Silver may be dissipated by Fire, provided it be extreamly violent and very lasting; yet it will not necessarily follow, that because the Fire was able at length to make the Silver lose a little of its weight, it was therefore able to dissipate it into its Principles. For first I might alledge that I have observ'd little Grains of Silver to lie hid in the small Cavities (perhaps glas'd over by a vitrifying heat) in Crucibles, wherein Silver has been long kept in Fusion, whence some Goldsmiths of my Acquaintance make a Benefit by grinding such Crucibles to powder, to recover out of them the latent particles of Silver. And hence I might argue, that perhaps *Claveus* was mistaken, and imagin'd that Silver to have been driven away by the Fire, that indeed lay in minute parts hid in his Crucible, in whose pores so small a quantity as he mist of so ponderous a Bodie might very well lie conceal'd.[5]

Carneades summarizes his arguments.

And thus, *Eleutherius*, (saies *Carneades*) having at length gone through the four Considerations I propos'd to Discourse unto you, I hold it not unfit, for fear my having insisted so long on each of them may have made you forget their *Series*, briefly to repeat them by telling you, that

Since, in the first place, it may justly be doubted whether or no the Fire be, as Chymists suppose it, the genuine and Universal Resolver of mixt Bodies;

Since we may doubt, in the next place, whether or no all the Distinct Substances that may be obtain'd from a mixt body by the Fire were pre-existent there in the formes in which they were separated from it;

Since also, though we should grant the Substances separable from mixt Bodies by the fire to have been their component Ingredients, yet the Number of such substances does not appear the same in all mixt Bodies; some of them being Resoluble into more differing substances than three, and Others not being resoluble into so many as three;

And Since, Lastly, those very substances that are thus separated are not for the most part pure and Elementary bodies, but new kinds of mixts;

Since, I say, these things are so, I hope you will allow me to inferr, that the Vulgar Experiments (I might perchance have Added, the Arguments too) wont to be Alledg'd by Chymists to prove, that their three Hypostatical Principles do adequately compose all mixt Bodies, are not so demonstrative as to induce a wary Person to acquiesce in their Doctrine, which, till they Explain and prove it better, will by its perplexing darkness be more apt to puzzle than satisfy considering men, and will to them appear incumbered with no small Difficulties.

And from what has been hitherto deduc'd (Continues *Carneades*) we may Learn, what to Judge of the common Practice of those Chymists, who because they have found that diverse compound Bodies (for it will not hold in All) can be resolv'd into, or rather can be brought to afford two or three differing Substances more than the Soot and Ashes, whereinto the naked fire commonly divides them in our Chymnies, cry up their own Sect

[5] *Ibid.*, pp. 49–59.

for the Invention of a New Philosophy, some of them, as *Helmont*, &c.
styling themselves Philosophers by the Fire; and the most part not only
ascribing, but as far as in them lies, engrossing to those of their Sect the
Title of PHILOSOPHERS.

But alas, how narrow is this Philosophy, that reaches but to some of
those compound Bodies, which we find but upon, or in the crust or outside
of our terrestrial Globe, which is it self but a point in comparison of the
vast extended Universe, of whose other and greater parts the Doctrine of
the *Tria Prima* does not give us an account! For what does it teach us,
either of the Nature of the Sun, which Astronomers affirme to be eight-
score & odd times bigger than the whole Earth? or of that of those numerous fixt Starrs, which, for ought we know, would very few, if any of them,
appear inferiour in bulke and brightness to the Sun, if they were as neer us
as He? What does the knowing that Salt, Sulphur and Mercury, are the
Principles of Mixt Bodies, informe us of the Nature of that vast, fluid,
and Aetherial Substance, that seems to make up the interstellar, and consequently much the greatest part of the World? for as for the opinion commonly ascrib'd to *Paracelsus*, as if he would have not only the four Peri-
patetick Elements, but even the Celestial parts of the Universe to consist
of his three Principles, since the modern Chymists themselves have not
thought so groundless a conceit worth their owning, I shall not think it
worth my confuting.

But I should perchance forgive the Hypothesis I have been all this
while examining, if, though it reaches but to a very little part of the
World, it did at least give us a satisfactory account of those things to
which 'tis said to reach. But I find not, that it gives us any other than a
very imperfect information even about mixt Bodies themselves: For how
will the knowledge of the *Tria Prima* discover to us the Reason, why the
Loadstone draws a Needle, and disposes it to respect the Poles, and yet
seldom precisely points at them? how will this Hypothesis teach Us how a
Chick is formed in the Egge, or how the Seminal Principles of Mint,
Pompions, and other Vegetables, that I mention'd to You above, can
fashion Water into Various Plants, each of them endow'd with its peculiar
and determinate shape, and with divers specifick and discriminating
Qualities? How does this Hypothesis shew us, how much Salt, how much
Sulphur, and how much Mercury must be taken to make a Chick or a
Pompion? and if We know that: what Principle is it that manages these
Ingredients, and contrives (for instance) such Liquors as the White and
Yolk of an Egge into such a variety of Textures as is requisite to fashion
the Bones, Veines, Arteries, Nerves, Tendons, Feathers, Blood, and other
parts of a Chick; and not only to fashion each Limbe, but to connect them
altogether, after that manner that is most congruous to the perfection of
the Animal which is to Consist of Them? For to say, that some more fine
and subtile part of either or all the Hypostatical Principles is the Director

in all this business, and the Architect of all this Elaborate structure, is to give one occasion to demand again, what proportion and way of mixture of the *Tria Prima* afforded this *Architectonick* Spirit, and what Agent made so skilful and happy a mixture? And the Answer to this Question, if the Chymists will keep themselves within their three Principles, will be lyable to the same Inconvenience, that the Answer to the former was. And if it were not to intrench upon the theame of a Friend of ours here present, I could easily prosecute the Imperfections of the Vulgar Chymists Philosophy, and shew you, that by going about to explicate by their three Principles, I say not, all the abstruse Properties of mixt Bodies, but even such Obvious and more familiar *Phaenomena* as *Fluidity* & *Firmness*, The Colours and Figures of Stones, Minerals, and other compound Bodies, The Nutrition of either Plants or Animals, the Gravity of Gold or Quicksilver compar'd with Wine or Spirit of Wine; By attempting, I say, to render a reason of these (to omit a thousand others as difficult to account for) from any proportion of the three simple Ingredients, Chymists will be much more likely to discredit themselves and their *Hypothesis*, than satisfy an intelligent Inquirer after Truth.[6]

In the appendix of the second edition of "The Sceptical Chymist" is to be found Boyle's much-quoted definition of an element. Although it is the first clear approach to our present concept, Boyle does not state what a true element is. This explains why his work was not more appreciated by his contemporaries, and why the concept of the four elements and the three principles still was used in the textbooks of the early eighteenth century. It was not until Lavoisier and his table of the chemical elements that Boyle's ideas took full effect.

And to prevent mistakes, I must advertize You, that I now mean by Elements, as those Chymists that speak plainest do by their Principles, certain Primitive and Simple, or perfectly unmingled bodies; which not being made of any other bodies, or of one another, are the Ingredients of which all those call'd perfectly mixt Bodies are immediately compounded, and into which they are ultimately resolved. . . .[7]

An illustration of Boyle's experimental methods is found in his work on combustion. His first experiments in this field were carried out with Robert Hooke, who was his assistant at Oxford. His observations are clear, but he attempts few explanations, although this work anticipated many later discoveries. The following selection is taken from his "New Experiments touching the Relation betwixt Flame and Air."[8]

[6] *Ibid.*, pp. 302–307.

[7] *Ibid.*, p. 354.

[8] "Tracts Written by the Honourable Robert Boyle, Containing New Experiments, touching the Relation betwixt *Flame* and *Air*. And about Explosions. An Hydrostatical Discourse occasion'd by some Objections of Dr. Henry More against some Explications of New Experiments made by the Author of these Tracts: To which is

THE FIRST TITLE.

OF THE DIFFICULTY OF PRODUCING FLAME WITHOUT AIRE.

EXPERIMENT I.

A Way of Kindling Brimstone in vacuo Boyliano Unsuccessfully Tried.

We took a small earthen melting Pot, of an almost Cylindrical figure, and well glaz'd (when it was first bak'd) by the heat; and into this we put a small cylinder of Iron of about an inch in thickness, and half as much more in Diameter, made red hot in the fire; and having hastily pump'd out the Air, to prevent the breaking of the Glass; when this vessel seem'd to be well emptied, we let down, by a turning key, a piece of Paper, wherein was put a convenient quantity of flower of Brimstone, under which the iron had been carefully plac'd; so that, being let down, it might fall upon the heated metal, which as soon as it came to do, that vehement heat did, as we expected, presently *destroy* the contiguous paper; whence the included Sulphur fell immediately upon the iron, whose upper part was a little concave, that it might contain the flowers when melted. But all the heat of the iron, though it made the Paper and Sulphur smoke, would not actually kindle either of them that we could perceive.

EXPERIMENT II.

An Ineffectual Attempt to Kindle Sulphur in Our Vacuum Another Way.

Another way I thought of to examine the inflammability of Sulphur without Air; which, though it may prove somewhat hazardous to put it in practice, I resolved to try, and did so after the following manner:

Into a glass-buble of a convenient size, and furnish'd with a neck fit for our purpose, we put a little flower of Brimstone (as likely to be more pure and inflammable than common Sulphur;) and having exhausted the Glass, and secured it against the return of the Air, we laid it upon burning coals, where it did not take fire, but rise all to the opposite part of the glass, in the form of a fine powder; and that part being turned downward and laid on coals, the Brimstone, without kindling, rose again in the form of an expanded substance, which (being removed from the fire) was, for the most part, transparent, not unlike a yellow varnish.

ADVERTISEMENT.

Though these unsuccessful attmpts to kindle Sulphur in our exhausted Receivers, were made more discouraging by some more, that were made

---

annex't, an *Hydrostatical Letter*, dilucidating an Experiment about a Way of Weighing Water in Water . . . ," London, 1672. See Fulton, *op. cit.*, pp. 70–73, for bibliographic details. The selection is taken from the first edition.

another way; yet judging that last way to be rational enough, we persisted somewhat obstinately in our endeavours, and conjecturing that there might be some unperceived difference between Minerals, that do all of them pass, and are sold for common Sulphur, I made trial, according to the way hereafter to be mentioned, with another parcel of brimstone, which differ'd not so much from the former, as to make it worth while to set down a description of it, that probably would not be useful.

But in this place, it may suffice to have given a general intimation of the possibility of the thing. The proof of it you will meet with under the *third Title*, when I come to tell you what use I endeavour'd to make of our sulphureous Flames.

EXPERIMENT III.

Shewing the Efficacy of Air in the Production of Flame, without Any Actually Flaming or Burning Body.

Having hitherto examin'd by the *presence* of the Air, what interest it has in kindling of Flame; it will not be impertinent to add an Experiment or two, that we tried to shew the same interest of the Air by the effects of its *admission* into our Vacuum. For I thought, it might reasonably be supposed, that if such dispositions were introduc'd into a body, as that there should not appear any thing wanting to turn it into Flame but the presence of the Air, an actual asccension of that body might be produced by the admitted Air, without the intervention of any actual Flame, or Fire, or even heated substance; the warrentableness of which supposition may be judged by the two following Experiments.

When we had made the Experiment, ere long to be related in its due place, (*viz. Title* II. Exper. the 2nd) to examine the presumption we had, that even when the Iron was not hot enough to keep the melted Brimstone in such a heat, as was requisite to make it burn without Air, or with very little, it would yet be hot enough to kindle the Sulphur, if the Air had access to it: to examine this (I say) we made two or three several Tryals, and found by them, that if some little while after the flame was extinguished, the Receiver were removed, the sulphur would Presently take fire again, and flame as vigorously as before. But I thought it might without absurdity be doubted, whether or no the agency of the Air in the production of the flame might not be somewhat less than these trials would perswade; because that, by taking off the Receiver, the Sulphur was not only exposed to fresh Air, but also advantaged with a free scope for the avolution of those fumes, which in a close Vessel might be presum'd to have been unfriendly to the Flame.

How far this doubt may, and how far it should, be admitted, we may be assisted to discern by the subjoined experiment, though made in great part for another purpose; which you will perceive by the beginning of the Memorial I made of it, that runs thus;

EXPERIMENT IV.

A Differing Experiment to the Same Purpose with the Former.

Having a mind to try, at how great a degree of rarefaction of the Air it was possible to make Sulphur flame by the assistance of an adventitious heat, we caused such an experiment as the above mention'd to be reiterated, and the pumping to be continued for some time after the flame of the melted flowers of Brimstone appeared to be quite extinguished, and the Receiver was judged by those that managed the Pump (and that upon probable signs) to be very well exhausted. Then, without stirring the Receiver, we let in at the stop-cock very warily a little Air, upon which we could perceive, though not a constant flame, yet divers little flashes, as it were, which disclosed themselves by their bleu colour to be sulphureous flames; and yet the Air, that had suffic'd to re-kindle the Sulphur, was so little, that two exsuctions more drew it out again, and quite depriv'd us of the mentioned flashes. And when a little Air was cautiously let in again at the stop-cock, the like flashes began again to appear, which, upon two exeuctions [*sic*] more did again quite vanish, though, upon the letting in a little fresh Air the third time, they did once more reappear.

Whether and how far such experiments as these may conduce to explicate what is related of Fires suddenly appearing in long undisclosed Vaults or Caves to those that first broke into them, I may perchance elsewhere consider; but shall not here enquire, especially being not yet fully satisfied of the truth of the matter of fact. . . .

THE SECOND TITLE.

OF THE DIFFICULTY OF PRESERVING FLAME WITHOUT AIR

Since it is generally, and in most cases justly, esteemed to be more easie to *preserve* Flame in a body that is already actually kindled, than to *produce* it there at first; we thought fit to try, whether at least bodies already burning might not be kept in that state without the concurrence of Air. And though in some of our formerly published Physico-mechanical experiments it happen'd that actually Flame would scarce last a minute or two in our *large* Pneumatical Receiver; yet because it seem'd not improbable, that mineral bodies once kindled might afford a vigorous and very durable flame; we thought fit to devise and make the following tryals: Whence probably we might receive some new information about the *Diversities*, and some other Phenomena of Flame, and the various *degrees*, wherein the Air is necessary or helpful to them.

Reciting an Attempt to Preserve the Flame of Brimstone without Air.

We put upon a thick metalline place a convenient quantity of flowers of Sulphur; and having kindled them in the Air, we nimbly conveyed them into a Receiver, and made haste to pump out some of the included Air, partly for other reasons, and partly that the cavity of the Receiver might be the sooner freed from smok, which would, if plentiful, both injure the flame, and hinder our sight. As soon as the Pump began to be plied, or presently after, the flame appear'd to be sensibly decayed, and continued to be lessen'd at every exsuction of the Air; and in effect, it expir'd before the Air was quite drawn out. Nor did it, upon the early removal of the Receiver, do any more than afford, for a very little while, somewhat more of smoak in the open Air, than it appear'd to do before.

The reiteration of this Experiment presently after, afforded us nothing new, worth mentioning in this place.

EXPERIMENT II.

*Relating a Tryal about the Duration of the Flame of Sulphur
in vacuo Boyliano.*

To vary a little the foregoing Experiment, and try to save some moments of time, which on these occasions is to be husbanded with the utmost care; having provided a Cylinder of iron larger than the former, that it might by its bulk, being once heated, both contribute to the asccension of the Sulphur, and to the lasting of its flame, we made a tryal, that I find registred to this effect:

We took a pretty big lump of Brimstone, and tied it to the turning-key; and having got what else was necessary in a readiness, we caus'd the iron-plate to be hastily brought red-hot from the fire, and put upon a Pedestal, that the flame might be the more conspicuous; and, having nimbly cemented on the Receiver, we speedily let down the suspended Brimstone, till it rested upon the red-hot iron, by which being kindled, it sent up a great flame with copious fumes, which hinder'd us not from plying the Pump, till we had, as we conjectur'd, emptied the Receiver; which we could not do without withdrawing together with the Air much sulphureous smok, (that was offensive enough both to the eyes and nostrils.) But notwithstanding this pumping out of the Air, though the flame did seem gradually to be somewhat impaired; yet it manifestly continued burning much longer, than by the short duration of other flames in our Receivers (when diligence is us'd to withdraw the air from them) one could have expected. And especially one time, (for the experiment was made more than once) the flame lasted, till the Receiver was judg'd to be well exhausted; and some thought it did so survive the exhaustion, that it went not out so much for want of Air, as Fuel; the Brimstone appearing, when we took off the Receiver, either· to have been consum'd by the fire that fed on it, or to have casually run off from the Iron, whose heat had kept it constantly melted.

In case you should have a mind to prosecute Experiments of the nature of this and the precedent, it may not prove useless, if I intimate to you the following Advertisements.

1. For the red-hot iron above mentioned, we thought it not amiss to provide, instead of the melting-pot imploy'd in the first experiment, a Pedestal (if I may so call it) made of a lump of dryed Tobacco-pipe-clay, that the vehement heat of the iron might neither fill the Receiver with the smok of what it lean'd on, nor injure the engine, if it should rest immediately upon that; And this Pedestal should be so plac'd, that the iron may be as far, as you can, from the sides of the Receiver, which else the excessive heat would indanger.

Robert Hooke

(1635–1703)

ROBERT Hooke extended the work of Boyle on combustion into the first rational theory explaining its nature. As an assistant to Robert Boyle, Hooke became familiar with experiments on combustion; there is little doubt that his own investigations began in this laboratory. He continued his work as the curator of experiments for the Royal Society (1662). The "Micrographia," which was printed in 1664 and submitted to the Royal Society, was published in April, 1665, and is his best known work.[1] This work, which has been termed the *magnum*

[1] "Micrographia: or some Physiological Descriptions of Minute Bodies made by Magnifying Glasses, with Observations and Inquiries thereupon . . . ," London, 1665 (with 38 copper-plates); reissued, with a new title, London, 1667.

A modernized edition of the "Micrographia" by the English naturalist, Henry Baker (1698–1774), appeared in 1745. It comprises the complete set of original plates illustrating microscopic objects as published in the "Micrographia." The plates were printed from the original coppers. "Micrographia Restaurata: or, the Copper-Plates of Dr. Hooke's Wonderful Discoveries by the Microscope, reprinted and fully explained; whereby the most valuable Particulars in that celebrated Author's Micrographia are brought together in a narrow Compass; and intermixed, occasionally, with many entertaining and instructive Discoveries and Observations in Natural History," London, 1745. A reissue of the Baker edition was published in 1780: "Microscopic

opus of early microscopy, is one of the most original books in the history of science. Using microscopes of his own construction, Hooke investigated and reported in this volume on crystals, seeds and other plant organs, fibers, hair, fungi, insects, feathers, etc. Among his descriptions are interspersed many reflections, some of a chemical nature, upon the constitution and properties of matter. It is here that his theory of combustion is found. Hooke gives no experimental details in his "Micrographia" but on the basis of unpublished work postulates 12 propositions as a theory of combustion. These are given in full in the selection that follows. Although the postulates are simply, clearly, and concisely stated, the theory made little impression on his contemporaries. This indifference is difficult to explain, although some believe that Hooke's work was responsible for delaying in England the adoption of the phlogiston theory. Hooke did unquestionably provide a great stimulus for the scientific work of the following generation. An extension of his work on combustion was his volume, "Lampas."[2] A theory of combustion similar to Hooke's appeared in 1674 in the "Tractatus Quinque Medico-Physici" of John Mayow (1641–1679). There are many conflicting opinions as to the originality and meaning of Mayow's work. The argument is treated critically by Patterson.[3]

Robert Hooke is also remembered for his work on gravitation and as the discoverer of Hooke's law.[4] He made contributions in other fields as well.[5]

Hooke's interpretation of combustion is found in Observ. XVI of his "Micrographia."[6]

OBSERV. XVI.

Of Charcoal, or Burnt Vegetables.

CHARCOAL, or a Vegetable burnt black, affords an object no less pleasant than instructive; for if you take a small round Charcoal, and break it short with your finger, you may perceive it to break with a very smooth and sleek surface, almost like the surface of black sealing Wax; this surface, if it be look'd on with an ordinary *Microscope*, does manifest

---

Observations; or Dr. Hooke's wonderful discoveries by the microscope," London, 1780.

A full facsimile reprint of the 1665 edition with preface by R. T. Gunther is available: "Micrographia, 1665. Facsimile reprint with preface by R. T. Gunther," London, 1938.

Extracts from the first edition of the "Micrographia" (1665), containing his work on combustion, are to be found in *Alembic Club Reprints*, No. 5, "Extracts from Micrographia: or some Physiological Descriptions of Minute Bodies made by Magnifying Glasses with Observations and Inquiries thereupon. by R. Hooke, Fellow of the Royal Society (1665)," Edinburgh, 1902; and "Extracts from Hooke's Micrographia . . . ," *Old Ashmolean Reprints*, VI, Oxford, 1926.

[2] "LAMPAS: or Descriptions of some Mechanical Improvements of Lamps and Waterpoises, with some other Physical and Mechanical Discoveries . . . ," London, 1677.

[3] T. S. Patterson, *Isis*, **15**: 47, 504 (1931).

[4] W. F. Magie, "A Source Book in Physics," New York, 1935, pp. 93–97.

[5] K. F. Mather and S. L. Mason, "A Source Book in Geology," New York, 1938, pp. 28–32.

[6] Baker edition, pp. 100–106; *Alembic Club Reprints, op. cit.*, pp. 39–49.

abundance of those pores which are also visible to the eye in many kinds of *Wood*, rang'd round the pith, both in a kind of circular order, and a radiant one. Of these there are a multitude in the substance of the Coal, every where almost perforating and drilling it from end to end; by means of which, be the Coal never so long, you may easily blow through it; and this you may presently find, by wetting one end of it with Spittle, and blowing at the other.

But this is not all, for besides those many great and conspicuous irregular spots or pores, if a better *Microscope* be made use of, there will appear an infinite Company of exceedingly small, and very regular pores, so thick and so orderly set, and so close to one another, that they leave very little room or space between them to be fill'd with a solid body, for the apparent *interstitia*, or separating sides of these pores seem so thin in some places, that the texture of a Honey-comb cannot be more porous. Though this be not every where so, the intercurrent partitions in some places being very much thicker in proportion to the holes. . . .

It is not my design at present, to examine the use and *Mechanisme* of these parts of Wood, that being more proper to another Enquiry; but rather to hint, that from this Experiment we may learn,

First, what is the cause of the blackness of many burnt bodies, which we may find to be nothing else but this; that the heat of the fire agitating and rarifying the waterish, transparent, and volatile water that is contain'd in them, by the continuation of that action, does so totally expel and drive away all that which before fill'd the pores, and was dispers'd also through the solid mass of it, and thereby caus'd an universal kind of transparency, that it not onely leaves all the pores empty, but all the *Interstitia* also so dry and *opacous*, and perhaps also yet further perforated, that that light onely is reflected back which falls upon the very outward edges of the pores, all they that enter into the pores of the body, never returning, but being lost in it.

Now, that the Charring or Coaling of a body is nothing else, may be easily believ'd by one that shall consider the means of its production, which may be done after this, or any such manner. The body to be charr'd or coal'd, may be put into a *Crucible*, Pot, or any other Vessel that will endure to be made red-hot in the Fire without breaking, and then cover'd over with Sand, so as no part of it be suffer'd to be open to the Air, then set into a good Fire, and there kept till the Sand has continu'd red hot for a quarter, half, an hour or two, or more, according to the nature and bigness of the body to be coal'd or charr'd, then taking it out of the Fire, and letting it stand till it be quite cold, the body may be taken out of the Sand well charr'd and cleans'd of its waterish parts; but in the taking of it out, care must be had that the Sand be very neer cold, for else, when it comes into the free air, it will take fire, and readily burn away.

This may be done also in any close Vessel of Glass, as a *Retort*, or the like, and the several fluid substances that come over may be receiv'd in a fit *Recipient*, which will yet further countenance this *Hypothesis*: And their manner of charring Wood in great quantity comes much to the same thing, namely, an application of a great heat to the body, and preserving it from the free access of the devouring Air; this may be easily learn'd from the History of Charring of Coal, most excellently describ'd and publish'd by that most accomplish'd Gentleman, Mr *John Evelin*, in the 100, 101, 103, pages of his *Sylva*, to which I shall therefore refer the curious Reader that desires a full information of it.

Next, we may learn what part of the Wood it is that is the *combustible* matter; for since we shall find that none, or very little of those fluid substances that are driven over into the Receiver are *combustible*, and that most of that which is left behind is so, it follows, that the solid *interstitia* of the Wood are the *combustible* matter. Further, the reason why uncharr'd Wood burns with a greater flame then that which is charr'd, is as evident, because those waterish or volatil parts issuing out of the fired Wood, every way, not onely shatter and open the body, the better for the fire to enter, but issuing out in vapours or wind they become like so many little *Aeolipiles*, or Bellows, whereby they blow and agitate the fir'd part, and conduce to the more speedy and violent consumption or dissolution of the body.

Thirdly, from the Experiment of Charring of Coals (whereby we see that notwithstanding the great heat, and the duration of it, the solid parts of the Wood remain, whilest they are preserv'd from the free access of the air undissipated) we may learn, that which has not, that I know of, been publish'd or hinted, nay, not so much as thought of, by any; and that in short is this.

First, *that the Air* in which we live, move, and breath, and which encompasses very many, and cherishes most bodies it encompasses, that this Air is the *menstruum*, or universal dissolvent of all *Sulphureous* bodies.

Secondly, *that this action* it performs not, till the body be first sufficiently heated, as we find requisite also to the dissolution of many other bodies by several other *menstruums*.

Thirdly, *that this action* of dissolution, produces or generates a very great heat, and that which we call Fire; and this is common also to many dissolutions of other bodies, made by *menstruums*, of which I could give multitudes of Instances.

Fourthly, *that this action* is perform'd with so great a violence, and does so minutely act, and rapidly agitate the smallest parts of the *combustible* matter, that it produces in the *diaphanous medium* of the Air, the action or pulse of light, which what it is, I have else-where already shewn.

Fifthly, *that the dissolution* of sulphureous bodies is made by a substance inherent, and mixt with the Air, that is like, if not the very same, with that which is fixt in *Salt-peter*, which by multitudes of Experiments that may be made with *Salt-peter*, will, I think, most evidently be demonstrated.

Sixthly, *that in this dissolution* of bodies by the Air, a certain part is united and mixt, or dissolv'd and turn'd into the Air, and made to fly up and down with it in the same manner as a *metalline* or other body dissolv'd into any *menstruums*, does follow the motions and progresses of that *menstruum* till it be precipitated.

Seventhly, That as there is one part that is dissoluble by the Air, so are there other parts with which the parts of the Air mixing and uniting, do make a *Coagulum*, or *precipitation*, as one may call it, which causes it to be separated from the Air, but this *precipitate* is so light, and in so small and rarify'd or porous clusters, that it is very volatil, and is easily carry'd up by the motion of the Air, though afterwards, when the heat and agitation that kept it rarify'd ceases, it easily condenses, and commixt with other indissoluble parts, it sticks and adheres to the next bodies it meets withall; and this is a certain *Salt* that may be extracted out of *Soot*.

Eighthly, that many indissoluble parts being very apt and prompt to be rarify'd, and so, whilest they continue in that heat and agitation, are lighter than the Ambient Air, are thereby thrust and carry'd upwards with great violence, and by that means carry along with them, not onely that *Saline concrete* I mention'd before, but many terrestrial, or indissoluble and irrarefiable parts, nay, many parts also which are dissoluble, but are not suffer'd to stay long enough in a sufficient heat to make them prompt and apt for that action. And therefore we find in Soot, not onely a part, that being continued longer in a competent heat, will be dissolv'd by the Air, or take fire and burn; but a part also which is fixt, terrestrial, and irrarefiable.

Ninthly, that as there are these several parts that will rarifie and fly, or be driven up by the heat, so are there many others, that as they are indissoluble by the *aerial menstruum*, so are they of such sluggish and gross parts, that they are not easily rarify'd by heat, and therefore cannot be rais'd by it; the volatility or fixtness of a body seeming to consist only in this, that the one is of a texture, or has component parts that will be easily rarify'd into the form of Air, and the other, that it has such as will not, without much ado, be brought to such a constitution; and this is that part which remains behind in a white body call'd Ashes, which contains a substance, or *Salt*, which Chymists call *Alkali*: what the particular natures of each of these bodies are, I shall not here examine, intending it in another place, but shall rather add that this *Hypothesis* does so exactly agree with all Phaenomena of Fire, and so genuinely explicate each particular circumstance that I have hitherto observ'd, that it is more than probable, that this cause which I have assign'd is the true adequate, real, and onely cause of those Phaenomena; And therefore I shall proceed a little further, to shew the nature and use of the Air.

Tenthly, therefore the dissolving parts of the Air are but few, that is, it seems of the nature of those *Saline menstruums*, or spirits, that have very much flegme mixt with the spirits, and therefore a small parcel of it is quickly glutted, and will dissolve no more; and therefore unless some fresh part of this *menstruum* be apply'd to the body to be dissolv'd, the action ceases, and the body leaves to be dissolv'd and to shine, which is the Indication of it, though plac'd or kept in the greatest heat; whereas *Salt-peter* is a *menstruum*, when melted and red-hot, that abounds more with those Dissolvent particles, and therefore as a small quantity of it will dissolve a great sulphureous body, so will the dissolution be very quick and violent.

Therefore in the *Eleventh* place, it is observable, that, as in other solutions, if a copious and quick supply of fresh *menstruum*, though but weak, be poured on, or applied to the dissoluble body, it quickly consumes it: So this *menstruum* of the Air, if by Bellows, or any other such contrivance, it be copiously apply'd to the shining body, is found to dissolve it as soon, and as violently as the more strong *menstruum* of melted *Nitre.*

Therefore twelfthly, it seems reasonable to think that there is no such thing as an Element of Fire that should attract or draw up the flame, or towards which the flame should endeavour to ascend out of a desire or appetite of uniting with that as its *Homogeneal* primitive and generating Element; but that that shining transient body which we call *Flame,* is nothing else but a mixture of Air, and volatil sulphureous parts of dissoluble or combustible bodies, which are acting upon each other whil'st they ascend, that is, flame seems to be a mixture of Air, and the combustible volatil parts of any body, which parts the encompassing Air does dissolve or work upon, which action, as it does intend the heat of the *aerial* parts of the dissolvent, so does it thereby further rarifie those parts that are acting, or that are very neer them, whereby they growing much lighter then the heavie parts of that *Menstruum* that are more remote, are thereby protruded and driven upward; and this may be easily observ'd also in dissolutions made by any other *menstruum*, especially such as either create heat or bubbles. Now, this action of the *Menstruum*, or *Air*, on the dissoluble parts, is made with such violence, or is such, that it imparts such a motion or pulse to the *diaphanous* parts of the Air, as I have elsewhere shewn is requisite to produce light.

This *Hypothesis* I have endeavoured to raise from an Infinite of Observations and Experiments, the process of which would be much too long to be here inserted, and will perhaps another time afford matter copious enough for a much larger Discourse, the Air being a Subject which (though all the world has hitherto liv'd and breath'd in, and been unconversant about) has yet been so little truly examin'd or explain'd, that a diligent enquirer will be able to find but very little information from what has been (till of late) written of it: But being once well understood, it will, I doubt not, inable a man to render an intelligible, nay probable, if not the true reason of all the *Phaenomena* of Fire, which, as it has been found by Writers and Philosophers of all Ages a matter of no small difficulty, as may be sufficiently understood by their strange *Hypotheses*, and unintelligible Solutions of some few *Phaenomena* of it; so will it prove a matter of no small concern and use in humane affairs, as I shall elsewhere endeavour to manifest when I come to show the use of the Air in respiration, and for the preservation of the life, nay, for the conservation and restauration of the health and natural constitution of mankind as well as all other aereal *animals*, as also the uses of this principle or propriety of the Air in chymical, mechanical, and other operations. In this place I have onely time to hint an *Hypothesis*, which, if God permit me life and opportunity, I may elsewhere prosecute, improve and publish. . . .

Nicolas Lemery

(1645–1715)

ONE of the most popular chemical works published before the birth of modern chemistry, at the end of the seventeenth century, was the "Cours de chymie" of Nicolas Lemery.[1] The popularity of this book was due in part to its easy and entertaining style, as well as to its simplicity. It has recently been shown convincingly that Lemery owed much of his material to the immediately preceding "Traité de la chymie" of Christophe Glaser (d. 1670–1673), which he nowhere acknowledged.[2] Nevertheless, Lemery was responsible for the dissemination of

[1] "Cours de Chymie, Contenant La Maniere De Faire les Operations qui sont en usage dans la Medecine, par une Methode facile. Avec des raisonnements sur chaque Operation, pour l'Instruction de ceux qui veulent s' appliquer à cette Science," Paris, 1675. The work appeared in 22 French editions.

The first English edition was published in 1677: "A Course of Chymistry. Containing The Easiest Manner of performing those Operations that are in Use in Physik. Illustrated With many Curious Remarks and Useful Discourses upon each Operation. Writ in French by Monsieur Nicholas Lemery. Translated by Walter Harris, Doctor of Physick. London, Printed for Walter Kettilby at the Bishop's Head in St. Paul's Church-Yard," 1677.

Other English editions appeared in 1686 and 1698, the last in 1720. German, Latin, Italian, and Spanish translations were also made.

[2] C. de Milt, *J. Chem. Education*, **19**: 53 (1942).

much chemical knowledge, whether his own or Glaser's. In his "Cours de chymie" Lemery makes use of the corpuscular theory of Descartes, which held that the properties of substances depend principally on the shapes of their particles. This is extended by Lemery to acids, whose properties he ascribes to a sharp, spiky form. This is an atomistic explanation, but it remained for Dalton, more than a century later, to replace these and other speculations with a sound atomic theory. The following passage is taken from the second English edition of "A Course of Chymistry" (London, 1686), pages 23 to 26, and contains the explanation of acids and bases.

The *Chymists* do assure us, but with little foundation for it, that in Terrestrious bodies, in *Metal's, Coral, Pearl,* and generally in all bodies that Ferment with *acids,* there is an hidden *Alkali* in them, which is one of the Principles of *Fermentation,* wherefore they give them the names of *Alkali's;* but because no manner of *Salt* can be drawn from them: to prove their Opinion, and they have no other rational Argument to perswade me, they must give me leave to think otherwise than they have done, and I conceive that the contrary to what they have established will serve me better to explicate the truth.

Following therefore the *Principle* I have laid, I believe that those Terrestrious bodies are themselves *Alkali's,* rather than that the *Ebullition* of *Acid* and *Alkali* proceeds from a *salt* supposed to be contained in them; and further that the *salts* are never *Alkali's* until they have undergone the force of fire, and been reduced into a *Calx.* I have proved, speaking of the nature of *Volatile salt,* that the fire did very much change the substances of things; and as I have shewn there is good reason to think there is but only one *species* of *salt* in Plants, and the *Volatile salt* is but a change wrought by fire; I shall proceed upon the same *Principle,* and affirm that there is no fixt *Alkali salt* in Plants, but that by *Calcination* the fire has fixt a part of the *acid Essential salt* with the earthy part that has serv'd to break the keenest of its points, and rendred them Porous, like a *Calx.* It is by reason of these Pores that this kind of *salt* grows humid, and melts so easily when exposed to the Air; and the Terrestrious parts do turn it into an *Alkali,* for if they were not mixed with it, it would continue still an *acid salt,* and opposed to *Alkali.* But to clear up this point the better, we must consider as nicely as may be the nature of an *Acid* and an *Alkali.*

Whereas the nature of a thing so obscure as that of *salt,* cannot better be explicated, than by admitting to its parts such figures as are answerable to the effects it produces; I shall affirm, that the *acidity* of any liquor does consist in keen particles of *salts,* put in motion; and I hope no body will offer to dispute whether an *acid* has points or no, seeing every ones experience does demonstrate it, they need but taste an *acid* to be satisfied of it, for it pricks the tongue like any thing keen, and finely cut; but a demonstrative and convincing proof that an *acid* does consist of pointed parts is, that not only all *acid salts* do *Crystallize* into edges, but all Dissolutions of different things, caused by *acid* liquors, do assume this figure in their *Crystallization;* these *Crystalls* consist of points differing both in length and bigness one from another, and this diversity must be attributed to the keener or blunter edges of the different sorts of *acids;* and so likewise this difference of the points in subtilty is the cause that one *acid* can penetrate and dissolve well one sort of *mixt*, that another can't rarifie at all: Thus *Vinegar* dissolves *Lead*, which *aqua fortis* can't: *Aqua fortis* dissolves *Quick-silver*, which *Vinegar* will not touch; *Aqua Regalis* dissolves *Gold*, whenas *Aqua fortis* cannot meddle with it; on the contrary *Aqua fortis* dissolves *Silver*, but can do nothing with *Gold*, and so of the rest.

As for *Alkali's*, they are soon known by pouring an *acid* upon them, for presently or soon after, there rises a violent *Ebullition*, which remains until the *acid* finds no more bodies to rarifie. This effect may make us reasonably conjecture that an *Alkali* is a terrestrious and solid matter, whose *pores* are figured after such a manner that the *acid* points entering into them do strike and divide whatsoever opposes their motion; and according as the parts of which the *Alkali* is compounded, are more or less solid, the *acids* finding more or less resistance, do cause a stronger or weaker *Ebullition*. So we see the *Effervescency* that happens in the dissolution of *Coral* is very much milder than that in the dissolution of *Silver*.

There are as many different *Alkali's*, as there are bodies that have different pores, and this is the reason why an *acid* will Ferment with one strongly, and with another not at all; for there must be a due proportion between the *acid* points, and the *pores* of the *Alkali*.

Johann Joachim Becher

(1635–1682)

CONTEMPORARY with the work of Boyle in England, a movement was initiated in Germany which was to play an important part in chemistry for the next century. This was the doctrine of phlogiston, which was first conceived by J. J. Becher, although the term itself was first generally used by Georg Ernst Stahl in his popularization of the ideas of Becher. Becher believed in the four elements and the three principles, with some modifications. He supposed that bodies were made up of air, water, and three earths. The latter corresponded to the sulfur, mercury, and salt of Paracelsus, but were known as *terra pinguis* (fatty or inflammable earth), *terra mercurialis* (mercurial earth), and *terra lapidia* (vitreous or stony earth). In combustion, the *terra pinguis* was released by the fire, fusibility was due to *terra mercurialis*, and *terra lapidia* remained as the calx after complete ignition of a metal or other substance. These new terms were an advance in a sense, for they removed the association of potential qualities with actual substances such as the sulfur of the iatrochemists. Combustion to Becher was the breakup of a body with expulsion of its more volatile constituent. These concepts were set forth in 1669 in his "Acta laboratorii chymici monacensis, seu physicae subterraneae."[1] The following selection has been taken from the 1681 edition.[2]

I say that there are three different earths in metals and stones; the first, aside from its own mixtures, is found in stones and alkali salt; the second in niter; the third in common salt. When these three earths are mixed together without any other additions, they constitute true and genuine metals, and also stones, according to the manner of formation. Hence, I conclude that stones and metals naturally belong together, as we will specifically show in the following chapters of this section and in Book 2; for this is our opinion, based on practice, that metals and stones are made up of three simple earths, and that the evidence for these comes not from the resulting bodies, since these are already mixed or can exist unmixed, but from the beginnings; in so far as these are miscible and mixed, they determine the body of which they constitute the principles. Thus, in this kind of philosophizing it is necessary to argue from the beginnings to the results, since the subjects are subterraneous, homogeneous, and insoluble, unless some new decomposition occurs. Now, our opinion having been explained in general, we will hurry on to the explanation of the three principles, namely, the three earths, according to our mind. . . .

CONCERNING THE FIRST PRINCIPLE OF METALS AND STONES, WHICH IS CALLED VITREOUS STONE, OR STONY EARTH [*terra lapidia*] AND IMPROPERLY SALT[3]

Up to now, we have been treating in general the principles of those things that are subterraneous. . . . Now we are going to explain each of the principles, of which there are three (that is three earths), and in this

[1] "Actorum Laboratorii Chymici Monacensis, seu Physicae Subterraneae Libri Duo quorum prior profundam subterraneorum genesin, nec non, admirandam Globi terratque—aerei et subterranei fabricam posterior specialem subterraneorum naturam, resolutionem in partes partiumque proprietates exponit; accessrunt sub finem mille hypotheses seu mixtiones chymicae ante hac nunquam visae, omnia plusquam mille experimentis stabilita, sumptibus et permissu Serenissimi Electoris Bavariae, etc. Domini sui clementissimi elaboravit et publicavit Joannes Joachimus Becherus, spirensis. . . . Francofurti, Imp. Joh. Davidis Zunneri. Anno 1669." Edito Altera, 1681.

[2] Book 1, Sec. 3, Cap. 1, pp. 118–119.

[3] *Ibid.*, Book 1, Sec. 3, Cap. 2, pp. 119–121.

chapter we are going to begin with the first, which is the mother and source of the other two. The kind of stone which melts in fire, and melting, produces glass, is found in all species of stones, of which there are three: for some stones melt, others do not melt, but in a strong fire are reduced to a calx, and still others do not melt nor are they reduced to a calx, but remain intact even in the strongest fire; still further, some of these always remain when glowing hot but when made ice cold break apart and crumble, but others get red hot or ice cold as often as you wish, and always remain unchanged.

Concerning this first species of stone, namely, stones that melt. . . . These are recognized by diverse properties, for mud, sand, flint, and many other stones melt in fire; but by this species we understand that which is the noblest of all, and is often called *calx* by the mineralogists. Without it no other mineral is of any value, or sends forth any fertility, for that stone is so necessary to minerals that, existing in the mountains either raw or without any other metal, it becomes an infallible sign of future metal . . . therefore we state and acknowledge this earth or stone . . . as the first principle of all metals, minerals, stones, and gems. . . . It is actually present in all metals and minerals, and also in all stones and gems. . . .

CONCERNING THE SECOND PRINCIPLE OF MINERALS, WHICH IS FATTY EARTH [*terra pinguis*], IMPROPERLY CALLED SULFUR[4]

We find the three earths in animals, vegetables, and minerals. . . . These three have a great affinity one for the other, and a great analogy. While it [*i.e. terra pinguis*] is related to the other earth which we have already treated and whence metals and stones obtain their liquidity and fusibility, it most certainly has a great relationship and analogy with the earth of vegetables, that, namely, which is present in the calcination of vegetables and the lixiviation of ashes. . . . It can also be prepared from all vegetables, for this earth, although it seems to be useless and of no value, has a very great analogy with the preceding earth of minerals and magnetism. This is apparent in the glassmaker's art, for when the glassmaker makes glass out of stone and flint, that is, from the aforementioned earth of minerals, which is thickened in flowing, either because of a lack of salt, or because of an excess of fire, so that it is again made hard and coagulates, nevertheless as soon as the preceding earth is injected from the ashes, not only is the whole mass of glass made more flowing, but also . . . takes on growth and augment. This not only proves the great affinity of vegetable earth with mineral, but even a great likeness, harmony, and analogy, since this earth per se can be made into glass. . . .

[4] *Ibid.*, Book 1, Sec. 3, Cap. 3, pp. 129–132.

CONCERNING THE THIRD PRINCIPLE OF MINERALS, WHICH IS
FLUID EARTH [*terra fluida*] IMPROPERLY CALLED MERCURY[5]

Especially in hidden things there is some third raw material, for the
idea cannot be denied that a stone gives to metals a likeness to itself,
and therefore a distinctive nature.   For the essence of metals is different
from the substance of stones in that they are of a malleable and extensible
nature. . . . That which makes a metal, metal, specifically comes from
this third principle. . . . But we also find an analogy to this substance
in vegetables and minerals.   In vegetables, indeed, since when they are
heated they not only exhibit salts of diverse shapes, but also sometimes
their volatile salts, is made manifest the old idea of a plant. . . . In
animals volatile salts are often noticed, especially from the horn of a deer,
which illustrates this idea very clearly.

Wherefore, I must necessarily state that there is a certain immortal
form hidden in things; a subtle earth. . . . Although some chemists call
it mercury, nevertheless, if you understand the true import of the word,
it is a salt which may actually exist in bodies, producing mercury. . . .
If it is said to be a principle, the fact that it may be a mixture or a mere
decomposition is contrary to the simplicity and unity of a principle, whose
definition is a simple, homogeneous, and unique being. I must therefore
conclude that this third earth is called *mercury* because of its mercurial
quality, *i.e.*, volatility . . . for if a metal is attacked out of proportion
by this earth, it is again made fluid and volatile.

Georg Ernst Stahl

(1660–1734)

THE formulation of the phlogiston theory, first conceived in principle by Johann
Becher, was finally due to his pupil, Georg Ernst Stahl. He accepted the doctrine
that combustible substances contain an ignitable matter, the *terra pinguis* of
Becher. To this Stahl gave the name *phlogiston* (derived from φλογίζειν, to in-
flame). Most of the chemists of the eighteenth century were believers in the
phlogiston theory, which, though erroneous, still provided a basis for the many
experiments that contributed to the birth of modern chemistry under the influence of Antoine Lavoisier. Stahl was one of the first to formulate a rational
system of chemistry on a structure of experimental observations.

[5] *Ibid.*, Book 1, Sec. 3, Cap. 4, pp. 149–152.

To Stahl, metals were compounds containing phlogiston in combination with metallic oxides (calces); on ignition the phlogiston was freed from the metal, leaving the oxide behind. When the oxide was heated with a substance rich in phlogiston, such as charcoal, the calx again took up phlogiston and regenerated the metal. Phlogiston was a definite substance, the same in all its combinations. To explain the gain in weight during calcination of metals, the concept of negative weight was introduced.

The first definition of phlogiston appeared in Stahl's "Zymotechnia fundamentalis,"[1] first published in 1697. Stahl speaks of his phlogiston in the following selection.[2]

The same thing works very well with sulfur, when certainly two parts, or better, three parts of alkali salt and one of pulverized sulfur are successively poured into and fused in a crucible. There is formed liver of sulfur. This, in the space of a quarter of an hour more or less, by fire alone, without any addition, can be converted to such a salt as is obtained from oil of sulfur *per campanum* [H_2SO_4] and salt of tartar, that which is commonly called *vitriolated tartar*. There is no more trace of sulfur or alkali salt, and in place of the red color of the liver, this salt is most white; in place of the very evil taste of the liver, this salt is very bitter; in place of the easy solution, nay, the spontaneous deliquescence of the liver, by reason of its alkali salt, this salt is the most difficult of all salts except tartar of wine to be dissolved; in place of the impossibility of crystallizing the liver, this is very prone to form almost octahedral crystals; in place of the fusibility of the liver, this is devoid of all fusion.

If this new salt, from the acid of sulfur and alkaline salt formed as stated above when the phlogiston has been used up, is treated with charcoal, in the space of a quarter of an hour the original liver of sulfur reappears, and this can be so converted a hundred times. . . .

I can indeed show by various other experiments how phlogiston from fatty substances and charcoal enters very promptly into metals them-

---

[1] "Zymotechnia fundamentalis seu Fermentationis Theoria generalis, qua nobilissimae hujus artis et partis chymiae, utilissimae ac subtillissimae, causae et effectus in genere, ex ipsis mechanico-physicis principiis, summo studio eruuntur . . . ," Halle, 1697.

This work also appears in the "Opusculum Chymico-Physico-Medicum" of Stahl, from which the extracts are, in part, taken: "Opusculum Chymico-Physico-Medicum, seu Schediasmatum a Pluribus Annis Variis Occasionibus In Publicum Emissorum Nunc Quadantenus Etiam Auctorum Et Deficientibus Passim Exemplaribus In Unum Volumen Jam Collectorum, Fasciculus Publicae Luci Redditus, Praemissa Praefationis Loco Authoris Epistola Ad Tit. Dn, Michaelem Alberti D. & Prof. Publ. Extraordinarium. Editonem hanc adcuratem. Halae Magdeburgicae, Typis & Impensis Orphantrophei. Anno 1715."

[2] "Opusculum Chymico-Physico-Medicum . . . ," pp. 144–145. This is a portion of Cap. XII of the "Zymotechnia."

selves and regenerates them from the burned calx into their own *fusible, malleable,* and *amalgamable* state.

The ideas which Stahl expressed in a rather scattered fashion in his "Zymotechnia" were later assembled more systematically in his work on sulfur.[3] The following expression of his theory is taken from pages 77 to 80 of this book.

Now the first thing to consider concerning the principle of sulfur is its properties, as follows:

1. Behavior toward fire
2. Display of colors
3. Subtle and intimate mixing with other metal substances
4. Behavior toward water and humidity
5. Its own great and wonderful subtlety
6. Its own form in the dry or fluid state
7. Where it can be found or occurs

According to these conditions and intentions, I now have demonstrable grounds to say, first,

Toward fire, this sulfur principle behaves in such a manner that it is not only suitable for the movement of fire but is also one and the same being, yes, even created and designed for it.

But also, according to a reasonable manner of speaking, it is the corporeal fire, the essential fire material, the true basis of fire movement in all inflammable compounds.

However, except in compounds, no fire at all occurs, but it dissipates and volatilizes in invisible particles, or at least, develops and forms a finely divided and invisible fire, namely, heat.

On the other hand, it is very important to note that this fire material, of and by itself and apart from other things, especially air and water, is not found united and active, either as a liquid or in an attenuated state. But if once by the movement of fire, with the addition of free air, it is attenuated and volatilized, then by this in all such conditions it is lost through unrecognizable subtlety and immeasurable attenuation, so that from this point on no science known to man, no human art, can collect it together or bring it into narrow limits, especially if this occurred rapidly and in quantity.

But how enormously attenuated and subtle material becomes through the movement of fire is shown by experience, which furnishes a field for thought and which also delights us.

From all these various conditions, therefore, I have believed that it

---

[3] "Zufällige Gedanken und nützliche Bedencken über den Streit von dem sogenannten Sulphure, und zwar sowohl dem gemeinen, verbrennlichen, oder flüchtigen, als unverbrennlichen oder fixen," Halle, 1718.

should be given a name, as the first, unique, basic, inflammable principle.
But since it cannot, until this hour, be found by itself, outside of all compounds and unions with other materials, and so there are no grounds or basis for giving a descriptive name based on properties, I have felt that it is most fitting to name it from its general action, which it customarily shows in all its compounds.   And therefore I have chosen the Greek name phlogiston, in German, *Brennlich* [inflammable]. . . .

The seventh and last consideration was where it could be found or occurred. The answer to this is now also in part easy to give from the discussion already presented, and from consideration that all corporeal compounded things have more or less of this substance, in all the so-called "kingdoms": vegetable, animal, and mineral. As then in the first two kingdoms there is contained a great amount of this principle, and all their parts are intimately penetrated and combined with it (except the watery parts which occur in them, but which still are not entirely free from it as long as they are in the body), then it is chiefly found in the fatty materials of both kingdoms.

In the mineral kingdom there is nothing but water, common salt, pure vitriolic salts, and light sand and stones in which the substance is little or not at all found. On the other hand, coal and bitumen are full of it; sulfur, not indeed in weight, but in the number of its finest particles, is completely possessed with it. Not less is it found in all inflammable, incomplete, and so-called "unripe" metals.

Stahl wrote several treatises on chemistry, of which "Fundamenta chymiae"[4] is the best known, since it had an important influence on chemists of the period. It is here that Stahl's often-quoted definition of chemistry is to be found.[5]

PRELIMINARIES

1. Universal chemistry is the Art of resolving *mixt, compound,* or *aggregate* Bodies into their *Principles;* and of composing *such Bodies* from those *Principles.*

[4] "Fundamenta chymiae dogmaticae et experimentalis, et quidem tum communioris physicae mechanicae pharmaceuticae ac medicae tum sublimioris sic dictae hermeticae atque alchymicae. Olim in privatos Auditorum usus posita, jam vero indultu. Autoris publicae luci exposita. Norimbergae, Sumptibus Wolfangi Mauritij, An. 1723."

This work was translated and used in part by Peter Shaw in his English edition, "Philosophical Principles of Universal Chemistry; or The Foundation of a scientifical Manner of Inquiring into and Preparing the Natural and Artificial Bodies for the Uses of Life: Both in the smaller Way of Experiment, and the larger Way of Business. Design'd as a General Introduction To the Knowledge and Practice of Artificial Philosophy: or Genuine Chemistry in all its Branches. Drawn from the *Collegium Jenense* of Dr. George Ernst Stahl. By Peter Shaw M.D. London: Printed for John Osborn and Thomas Longman, at the Ship in Paternoster-Row," 1730.

[5] *Ibid.,* p. 1.

2. It has for its *Subject* all the *mix'd*, *compound*, and *aggregate Bodies* that are *resolvable* and *combinable;* and *Resolution* and *Combination*, or Destruction and Generation, for its *Object*.

3. Its *Means* in general are either *remote* or *immediate;* that is, either *Instruments* or the *Operations* themselves.

4. Its *End* is either *philosophical* and *theoretical;* or *medicinal, mechanical, economical*, and *practical*.

5. Its *efficient Cause* is the *Chemist*.

In his discussion of the composition of substances, Stahl divides all matter into several classes, depending on their chemical nature. He uses the usual four elements and three principles. The combination of the original principles into simple compounds he terms *mixts*. A further union of mixts forms *compounds*, whereas a miscellaneous group of substances are designated *aggregates*. The following selection illustrates his treatment of the subject.[6]

THE STRUCTURE OF SIMPLE, MIX'D, COMPOUND AND AGGREGATE MATTER

1. As *mix'd, compound*, and *aggregate Bodies* are, according to our Definition, the Subject of *Chemistry*, 'tis necessary that we here consider their *chemical Structure*.

2. All *natural Bodies* are either *simple* or *compounded:* the *simple* do not consist of *physical parts;* but the *compounded* do.   The *simple* are *Principles,* or the first material causes of *Mixts;* and the *compounded*, according to the difference of their mixture, are either *mix'd, compound or aggregate: mix'd*, if composed merely of Principles; *compound*, if formed of Mixts into any determinable single thing; and *aggregate*, when several such things form any other entire parcel of matter, whatsoever it be.

3. A *Principle* is defined, *à priori*, that in mix'd matter, which *first existed;* and *à posteriori*, that into which it is *at last resolved*.

4. Both these definitions are exact, if we allow of a *pure, natural resolution:* but as this is not easily obtainable from the Chemistry of these days, and so can hardly be come at by Art, a difference, at present, prevails between the *physical* and *chemical Principles* of mix'd Bodies.

5. Those are called *physical Principles* whereof a Mixt is really composed, but they are not hitherto settled: for the four *Peripatetical Elements*, according to their vulgar acceptation, do not deserve this title. And those are usually termed *chemical Principles*, into which all Bodies are found reducible by the chemical operations hitherto known.

6. These *chemical Principles* are called *Salt, Sulphur*, and *Mercury;* the analogy being taken from Minerals: or, *Salt, Oil*, and *Spirit;* to which Dr. *Willis* adds *Phlegm* and *Earth;* but improperly, since *Phlegm* is comprehended under *Spirit:* for inflammible Spirits cannot be here meant; these consisting manifestly of Water, Oil and Salt, as we shall see hereafter.

[6] *Ibid.*, p. 3.

7. But as the four *Peripatetic Elements*, howsoever understood, cannot have place, if supposed specifically the same in all Subjects; so neither can the *Chemical Principles:* for no-one has hitherto pretended to shew that these *Principles* are specifically the same in all Bodies. But if consider'd only as to their *generical qualities*, they may be allow'd in *Compounds*.

8. We say particularly in *Compounds*, because all the darkness and disputes about *Principles* arise from a neglect of that *real distinction* between *original* and *secondary Mixts*, or *Mixts consisting of Principles* and *Bodies compounded of Mixts*. Whilst these two are confounded, and supposed to be resolved by an operation that is contrary to Nature, the common *chemical Principles* of vegetables, animals and minerals are produced, and prove in reality *artificial Mixts:* but when *Compounds* are separated by bare resolution, without the least combination, their *Principles* are *natural Mixts*.

9. By justly distinguishing between *Mixts* and *Compounds*, without directly undertaking to exhibit the *first Principles* of the latter, we may easily settle this affair. *Helmont* and *Becher* have attempted it; the former taking *Water* for the first and only *material Principle* of all things; and the other, *Water* and *Earth;* but distinguishing the *Earth* into *three kinds*.

Hermann Boerhaave

(*1668–1738*)

HERMANN Boerhaave was one of the greatest exponents of chemistry of the eighteenth century. Although a chemist of skill, he made no discoveries of consequence; it was rather his textbook, "Elementa chemiae," and his teaching that made him famous. The first appearance of this book was a pirated edition which his students, impatient for a text, collated and edited from their notes.[1] Boerhaave disowned the spurious work and soon published his own edition, in order to correct what he considered the numerous errors of the unauthorized work.[2] It was

[1] "Institutiones et Experimenta Chemiae, Parisus," 1724. It was probably printed in Leiden, not Paris.

[2] "Elementa Chemiae, Quae Anniversaria Labore Docuit, In Publicis, Privatisque, Scholis, Hermannus Boerhaave. Tomus Primus qui continet Historiam et Artis Theoriam cum Tabulis Aeneis. Tomus Secundus qui continet Operationes Chemicas. Lugduni Batovorum, Apud Isaacum Severinum," 1732. On the reverse of the title page is Boerhaave's signature, which he placed on each copy as a guarantee of genuineness.

The third English edition of this work (actually the second, for the first was the

one of the most successful works of its day and soon was translated into English, German, and French. The influence of the "Elementa chemiae" was felt for half a century. To the historian of chemistry it has a special interest, for Part I contains one of the finest accounts of the development of chemistry written up to that time. Although Boerhaave was free from iatrochemical concepts, he still believed in the possibility of the transmutation of metals and in the four elements. In spite of this, the book is a complete survey of the chemical knowledge of his day, and it is characteristically free from obscurity. He does not mention Stahl and the doctrine of phlogiston, which is remarkable, for this idea was then dominant. It probably indicates that he was not convinced of its importance.

The following selection is an excellent example of Boerhaave's style and gives an unusually good exposition of the principles of alchemy. The logical character of the basic beliefs as shown here explains why even such a rational mind as that of Boerhaave could accept the possibility of transmutation. The selection is taken from the English edition of 1753, Vol. I, page 200.

ALCHEMY

37. I come now to add a few, but candid and ingenuous considerations, on the great use of chemistry in alchemy. To speak my mind freely, I have not met any writers on natural philosophy, who tread [sic] of the nature of bodies, and the manner of changing them, so profoundly, or explain'd them so clearly, as those called alchemists. To be convinced of this, read carefully their genuine writings: for instance, that piece of *Raymund Lully*, which he entitled *Experiments;* you will find him with the utmost clearness and simplicity, relating experiments, which explain the nature and actions of animals, vegetables, and fossils. After this, you will hardly be able to name an author, wherein physical things are treated of to so much advantage.

38. The bodies, which chemistry resolves before our eyes, afford demonstrations which call for our assent, infinitely more cogently than any words could do; by these we do what we say, and what we teach we perform: Insomuch, that these writers seem to have attempted to build that body of philosophy, wish'd for by the great Lord *Bacon; viz.* a philosophy, which should lay down such powers of bodies, as the bodies themselves, when present, really exhibit effects to warrent; and consequently should

---

pirated edition) has been used for the selections given here: "A New Method of Chemistry, including the History, Theory, and Practice of the Art; Translated from the Original Latin of Dr. Boerhaave'es Elementa Chemiae as Published by Himself. To which are added, Notes; and an Appendix, shewing the necessity and utility of enlarging the Bounds of Chemistry. With Sculptures. By Peter Shaw. The Third Edition corrected. London, T. and T. Longman," 1753, 2 vols.

For a critical discussion of all the editions of the "Elementa Chemiae," see T. L. Davis, *Isis*, **10**: 33–46 (1928); M. Hertzberger, "Short-title Catalogue of Books Written and Edited by Boerhaave," Amsterdam, 1927.

assign such causes of things, as being given, will readily produce the things themselves: so that when it pleased it could do what it taught.

39. They laugh'd at those subtile universal causes, sought for only by speculation; the knowledge whereof did not render the inquirers more fit for effecting any thing, and of which the schoolmen obtruded more than enough. Hence they are continually inculcating, that man cannot by any art go beyond the powers impress'd by the Creator on bodies; of which powers such as are of necessary use to life, are obvious enough; but others lie less apparent, and are only revealed to those who seek them with great labour and industry, but that both are equally natural. That a man, therefore, possessed of all knowledge of things, both past and to come, would never be able to create, or make the least thing; for instance, a grain of mustard-seed; or produce it out of matter, which was not mustard-seed before. That wise men observe the works of nature as they offer themselves, and then by experiments endeavour to learn the laws; which the Creator has impressed on his work, and in what manner each thing, according to its peculiar nature, arises, is produced, or perfected; the principal of which laws is, that all things arise from other similar pre-existent ones; plants from plants, animals from animals, and fossils from fossils. That all power of propagating is contained in the seminal matter alone; which converts every crude thing it takes, into its own form, and assimilates it to itself. That to have an offspring from this semen always requires a male father, and female mother; so that nothing is ever produced without the natural copulation of these two. A prolific seed being given, lodg'd duly in a *matrix* intended for it, and supplied and cherished with due food and warmth for a proper time, an offspring arises like the parent: But if these be disturbed, an abortion will arise, instead of the thing desired. So that since the creation was compleated, no new thing can possibly arise; but only similar things to those already in being are produced from them by means of seeds. That after this manner any created being may be multiplied *ad infinitum*, supposing, we mean, a proper seed. So that the whole earth, for instance, might be cover'd with femel, if the seeds it yields yearly were sown again, and duly cultivated. They have also observed, that certain of the more simple bodies have ordinarily no seminal power, and consequently do not increase nor transmute others into their own nature; but either serve for giving motion to other bodies, as fire; or as a vehicle for conveyance of the nutriment, as water; or to give firmness and solidity to bodies, as in true and pure earth: All which being found, by a multitude of experiments, to obtain throughout all nature; they conclude, by parity of reason, that the same must also obtain in fossils. For, the great simplicity of the constitution of these, excluded all organical structure of seed; yet there was found some innate power, whereby they were able to prepare and apply their proper nutri-

ment, and thus continually propagate themselves. They also taught, that the spirits, called presiding spirits, sealed up in metals, do not indeed appear in the dead metals, but become manifest in them when resolved, opened and revivified; and thus produce obvious and extraordinary effects. They further teach, that something like marriage and generation obtains here; there being an impregnating male, and fecundified female, by whose genital power a propagation *sui generis* is effected in living metals. Nor are they silent on the manner wherein living metals may be made, with what fire to be governed, in what proportion mixed, and with what pabulum fed, that they may be perpetually multiplied. They add also, that metals alone, by reason of their extreme simplicity, admit of being produced in the shortest time, from a heavy mercurial fluid, and a fixing seminal sulphurous power, intimately mixed by force of fire, and thus united together in an indissoluble bond, so that mercury, or *argentum vivum*, does the office of mother, and *sal vivus*, that of father: that, after this manner, what is performed, in the bosom of the earth by subterraneous fire in a long series of years, may here be effected instantaneously, in metals properly vivified by art. They allow also, that among animals and vegetables, this power of generation is always limited by its proper time, which is prescribed by nature: that it could not possibly be otherwise, by reason of the smallness of the seminal fabrick, and the numerous different parts, out of which it is intricately composed; as also by reason the live spark, or embryo, in the centre of the prolific sulphur, is so easily spoil'd. But at the same time they advance, that in the purer metals, as gold and silver, and the mother of these, mercury, the parts are so similar, that every minute particle is of the same nature as the largest mass: that they are likewise so immutable, as not to be corrupted either by a small, or even the greatest fire. That the prolific virtue, therefore, of the seed resides in the fire; and thence acts very speedily, and in a moment's time assimilates a convenient mercurial matter to itself: and that on this principle it is, that metals may be generated or multiplied; and that the philosopher's stone may be made; concerning which last, if I were ask'd my opinion I should answer, that the wise *Socrates*, after reading a most abstruse book of *Heraclitus*, being ask'd what he thought of it; replied, that where he understood it, he found it excellent, and believ'd it to be so in those other parts he could not comprehend, which required the greatest penetration to come at. So where-ever I understand the alchemists, I find them describe the truth in the most simple and naked terms, without deceiving us, or being deceived themselves. When therefore I come to places where I do not comprehend the meaning; why should I change [*sic*] them with falshood, who have shewn themselves so much better skill'd in the art than myself; from whom I have learnt many things, in those parts of their writings where they thought proper to speak plain? It is said when they come to reveal the perfection of the art, they then only write that the art is true, in order to animate others to the pursuit of it; but that they may not publish a secret, capable of being abused to such ill purposes, that it is enough for them to point out the way, and guard from error. I therefore rather lay the blame on my own ignorance than on their vanity. Yet I have often doubted, upon reading their secrets, whether these skillful persons, after they had discovered so many extraordinary things by naked observation, might not by a too great quickness of apprehension anticipate, and relate things for facts, which they concluded might be done; or even must of necessity have been done, if they had perfected in the pursuit.

Étienne-François Geoffroy

(1672–1731)

THE first attempt to compare and summarize a large number of chemical facts in a concise tabular form was made in the table of affinities by Étienne-François Geoffroy, called Geoffroy the Elder to distinguish him from his brother, who was also a scientist. It had a considerable effect upon the development of the ideas of affinity and was much used in a more or less revised form during the eighteenth century. Geoffroy's original memoir, entitled "Table des differents rapports observés en chimie entre differentes substances," was presented at the Academy of Sciences at Paris on August 27, 1718, and published in the *Mémoires* for that year.[1] Geoffroy used an elaborate set of symbols for the reacting substances, arranging them in tabular form in order of their degree of attraction. Each vertical column has the diminishing affinity of the first substance for the others arranged below. No substance beneath a combination of the first reactant with another member of the column can displace the complex, but the reverse, that is the replacement by any above, can occur. He considers these reactions in his discussion of the table. It is evident from this scheme that Geoffroy had a clear concept of the reactivities of different chemical substances. The table is also an interesting example of early chemical symbolism. The memoir is here given in its entirety.

CONCERNING THE DIFFERENT AFFINITIES OBSERVED IN CHEMISTRY BETWEEN DIFFERENT SUBSTANCES

We observe in chemistry certain affinities between different bodies according to which they unite easily, one with another. These affinities have their degrees and are governed by their laws. We observe their dif-

[1] *Mémoires de l'Académie royale des sciences*, **1718**: 202–212.

ferent degrees when, among many mixed materials which have some disposition to unite, we note that one of the substances invariably unites with a certain other one in preference to all the rest.

For the laws of these affinities I have observed that when two substances having a disposition to unite together are combined and a third added, the third may part the two, taking one or the other. Some other substances neither join with the one or the other and do not lessen them at all. From this it appears to me that we may with some certainty conclude that those substances which were joined to one of the two had more affinity of union or disposition to unite to it than the substances which were displaced, and I believe that one can deduce from these observations the following proposition which is very general, although one cannot give it as general without having examined all possible combinations to assure that there is nothing to the contrary.

Whenever two substances which have some disposition to unite, the one with the other, are united together and a third which has more affinity for one of the two is added, the third will unite with one of these, separating it from the other.

This proposition is very general in chemistry where one encounters, so to speak at every step, the effects of this affinity. It is this property upon which depends the greater part of the hidden movements which follow the mixing of bodies and which are nearly impenetrable without this key. But since the order of these affinities is little known, I have believed that it would be very useful to mark those affinities which the substances commonly met with in chemistry show to each other and to construct a table where at a glance one could see the different affinities which substances have for one another.

I show today in this table the different affinities which I have collected as much from the experiments and observations of other chemists as from my own.

By this table those who are beginning to learn chemistry may form in a short time an adequate idea of the affinities which exist between different substances, and the chemists will there find an easy method to determine what takes place in many of their operations which are difficult to disentangle and to predict what should result when they mix different bodies.

The first line of this table includes different substances used in chemistry. Below each substance different types of materials are arranged in columns in the order of their affinity for that substance such that that which is nearest has the greatest affinity for the substance and cannot be displaced by any of the materials below it, but that it may remove any of the lower ones when they are joined to the substance. Thus in the first column the acid spirits are the substances with which I compare the four other kinds of substances which are below, that is, the fixed alkali salts, the volatile alkali salts, the absorbent earths, and metallic substances.

The fixed alkali salts are placed in the column immediately below the acid spirits, since I know of no substance which will separate these once they are united, and on the other hand whenever one of the three types of substance below is united to acid spirits, it abandons its place in favor of fixed alkali salts which when added combine directly with the acid.

In the third position are the volatile alkali salts, which have more affinity for acid spirits than the earthy substances or metals which are below but less than the fixed alkali salts which are above, so that if one or the

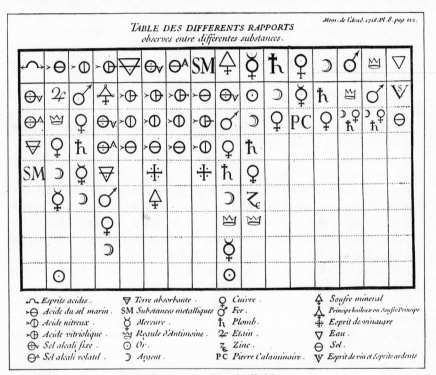

Geoffroy's table of affinities.

other of these lower substances be joined to an acid spirit, it can displace them and unite with the acid itself. These same volatile alkali salts have less affinity for acid spirits than the fixed alkali salts: thus these have no effect upon these two substances united: on the contrary, when the volatile alkali salts are united with acid spirits they leave them in the presence of fixed alkali salts which take their place.

We may say the same thing of the absorbent earths in the fourth position. These have no action on fixed or volatile alkali salts joined with acid spirits: and when these earthy substances are united with acid spirits they may be displaced by one or the other of these salts. Actually these absorbent earths are more compatible with acid spirits than the metallic substances which are below: thus when the latter are united to acid spirits they may give place to absorbent earths.

Any of these upper three substances being united with acids cannot be displaced by the metallic substances which are below, and each of the three may displace metals attached to acid spirits.

Since metallic substances differ in their compatibility with acid spirits, the acid of common salt dissolving certain metals which nitric acid does not dissolve at all, etc., I have disposed each of the three mineral acid spirits at the heads of the three following columns; namely, the acid of common salt, nitric acid, and vitriolic acid, and I have arranged under them in each column the various metallic substances, according to the order of the different affinities I have observed.

The fifth column shows the affinities between the various acid salts and the absorbent earths.

The sixth gives us the affinities between the fixed alkali salts and the acid spirits and common sulfur.

The following presents the different affinities between the volatile alkali salts and the various acids.

The eighth represents the affinities of these acids with metallic substances, these being slightly different from their affinities for the earths and alkali salts; the acid of common salt having a stronger affinity for metallic substances than nitric or vitriolic acids, and this same acid having less than the two others for the earths and alkali salts.

The ninth column, assigned to common sulfur, presents the order of the affinities of several substances with this mineral.

The tenth includes those substances which have some affinity for quicksilver.

The eleventh shows the order of affinity of silver and copper toward lead.

The twelfth gives the different affinities of mercury and calamine for copper.

The thirteenth likewise marks the order of the affinities of copper and lead with silver.

The fourteenth gives the affinities of regulus of antimony, silver, copper, and lead toward iron.

The fifteenth gives the affinities of iron, silver, copper, and lead with the regulus of antimony.

In these last two columns the silver, copper, and lead are found in the same positions because the difference between their affinities toward Mars or toward the regulus of antimony is not yet known, although it is well known that these metals have less compatibility with Mars than

with the regulus of antimony and less with the regulus of antimony than
with Mars, as we shall explain in the proper place.

Finally, the sixteenth column shows the affinity of water with ardent
spirits and with salts.

To show now to what use this table may be put in discovering what
takes place in various mixtures of combined bodies or in predicting what
may result, let us take for example the preparation of corrosive sublimate—a very common preparation, yet one whose theory is but very
slightly known.

This preparation is ordinarily carried out by taking vitriol, calcined
nearly to redness, that is to say, extremely dephlegmated, decrepitated
common salt, and a nitrous mercurial salt formed by the solution of mercury in the spirit of niter evaporated to dryness. These three substances
are exactly mixed together, and immediately upon mixture the odor of the
spirit of niter becomes evident and yellow vapors arise. If the mixture is
distilled in a retort with a very moderate fire, an acid spirit comes off
which is for the most part spirit of niter, mixed with a little acid spirit of
salt, thus making a weak aqua regia. When the fire is increased there rises
to the top of the retort a white, crystalline, saline mass and there remains
at the bottom a reddish mass from which by lixiviation may be separated
a white salt and a red metallic earth.

The substances which are obtained in this operation are very different,
as we shall see, from those which were used.

The vitriol which is used is a compound salt composed of acid of vitriol
and of iron dissolved by this acid and very closely united with it. The
common salt is also a compound salt, formed of the acid of salt and an
absorbent earth closely united together. The nitrous mercurial salt is
composed of mercury united with the acid of niter.

It is necessary to examine the affinities of the six substances of which
these three mixtures are formed in order to judge the manner in which
they react upon each other.

I consider that these three mixtures are composed of different acid salts,
of which one, the acid of common salt, has for a base an absorbent earth,
and the two others, that is the vitriolic acid and nitric acid, have metallic
substances for bases. I find from the first column of my table under *acid
spirits* that acids in general have more affinity for the absorbent earth of
common salt than for iron and mercury, and by the fifth column under
absorbent earths that vitriolic acid in particular has more affinity for this
earth than either nitric acid or the acid of common salt to which it is already united: from which I judge, following my proposition, that the
vitriolic acid should leave its metal to join the earth of the common salt;
and this in effect takes place. The acid of the common salt departs at the
approach of the vitriolic acid and, being volatile by nature, disperses in

the air; if it does not come into contact with the metallic substances toward which it has more affinity than the other acids, as it appears in the eighth column under *metallic substances*. It, then, attacks both the iron of the vitriol and the mercury of the niter.

As this acid of common salt is more compatible with the mercury than is nitric acid, it forces this latter to abandon the mercury. This nitric acid, being free and finding nothing else to attach itself to, dissipates itself in the air and comes forth from the vessel in reddish or yellowish vapors.

At the same time that a portion of the acid of common salt attaches itself to the mercury, another and far larger part combines with the iron, where it remains attached until the force of the fire, which is increased and rendered strong during the sublimation, forces this portion of acid to detach itself from the feruginous substance, which is itself too fixed to rise; this acid, reliberated by the fire, meeting the mercurial portions which had not yet been completely detached from the nitric acid, joins to them and completely removes the nitric acid, which dissipates in yellowish vapors, while the combination of the acid of common salt and mercurial parts produces a saline mercurial concretion sufficiently volatile to rise, or (as the chemists say) to sublime to the top of the vessel—whence it is named mercury sublimate.

That which comes off in reddish or yellowish vapors is largely nitrous. This is the acid of niter which has been detached from the mercury by the acid of common salt, largely, I say, because there is also a small quantity of the acid of common salt which has been forced up so far into the empty space of the retort by the violence of the fire that it cannot return to the solid residue.

There remains at the bottom of the vessel a reddish mass which is metallic earth or the saffron of Mars, which before the operation was united with the vitriolic acid from which it was presently detached. For this vitriolic acid left the metal and joined the earth of the common salt, and together they formed a compound salt which is still actually confused with saffron of Mars without, however, being connected with it in any fashion. Indeed, this salt may be separated very easily by lixiviation and is of the same nature as Glauber's marvellous salt. The colcothar or saffron of Mars remains after the lixiviation completely deprived of its acid when just a sufficient proportion of this salt has been used.

In this operation, the acid of the niter should attach itself to portions of the iron abandoned by the acid of the vitriol, provided the strong heat does not disperse these acid particles and drive them out of the vessel.

It is apparent, thus, that the acid of niter serves no purpose in this operation, since it leaves the mercury and escapes and has no action on any of these substances. Actually, some omit the solution of the mercury in the spirit of niter. They simply mix the vitriol, the common salt, and the

mercury just as it is, and the sublimation takes place just as well. It is to
be observed, it is true, that in this operation it is necessary to triturate the
mixture a long time in order to pulverize the material well and mix it
intimately—an operation which is tiresome and even dangerous for the
operator because of the parts which arise from the mixture during the
trituration. On the other hand, the mercury being dissolved in the spirit
of niter, this metallic liquor is already very well divided by the act of solution and much better prepared to unite promptly and intimately with the
acid of the common salt.

Another reason for adding this nitric acid is that it is claimed that it
attenuates and considerably volatilizes the acid of the common salt and
thus puts it in a condition to unite more closely with the mercury—much
as the spirit of common salt, which by itself will scarcely dissolve gold,
will dissolve it rapidly if it be animated with a little of the spirit of niter.
This takes place, according to the opinion of some of us, by virtue of a
very subtle sulfurous principle contained in the spirit of niter and which is
communicated by this means to the acid of common salt. This is not the
place to examine this subject thoroughly. It is sufficient to say that the
sublimation may be carried out without nitric acid or with it, and that it
proceeds more promptly when the mercury is dispersed by this acid and a
little less easily when it is not so divided.

Another observation is that when mercury, reduced to a salt with spirit
of niter, is used, the vitriol may be dispensed with. If pure running mercury is used thus without vitriol, the operation fails completely. The
reason is clear in the light of our principles. The acid of the common salt,
having more affinity for its earth than for metallic substances, as it is
shown in the first column (*acid spirits*), will not move at all to attach
itself to the mercury, unless it is caused to do so. It will not attack the
mercury alone at all. But if mercury reduced to a salt by nitric acid is
used, the nitric acid, having a greater affinity for the earth of the common
salt than has the acid of the salt, as appears by the fifth column of the
table (*absorbent earths*), and this same nitric acid having also more affinity
for the earth than for the mercury, as may be seen in the first column
(*acid spirits*), initiates the reaction. It leaves the mercury to attach itself
to the earth of the salt, detaching the acid therefrom. This acid of the
common salt become free from its earth, meets then the freed mercury,
joins to it, and these two substances form together the compound of the
sublimate which rises to the top of the vessel. Meanwhile, the nitric acid
and the earth of the common salt form a compound salt which remains
fixed at the bottom of the vessel and is good saltpeter.

Some also make corrosive sublimate by dissolving quicksilver in spirit
of niter, adding to the solution a solution of common salt in water which
produces a white precipitate. When the liquid has cleared it is decanted

and the white powder which lies at the bottom of the vessel is separated. This is the white precipitated mercury. It is dried and then sublimated into a compact white saline mass which is corrosive sublimate.

If the clear liquor which was decanted be evaporated, a very good saltpeter is obtained.

The theory of this operation is the same as that of the preceding one; here it was carried out in solution—there, in the dry materials.

In both cases the acid of the niter quit the mercury which it had grasped on solution and attached itself to the earth of the common salt, in the meantime freeing the acid of this salt, which in turn attached itself to the mercury and was precipitated with it in a white powder. The fire then raised this powder into a white salt.

Corrosive sublimate may also be made with the simple acid of common salt, without using its earth, by pouring little by little the spirit of salt upon a solution of quicksilver in spirit of niter. A white precipitate is then first formed as in the preceding operation. If the precipitate be promptly separated it may be sublimed in the same manner. However, if it is left for some time in the liquor, a part of the precipitate redissolves in the liquor, which became aqua regia as soon as the spirit of niter and the spirit of salt were united together intimately.

But if a much larger quantity of sublimate by this method is desired, the whole is placed in a retort and distilled with a controlled fire. At first an aqua regia comes off, composed of the spirit of niter from the mercury, some spirit of common salt, and even some mercurial parts which were carried over in the distillation. There remains at the bottom of the retort a saline mass composed of mercury and the acid of common salt. When the fire is increased this saline mass sublimes into a white salt which is corrosive sublimate.

In this operation the acid of the spirit of salt begins the action. Being free and not held by its earth as in the other operations, it immediately attacks the mercurial particles, with which it is more compatible than is nitric acid, as appears by the eighth column (*metallic substances*). The nitric acid set free is then forced up by a moderate fire past the neck of the retort into the receiver, while the acid of common salt joined with the mercury remains in a saline mass at the bottom of the retort, and a much stronger fire is required to sublime it to the top of the vessel.

Although this table contains a rather large number of substances whose affinities are compared, I have no doubt that many others might be added if one but determined by experiment their various affinities.

I will give later, if it be judged appropriate, all the experiments upon which the affinities of different substances in the table are founded and which have led me to arrange them in the order in which you see them.

It should be noted that in many of these experiments the separation of materials is not perfectly exact and precise. This arises from several causes which are impossible to eliminate, such as the viscosity of the liquid, its movement, the character of the precipitant or precipitate, and other such things which prevent a prompt precipitation or an exact separation of all the parts. These errors are nevertheless not so large as to prevent one from regarding the rules as constant.

Guillaume-François Rouelle

(1703–1770)

AS A teacher Guillaume-François Rouelle was one of the greatest in France; many of his students were destined to be eminent chemists—Proust, Leblanc, Lavoisier. It is unfortunate that his lectures, which did so much to stimulate chemistry in France, were never published. The most important of his few publications appeared in the *Mémoires* of the French Academy of Sciences. His chief contribution to chemistry lay in his ideas concerning salts that were published in the *Mémoires* for 1744 and 1754.[1] In the latter paper he states that the name *salt* (*sel*) had previously been applied only to water-soluble, saline-tasting solids. He goes on to introduce what is essentially the modern definition of a salt and demonstrates how widespread this type of compound is. Rouelle was, further, the first to distinguish between acid, neutral, and basic salts and the first to consider calomel and such insoluble compounds also as salts. It was not, however, until the work of Lavoisier that these concepts on salts were generally accepted.

The following is translated from Rouelle's memoir of 1754, cited above. Some of his examples of basic salts hardly fall within the modern definition. The word *base* had only recently been introduced, and its use here indicates its origin.

In order to give an adequate idea of the various kinds of salts which I shall mention, it seems to me appropriate to give a brief account of neutral salts and to recall their definitions.

Some authors have defined as neutral those which have been formed by the union of acids with alkalis, which are soluble in water, and which have a saline taste to the tongue. Because of this latter they also call them *saline salts*.

The number of neutral salts was at first very small, hardly more than common salt and niter being known; but the number was soon increased, especially by the work of Glauber.

Others which had as bases volatile alkali or absorbent earth were then

---

[1] *Mémoires de l'Académie royale des sciences*, **1744**: 353–364; **1754**: 572–588.

added and finally, those salts formed by the union of acids with metallic substances.

It was at first required of a perfect neutral salt that it be formed of an exact proportion of acid and of alkali—a state which was easy to determine, since when it had been attained in the addition of acid to alkali, movement or effervescence ceased. This is called the *point of saturation.*

It was further required as an essential proof of complete saturation that the blue color of the syrup of violets should not be changed. It is known that acids change this color to red and alkalis to green.

Other authors are not content with this exact combination; they require of a perfect neutral salt that it resist the violence of fire without decomposing. In restricting thus the definition of neutral salts they have practically reduced them to vitriolated tartar and Glauber's admirable salt.

Their analysis, their artificial preparation, and Stahl's discovery of the nature of sulfur have shown these latter salts equally susceptible to decomposition. That illustrious chemist has also proposed, in the form of a question, the decomposition of vitriolated tartar in the hollow of the hand [*i.e.*, at room temperature]. This problem greatly stimulated chemists; it was reserved for the scholarly Mr. Pott to solve it. This salt then falls in the same class with the others; it can be decomposed even without recourse to fire.

There is very little accord among chemists concerning neutral salts formed by the combination of acids with alkaline earths and metallic substances. There are some of these salts which do not change the color of the syrup of violets, while others turn it red and still others green. These salts are also different in other properties, and it is this which has occasioned the diversity in opinion among chemists. Some prefer to class them with neutral salts, others in a separate class. The most enlightened have regarded the solution of this problem as very difficult, since these salts have not yet been sufficiently examined.

In a memoir which I presented to the Academy in 1744 on the crystallization of neutral salts, I extended the number of these salts as far as possible by defining a neutral salt as one formed by the union of an acid with any substance whatsoever which would serve it as a base and give it a concrete or solid form. In that same memoir I not only extended the number of intermediate salts [*sels moyens, i.e.*, intermediate between acids and bases] by reference to the phenomena of crystallization, but I had particularly in mind this new work which I present today.

I understand by a neutral salt which has an excess or a superabundance of acid an intermediate salt which besides the exact quantity of acid necessary to make it perfectly neutral has also a further quantity of acid. It is not sufficient that the acid be simply mixed with the neutral salt; there must be a coherence between this acid and the other parts in order that it combine, and this in exact quantity. The excess of acid has also its saturation point.

Salts which have an excess of acid are very soluble compared with the same species of salt which has no more acid than the least possible. Many of these salts even attract the moisture of the air and fall in deliquium [*i.e.*, deliquesce].

These salts all turn the blue tincture of violets red; they nearly all effervesce with fixed and with volatile alkali. There is, however, one exception to this general rule; instead of reddening the blue color of violets it turns it to green, and with fixed or volatile alkalis it gives no effervescence, although with metallic substances it gives a very sensible one. This singularity forms, as I said, an exception to the rule and shows us how we ought in view of the slight extent of our knowledge guard against the temptation of making axioms in chemistry.

I call perfect or saline those neutral salts the saturation of which is exact and which have an exact quantity of acid and a moderate degree of solubility. Such are the salts formed by the combination of acids with alkali salts. These salts do not change the syrup of violets: among them are numbered vitriolated tartar, Glauber's admirable salt, the vitriolic ammoniacal salt or secret salt of Glauber, niter, quadrangular niter, nitrous ammoniacal salt, common salt, common salt regenerated by fixed alkali, sal ammoniacal, etc.

The third class is composed of those which I have called neutral salts having less acid than is possible or very slightly soluble or even insoluble neutral salts such as horn silver. These salts have very little acid in their composition, whence their slight solubility. They are in a perfectly neutral state, having for the most part no effect upon the syrup of violets and not effervescing with volatile or fixed alkali.

The phenomenon of an excess of acid in some saline substances is not unknown in chemistry, and it has always appeared astonishing to me that the new discovery which I offer has escaped the wisdom of some of our celebrated artists such as Glauber, Kunckel, Becher, and Stahl, who have been much occupied in revealing the nature of these salts. They had under their eyes striking phenomena and a neutral salt whose excess of acid is known to all the world, which ought to have enlightened them and to have set them on the path of observation.

I will report but a small number of these salts to serve as examples in explaining all the others and to show the necessity for the new distinctions which I propose.

The limits which I have prescribed for myself do not permit me to enter into the details, though they are very interesting. I reserve them for another time and content myself with speaking today of the combination of the acid of common salt and of vitriolic acid with mercury, the acid of the same common salt with the regulus of antimony, of nitric acid with bismuth, and of vitriolic acid with fixed alkali. These first three salts are among the number of those which I give in my lessons in chemistry as examples of salts with an excess of acid; the two latter ones have not been published.

From among the saline substances I will first choose one whose excess of acid is perfectly well known and which moreover, first gave me light on this discovery; I wish to speak of corrosive sublimate of mercury.

Corrosive mercury sublimate is a neutral salt formed by the union of the acid of common salt and mercury, or quicksilver. We know that this sublimate has such an abundance of acid that it is able to dissolve a new quantity of mercury, since four parts of it dissolve more than three parts of fresh mercury. Sublimed mercury, thus deprived of its acid, is known in chemistry and in medicine under the name of *mild mercury* [*mercure doux*]. One treats it in vain with new mercury; it will not take on any more.

This new salt or mild mercury is then in the perfect state of a neutral salt; that is to say, the acid and the base are in exact proportion. It has less acid than it might possibly have, while corrosive mercury sublimate on the other hand is a neutral salt having an excess of the acid of common salt.

Several chemists have thought to add new acid to corrosive sublimate by subliming it several times with fresh common salt and vitriol. There are many things to be said about this procedure, but it will suffice my purpose to make it known that corrosive sublimate will not take the new acid of common salt. The latter rises with the mercury sublimate and a little iron united to the acid of the salt, while a portion of the mercury sublimate remains in the *caput mortuum*, from whence it is nearly impossible to separate it by sublimation. I wish some day to present to the Academy my work on this sublimate, which was used by the ancients in the composition of a peculiar menstruum. If in the sublimation of corrosive sublimate we double the quantity of common salt and of vitriol, the mercury takes no more acid.

I have unsuccessfully attempted to add a new acid to corrosive sublimate by dissolving it in the acid of common salt and subliming it in a retort in order to obtain it in a concrete form free of ununited phlegm and acid. All the acid of the salt comes over in the distillation, while the corrosive sublimate rises to the neck of the retort, where it is found unaugmented.

The union of the acid of common salt with mercury furnishes us with two intermediate salts—one in a neutral state and the other having an excess of acid. It is certain that the acid which is in excess in this latter case is not simply mixed with the mercury but is combined and united with it, since it takes with it a concrete form, sublimes without separating from it, and crystallizes from water with it. The sublimation, then, gives the exact point of saturation of the excess of acid.

Corrosive sublimate will not turn in deliquium, and it requires for its solution a far greater quantity of water than most other such salts—thus making an exception to the general rule.

This corrosive sublimate, dissolved in distilled rain water (which is what I have used in all my experiments), crystallizes, as is already known.

This solution turns to green the blue tincture of the syrup of violets, while fixed and volatile alkali precipitate it, but without effervescence. It is this salt which constitutes a new exception to the general rule of salts having an excess of acid which I spoke of above. However, while it does not effervesce with alkalis, it does so with many metallic substances for which the acid of common salt has a greater affinity than for mercury. Such are arsenic, regulus of antimony, tin, etc.

The perfectly neutral salt or mild mercury, which has the least acid possible, is very slightly soluble compared with corrosive sublimate. It requires for its solution a large quantity of water and sustained boiling. Here is the method which I have used for its solution as well as for the solution of all other slightly soluble salts of the same class.

I take a half ounce of powdered mild mercury and grind it in a glass mortar with a little water for a good half hour in order to powder it more and make it much more easily soluble. I put this salt then in a matrass with 4 ounces of distilled water in such a manner that a third of the vessel is left empty. I let it digest and boil on a sand bath for three-quarters of an hour, adding from time to time a little boiling water to replace that which evaporates. The liquor being cooled, I decant and filter it, taking care previously to wash the filter paper with boiling water.

The quantity of mild mercury thus dissolved is so small that it takes more than 1,100 parts of water to dissolve 1 part of salt. This is what I have found by precipitating it with alkali; 1 grain of this mercury is held in solution by more than 2 ounces of water. The slight solubility of this salt and of many others renders them very distinct from other neutral salts, which I have called saline or perfect, and from those which have an excess of acid. It is then absolutely necessary to place them in a class apart and distinguish them from others, calling them *neutral insoluble* or nearly insoluble salts (for there are in effect some which are insoluble).

Joseph Black

(1728–1799)

UNTIL the eighteenth century there had been no clear distinction made between various gases, and air itself was generally considered an element. Early in the century Stephen Hales (1677–1761) demonstrated that gases could be experimentally handled with a pneumatic trough. The discovery, by Joseph Black, using the technique of Hales, that carbon dioxide (the *gas sylvestre* of Van Helmont) was a definite chemical entity different from air ushered in the era of pneumatic chemistry. It was to culminate in the discovery of oxygen and the composition of water and contribute to Lavoisier's classical studies.

Joseph Black distinguished himself as both a physicist and a chemist. In physics he was the discoverer of latent heat and the founder of calorimetry.[1] In chemistry his major contribution was the investigation of the role of carbon dioxide (or *fixed air*, as he termed it) in the reactions of the carbonates—especially magnesium carbonate or *magnesia alba*. This compound was first discussed in his inaugural dissertation for the degree of Doctor of Medicine at the University of Edinburgh, in 1754; "De humore acido a cibis orto, et magnesia alba" ("On the Acid Humour Arising from Food, and Magnesia Alba").[2] The dissertation deals principally with stomach acidity and the value of magnesia as an antacid. In its appendix Black has detailed his experiments, which contain the work on the relation between mild and strong alkalis. This was read in an extended form before the Philosophical Society at Edinburgh in June, 1755, and was soon published as "Experiments upon Magnesia Alba, Quick-lime, and some other Alcaline Substances" (1756).[3] This paper contains the first correct explana-

---

[1] W. F. Magie, "A Source Book in Physics," New York, 1935, pp. 134–145; D. McKie, and N. H. de V. Heathcote, "The Discovery of Specific and Latent Heats," London, 1935.

[2] A. Crum Brown has translated both parts of Black's medical dissertation: "On the Acid Humour Arising from Food," *J. Chem. Education*, **12**: 225–228 (1935); "On Magnesia Alba," *ibid.*, 268–273 (1935).

[3] "Essays and Observations, Physical and Literary. Read before a Society in Edinburgh and Published by them," Edinburgh, 1756, vol. 2, pp. 157–225. The paper has been reprinted in its entirety in *Alembic Club Reprints*, No. 1, "Experiments upon Magnesia Alba, Quick-lime, and some other Alcaline Substances. By Joseph Black, M.D., 1755," Edinburgh, 1898. It was reprinted in later editions of the Essays and was also issued in separate form.

The first edition in book form, which also contained a section by William Cullen, was published together with Black's essay on latent heat and specific heat: "Experiments upon Magnesia Alba, Quick-Lime, and other Alcaline Substances: with Essay on the Cold produced by Evaporating Fluids, and of some other Means of Producing Cold by William Cullen, M.D.," Edinburgh, 1777; 2d ed., 1782.

tion of some of the reactions of the mild and caustic alkalis (carbonates and hydroxides). Black found that *magnesia alba* (magnesium carbonate) gave off "fixed air" on heating and that the resultant loss in weight was regained when the calcined *magnesia alba* recombined with the same gas. He further demonstrated that in the conversion of limestone to quicklime a loss of half the weight occurred, the result of a loss of "fixed air." The following portions of his paper are self-evident in their content. It is an early model of a carefully planned experimental investigation and contains well-conceived quantitative methods.

By the following experiments, I proposed to know whether this substance could be reduced to a quick-lime.

An ounce of *magnesia* was exposed in a crucible for about an hour to such a heat as is sufficient to melt copper. When taken out, it weighed three drams and one scruple, or had lost $\frac{7}{12}$ of its former weight.

I repeated, with the *magnesia* prepared in this manner, most of those experiments I had already made upon it before calcination, and the result was as follows.

It dissolves in all the acids, and with these composes salts exactly similar to those described in the first set of experiments: but what is particularly to be remarked, it is dissolved without any the least degree of effervescence.

It slowly precipitates the corrosive sublimate of mercury in the form of a black powder.

It separates the volatile alkali in a salt-ammoniac from the acid, when it is mixed with a warm solution of that salt. But it does not separate an acid from a calcarious earth, nor does it induce the least change upon lime-water.

Lastly, when a dram of it is digested with an ounce of water in a bottle for some hours, it does not make any the least change in the water. The *magnesia*, when dried, is found to have gained ten grains; but it neither effervesces with acids, nor does it sensibly affect lime-water.

Observing *magnesia* to lose such a remarkable proportion of its weight in the fire, my next attempts were directed to the investigation of this volatile part, and, among other experiments, the following seemed to throw some light upon it.

Three ounces of *magnesia* were distilled in a glass retort and receiver, the fire being gradually increased until the *magnesia* was obscurely red hot. When all was cool, I found only five drams of a whitish water in the receiver, which had a faint smell of the spirit of hartshorn, gave a green colour to the juice of violets, and rendered the solutions of corrosive sublimate and of silver very slightly turbid. But it did not sensibly effervesce with acids.

The *magnesia*, when taken out of the retort, weighed an ounce, three drams, and thirty grains, or had lost more than half of its weight. It still effervesced pretty briskly with acids, tho' not so strongly as before this operation.

The fire should have been raised here to the degree requisite for the perfect calcination of *magnesia*. But even from this imperfect experiment, it is evident, that of the volatile parts contained in that powder, a small proportion only is water; the rest cannot, it seems, be retained in vessels, under a visible form. Chemists have often observed, in their distillations, that part of a body has vanished from their senses, notwithstanding the utmost care to retain it; and they have always found, upon further inquiry, that subtile part to be air, which having been imprisoned in the body, under a solid form, was set free, and rendered fluid and elastic by the fire. We may therefore safely conclude, that the volatile matter, lost in the calcination of *magnesia*, is mostly air; and hence the calcined *magnesia* does not emit air, or make an effervescence when mixed with acids.

The water, from its properties, seems to contain a small portion of volatile alkali, which was probably formed from the earth, air, and water, or from some of these combined together; and perhaps also from a small quantity of inflammable matter which adhered accidentally to the *magnesia*. Whenever Chemists meet with this salt, they are inclined to ascribe its origin to some animal, or putrid vegetable, substance; and this they have always done, when they obtained it from the calcarious earths, all of which afford a small quantity of it. There is, however, no doubt that it can sometimes be produced independently of any such mixture, since many fresh vegetables and tartar afford a considerable quantity of it. And how can it, in the present instance, be supposed, that any animal or vegetable matter adhered to the *magnesia*, while it was dissolved by an acid, separated from this by an alkali, and washed with so much water?

Two drams of *magnesia* were calcined in a crucible, in the manner described above, and thus reduced to two scruples and twelve grains. This calcined *magnesia* was dissolved in a sufficient quantity of spirit of vitriol, and then again separated from the acid by the addition of an alkali, of which a large quantity is necessary for this purpose. The *magnesia* being very well washed and dried, weighed one dram and fifty grains. It effervesced violently, or emitted a large quantity of air, when thrown into acids, formed a red powder when mixed with a solution of sublimate, separated the calcarious earths from an acid, and sweetened lime-water: and had thus recovered all those properties which it had but just now lost by calcination: Nor had it only recovered its original properties, but acquired besides an addition of weight nearly equal to what had been lost in the fire; and, as it is found to effervesce with acids, part of the addition must certainly be air.

This air seems to have been furnished by the alkali from which it was separated by the acid; for Dr. *Hales* has clearly proved, that alkaline salts contain a large quantity of fixed air, which they emit in great abundance when joined to a pure acid. In the present case, the alkali is really joined to an acid, but without any visible emission of air; and yet the air is not retained in it: for the neutral salt, into which it is converted, is the same in quantity, and in every other respect, as if the acid employed had not been previously saturated with *magnesia*, but offered to the alkali in its pure state, and had driven the air out of it in their conflict. It seems therefore evident, that the air was forced from the alkali by the acid, and lodged itself in the *magnesia*.

These considerations led me to try a few experiments, whereby I might know what quantity of air is expelled from an alkali, or from *magnesia*, by acids.

Two drams of a pure fixed alkaline salt, and an ounce of water, were put into a Florentine flask, which, together with its contents, weighed two ounces and two drams. Some oil of vitriol diluted with water was dropt in, until the salt was exactly saturated; which it was found to be, when two drams, two scruples, and three grains of this acid had been added. The phial with its contents now weighed two ounces, four drams, and fifteen grains. One scruple, therefore, and eight grains were lost during the ebullition, of which a trifling portion may be water, or something of the same kind. The rest is air.

The celebrated *Homberg* has attempted to estimate the quantity of solid salt contained in a determined portion of the several acids. He saturated equal quantities of an alkali with each of them; and, observing the weight which the alkali had gained, after being perfectly dryed, took this for the quantity of solid salt contained in that share of the acid which performed the saturation. But we learn from the above experiment, that his estimate was not accurate, because the alkali loses weight as well as gains it.

Two drams of *magnesia*, treated exactly as the alkali in the last experiment, were just dissolved by four drams, one scruple, and seven grains of the same acid liquor, and lost one scruple and sixteen grains by the ebullition.

Two drams of *magnesia* were reduced, by the action of a violent fire, to two scruples and twelve grains, with which the same process was repeated, as in the two last experiments; four drams, one scruple, and two grains of the same acid, were required to compleat the solution, and no weight was lost in the experiment.

As in the separation of the volatile from the fixed parts of bodies, by means of heat, a small quantity of the latter is generally raised with the former; so the air and water, originally contained in the *magnesia*, and afterwards dissipated by the fire, seem to have carried off a small part of the fixed earth of this substance. This is probably the reason, why calcined *magnesia* is saturated with a quantity of acid, somewhat less than what is required to dissolve it before calcination: and the same may be assigned as one cause which hinders us from restoring the whole of its original weight, by solution and precipitation.

I took care to dilute the vitriolic acid, in order to avoid the heat and ebullition which it would otherwise have excited in the water; and I chose a Florentine flask, on account of its lightness, capacity, and shape, which is peculiarly adapted to the experiment; for the vapours raised by the ebullition circulated for a short time, thro' the wide cavity of the phial, but were soon collected upon its sides, like dew, and none of them seemed to reach the neck, which continued perfectly dry to the end of the experiment.

We now perceive the reason why crude and calcined *magnesia*, which differ in many respects from one another, agree however in composing the same kind of salt, when dissolved in any particular acid; for the crude *magnesia* seems to differ from the calcined chiefly by containing a considerable quantity of air, which air is unavoidably dissipated and lost during the dissolution.

From our experiments, it seems probable, that the increase of weight which some metals acquire, by being first dissolved in acids, and then separated from them again by alkalis, proceeds from air furnished by the alkalis. And that in the *aurum fulminans*, which is prepared by the same means, this air adheres to the gold in such a peculiar manner, that, in a moderate degree of heat, the whole of it recovers its elasticity in the same instant of time; and thus, by the violent shock which it gives to the air around, produces the loud crack or fulmination of this powder. Those who will imagine the explosion of such a minute portion of fixed air, as can reside in the *aurum fulminans*, to be insufficient for the excessive loudness of the noise, will consider, that it is not a large quantity of motion communicated to the air, but rather a smart stroke which produces sound, and that the explosion of but a few particles of fixed air may be capable of causing a loud noise, provided they all recover their spring suddenly, and in the same instant.

The above experiments lead us also to conclude, that volatile alkalis, and the common absorbent earths, which lose their air by being joined to acids, but shew evident signs of their having recovered it, when separated from them by alkalis, received it from these alkalis which lost it in the instant of their joining with the acid.

The following are a few experiments upon three of the absorbent earths, made in order to compare them with one another, and with *magnesia*.

Suspecting that *magnesia* might possibly be no other than a common calcarious earth, which had changed its nature by having been previously combined with an acid, I saturated a small quantity of chalk with the muriatic acid, separated the acid from it again by means of a fixed alkali, and carefully washed away the whole of the salt.

The chalk when dryed was not found to have suffered any alteration; for it effervesced with the vitriolic acid, but did not dissolve in it; and when exposed to a violent fire, was converted into a quick-lime, in all respects similar to that obtained from common chalk.

In another experiment of the same kind, I used the vitriolic acid with the same event.

Any calcarious matter reduced to a fine powder, and thrown into a warm solution of alum, immediately raises a brisk effervescence. But the powder is not dissolved; it is rather increased in bulk: and if the addition be repeated until it is no longer accompanied with effervescence, the liquor loses all taste of the alum, and yields only a very light cloud upon the admixture of an alkali.

From this experiment we learn, that acids attract the calcarious earth more strongly then they do the earth of alum; and as the acid in this salt is exactly the same with the vitriolic, it composes with the calcarious earth a neutral substance, which is very difficultly soluble in water, and therefore falls down to the bottom of the vessel along with the earth of alum, which is deprived of its acid. The light cloud formed by the alkali proceeds from the minute portion of the calcarious compound which saturates the water.

The earth of animal bones, when reduced to a fine powder and thrown into a diluted vitriolic acid, gradually absorbs the acid in the same manner as the calcarious earths, but without any remarkable effervescence. When it is added to the nitrous or to the muriatic acid, it is slowly dissolved. The compound liquor thence produced is extremely acrid, and still changes the colour of the juice of violets to a red, even after it is fully saturated with the absorbent. Distilled vinegar has little or no effect upon this earth; for after a long digestion it still retains its sour taste, and gives only a light cloud upon the addition of an alkali.

By dropping a dissolved fixed alkali into a warm solution of alum, I obtained the earth of this salt, which, after being well washed and dried, was found to have the following properties:

It is dissolved in every acid but very slowly, unless assisted by heat. The several solutions, when thoroughly saturated, are all astringent with a slight degree of an acid taste, and they also agree with a solution of alum in this, that they give a red colour to the infusion of turnsol.

Neither this earth, nor that of animal bones, can be converted into quick-lime by the strongest fire, nor do they suffer any change worth notice. Both of them seem to attract acids but weakly, and to alter their properties less when united to them than the other absorbents.

PART II.

In reflecting afterwards upon these experiments, an explication of the nature of lime offered itself, which seemed to account, in an easy manner, for most of the properties of that substance.

It is sufficiently clear, that the calcarious earths in their native state, and that the alkalis and *magnesia* in their ordinary condition, contain a large quantity of fixed air, and this air certainly adheres to them with considerable force, since a strong fire is necessary to separate it from *magnesia*, and the strongest is not sufficient to expel it entirely from fixed alkalis, or take away their power of effervescing with acid salts.

These considerations led me to conclude, that the relation between fixed air and alkaline substances was somewhat similar to the relation between these and acids; that as the calcarious earths and alkalis attract acids strongly and can be saturated with them, so they also attract fixed air, and are in their ordinary state saturated with it: and when we mix an acid with an alkali or with an absorbent earth, that the air is then set at liberty, and breaks out with violence; because the alkaline body attracts it more weakly than it does the acid, and because the acid and air cannot both be joined to the same body at the same time.

I also imagined that, when the calcarious earths are exposed to the action of a violent fire, and are thereby converted into quick-lime, they suffer no other change in their composition than the loss of a small quantity of water and of their fixed air. The remarkable acrimony which we perceive in them after this process, was not supposed to proceed from any additional matter received in the fire, but seemed to be an essential property of the pure earth, depending on an attraction for those several substances which it then became capable of corroding or dissolving, which attraction had been insensible as long as the air adhered to the earth, but discovered itself upon the separation.

This supposition was founded upon an observation of the most frequent consequences of combining bodies in chemistry. Commonly when we join two bodies together, their acrimony or attraction for other substances becomes immediately either less perceivable or entirely insensible; altho' it was sufficiently strong and remarkable before their union, and may be rendered evident again by disjoining them. A neutral salt, which is composed of an acid and alkali, does not possess the acrimony of either of its constituent parts. It can easily be separated from water, has little or no effect upon metals, is incapable of being joined to inflammable bodies, and of corroding and dissolving animals and vegetables; so that the attraction both of the acid and alkali for these several substances seems to be suspended till they are again separated from one other.

Crude lime was therefore considered as a peculiar acrid earth rendered mild by its union with fixed air: and quick-lime as the same earth, in which, by having separated the air, we discover that acrimony or attraction for water, for animal, vegetable, and for inflammable substances.

That the calcarious earths really lose a large quantity of air when they are burnt to quick-lime, seems sufficiently proved by an experiment of Mr. *Margraaf*, an exceedingly accurate and judicious Chemist. He subjected eight ounces of *osteocolla* to distillation in an earthen retort, finishing his process with the most violent fire of a reverberatory, and caught in the receiver only two drams of water, which by its smell and properties shewed itself to be slightly alkaline. He does not tell us the weight of the *osteocolla* remaining in the retort, and only says, that it was converted into quick-lime; but as no calcarious earth can be converted into quick-lime, or bear the heat which he applied without losing above a third of its weight, we may safely conclude, that the loss in his experiment was proportional, and proceeded chiefly from the dissipation of fixed air.

According to our theory, the relation of the calcarious earth to air and water appeared to agree with the relation of the same earth to the vitriolic and vegetable acids. As chalk for instance has a stronger attraction for the vitriolic than for the vegetable acid, and is dissolved with more difficulty when combined with the first, than when joined to the second: so it also attracts air more strongly than water, and is dissolved with more difficulty when saturated with air than when compounded with water only.

A calcarious earth deprived of its air, or in the state of quick-lime, greedily absorbs a considerable quantity of water, becomes soluble in that fluid, and is then said to be slaked; but as soon as it meets with fixed air, it is supposed to quit the water and join itself to the air, for which it has a superior attraction, and is therefore restored to its first state of mildness and insolubility in water.

When slaked lime is mixed with water, the fixed air in the water is attracted by the lime, and saturates a small portion of it, which then becomes again incapable of dissolution, but part of the remaining slaked lime is dissolved and composes lime-water.

If this fluid be exposed to the open air, the particles of quick-lime which are nearest the surface gradually attract the particles of fixed air which float in the atmosphere. But at the same time that a particle of lime is thus saturated with air, it is also restored to its native state of mildness and insolubility; and as the whole of this change must happen at the surface, the whole of the lime is successively collected there under its original form of an insipid calcarious earth, called the cream or crusts of lime-water.

When quick-lime itself is exposed to the open air, it absorbs the particles of water and of fixed air which come within its sphere of attraction, as it meets with the first of these in greatest plenty, the greatest part of it assumes the form of slaked lime; the rest is restored to its original state;

and if it be exposed for a sufficient length of time, the whole of it is gradually saturated with air, to which the water as gradually yields its place.

We have already shewn by experiment, that *magnesia alba* is a compound of a peculiar earth and fixed air. When this substance is mixed with lime-water, the lime shews a stronger attraction for fixed air than that of the earth of *magnesia;* the air leaves this powder to join itself to the lime. And as neither the lime when saturated with air, nor the *magnesia* when deprived of it, are soluble in water, the lime-water becomes perfectly pure and insipid, the lime which it contained being mixed with the *magnesia.* But if the *magnesia* be deprived of air by calcination before it is mixed with the lime-water, this fluid suffers no alteration.

If quick-lime be mixed with a dissolved alkali, it likeways shews an attraction for fixed air superior to that of the alkali. It robs this salt of its air, and thereby becomes mild itself, while the alkali is consequently rendered more corrosive, or discovers its natural degree of acrimony or strong attraction for water, and for bodies of the inflammable, and of the animal and vegetable kind; which attraction was less perceivable as long as it was saturated with air. And the volatile alkali when deprived of its air, besides this attraction for various bodies, discovers likeways its natural degree of volatility, which was formerly somewhat repressed by the air adhering to it, in the same manner as it is repressed by the addition of an acid.

This account of lime and alkalis recommended itself by its simplicity, and by affording an easy solution of many *phaenomena*, but appeared upon a nearer view to be attended with consequences that were so very new and extraordinary, as to render suspicious the principles from which they were drawn.

I resolved however to examine, in a particular manner, such of these consequences as were the most unavoidable, and found the greatest number of them might be reduced to the following propositions:

I. If we only separate a quantity of air from lime and alkalis, when we render them caustic they will be found to lose part of their weight in the operation, but will saturate the same quantity of acid as before, and the saturation will be performed without effervescence.

II. If quick-lime be no other than a calcarious earth deprived of its air, and whose attraction for fixed air is stronger than that of alkalis, it follows, that, by adding to it a sufficient quantity of alkali saturated with air, the lime will recover the whole of its air, and be entirely restored to its original weight and condition: and it also follows, that the earth separated from lime-water by an alkali, is the lime which was dissolved in the water now restored to its original mild and insoluble state.

III. If it be supposed that slaked lime does not contain any parts which are more firey, active, or subtile than others, and by which chiefly it communicates its virtues to water; but that it is an uniform compound of lime and water: it follows, that, as part of it can be dissolved in water, the whole of it is also capable of being dissolved.

IV. If the acrimony of the caustic alkali does not depend on any part of the lime adhering to it, a caustic or soap-ley will consequently be found to contain no lime, unless the quantity of lime employed in making it were greater than what is just sufficient to extract the whole air of the alkali; for then as much of the superfluous quick-lime might possibly be dissolved by the ley as would be dissolved by pure water, or the ley would contain as much lime as lime-water does.

V. We have shewn in the former experiments, that absorbent earths lose their air when they are joined to an acid; but recover it, if separated again from that acid, by means of an ordinary alkali: the air passing from the alkali to the earth, at the same time that the acid passes from the earth to the alkali.

If the caustic alkali therefore be destitute of air, it will separate *magnesia* from an acid under the form of a *magnesia* free of air, or which will not effervesce with acids; and the same caustic alkali will also separate a calcarious earth from acids under the form of a calcarious earth destitute of air, but saturated with water, or under the form of slaked lime.

These were all necessary conclusions from the above suppositions. Many of them appeared too improbable to deserve any further attention: some however, I found upon reflection, were already seconded by experience. Thus *Hoffman* has observed, that quick-lime does not effervesce with spirit of vitriol; and it is well known that the caustic spirit of urine, or of salt ammoniac, does not emit air, when mixed with acids. This consideration excited my curiosity, and determined me to inquire into the truth of them all by way of experiment. I therefore engaged myself in a set of trials; the history of which is here subjoined. Some new facts are likeways occasionally mentioned; and here it will be proper to inform the reader, that I have never mentioned any, without satisfying myself of their truth by experiment, tho' I have sometimes taken the liberty to neglect describing the experiments when they seemed sufficiently obvious.

Desiring to know how much of an acid a calcarious earth will absorb, and what quantity of air is expelled during the dissolution, I saturated two drams of chalk with diluted spirit of salt, and used the Florentine flask, as related in a similar experiment upon *magnesia*. Seven drams and one grain of the acid finished the dissolution, and the chalk lost two scruples and eight grains of air.

This experiment was necessary before the following, by which I proposed to inquire into the truth of the first proposition so far as it relates to quick-lime.

Two drams of chalk were converted into a perfect quick-lime, and lost two scruples and twelve grains in the fire. This quick-lime was slaked or reduced to a milky liquor with an ounce of water, and then dissolved in the same manner, and with the same acid, as the two drams of chalk in the preceding experiment. Six drams, two scruples and fourteen grains of the acid finished the saturation without any sensible effervescence or loss of weight.

It therefore appears from these experiments, that no air is separated from quick-lime by an acid, and that chalk saturates nearly the same quantity of acid after it is converted into quick-lime as before.

With respect to the second proposition, I tried the following experiments.

A piece of perfect quick-lime made from two drams of chalk, and which weighed one dram and eight grains, was reduced to a very fine powder, and thrown into a filtrated mixture of an ounce of a fixed alkaline salt and two ounces of water. After a slight digestion, the powder being well washed and dried, weighed one dram and fifty eight grains. It was similar in every trial to a fine powder of ordinary chalk, and was therefore saturated with air which must have been furnished by the alkali.

A dram of pure salt of tartar was dissolved in fourteen pounds of lime-water, and the powder thereby precipitated, being carefully collected and dried, weighed one and fifty grains. When exposed to a violent fire, it was converted into a true quick-lime, and had every other quality of a calcarious earth.

This experiment was repeated with the volatile alkali, and also with the fossil or alkali of sea-salt, and exactly with the same event.

The third proposition had less appearance of probability than the foregoing; but, as an accurate experiment was the only test of its truth, I reduced eight grains of perfect quick-lime made of chalk, to an exceedingly subtile powder, by slaking it in two drams of distilled water boiling hot, and immediately threw the mixture into eighteen ounces of distilled water in a flask. After shaking it, a light sediment, which floated thro' the liquor, was allowed to subside; and this, when collected with the greatest care, and dryed, weighed, as near as I could guess, one third of a grain. The water tasted strongly of the lime, had all the qualities of lime-water, and yielded twelve grains of precipitate, upon the addition of salt of tartar. In repeating this experiment, the quantity of sediment was sometimes less than the above, and sometimes amounted to half a grain. It consisted partly of an earth which effervesced violently with *aqua fortis*, and partly of an ochry powder, which would not dissolve in that acid. The ochry powder, as it usually appears in chalk to the eye, in the form of veins running thro' its substance, must be considered only as an accidental or foreign admixture; and, with respect to the minute portion of alkaline earth which composed the remainder of the sediment, it cannot be supposed to have been originally different from the rest, and incapable, from its nature, of being converted into quick-lime, or of being dissolved in water; it seems rather to have consisted of a small part of the chalk in its mild state, or saturated with air, which had either remained, for want of a sufficient fire to drive it out entirely, or had been furnished by the distilled water.

I indeed expected to see a much larger quantity of sediment produced from the lime, on account of the air which water constantly contains, and with a view to know whether water retains its air when fully saturated with lime, a lime-water was made as strong as possible; four ounces of which were placed under the receiver of an air-pump, together with four ounces of common water in a phial of the same size; and, upon exhausting the receiver, without heating the phials, the air arose from each, in nearly the same quantity: from whence it is evident, that the air, which quick-lime attracts, is of a different kind from that which is mixed with water. And that it is also different from common elastic air, is sufficiently proved by daily experience; for lime-water, which soon attracts air, and forms a crust when exposed in open and shallow vessels, may be preserved, for any time, in bottles which are but slightly corked, or closed in such a manner as would allow free access to elastic air, were a vacuum formed in the bottle. Quick-lime therefore does not attract air when in its most ordinary form, but is capable of being joined to one particular species only, which is dispersed thro' the atmosphere, either in the shape of an exceedingly subtle powder, or more probably in that of an elastic fluid. To this I have given the name of fixed air, and perhaps very improperly; but I thought it better to use a word already familiar in philosophy,[4] than to invent a new name, before we be more fully acquainted with the nature and properties of this substance, which will probably be the subject of my further inquiry.

[4] [Robert Boyle had used it.]

Torbern Bergman

(1735–1784)

ONE of the first branches of physical chemistry studied was the theory of affinity. Geoffroy's (1718) system was one of the earliest. This was extended by Torbern Bergman (1775) in a paper presented at the Upsala Academy.[1] Bergman utilized two sets of tables, one for ordinary low temperatures in the wet way, the other at high temperatures in the dry fused state. He was the first to recognize the effect of heat on affinity, and he also indicated that some reactions require an excess of reagent for completion. The two tables of affinity are for 59 substances, headed by acids, alkalies, calces, etc., with all the known combinable substances arranged below in order of their supposed affinity. One could predict from the charts the course of a reaction. Bergman defined the amount of acid needed to neutralize a given amount of base as the measure of affinity of that acid for that base. Unfortunately he drew erroneous conclusions in this work which were later clarified by Berthollet. He differentiated two types of affinity: the affinity of aggregation between homogeneous substances whose combination only increases the mass, and the affinity of composition between heterogeneous substances to form compounds. The combination of two out of three substances together was termed, by Bergman, *single elective attraction*, and double attraction was the exchange of constituents of two compounds. He stated that a change in affinity could only be brought about by heat.

The results of the classification were utilized by Bergman in setting up a theory of affinity which was accepted for many years. The chief point of his theory is that the affinity value between two chemically active substances reacting upon one another is constant under like conditions and is independent of the mass of the substance. Bergman postulated that gravity was the cause of affinity, which was modified by the form and position of the reacting body particles. He recognized the impossibility of carrying out absolute affinity determinations, constructing his tables with relative values. The citation is from the Cullen translation.[2]

[1] "De attractionibus electivis," *N. Actes d' Upsal*, **3** (1775). This was augmented and republished in the third volume of his "Opuscula." "Opuscula Physica et Chemica, pleraque antea seorsim edita jam ab auctore collecta, revisa et aucta," Stockholm, Upsala, 1783. The complete works appeared in six volumes (1779 to 1790); the last three were edited after Bergman's death.

An English edition of the complete set, except for his "Elective Attractions," was made by Edmund Cullen: "Physical and Chemical Essays, translated from the original Latin, with Notes and Illustrations, by Edmund Cullen, M.D., . . . ," Edinburgh, 1788–1791.

[2] "A Dissertation on Elective Attractions. By Torbern Bergman. Late Professor of Chemistry at Upsal, and Knight of the Royal Order of Vasa. Translated from the Latin by the Translator of Spallanzani's Dissertations. London, Printed for J. Murray,

Several species of contiguous attraction may be distinguished. I shall here briefly mention the principal. When homogeneous bodies tend to union, an increase of mass only takes place, the nature of the body remaining still the same; and this effect is denominated the *attraction of aggregation.* But heterogeneous substances, when mixed together, and left to themselves to form combinations, are influenced by difference of quality rather than of quantity. This we call *attraction of composition;* and when it is exerted in forming a mere union of two or more substances, it receives the name of *attraction of solution* or *fusion,* according as it is effected either in the moist or the dry way. When it takes place between three respectively, to the exclusion of one, it is said to be a *single elective attraction;* when between two compounds, each consisting of only two proximate principles, which are exchanged in consequence of mixture, it is intitled *double attraction.* I am particularly to consider the two last species.

II. SINGLE ELECTIVE ATTRACTIONS.

Suppose A to be a substance for which other heterogeneous substances a, b, c, &c. have an attraction; suppose further, A combined with c to saturation, (this union I shall call Ac), should, upon the addition of b, tend to unite with it to the exclusion of c, A is then said to attract b more strongly than c, or to have a stronger elective attraction for it; lastly, let the union of Ab, on the addition of a, be broken, let b be rejected, and a chosen in its place, it will follow, that a exceeds b in attractive power, and we shall have a series, a, b, c, in respect of efficacy. What I here call attraction, others denominate affinity; I shall employ both terms promiscuously in the sequel, though the latter, being more metaphorical, would seem less proper in philosophy.

Geoffroy, in 1718, first exhibited at one view the series of elective attractions, by arranging in a table the chemical signs, according to a certain order; but this admirable contrivance, while it is commended by some, is blamed by others; one party contending, that affinities are governed by fixed laws, and the other affirming, that they are vague, and to be ascribed to circumstances alone.

Now, since all chemical operations consist either in analysis or synthesis, composition or decomposition, and both the one and the other depend on attraction, it will certainly be of great importance to determine this dispute. Let us not then lightly, and on account of one or two irregularities, perhaps ill understood, reject the whole doctrine, but let us rather proceed in our examination with caution and care. Should we even at last find that attractions depend on circumstances, shall we therefore conclude, that it will be useless to know the several conditions that forward or

No. 32, Fleet Street; and Charles Elliot," Edinburgh, 1785, pp. 5–17, 64–75. This work was translated by Edmund Cullen.

impede or disturb them? By no means, but rather that it will be of extensive utility. There does not exist in all nature a single phaenomenon but what is so connected with certain conditions, that when they are absent, the phaenomenon shall either not appear, or be varied occasionally. It is of consequence to science, that the changes and the combination of causes in every operation should be accurately known, as far as a knowledge of them is attainable; and the utility of a strict inquiry into attractions will, I hope, clearly appear from many instances in the following pages.

But if, on the contrary, a fixed order does really take place, will it not, when once ascertained by experience, serve as a key to unlock the innermost sanctuaries of nature, and to solve the most difficult problems, whether analytical or synthetical? I maintain, therefore, not only that the doctrine deserves to be cultivated, but that the whole of chemistry rests upon it, as upon a solid foundation, at least if we wish to have the science in a rational form, and that each circumstance of its operations should be clearly and justly explained. Let him who doubts of this consider the following observations without prejudice, and bring them to the test of experiment.

III. WHETHER THE ORDER OF ATTRACTIONS BE CONSTANT.

This question can only be properly answered from what follows. But let us now slightly consider whether a constant series, such as is mentioned in the last paragraph, is to be expected. Does *a* expel *b*, and *b* *a* reciprocally, according to circumstances? Does *c* perchance expel *a*, while it always gives way to *b*? Let us consult Experiment, the oracle of nature, with due care and patience, and we shall doubtless find the proper clue to guide us out of this labyrinth.

I am far from approving of those general rules which affirm, that earths and metals are in all cases precipitated by alkalis, and metals by earths, for they are often fallacious. We have, however, many particular observations which, when every thing is properly disposed, never mislead. We know, for instance, that volatile alkali is dislodged by fixed alkali and pure calcareous earth; that quicksilver and silver are precipitated from nitrous and vitriolic acids on the addition of copper, which is again separated by iron. Silver, quicksilver, and lead, which were called the white metals by the ancients, are separated from the nitrous acid both by the vitriolic and marine. Do not these, and other facts long since known, shew, that there prevails a constant order among these several substances? Many other clear proofs occur in the explanation of the new table of attractions, which I shall reserve for their proper places, (XII.–LXX.). The difficulties, when closely examined, disappear; and none has yet, as far as I know, been pointed out which is really inconsistent with a continued series. But should there occur in this, as in other branches of natural philosophy, a few phaenomena, which appear to deviate from the ordinary track, they should be considered as comets, of which the orbits cannot yet be determined, because they have not been sufficiently observed. Repeated observations, and proper experiments, will in time dispel the darkness.

That the effect of three substances mixed together may appear at one view, I have contrived a way of representing it by symbols. It will be proper to illustrate it by example.

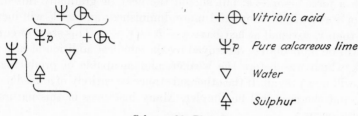

+⊕ *Vitriolic acid*

♄p *Pure calcareous lime*

▽   *Water*

♀   *Sulphur*

Scheme 20. Plate I.

Scheme 20. Pl. I. exhibits the decomposition of calcareous hepar by the vitriolic acid. On the left side appears the hepar, indicated by the signs of its proximate principles united; but within the vertical bracket these principles are seen separate, one above the other. On the right, opposite the calcareous earth, is placed the sign of vitriolic acid; in the middle stands the sign of water, intimating that the three surrounding bodies freely exercise their attractive powers in it. Now, as vitriolic acid attracts calcareous earth more forcibly than sulfur does, it destroys the composition of the hepar; the extruded sulfur being by itself insoluble falls to the bottom, which is signified by the point of the lower horizontal half-bracket being turned downwards; and as the new compound, vitriolated calcareous earth (gypsum), also subsides, unless the quantity of water be very large, the point of the upper bracket is likewise turned downwards. The complete horizontal bracket indicates a new combination, but the half-bracket serves merely to shew by its point whether the substance from which it is drawn remains in the liquor, or falls to the bottom. The absence of horizontal brackets indicates that the original compound remains entire. Such a combination only as continues unaltered can have a place on the right side, for if it be likewise decomposed, a new case arises, which will be noticed hereafter, (V.). Those operations which are performed in the dry way, are distinguished by the character of fire, which is placed in the middle.

IV. A DIFFERENCE IN THE DEGREE OF HEAT SOMETIMES PRODUCES A DIFFERENCE IN ELECTIVE ATTRACTIONS.

The only external condition, which either weakens or totally inverts the affinities of bodies subjected to experiments, is the different intensity of heat. But this cause can only operate in cases where the same temperature renders some bodies remarkably volatile in comparison of others.

Suppose A to be attracted by two other substances; and let the more powerful act at the ordinary temperature with the force a, the weaker with the force b: suppose, at the same time, the former to be the more volatile; let its effort to arise be expressed by V, and that of the other by v. When these three substances are mixed together, the stronger will attract A with a force $= a - b$: but should the heat be gradually raised, this superior force will be more and more diminished; and as V will increase faster than v, we shall at last have $a - b = V - v$. This state of equilibrium will be immediately destroyed by the smallest addition of heat; and thus b, which was before the weaker, and incapable of producing any effect, will now prevail. If the other substance be entirely of a fixed nature, $v = o$, and the case will be simpler. Many instances of this nature will hereafter occur.

Hence, I think it in general obvious, that those are the genuine attractions, which take place when bodies are left to themselves: too high a degree of heat is an external cause, which forcibly weakens the real affinities more or less, nay, in some cases, even totally alters them. Since, however, many operations cannot be carried on without the aid of heat, and the power therefore of this most subtile fluid is highly worthy of being observed, I think the table of elective attractions ought to be divided into two areas; of which the upper may exhibit the free attractions, that take place in the moist way, as the expression is; and the lower, those which are effected by the force of heat. This may easily be done, since we are as yet unacquainted with any other external condition which deserves here to be taken into the account; if the internal conditions ever cause any deviation, it is either only apparent, or else a real change in the nature of the substances is produced. It cannot indeed be denied, that volatile bodies are actually changed by a combination with the matter of heat; but the change is of short duration, as it totally disappears on refrigeration, though not till after the desired decomposition has been effected.

It is hence evident, what opinion we are to form concerning the various arguments brought against the constancy of affinities, from the distillation, sublimation, or fusion of mixtures: such sometimes is the efficacy of heat, that strong digestion, or even that degree of warmth which is produced by the combination of certain substances, is sufficient to disturb the usual order. . . .

X. HOW WE ARE TO DETERMINE THE SINGLE ELECTIVE ATTRACTIONS.

After this view of the difficulties which may occur, let us hasten to our subject. Suppose a, b, c, d, &c. to be different substances, of which the attractive forces for A are to be ascertained.

a.) Let *Ad*, (i.e. *A* saturated with *d*,) be dissolved in distilled water, and then add a small quantity of *c*, which may either be soluble in water by itself or not. First let it be soluble; then a concentrated solution ought to be employed, which, when dropped into a solution of *Ad*, sometimes immediately affords a precipitate, which, being collected and washed, either proves to be a new combination, *Ac*, with peculiar properties, or *d* is extruded, or sometimes both. It now remains to be examined, whether the whole of *d* can be dislodged by a sufficient quantity of *c* from its former union. It should be carefully noted in general, that there is occasion for twice, thrice, nay sometimes six times the quantity of the decomponent *c*, than is necessary for saturating *A* when uncombined. If *c* effect no separation, not even in several hours, let the liquor stand to crystallize, or at least become dry by a spontaneous evaporation; high degrees of heat must be avoided, less they disturb the affinities, (IV.). Here the knowledge of the form, taste, solubility, tendency to effloresce, and other properties, even those which, in other respects, appear of no consequence, of the substances, is of great use in enabling us to judge safely and readily, whether any, and what decomposition has taken place. Sometimes the disengaged substance, whether that which was added or expelled, gives the operator much trouble, by concealing the genuine properties of the other, and therefore, if possible, should be removed, according to circumstances, either by water or spirit of wine.

Next, suppose *c* to be insoluble, as, for instance, a metal, let a bright and clean plate of it be put into the solution of *Ad*, and let it be observed, whether any thing is precipitated. By putting several laminae in succession, we find at last whether a part only of *d*, or the whole, is separated. Sometimes no decomposition is effected, though the surface of the metal should have been lately filed, unless there be a small excess of acid; and as far as I have hitherto been able to collect, it is not always of consequence that the superfluous acid should be of the same nature as that which *Ad* contains or not.

If only one of the compounds *Ad* and *Ac* be soluble in highly rectified spirit of wine, there is scarce any need of evaporation; for if the mixture be made, and left a few hours at rest, and then spirit of wine be added, that which cannot be dissolved in it is separated.

The smell also often indicates what is taking place. Thus, vinegar, acid of ants, of salt, nitre, volatile alkali, are easily distinguished when set free. The taste likewise often informs an experienced tongue.

b.) Let *Ad* then be treated with *b* and *a*, &c. separately in the same manner.

c.) In like manner, let *Ac*, *Ab*, *Aa*, be examined in their order.

By such an examination properly conducted, the order of attractions is discovered. This task, however, exercises all the patience, and diligence, and accuracy, and knowledge, and experience of the chemist. Let us suppose only a series of five terms, *a, b, c, d,* and *e,* to be examined with respect to *A,* twenty different experiments are requisite, of which each involves several others: a series of ten terms requires ninety experiments, and, in general, if *a* be the number of the series, $n \cdot \overline{n - 1}$ will be the number of experiments.

d.) In like manner, each compound with *a, c, b,* should be examined in the dry way; but it must be in a crucible, or, if possible, in a retort heated to incandescence, that the volatile part may be collected at the same time.

Such, in general, is the method which I have followed; the continuance of this labour will perhaps discover various shorter paths, which will at least be convenient in certain cases. But we should be cautious in guarding against fallacies arising from the apparent exceptions above described.

XI. THE NECESSITY FOR A NEW TABLE OF ATTRACTIONS.

The tables which we have at present contain only a few substances, and each of these compared only with a few others. This is no reproach to the authors of them, for the task is laborious and long. Although, therefore, I have been employed upon it with all the diligence I could exert, and as much as my many other engagements would permit, yet I am very far from venturing to assert, that that which I offer is perfect, since I know with certainty, that the slight sketch now proposed will require above 30,000 exact experiments before it can be brought to any degree of perfection. But when I reflected on the shortness of life, and the instability of health, I resolved to publish my observations, however defective, lest they should perish with my papers, and I shall relate them as briefly as possible. In itself it is of small consequence by whom science is enriched; whether the truths belonging to it are discovered by me or by another. Meanwhile, if God shall grant me life, health, and the necessary leisure, I will persevere in the task which I have begun. I shall now explain the end I had in view, and my plan; should they be approved by the masters of the science, I hope that many will lend me their assistance, for it is easier to accomplish one or two columns, than to bring all to perfection: I exhibit a great number of the more simple substances which occur in chemistry. Many of these are not only compounded, but are easily resolved into their proximate principles, such as hepar, sulphur, the imperfect metals, &c.; but they do not come into view here, but inasmuch as they effect composition and decomposition in their entire state; but when their proximate constituent parts are separated, double attractions take place, which are not considered in this table.

Moreover, I have inserted many lately discovered, of uncertain origin and composition, such as the acids of fluor, arsenic, tartar, sugar, and sorrel; of earths, magnesia and terra ponderosa; of metals, platina, nickle, manganese, and siderite, of which more in the place belonging to each. In the obscurity of their origin, these substances agree with others that have been the longest known. Should they be derived from others, they ought not, on this account, to be excluded, for they are now different, have constant properties, exercise their attractive powers without decomposition, and can at pleasure be obtained perfectly alike. It is therefore proper to inquire into their powers. Every substance that we employ is probably compounded, and although we are at present ignorant of its principles, they may hereafter be detected.

The upper stratum of the table, if I may so call it, contains fifty-nine rectangles horizontally placed, which exhibit fifty-nine different substances, denoted by signs formerly in use, or by new ones, which I shall now therefore enumerate in order of the adjacent numbers, for there is scarce any one in the following which does not appear in the first: 1. Is vitriolic acid; 2. Phlogisticated vitriolic acid; 3. Nitrous acid; 4. Phlogisticated nitrous acid; 5. Muriatic acid; 6. Dephlogisticated muriatic acid; 7. Aqua regia; 8. Fluor acid; 9. Arsenical acid; 10. Acid of borax; 11. Acid of sugar; 12. Acid of tartar; 13. Acid of sorrel; 14. Acid of lemon; 15. Acid of benzoin; 16. Acid of amber; 17. Acid of sugar of milk; 18. Distilled vinegar; 19. Acid of milk; 20. Acid of ants; 21. Acid of fat; 22. Acid of phosphorus; 23. Acidum perlatum; 24. Acid of Prussian blue; 25. Aerial acid; 26. Pure fixed vegetable alkali; 27. Pure fixed mineral alkali; 28. Pure volatile alkali; 29. Pure ponderous earth; 30. Pure lime; 31. Pure magnesia; 32. Pure clay; 33. Pure siliceous earth; 34. Water; 35. Vital air; 36. Phlogiston; 37. Matter of heat; 38. Sulphur; 39. Saline liver of sulphur; 40. Alcohol; 41. Aether; 42. Essential oil; 43. Unctuous oil; 44. Gold; 45. Platina; 46. Silver; 47. Mercury; 48. Lead; 49. Copper; 50. Iron; 51. Tin; 52. Bismuth; 53. Nickle; 54. Arsenic; 55. Cobalt; 56. Zinc; 57. Antimony; 58. Manganese; and, 59. Siderite.

These substances are, as it were, the heads of each column, at the top of which they respectively stand: to these those that are placed below bear this relation, that the nearer they stand, the stronger attraction they must be understood to have. Every column, therefore, not only must exhibit every one of the fifty-nine substances which is capable of being combined with the principal substance at the top, but also the order which such combinations follow. The double line distinguishes from the others the thirtieth stratum, which is the first that belongs to the dry way. The substances which occur in these rows refer also to the heads of the columns.

Lastly, I have distinguished the horizontal rows, as well as the columns, by numbers on each side, that each rectangle might be more readily found and quoted. On account of the new substances, I am obliged to divide the table of single elective attractions into two parts; and when, from multi-

1 VITRIOLIC ACID	2 PHLOGISTICATED VITRIOLIC ACID	3 NITROUS ACID	4 PHLOGISTICATED NITROUS ACID	5 MARINE ACID	6 DEPHLOGISTICATED MARINE ACID	7 AQUA REGIA
2 Pure ponderous earth	Pure ponderous earth	Pure vegetable alkali?	Pure vegetable alkali?	Pure vegetable alkali	Pure vegetable alkali?	Pure vegetable alkali?
3 Pure vegetable alkali	Pure vegetable alkali	Pure fossil alkali?	Pure fossil alkali?	Pure fossil alkali?	Pure fossil alkali?	Pure fossil alkali?
4 Pure fossil alkali	Pure fossil alkali	Pure ponderous earth?	Pure ponderous earth?	Pure ponderous earth?	Pure ponderous earth?	Pure ponderous earth?
5 Lime	Lime	Lime	Lime	Lime	Lime	Lime
6 Pure magnesia	Pure magnesia	Pure magnesia	Pure magnesia	Pure magnesia	Pure magnesia	Pure magnesia
7 Pure volatile alkali	Pure volatile alkali	Pure volatile alkali	Pure volatile alkali	Pure volatile alkali	Pure volatile alkali	Pure volatile alkali
8 Pure clay	Pure clay	Pure clay	Pure clay	Pure clay	Pure clay	Pure clay
9 Calx of zinc	Calx of zinc	Calx of zinc	Calx of zinc	Calx of zinc	Calx of zinc	Calx of zinc
10 Calx of iron	Calx of iron	Calx of iron	Calx of iron	Calx of iron	Calx of iron	Calx of iron
11 Calx of manganese	Calx of manganese	Calx of manganese	Calx of manganese	Calx of manganese	Calx of manganese	Calx of manganese
12 Calx of cobalt	Calx of cobalt	Calx of cobalt	Calx of cobalt	Calx of cobalt	Calx of cobalt	Calx of cobalt
13 Calx of nickle	Calx of nickle	Calx of nickle	Calx of nickle	Calx of nickle	Calx of nickle	Calx of nickle
14 Calx of lead	Calx of lead	Calx of lead	Calx of lead	Calx of lead	Calx of lead	Calx of lead
15 Calx of tin	Calx of tin	Calx of tin	Calx of tin	Calx of tin	Calx of tin	Calx of tin
16 Calx of copper	Calx of copper	Calx of copper	Calx of copper	Calx of copper	Calx of copper	Calx of copper
17 Calx of bismuth	Calx of bismuth	Calx of bismuth	Calx of bismuth	Calx of bismuth	Calx of bismuth	Calx of bismuth
18 Calx of antimony	Calx of antimony	Calx of antimony	Calx of antimony	Calx of antimony	Calx of antimony	Calx of antimony
19 Calx of arsenic	Calx of arsenic	Calx of arsenic	Calx of arsenic	Calx of arsenic	Calx of arsenic	Calx of arsenic
20 Calx of mercury	Calx of mercury	Calx of mercury	Calx of mercury	Calx of mercury	Calx of mercury	Calx of mercury
21 Calx of silver	Calx of silver	Calx of silver	Calx of silver	Calx of silver	Calx of silver	Calx of silver
22 Calx of gold	Calx of gold	Calx of gold	Calx of gold	Calx of gold	Calx of gold	Calx of gold
23 Calx of platina	Calx of platina	Calx of platina	Calx of platina	Calx of platina	Calx of platina	Calx of platina
24 Water	Water	Water	Water	Water	Water	Water
25 Spirit of wine	Spirit of wine	Spirit of wine	Spirit of wine	Spirit of wine	Spirit of wine	Spirit of wine
26 Phlogiston	Phlogiston	Phlogiston	Phlogiston	Phlogiston	Phlogiston	Phlogiston
27						
28						
29						
30						
31 Phlogiston		Phlogiston		Phlogiston		Phlogiston
32 Pure vegetable alkali		Pure ponderous earth?		Pure ponderous earth?		Pure ponderous earth?
33 Pure fossil alkali		Pure vegetable alkali		Pure vegetable alkali		Pure vegetable alkali
34 Pure pond. earth		Pure fossil alkali		Pure fossil alkali		Pure fossil alkali
35 Lime		Lime		Lime		Lime
36 Pure magnesia		Pure magnesia		Pure magnesia		Pure magnesia
37 Metallic calces		Metallic calces		Metallic calces		Metallic calces
38 Pure volatile alkali		Pure volatile alkali		Pure volatile alkali		Pure volatile alkali
39 Pure clay		Pure clay		Pure clay		Pure clay
40						
41						
42						
43						
44						
45						
46						
47						
48						
49						
50						

A portion of Bergman's table of affinities from "A Dissertation on Elective Attraction," London, 1785.

plied experiments, more [material] than two can contain shall require admission, it may be conveniently divided into four parts; the first for the acids, the second for the alkalis and earths, the third for the inflammables, and the fourth for the metals.

Carl Wilhelm Scheele

(1742–1786)

FEW, if any, chemists have discovered more new substances than the Swedish apothecary chemist, Carl Wilhelm Scheele. Always in poor circumstances, he could devote only his spare time to chemistry, but this he did with such vigor and perspicuity that in his short life he published many papers, in almost each one of which was a discovery of major importance. In manipulative skill he probably surpassed even Priestley, but like his English contemporary he was a phlogistonist and, therefore, contributed little to the theory of chemistry. Unfortunately, Scheele was not so careful as Priestley to publish his investigations promptly, so that many of his discoveries have been credited to others.

Scheele's investigations are far too numerous even to enumerate. Among the most important were the discoveries of chlorine and oxygen. Scheele found the latter a short time before Priestley. Unfortunately, his publication was delayed by the printer for several years, so he lost his claim to priority. Some consider his isolation of glycerol almost as important as the discovery of chlorine and oxygen.

A host of important substances were characterized by C. W. Scheele: silicon fluoride, hydrofluoric acid, arsenic acid, molybdic acid, tungstic acid, arsine, and copper arsenite ("Scheele's green") are among the inorganic substances. His work on organic acids was outstanding, for he discovered tartaric, mucic, pyromucic, uric, hydrocyanic, oxalic, citric, malic, gallic, pyrogallic, and lactic acids.

Many of the papers of Scheele were originally published in the *Memoirs* of the Stockholm Academy of Sciences. Scheele's work on oxygen is contained in his only book, "Chemische Abhandlung von der Luft und dem Feuer," which was published in 1777.[1] In this volume he proves that air consists of two "elastic fluids," one of which supports combustion while the other does not. He removed the oxygen from the air with potassium persulfide (liver of sulfur) and by other

---

[1] "Chemische Abhandlung von der Luft und dem Feuer. Nebst einem Vorbericht von Torbern Bergman. Upsala und Leipzig, Magn. Swederus," 1777. The manuscript was delivered to the printer Swederus in 1775, and much of the experimental work had been performed before 1773. It is not known what caused the delay in printing.

The first English edition appeared in 1780: "Chemical Observations and Experiments on Air and Fire. By William Scheele, Member of the Royal Academy at Stockholm; With a prefatory introduction By Torbern Bergman; Translated from the

means. Scheele further identified it with the gas obtained from nitric acid, saltpeter, and black oxide of manganese. The discovery of oxygen was difficult to reconcile with the phlogiston theory; this is all too apparent in Scheele's involved explanations of combustion. The passages which follow, on the discovery of oxygen, are from the translation of Leonard Dobbin.[2]

CHEMICAL TREATISE ON AIR AND FIRE.

PREFACE.

The investigation of the air is an important object of chemistry at the present time. This elastic fluid is endowed, too, with so many special properties that it can furnish material enough for new discoveries to anyone who takes such experiments in hand. Fire, this product of chemistry which is so wonderful, shows us that it cannot be generated without air; and do I, indeed, err if I have undertaken to adduce proofs in this treatise, which is only to be looked upon as an attempt towards a chemical theory of fire, that an air existent in our atmosphere is to be regarded as a true consituent of fire and consequently contributes materially to flame; wherefore I have named this air fire air? Certainly. I shall not be so bold as to press my readers to believe this. No, there are clear experiments which tell in my favour, experiments that I have made on more than a single occasion, and in which, if I do not mistake, I have sufficiently nearly attained my object of learning to understand fire as clearly as possible. And this is the reward which I have obtained for my labour, and which has occasioned me a true satisfaction that I cannot possibly retain for myself alone. This, and no other, is the reason why I make this work known to my readers. I had already carried out the greater part

German by J. R. Forster, L.L.D. and S.A., Member of several Learned Societies and Academies in Europe. To which are added Notes, by Richard Kirwin, Esq. F.R.S. with a letter to him from Joseph Priestley, L.L.D., F.R.S. London, Printed for J. Johnson, no. 72 St. Paul's Churchyard," 1780. This edition contains some interesting notes by Kirwin and an important letter by Joseph Priestley to him on his differences with Scheele. It is, therefore, more than a translation.

The German edition has been reprinted as No. 58 of Ostwald's *Klassiker:* "Chemische Abhandlung von der Luft und dem Feuer. (1777). Herausgegeben von W. Ostwald," Leipzig, 1894.

A French translation of a portion has been reprinted in "Les Classiques de la Découverte Scientifique. Halogènes et composés oxygénés du chlore. Mémoires de Scheele, Berthollet, Gay-Lussac et Thenard, H. Davy, Balard, Courtois, H. Moissan, Millon. Avant-Propos par M. A. Damiens," Paris, 1938.

Portions of the original issue have been translated by Leonard Dobbin in *Alembic Club Reprints*, No. 8, "The Discovery of Oxygen, Part 2. Experiments by Carl Wilhelm Scheele. (1777)," Edinburgh, 1901.

A complete translation of "Luft und dem Feuer" appears in Dobbin's "The Collected Papers Translated from the Swedish and German Originals," London, 1931.

[2] Dobbin, "Collected Papers," pp. 87–178.

of these experiments when I obtained sight of Priestley's elegant observations. . . .

1. It is the object and chief business of chemistry skilfully to separate substances into their constituents, to discover their properties, and to compound them in different ways.

Carl Wilhelm Scheele's
d. Königl. Schwed. Acad. d. Wissenschaft. Mitgliedes,

Chemische Abhandlung
von der

Luft und dem Feuer.

Nebst einem Vorbericht
von

Torbern Bergman,
Chem, und Pharm. Prof. und Ritter; verschied.
Societ. Mitglied.

Upsala und Leipzig,
Verlegt von Magn. Swederus, Buchhändler;
zu finden bey S. L. Crusius.
1777.

Title page from Scheele's "Luft und dem Feuer," Upsala, 1777. (*Courtesy of the American Philosophical Society, Philadelphia.*)

How difficult it is, however, to carry out such operations with the greatest accuracy can only be unknown to one who either has never undertaken this occupation, or at least has not done so with sufficient attention.

2. Hitherto chemical investigators are not agreed as to how many elements or fundamental materials compose all substances. This is indeed

one of the most difficult problems. Some hold that there remains no further hope of searching out the elements of substances. Poor comfort for those who feel their greatest pleasure in the investigation of natural things! Far mistaken is anyone who endeavours to confine chemistry, this noble science, within such narrow bounds! . . .

GENERAL PROPERTIES OF ORDINARY AIR.

7. (1) Fire must burn for a certain time in a given quantity of air. (2) If, so far as can be seen, this fire does not produce during combustion any fluid resembling air, then, after the fire has gone out of itself, the quantity of air must be diminished between a third and a fourth part. (3) It must not unite with common water. (4) All kinds of animals must live for a certain time in a confined quantity of air. (5) Seeds, as for example peas, in a given quantity of similarly confined air, must strike roots and attain a certain height with the aid of some water and of a moderate heat.

Consequently, when I have a fluid resembling air in its external appearance, and find that it has not the properties mentioned, even when only one of them is wanting, I feel convinced that it is not ordinary air.

AIR MUST BE COMPOSED OF ELASTIC FLUIDS OF TWO KINDS.

8. *First Experiment.* I dissolved one ounce of alkaline liver of sulphur[3] in eight ounces of water; I poured four ounces of this solution into an empty bottle capable of holding twenty-four ounces of water and closed it most securely with a cork; I then inverted the bottle and placed the neck in a small vessel with water; in this position I allowed it to stand for fourteen days. During this time the solution had lost a part of its red colour and had also deposited some sulphur: afterwards I took the bottle and held it in the same position in a larger vessel with water, so that the mouth was under and the bottom above the water-level, and withdrew the cork under the water; immediately water rose with violence into the bottle. I closed the bottle again, removed it from the water, and weighed the fluid which it contained. There were ten ounces. After subtracting from this the four ounces of solution of sulphur there remain six ounces, consequently it is apparent from this experiment that of twenty parts of air six parts have been lost in fourteen days. . . .

13. *Sixth Experiment.* I collected in a bladder the nitrous air which arises on the dissolution of the metals in acid of nitre, and after I had tied the bladder tightly I laid it in a flask and secured the mouth very carefully with a wet bladder. The nitrous air gradually lost its elasticity, the bladder collapsed, and became yellow as if corroded by *aqua fortis.* After fourteen days I made a hole in the bladder tied over the flask, having previously

[3] [A mixture of potassium polysulfides produced by the fusion of potassium carbonate with sulphur.]

held it, inverted, under water; the water rose rapidly into the flask, and it remained only two thirds empty.

14. *Seventh Experiment.* (a) I immersed the mouth of a flask in a vessel with oil of turpentine. The oil rose in the flask a few lines every day. After the lapse of fourteen days the fourth part of the flask was filled with it; I allowed it to stand for three weeks longer, but the oil did not rise higher. All those oils which dry in the air and become converted into resinous substances, possess this property. Oil of turpentine, however, and linseed oil rise up sooner if the flask is previously rinsed out with a concentrated corrosive ley. (b) I poured two ounces of colourless and transparent animal oil of Dippel[4] into a bottle and closed it very tightly; after the expiry of two months the oil was thick and black. I then held the bottle, inverted, under water and drew out the cork; the bottle immediately became one fourth filled with water.

15. *Eighth Experiment.* (a) I dissolved two ounces of vitriol of iron in thirty-two ounces of water, and precipitated this solution with a caustic ley. After the precipitate had settled, I poured away the clear fluid and put the dark green precipitate of iron so obtained, together with the remaining water, into the before-mentioned bottle (§8) and closed it tightly. After fourteen days (during which time I shook the bottle frequently) this green calx of iron had acquired the colour of crocus of iron,[5] and of forty parts of air twelve had been lost. (b) When iron filings are moistened with some water and preserved for a few weeks in a well-closed bottle, a portion of the air is likewise lost. (c) The solution of iron in vinegar has the same effect upon air. In this case the vinegar permits the dissolved iron to fall out in the form of a yellow crocus and becomes completely deprived of the metal. (d) The solution of copper prepared in closed vessels with spirit of salt likewise diminishes air. In none of the foregoing kinds of air can either a candle burn or the smallest spark appear.

16. It is seen from these experiments that phlogiston, this simple inflammable principle, is present in each of them. It is known that the air strongly attracts to itself the inflammable matter of substances and deprives them of it: not only may this be seen from the experiments cited, but it is at the same time evident that on the transference of the inflammable matter to the air a considerable part of the air is lost. . . .

It may also be seen from the above experiments, that a given quantity of air can only unite with, and at the same time saturate, a certain quantity of the inflammable principle: . . . Thus much I see from the experiments mentioned, that the air consists of two fluids differing from each other, the one of which does not manifest in the least the property of attracting phlogiston while the other, which composes between the third

---

[4] [An oil obtained by the destructive distillation of bones.]
[5] [Ferric oxide.]

and the fourth part of the whole mass of the air, is peculiarly disposed to such attraction. But where this latter kind of air has gone to after it has united with the inflammable matter, is a question which must be decided by further experiments, and not by conjectures. . . .

17. *First Experiment*. I placed nine grains of phosphorus from urine in a thin flask, which was capable of holding thirty ounces of water, and closed its mouth most securely. I then heated, with a burning candle, the part of the flask where the phosphorus lay; the phosphorus began to melt, and immediately afterwards took fire; the flask became filled with a white cloud, which attached itself to the sides like white flowers; this was the dry acid of phosphorus. After the flask had become cold again, I held it, inverted, under water and opened it; scarcely had this been done when the external air pressed water into the flask; this water amounted to nine ounces.

18. *Second Experiment*. When I placed pieces of phosphorus in the same flask and allowed it to stand, closed, for six weeks, or until it no longer glowed, I found that one third of the air had been lost.

19. *Third Experiment*. I placed three teaspoonfuls of iron filings in a bottle capable of holding two ounces of water; to this I added an ounce of water, and gradually mixed with them half an ounce of oil of vitriol. A violent heating and fermentation took place. When the froth had somewhat subsided, I fixed into the bottle an accurately fitting cork, through which I had previously fixed a glass tube *A* (Fig. 1). I placed this bottle in a vessel filled with hot water, *B B* (cold water would greatly retard the solution). I then approached a burning candle to the orifice of the tube, whereupon the inflammable air took fire and burned with a small yellowish-green flame. As soon as this had taken place, I took a small flask *C* which was capable of holding twenty ounces of water, and held it so deep in the water that the little flame stood in the middle of the flask. The water at once began to rise gradually into the flask, and when the level had reached the point *D* the flame went out. Immediately afterwards the water began to sink again, and was entirely driven out of the flask. The space in the flask up to *D* contained four ounces, therefore the fifth part of the air had been lost. I poured a few ounces of lime water into the flask in order to see whether any aerial acid had also been produced during the combustion, but I did not find any. I made the same experiment with zinc filings, and it proceeded in every way similarly to that just mentioned. I shall demonstrate the constituents of this inflammable air further on; for, although it seems to follow from these experiments that it is only phlogiston, still other observations are contrary to this. . . .

29. I took a glass retort which was capable of holding eight ounces of water, and distilled fuming acid of nitre according to the usual method. In the beginning the acid went over red, then it became colourless, and

finally all became red again; as soon as I perceived the latter, I took away the receiver and tied on a bladder, emptied of air, into which I poured some thick milk of lime in order to prevent the corrosion of the bladder. I then proceeded with the distillation. The bladder began to expand gradually. After this I permitted everything to cool, and tied up the bladder. Lastly I removed it from the neck of the retort. I filled a bottle, which contained ten ounces of water, with this gas. I then placed a small lighted

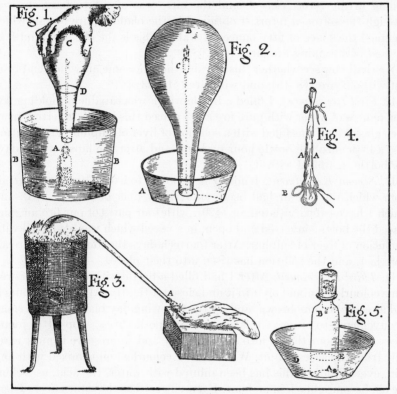

Apparatus of Scheele. (*Courtesy of the American Philosophical Society, Philadelphia.*)

candle in it; scarcely had this been done when the candle began to burn with a large flame, whereby it gave out such a bright light that it was sufficient to dazzle the eyes, I mixed one part of this air with three parts of that kind of air in which fire would not burn; I had here an air which was like the ordinary air in every respect. Since this air is necessarily required for the origination of fire, and makes up about the third part of our common air, I shall call it after this, for the sake of shortness, Fire Air; but the other air which is not in the least serviceable for the fiery phenomenon, and makes up about two thirds of our air, I shall designate after this with the name already known, of Vitiated Air. . . .

I have stated that even nitre alone decomposes the matter of heat.[6] The following experiment proves this.   . . .

35. *Fourth Experiment.* I put an ounce of purified nitre into a glass retort for distillation and made use of a bladder, moistened and emptied of air, in place of a receiver (Fig. 3). As soon as the nitre began to be red-hot it also began to boil, and at the same time the bladder was expanded by the air that passed over. I proceeded with the distillation until the boiling in the retort ceased, and the nitre was about to force its way through the softened retort. I obtained in the bladder pure fire air which occupied the space of fifty ounces of water. This is the cheapest and best method of obtaining fire air.   . . .

We shall now see whether this fire air is not the same air which had been lost without fire (§8–15), and with fire (§17–23).[7]   . . .

42. *First Experiment.* I filled a bottle which was capable of holding sixteen ounces of water with pure fire air. I placed this bottle, inverted, in an open glass which was filled with a solution of liver of sulphur. The solution rose a little into the bottle hour by hour, and after the lapse of two days the bottle was filled with it.

43. *Second Experiment.* I mixed in a bottle fourteen parts of that air from which the fire air had been removed by liver of sulphur (§8), and which I have called vitiated air (§29), with four parts of our fire air, and placed the bottle, inverted and open, in a vessel which was also filled with a solution of liver of sulphur. After fourteen days the four parts of fire air were lost, and the solution has risen into their place.

44. *Third Experiment.* After I had filled a bottle with our air, I poured some colourless animal oil into it and closed it tightly. After a few hours it had already become brown, and by the following day black. It is no small inconvenience to preserve this oil white in apothecaries' shops. It is found necessary to pour the oil into small bottles, and to preserve it most carefully from the access of air. When such a colourless oil is mixed with any acid, even although this has been diluted with water, the acid, as well as the oil, becomes black in an hour. Even vinegar has the same effect. There is no other reason, therefore, why the oil becomes at once black in the air than that the fire air present in the air deprives it of its phlogiston, and thereby develops a subtle acid, previously united with this phlogiston, which produces the blackness.   . . .

47. *Sixth Experiment.* I laid some red-hot pieces of charcoal upon the stand, and placed over them a flask which was filled with fire air. The charcoal had not even reached the air in the flask before it began to burn very brilliantly.

After everything had become cold, I made an aperture under the flask,

[6] [Scheele thought that heat was a compound of "fire air" and phlogiston.]

[7] [As with liver of sulfur and with a candle, for instance.]

whereupon the fourth part became filled with water. But when I removed, by means of milk of lime, the aerial acid which was present in the residual air there remained in the flask only the fourth part. In this air a candle could still burn. . . .

49. I have mentioned (§16) that I found vitiated air lighter than ordinary air. Must it not follow from this that fire air is heavier than our air? As a matter of fact, I actually found, when I accurately weighed as much fire air as occupied the space of twenty ounces of water, that this was almost two grains heavier than the same bulk of common air.

50. These experiments show, therefore, that this fire air is just that air by means of which fire burns in common air; only it is there mixed with a kind of air which seems to possess no attraction at all for the inflammable principle, and this it is which places some hindrance in the way of the otherwise rapid and violent inflammation. And in fact, if air consisted of nothing but fire air, water would surely render small service in extinguishing outbreaks of fire. Aerial acid mixed with this fire air, has the same effect as vitiated air.

One of the most interesting and important chapters in chemistry is the history of chlorine. The first paper describing the discovery of chlorine was published by Scheele in 1774, "Om Brunsten, eller Magnesia, och dess Egenskaper."[8] He gives a full and accurate description of the nature of chlorine in a remarkably small space.[9]

ON MANGANESE OR MAGNESIA; AND ITS PROPERTIES.[10]

[BEHAVIOR OF MANGANESE] WITH THE ORDINARY ACID OF SALT.[11]

. . . 6. (a) One ounce of pure spirit of salt was poured upon half an ounce of finely ground manganese. After this mixture had stood one hour in the cold, the acid had assumed a dark brown colour. Part of this solution was poured into a bottle, which was left open in a warm place. The solution gave off a smell like warm *aqua regia*, and after the lapse of a quarter of an hour it was clear and colorless as water, and the smell was gone. (b) The remainder of the brown mixture was set to digest, in order to

---

[8] *Kong. Vetenskaps Academiens Handlingar*, **35**: 89–116 (1774).

[9] Citation from the Dobbin translation of the "Collected Papers"; also to be found in *Alembic Club Reprints*, No. 13, "The Early History of Chlorine. Papers by Carl Wilhelm Scheele (1774). C. L. Berthollet (1785). Guyton de Morveau (1787). J. L. Gay-Lussac and L. J. Thenard (1809)," Edinburgh, 1905.

For a continuation of the history of chlorine see also *Alembic Club Reprints*, No. 9, "The Elementary Nature of Chlorine. Papers by Humphry Davy (1809–1818)," Edinburgh, 1902.

[10] [Pyrolusite or manganese dioxide was called *magnesia nigra*. Here it is referred to simply as *manganese*.]

[11] Dobbin, "Collected Papers," pp. 20, 28–32.

see whether the acid of salt would saturate itself with manganese. As soon as the mixture grew hot, its smell of *aqua regia* became considerable augmented; an effervescence also arose, which continued till the following day, when the acid was found to be saturated. One ounce of spirit of salt was again poured upon the residue which could not be dissolved, whereupon all the above-mentioned phenomena occurred, and the manganese became completely dissolved, except a little siliceous earth. . . .

23. The sixth paragraph shows the behaviour with acid of salt. It might not at first be so easily perceived in this case whence the manganese has obtained phlogiston; nothing inflammable is added here, and nevertheless the complete dissolution of manganese can be effected without heat. In fact, a phenomenon takes place here which proves that phlogiston is quite certainly present in the acid of salt—a property which would have been attributed to the acid of nitre; because chemists, since Stahl, have believed that this principle is required in considerable quantity as one of its constituents. That, however, we may now reverse and attribute to the acid of salt.

When the acid of salt stood over manganese in the cold, it acquired a reddish brown colour (§6(a)). As manganese does not give any colourless solution without uniting with phlogiston, it follows that the acid of salt can dissolve it without this principle. But such a solution has either a blue or a red colour. The colour here is more brown than red; the reason is that the very finest portions of the manganese, which do not sink so easily, float in the red solution; for without these fine particles this solution is red, and red mixed with black makes brown. The manganese has here attached itself so loosely to the acid of salt that water can precipitate it, and this precipitate behaves like ordinary manganese. When, now, the mixture of manganese and spirit of salt was set to digest, an effervescence and smell of *aqua regia* arose (§6(b)).

In order to understand this novelty clearly, I took a retort in which there was a mixture of manganese and acid of salt. In front of the neck I attached a bladder empty of air, and placed the retort in hot sand. The bladder became expanded by the effervescence in the retort. When the acid no longer effervesced, which was an indication of its saturation, I removed the bladder, and found that this air had coloured it yellow, as if by *aqua fortis*, but it had not any trace of fixed air; it had, however, a very perceptible suffocating smell, which was most oppressive to the lungs: it resembled the smell of warm *aqua regia*. . . .

24. This acid of salt, deprived of phlogiston as one of its constituents, unites with water in very small quantity, and gives the water a slightly acid taste; but as soon as it meets with inflammable matter it becomes again a true acid of salt. In order to investigate the properties of this air, it is best to put it to the test in the elastic condition. Ordinary acid of salt is

mixed with finely ground manganese, as much as is desired, in a glass retort which is placed on warm sand. Small bottles which hold about twelve ounces of water are employed as receivers. About two drachms of water are put into each bottle, and the joints are not luted further than that grey absorbent paper is wrapped round the neck of the retort, and on this the bottle is fixed. When such a bottle has been attached for a quarter of an hour or more, it is found, according to the quantity of the elastic acid in the receiver, that the air in it acquires a yellow colour; the bottle is then removed from the retort. If the paper luting has held tight, a part of the air escapes with force. A previously fitted cork is then immediately inserted into the bottle, and another bottle is attached to the neck of the retort in its stead. In this way several bottles can be partly filled with dephlogisticated acid of salt. It is here to be noted that the retort is placed in such a position that in case drops should rise up into the neck they can flow back. The water in these bottles serves this purpose, that, if any vapour of the acid of salt should pass over, it may then have this water to betake itself to. I take more than one bottle, so that I have no need to start such a distillation anew before each experiment I make. It is not advantageous to fill large vessels, as a good part of the acid disappears into the air each time they are opened.

25. Whatever was examined in this dephlogisticated acid of salt was hung on a glass tube which I fastened into the cork. Then (*a*) the corks in the bottles became yellow, as if from *aqua fortis*, and during the distillation the luting was likewise attacked. (*b*) Blue litmus paper became almost white; all vegetable flowers—red, blue, and yellow—became white in a short time; the same thing also occurred with green plants. In the meantime the water in the bottle became changed to a weak and pure acid of salt. (*c*) The former colours of these flowers, as well as that of the green plants, could not be restored either by alkalis or by acids. (*d*) Expressed oils and animal fats, when they hung as drops, or were rubbed, upon the glass tube, became in a short time as tough as turpentine. (*e*) Cinnabar became white on the surface, and when the piece was washed in water a pure solution of mercurial sublimate was obtained, but the sulphur was not altered. (*f*) Vitriol of iron became red and deliquesced. Vitriols of copper and zinc were not altered. (*g*) Iron filings were put into such a bottle and they dissolved. This solution was evaporated to dryness and distilled with addition of oil of vitriol, when a pure acid of salt, which did not dissolve gold, again passed over. (*h*) All metals were attacked, and in the case of gold it is noteworthy that its solution in this dephlogisticated acid of salt forms fulminating gold with volatile alkali. (*i*) When spirit of sal ammoniac, prepared with lime, hung in drops upon the tube, a white cloud arose, and from the drops a quantity of air bubbles escaped, which gave off a smoke when they burst asunder. (*k*) Fixed alkali was converted

into common salt, which decrepitated on charcoal but did not detonate. (*l*) Arsenic deliquesced in these vapours. (*m*) Insects immediately died in them, and (*n*) a flame was instantly extinguished by them.

26. This proves sufficiently the great attraction which dephlogisticated acid of salt has for the inflammable principle.

Joseph Priestley

(*1733–1804*)

IT IS ironic that the greatest discovery of Joseph Priestley, that of oxygen, in the hands of Lavoisier soon destroyed the phlogiston theory, of which he was the last ardent follower. Self-taught in chemistry, he was essentially an explorer, a man of great curiosity and manipulative skill. He isolated and for the first time characterized the gases ammonia, hydrogen chloride, carbon monoxide, sulfur dioxide, nitrous oxide, nitric oxide, and oxygen. Priestley's writings in chemistry are extensive and are to be found chiefly in a series of books published from 1774 to 1786.[1] These works exhibit little order, as Priestley believed in the immediate publication of any new experiments, which are therefore presented here in the order in which they were carried out, with revisions, additions, and corrections appearing in later volumes. One should not conclude from this random presentation that Priestley's researches were but a disorderly series of experiments, dictated by chance. Priestley was the first pneumatic chemist and made important contributions in spite of the fact that many of his inferences were erroneous. His staunch belief in phlogiston did not help matters.

On August 1, 1774, Priestley first prepared oxygen, which to him was dephlogisticated air. He told Lavoisier of his discovery some two months later, on a visit to Paris. It was his most important discovery and is well described in the following account taken from "Experiments and Observations on Different Kinds of Air" vol. II, pages 29 to 48. It should be noted that, although Priestley was the first to publish the discovery of oxygen, Scheele had earlier reached the same result independently. His results were delayed in publication.[2] The *mercurius*

[1] "Experiments and Observations on Different Kinds of Air," London, 1774, 1775, and 1777, 3 vols.; "Experiments and Observations Relating to Various Branches of Natural Philosophy; with a Continuation of the Observations on Air," London, 1779, 1 vol., and Birmingham, 1781 and 1786, 2 vols. An abridgment of the six volumes was published in three in 1790: "Experiments and Observations on Different Kinds of Air, and other Branches of Natural Philosophy, connected with the Subject. In three Volumes; being the former six Volumes abridged and methodized, with many Additions. Birmingham, printed by Thomas Pearson," 1790.

[2] *Alembic Club Reprints*, No. 7, "The Discovery of Oxygen, Part I. Experiments

calcinatus per se is mercuric oxide, also referred to as the *red precipitate*. From Priestley's experiments on the contraction of gaseous mixtures with nitric oxide dates the beginning of eudiometric methods for the determination of the purity of air.

SECTION III.

OF DEPHLOGISTICATED AIR, AND OF THE CONSTITUTION OF THE ATMOSPHERE.

The contents of this section will furnish a very striking illustration of the truth of a remark, which I have more than once made in my philosophical writings, and which can hardly be too often repeated, as it tends greatly to encourage philosophical investigations; viz. that more is owing to what we call *chance*, that is, philosophically speaking, to the observation of *events arising from unknown causes*, than to any proper *design*, or pre-conceived *theory* in this business. This does not appear in the works of those who write *synthetically* upon these subjects; but would, I doubt not, appear very strikingly in those who are the most celebrated for their philosophical acumen, did they write *analytically* and ingenuously.

For my own part, I will frankly acknowledge, that, at the commencement of the experiments recited in this section, I was so far from having formed any hypothesis that led to the discoveries I made in pursuing them, that they would have appeared very improbable to me had I been told of them; and when the decisive facts did at length obtrude themselves upon my notice, it was very slowly, and with great hesitation, that I yielded to the evidence of my senses. And yet, when I re-consider the matter, and compare my last discoveries relating to the constitution of the atmosphere with the first, I see the closest and the easiest connexion in the world between them, so as to wonder that I should not have been led immediately from the one to the other. That this was not the case, I attribute to the force of prejudice, which, unknown to ourselves, biasses not only our *judgments*, properly so called, but even the perceptions of our senses: for we may take a maxim so strongly for granted, that the plainest evidence of sense will not intirely change, and often hardly modify our persuasions; and the more ingenious a man is, the more effectually he is entangled in his errors; his ingenuity only helping him to deceive himself, by evading the force of truth.

There are, I believe, very few maxims in philosophy that have laid firmer hold upon the mind, than that air, meaning atmospherical air (free from various foreign matters, which were always supposed to be dissolved,

---

by Joseph Priestley, LLD. (1775)," Edinburgh, 1901, contains the full version of Priestley's work on oxygen. *Alembic Club Reprints*, No. 8, "The Discovery of Oxygen, Part 2. Experiments by Carl Wilhelm Scheele, (1777)," Edinburgh, 1901, should be consulted for Scheele's work.

and intermixed with it) is *a simple elementary substance*, indestructible, and unalterable, at least as much so as water is supposed to be. In the course of my inquiries, I was, however, soon satisfied that atmospherical air is not an unalterable thing; for that the phlogiston with which it becomes loaded from bodies burning in it, and animals breathing it, and various other chemical processes, so far alters and depraves it, as to render it altogether unfit for inflammation, respiration, and other purposes to which it is subservient; and I had discovered that agitation in water, the process of vegetation, and probably other natural processes, by taking out the superfluous phlogiston, restore it to its original purity. But I own I had no idea of the possibility of going any farther in this way, and thereby procuring air purer than the best common air. I might, indeed, have naturally imagined that such would be air that should contain less phlogiston than the air of the atmosphere; but I had no idea that such a composition was possible.

It will be seen in my last publication, that, from the experiments which I made on the marine acid air, I was led to conclude that common air consisted of some acid (and I naturally inclined to the acid that I was then operating upon) and phlogiston; because the union of this acid vapour and phlogiston made inflammable air; and inflammable air, by agitation in water, ceases to be inflammable, and becomes respirable. And though I could never make it quite so good as common air, I thought it very probable that vegetation, in more favourable circumstances than any in which I could apply it, or some other natural process, might render it more pure.

Upon this, which no person can say was an improbable supposition, was founded my conjecture, of volcanos having given birth to the atmosphere of this planet, supplying it with a permanent air, first inflammable, then deprived of its inflammability by agitation in water, and farther purified by vegetation.

Several of the known phenomena of the *nitrous acid* might have led me to think, that this was more proper for the constitution of the atmosphere than the marine acid: but my thoughts had got into a different train, and nothing but a series of observations, which I shall now distinctly relate, compelled me to adopt another hypothesis, and brought me, in a way of which I had then no idea, to the solution of the great problem, which my reader will perceive I have had in view ever since my discovery that the atmospherical air is alterable, and therefore that it is not an elementary substance, but a *composition*, viz. what this composition is, or *what is the thing that we breathe*, and how is it to be made from its constituent principles.

At the time of my former publication, I was not possessed of a *burning lens* of any considerable force; and for want of one, I could not possibly make many of the experiments that I had projected, and which, in theory, appeared very promising. I had, indeed, a *mirror* of force sufficient for my purpose. But the nature of this instrument is such, that it cannot be applied, with effect, except upon substances that are capable of being suspended, or resting on a very slender support. It cannot be directed at all upon any substance in the form of a *powder*, nor hardly upon any thing that requires to be put into a vessel of quicksilver; which appears to me to be the most accurate method of extracting air from a great variety of substances, as was explained in the Introduction to this volume. But having

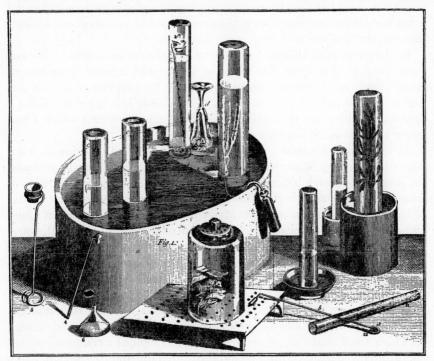

Folding frontispiece from Priestley's "Experiments and Observations on Different Kinds of Air," London, 1774.

afterwards procured a lens of twelve inches diameter, and twenty inches focal distance, I proceeded with great alacrity to examine, by the help of it, what kind of air a great variety of substances, natural and factitious, would yield, putting them into the vessels represented fig. *a*, which I filled with quicksilver, and kept inverted in a bason of the same. Mr. Warltire, a good chymist, and lecturer in natural philosophy, happening to be at that time in Calne, I explained my views to him, and was furnished by him with many substances, which I could not otherwise have procured.

With this apparatus, after a variety of other experiments, an account of which will be found in its proper place, on the 1st of August, 1774, I endeavoured to extract air from *mercurius calcinatus per se;* and I presently found that, by means of this lens, air was expelled from it very readily. Having got about three or four times as much as the bulk of my materials, I admitted water to it, and found that it was not imbibed by it. But what surprized me more than I can well express, was, that a candle burned in this air with a remarkably vigorous flame, very much like that enlarged flame with which a candle burns in nitrous air, exposed to iron or liver of sulphur; but as I had got nothing like this remarkable appearance from any kind of air besides this particuluar modification of nitrous air, and I knew no nitrous acid was used in the preparation of *mercurius calcinatus*, I was utterly at a loss how to account for it.

In this case, also, though I did not give sufficient attention to the circumstance at that time, the flame of the candle, besides being larger, burned with more splendor and heat than in that species of nitrous air; and a piece of red-hot wood sparkled in it, exactly like paper dipped in a solution of nitre, and it consumed very fast; an experiment which I had never thought of trying with nitrous air.

At the same time that I made the above mentioned experiment, I extracted a quantity of air, with the very same property, from the common *red precipitate*, which being produced by a solution of mercury in spirit of nitre, made me conclude that this peculiar property, being similar to that of the modification of nitrous air above mentioned, depended upon something being communicated to it by the nitrous acid; and since the *mercurius calcinatus* is produced by exposing mercury to a certain degree of heat, where common air has access to it, I likewise concluded that this substance had collected something of *nitre*, in that state of heat, from the atmosphere.

This, however, appearing to me much more extraordinary than it ought to have done, I entertained some suspicion that the mercurius calcinatus, on which I had made my experiments, being bought at a common apothecary's, might, in fact, be nothing more than red precipitate; though, had I been any thing of a practical chymist, I could not have entertained any such suspicion. However, mentioning this suspicion to Mr. Warltire, he furnished me with some that he had kept for a specimen of the preparation, and which, he told me, he could warrant to be genuine. This being treated in the same manner as the former, only by a longer continuance of heat, I extracted much more air from it than from the other.

This experiment might have satisfied any moderate sceptic: but, however, being at Paris in the October following, and knowing that there were several very eminent chymists in that place, I did not omit the opportunity, by means of my friend Mr. Magellan, to get an ounce of mercurius calcinatus prepared by Mr. Cadet, of the genuineness of which there could not possibly be any suspicion; and at the same time, I frequently mentioned my surprize at the kind of air which I had got from this preparation to Mr. Lavoisier, Mr. le Roy, and several other philosophers, who honoured me with their notice in that city; and who, I dare say, cannot fail to recollect the circumstance.

At the same time, I had no suspicion that the air which I had got from the mercurius calcinatus was even wholesome, so far was I from knowing what it was that I had really found; taking it for granted, that it was nothing more than such kind of air as I had brought nitrous air to be by the processes above mentioned; and in this air I have observed that a candle would burn sometime quite naturally, and sometimes with a beautiful enlarged flame, and yet remain perfectly noxious.

At the same time that I had got the air above mentioned from mercurius calcinatus and the red precipitate, I had got the same kind from *red lead* or *minium*. In this process, that part of the minium on which the focus of the lens had fallen, turned yellow. One third of the air, in this experiment, was readily absorbed by water, but, in the remainder, a candle burned very strongly, and with a crackling noise.

That fixed air is contained in red lead I had observed before; for I had expelled it by the heat of a candle, and had found it to be very pure. I imagine it requires more heat than I then used to expel any of the other kind of air.

This experiment with *red lead* confirmed me more in my suspicion, that the *mercurius calcinatus* must get the property of yielding this kind of air from the atmosphere, the process by which that preparation, and this of red lead is made, being similar. As I never make the least secret of any thing that I observe, I mentioned this experiment also, as well as those with the mercurius calcinatus, and the red precipitate, to all my philosophical acquaintance at Paris, and elsewhere; having no idea, at that time, to what these remarkable facts would lead.

Presently after my return from abroad, I went to work upon the *mercurius calcinatus*, which I had procured from Mr. Cadet; and, with a very moderate degree of heat, I got from about one fourth of an ounce of it, an ounce-measure of air, which I observed to be not readily imbibed, either by the substance itself from which it had been expelled (for I suffered them to continue a long time together before I transferred the air to any other place) or by water, in which I suffered this air to stand a considerable time before I made any experiment upon it.

In this air, as I had expected, a candle burned with a vivid flame; but what I observed new at this time (Nov. 19), and which surprized me no less than the fact I had discovered before, was, that, whereas a few moments agitation in water will deprive the modified nitrous air of its property of admitting a candle to burn in it; yet, after more than ten times as much agitation as would be sufficient to produce this alteration in the nitrous air, no sensible change was produced in this. A candle still burned in it with a strong flame; and it did not, in the least, diminish common air, which I have observed that nitrous air, in this state, in some measure, does.

But I was much more surprized, when, after two days, in which this air had continued in contact with water (by which it was diminished about one twentieth of its bulk) I agitated it violently in water about five min-

Folding plate, facing page 324, from Priestley's "Experiments and Observations on Different Kinds of Air," London, 1774. A view of his laboratory.

utes, and found that a candle still burned in it as well as in common air. The same degree of agitation would have made phlogisticated nitrous air fit for respiration indeed, but it would certainly have extinguished a candle.

These facts fully convinced me, that there must be a very material difference between the constitution of the air from mercurius calcinatus, and that of phlogisticated nitrous air, notwithstanding their resemblance in some particulars. But though I did not doubt that the air from *mercurius calcinatus* was fit for respiration, after being agitated in water, as every kind of air without exception, on which I had tried the experiment, had been, I still did not suspect that it was respirable in the first instance; so far was I from having any idea of this air being, what it really was, much superior, in this respect, to the air of the atmosphere.

In this ignorance of the real nature of this kind of air, I continued from this time (November) to the 1st of March following; having, in the mean time, been intent upon my experiments on the vitriolic acid air above recited, and the various modifications of air produced by spirit of nitre, an account of which will follow. But in the course of this month, I not only ascertained the nature of this kind of air, though very gradually, but was led by it to the complete discovery of the constitution of the air we breathe.

Till this 1st of March, 1775, I had so little suspicion of the air from mercurius calcinatus, &c. being wholesome, that I had not even thought of applying to it the test of nitrous air; but thinking (as my reader must imagine I frequently must have done) on the candle burning in it after long agitation in water, it occurred to me at last to make the experiment; and putting one measure of nitrous air to two measures of this air, I found, not only that it was diminished, but that it was diminished quite as much as common air, and that the redness of the mixture was likewise equal to that of a similar mixture of nitrous and common air.

After this I had no doubt but that the air from mercurius calcinatus was fit for respiration, and that it had all the other properties of genuine common air. But I did not take notice of what I might have observed, if I had not been so fully possessed by the notion of there being no air better than common air, that the redness was really deeper, and the diminution something greater than common air would have admitted.

Moreover, this advance in the way of truth, in reality, threw me back into error, making me give up the hypothesis I had first formed, viz. that the mercurius calcinatus had extracted spirit of nitre from the air; for I now concluded, that all the constituent parts of the air were equally, and in their proper proportion, imbibed in the preparation of this substance, and also in the process of making red lead. For at the same time that I made the above-mentioned experiment on the air from mercurius calcinatus, I likewise observed that the air which I had extracted from red lead, after the fixed air was washed out of it, was of the same nature, being diminished by nitrous air like common air: but, at the same time, I was puzzled to find that air from the red precipitate was diminished in the same manner, though the process for making this substance is quite different from that of making the two others. But to this circumstance I happened not to give much attention.

I wish my reader be not quite tired with the frequent repetition of the word *suprize*, and others of similar import; but I must go on in that style a little longer. For the next day I was more surprized than ever I had been before, with finding that, after the above-mentioned mixture of nitrous air and the air from mercurius calcinatus, had stood all night, (in which time the whole diminution must have taken place; and, consequently, had it been common air, it must have been made perfectly noxious, and intirely unfit for respiration or inflammation) a candle burned in it, and even better than in common air.

I cannot, at this distance of time, recollect what it was that I had in view in making this experiment; but I know I had no expectation of the real issue of it. Having acquired a considerable degree of readiness in making experiments of this kind, a very slight and evanescent motive would be sufficient to induce me to do it. If, however, I had not happened, for some other purpose, to have had a lighted candle before me, I should probably never have made the trial; and the whole train of my future experiments relating to this kind of air might have been prevented.

Still, however, having no conception of the real cause of this phenomenon, I considered it as something very extraordinary; but as a property that was peculiar to air extracted from these substances, and *adventitious;* and I always spoke of the air to my acquaintance as being substantially the same thing with common air. I particularly remember my telling Dr. Price, that I was myself perfectly satisfied of its being common air, as it appeared to be so by the test of nitrous air; though, for the satisfaction of others, I wanted a mouse to make the proof quite complete.

On the 8th of this month I procured a mouse, and put it into a glass vessel, containing two ounce-measures of the air from mercurius calcinatus. Had it been common air, a full-grown mouse, as this was, would have lived in it about a quarter of an hour. In this air, however, my mouse lived a full half hour; and though it was taken out seemingly dead, it appeared to have been only exceedingly chilled; for, upon being held to the fire, it presently revived, and appeared not to have received any harm from the experiment.

By this I was confirmed in my conclusion, that the air extracted from mercurius calcinatus, &c. was, *at least, as good* as common air; but I did not certainly conclude that it was any *better;* because, though one mouse would live only a quarter of an hour in a given quantity of air, I knew it was not impossible but that another mouse might have lived in it half an hour; so little accuracy is there in this method of ascertaining the goodness of air: and indeed I have never had recourse to it for my own satisfaction, since the discovery of that most ready, accurate, and elegant test that nitrous air furnishes. But in this case I had a view to publishing the most generally-satisfactory account of my experiments that the nature of the thing would admit of.

This experiment with the mouse, when I had reflected upon it some time, gave me so much suspicion that the air into which I had put it was better than common air, that I was induced, the day after, to apply the test of nitrous air to a small part of that very quantity of air which the mouse had breathed so long; so that, had it been common air, I was satisfied it must have been very nearly, if not altogether, as noxious as possible, so as not to be affected by nitrous air; when, to my surprize again, I found that though it had been breathed so long, it was still better than common air. For after mixing it with nitrous air, in the usual proportion of two to one, it was diminished in the proportion of $4\frac{1}{2}$ to $3\frac{1}{2}$; that is, the nitrous air had made it two ninths less than before, and this in a very short space of time; whereas I had never found that, in the longest time, any common air was reduced more than one fifth of its bulk by any proportion of nitrous air, nor more than one fourth by any phlogistic process whatever. Thinking of this extraordinary fact upon my pillow, the next morning I put another measure of nitrous air to the same mixture, and, to my utter astonishment, found that it was farther diminished to almost one half of its original quantity. I then put a third measure to it; but this did not diminish it any farther: but, however, left it one measure less than it was even after the mouse had been taken out of it.

Being now fully satisfied that this air, even after the mouse had breathed it half an hour, was much better than common air; and having a quantity of it still left, sufficient for the experiment, viz. an ounce-measure and a half, I put the mouse into it; when I observed that it seemed to feel no shock upon being put into it, evident signs of which would have been visible, if the air had not been very wholesome; but that it remained perfectly at its ease another full half hour, when I took it out quite lively and vigorous. Measuring the air the next day, I found it to be reduced from $1\frac{1}{2}$ to $\frac{2}{3}$ of an ounce-measure. And after this, if I remember well (for in my *register* of the day I only find it noted, that it was *considerably diminished* by nitrous air) it was nearly as good as common air. It was evident, indeed, from the mouse having been taken out quite vigorous, that the air could not have been rendered very noxious.

For my farther satisfaction I procured another mouse, and putting it into less than two ounce-measures of air extracted from mercurius calcinatus and air from red precipitate (which, having found them to be of the same quality, I had mixed together) it lived three quarters of an hour. But not having had the precaution to set the vessel in a warm place, I suspect that the mouse died of cold. However, as it had lived three times as long as it could probably have lived in the same quantity of common air, and I did not expect much accuracy from this kind of test, I did not think it necessary to make any more experiments with mice.

Being now fully satisfied of the superior goodness of this kind of air, I proceeded to measure that degree of purity, with as much accuracy as I could, by the test of nitrous air; and I began with putting one measure of nitrous air to two measures of this air, as if I had been examining common air; and now I observed that the diminution was evidently greater than common air would have suffered by the same treatment. A second measure of nitrous air reduced it to two thirds of its original quantity, and a third measure to one half. Suspecting that the diminution could not proceed much farther, I then added only half a measure of nitrous air, by which it was diminished still more; but not much, and another half measure made it more than half of its original quantity; so that, in this case, two measures of this air took more than two measures of nitrous air, and yet remained less than half of what it was. Five measures brought it pretty exactly to its original dimensions.

At the same time, air from *red precipitate* was diminished in the same proportion as that from *mercurius calcinatus*, five measures of nitrous air being received by two measures of this without any increase of dimensions. Now as common air takes about one half of its bulk of nitrous air, before it begins to receive any addition to its dimensions from more nitrous air, and this air took more than four half-measures before it ceased to be diminished by more nitrous air, and even five half-measures made no addition to its original dimensions, I conclude that it was between four and five times as good as common air. It will be seen that I have since procured air better than this, even between five and six times as good as the best common air that I have ever met with.

Priestley had observed in August, 1771, which was before his discovery of oxygen, that a sprig of mint when placed in air in which a candle had burned out, would after a time enable the candle to be lit again. He repeated this experiment seven years later and ascertained that this purification of air was due to the emission from plants of dephlogisticated air. Although Priestley now had enough information to enable him to understand something of the nature of photosynthesis, he did not continue the work, and it was left to Ingenhousz, Senebier, and others to lay the foundations of this subject. The citation below contains Priestley's discovery of the role of green plants in revivifying air.[3]

When air has been freshly and strongly tainted with putrefaction, so as to smell through the water, sprigs of mint have presently died, upon being put into it, their leaves turning black; but if they do not die presently, they thrive in a most surprizing manner. In no other circumstances have I ever seen vegetation so vigorous as in this kind of air, which is immediately fatal to animal life. Though these plants have been crouded in jars filled with this air, every leaf has been full of life; fresh shoots have branched out in various directions, and have grown much faster than other similar plants, growing in the same exposure in common air.

This observation led me to conclude, that plants, instead of affecting

[3] "Experiments and Observations . . . ," 1790, vol. 1, pp. 86–88; vol. 3, pp. 293–296, 304.

the air in the same manner with animal respiration, reverse the effects of breathing, and tend to keep the atmosphere sweet and wholesome, when it is become noxious, in consequence of animals either living and breathing, or dying and putrefying in it.

In order to ascertain this, I took a quantity of air, made thoroughly noxious, by mice breathing and dying in it, and divided it into two parts; one of which I put into a phial immersed in water; and to the other (which was contained in a glass jar, standing in water) I put a sprig of mint. This was about the beginning of August 1771, and after eight or nine days, I found that a mouse lived perfectly well in that part of the air, in which the sprig of mint had grown, but died the moment it was put into the other part of the same original quantity of air; and which I had kept in the very same exposure, but without any plant growing in it.

This experiment I have several times repeated; sometimes using air in which animals had breathed and died; sometimes using air tainted with vegetable or animal putrefaction, and generally with the same success.

Once, I let a mouse live and die in a quantity of air which had been noxious, but which had been restored by this process, and it lived nearly as long as I conjectured it might have done in an equal quantity of fresh air; but this is so exceedingly various, that it is not easy to form any judgment from it; and in this case the symptom of *difficult respiration* seemed to begin earlier than it would have done in common air.

Since the plants that I have made use of manifestly grow and thrive in putrid air; since putrid matter is well known to afford proper nourishment for the roots of plants; and since it is likewise certain that they receive nourishment by their leaves as well as by their roots, it seems to be exceedingly probable, that the putrid effluvium is in some measure extracted from the air, by means of the leaves of plants, and therefore that they render the remainder more fit for respiration.

SECTION VII.

OF THE PURIFICATION OF AIR BY PLANTS AND THE INFLUENCE OF LIGHT ON THAT PROCESS.

One of my earliest observations on the subject of air, but made casually, when, in fact, I expected a contrary result from the process, was the purification of air injured by respiration or putrefaction, by the vegetation of plants. But at that time I was altogether ignorant of the part that *light* had to act in the business. At the publication of the experiments recited in the last section, I had fully ascertained the influence of light in the production of dephlogisticated air in water by means of a *green substance*, which I at first supposed to be a plant, but not being able to discover the form of one, I contented myself with calling it simply *green matter*.

Several of my friends, however, better skilled in botany than myself, never entertained any doubt of its being a plant; and I had afterwards the fullest conviction that it must be one. Mr. Bewly has lately observed the regular form of it by a microscope. My own eyes having always been weak, I have, as much as possible, avoided the use of a microscope.

The principle reason that made me question whether this green matter was a plant, besides my not being able to discover the form of it, was its being produced, as I then thought, in a vial close stopped. But this being only with a common cork, the seeds of this plant, which must float invisibly in the air, might have insinuated themselves through some unperceived fracture in it; or the seeds might have been contained in the water previous to its being put into the phial. Both Mr. Bewly and myself found, in the course of the last summer, that when distilled water was exposed to the sun, in phials filled in part with quicksilver, and in part with distilled water, and inverted in basons of quicksilver, none of this green matter was ever produced; no seed of this plant having been able to penetrate through the mercury, to reach the water incumbent upon it, though, in several cases, it will be seen, that these seeds diffuse and insinuate themselves, in a manner that is truly wonderful.

Without light, it is well known, that no plant can thrive; and if it do grow at all in the dark, it is always white, and is, in all other respects, in a weak and sickly state. Healthy plants are probably in a state similar to that of *sleep* in the absence of light, and do not resume their proper functions, but by the influence of light, and especially the action of the rays of the sun. This was the reason why no green matter was ever produced by means of mere *warmth* in my former experiments, and that in jars standing in the same exposure, but covered so that the light had no access to them, no pure air was collected, none of the green matter being then found in them.

This I verified most completely by covering the greatest part of a glass jar with black sealing-wax, which made it thoroughly opaque; and besides answering that purpose better than brown paper, as I made the experiment before mentioned, did not imbibe any of the water, and therefore did not promote the evaporation of it. To be able to observe whether any air was collected in these jars, or not, the upper part of them was not coated with sealing-wax, but had a thick movable cap of paper, which I could easily take off, and then inspect the surface of the water.

In order to satisfy myself as fully as possible with respect to this remarkable circumstance, I also made the following experiments, the results of which are, indeed, very decisive in favour of the influence of *light* in this case.

Having a large trough of water, full of recent green matter, giving air very copiously, so that all the surface of it was covered with froth, and jars filled with it, and inverted, collected great quantities of it, and very fast; I filled a jar with it, and, inverting it in a bason of the same, I placed it in a dark room. From that instant no more air was yielded by it, and in a few days it had a very offensive smell, the green vegetable matter with which it abounded being then all dead, and putrid.

Again, having filled a receiver with fresh pump water, and having waited till it was in a state of giving air copiously, I removed it into a dark room; and from that time the production of air from it intirely ceased. When I placed it again in the sun, it gave no air till about ten days after, when it had more green matter, the former plants being probably all dead; and no air could be produced till new ones were formed. . . .

It appears from these experiments, that air combined with water is liable to be phlogisticated by respiration, and to be dephlogisticated by vegetation, as much as air in an elastic state, out of water. For fishes, as I shall observe, foul the air contained in the water in which they are confined, and water plants now appear to purify it. This is no doubt one of the great uses of weeds, and other aquatic plants, with which fresh water lakes, and even seas abound, as well as their serving for food to a great number of fishes.

Jan Ingenhousz

(1730–1799)

PRIESTLEY'S investigations upon the role of plants in purifying the atmosphere stimulated the Dutch physician Jan Ingenhousz to study the phenomena more completely. His work provided a firm foundation for the subsequent study of photosynthesis and respiration. Ingenhousz had the ability to draw essentially correct conclusions from his studies. The results of his investigations were first published in a volume, "Experiments upon Vegetables . . . ," (1779).[1] Ingen-

[1] "Experiments upon Vegetables, Discovering Their great Power of purifying the Common Air in the Sun-shine, and of Injuring it in the Shade and at Night. To Which is Joined, A new Method of examining the accurate Degree of Salubrity of the Atmosphere," London, 1779.

The first French edition, which was a translation of the English edition, appeared in 1780. Ingenhousz subsequently rewrote the French edition, which was issued in two volumes in 1787 and 1789. This, the second French edition, contains new material.

The text of the English edition of 1779, with some interpolations from the French edition of 1787, has recently been published with annotations by H. S. Reed, "Jan Ingenhousz. *Plant Physiologist*. With a History of the Discovery of Photosynthesis," Waltham, 1949. This constitutes *Chronica Botanica*, vol. 11, number 5/6.

housz made the additional discovery that plants exhale carbon dioxide. The work contains a demonstration that plants when exposed to light fix the free carbon dioxide in the atmosphere but have no such power in darkness. In many ways, however, Ingenhousz failed to see the full importance of his experiments, and it remained for others, such as Jean Senebier (1742–1809) to unravel further the problem of photosynthesis. The selection below, which contains Ingenhousz's principal results, is taken from the 1779 English edition.[2]

SECTION I.

Some General Remarks on the Nature of the Leaves of Plants, and Their Use.

It seems to be more than probable, that the leaves, with which the most part of plants are furnished during the summer in temperate climates, and perpetually in hot countries, are destined to more than one purpose. Such a great apparatus, which nature displays as soon as the sun begins to afford a certain degree of warmth upon the surface of the earth, can scarcely be considered as solely destined either to ornament, to nourishment of the plant, to its growth, to ripen its fruit, or for any other peculiar and single use. It seems probable, that they are useful to the growth of the tree; for, by depriving the tree of all its leaves, it is in danger of decay. By taking a considerable part of the leaves from a fruit tree, the fruit is less perfect; and by taking them all away, the fruit decays and falls before its maturity. It is also probable, that the tree receives some advantage from the leaves absorbing, by their means, moisture from the air, from rain, and from dew; for it has been found a considerable advantage to the growth of a tree, to water the stem and the leaves now and then. But I leave the discussion of those articles to others, who have made these considerations an object of their pursuits. The late Mr. Baker has published to the world his microscopical observations on the subject. Mr. Bonnet, of Geneva, has published a very elaborate work upon the same, entitled, *Recherches sur l'usage des Feuilles dans les Plantes, et sur quelques autres Sujets relatif à l'Histoire de la Végétation, par* Charles Bonnet, *à* Gottingen *et* Leiden, 1754. This work contains a great deal of interesting inquiries upon the nature, properties, and utilities of those wonderful organs; all of which have been treated with the greatest attention, and have thrown much light upon this subject.

This celebrated author has taken a great deal of notice of those air bubbles which cover the leaves when plunged under water. He says, p. 26, that the leaves draw these bubbles from the water. He is the more persuaded that this is the case, because he found these bubbles did not appear when the water had been boiled some time, and appeared more when the

[2] *Op. cit.*, pp. 1–16, 22–36.

water is impregnated with air, by blowing in it. He had also observed, that they did not appear after sunset. Page 31, he explains his opinion farther upon this head: he says, that these air bubbles are produced by common air adhering to the external surface of the leaves, which swells up into bubbles by the heat of the sun; and that the cold of the night is the reason why these air bubbles do not make their appearance at that time. As he found that dry leaves put under water gather such bubbles also upon their surface, he concludes, p. 33, that the appearance of these bubbles cannot be owing to any vital action in the leaves.

I took some pains to disclose the cause of these bubbles, which, I think, are of more importance than Mr. Bonnet at that time imagined them to be; and found the fact to be generally this:

The most part of leaves gather these bubbles upon their surface, when plunged in any water in the sun-shine or by day-time in the open air; but infinitely more in fresh pump water than in any other. In clear river water they appear later, less in number and in size; less so in rain water, and the least of all in boiled water, in stagnating, and in distilled water.

They are not produced by the warmth of the sun rarifying the air adhering to the leaves; for many kinds of leaves produce them almost as soon as plunged under water, though the water be very cold, and the leaves warm from the sun-shine be plunged in it.

They do not appear after sun-set, at least not in any considerable number; but those that already exist do not shrink in or disappear by the cold of the night.

As soon as the sun begins to diffuse its warmth over the surface of the earth in the spring, and to promote that general tendency to corruption which all dead bodies of the animal and vegetable kingdom, and many other substances, are so liable to, the trees display in a few days, the most wonderful scene that can be imagined. Contracted as they were in that state of stupor and inactivity in which they remain during the winter, exposing to the air no other surface than that of their trunk and branches, as if they wanted to have as little to do as possible with the external air, they all at once increase, perhaps more than a thousand times, their surface by displaying those kind of numberless fans which we call leaves. Some of them produce their leaves a long while before any flowers appear upon them; others a good while after the flowers are formed, and the fructification is already in an advanced state; and keep their leaves in the best condition, and even push out continually new ones, long after the whole fructification is finished; which seems to indicate, that the chief use of these fans is not to assist the fructification and propagation of their species. These fans, when compleated, seem to compose or arrange themselves in such a manner as to expose their upper and varnished surface to the direct influence of the sun, and to hide as much as they can their under surface from the direct influence of this luminary. It seems as if they required rather the light of the sun than the influence of its heat, as their polished surfaces must reflect some of the rays of the sun, and thus moderate the degree of heat.

It will, perhaps, appear probable, that one of the great laboratories of nature for cleansing and purifying the air of our atmosphere is placed in the substance of the leaves, and put in action by the influence of the light, and that the air thus purified, but in this state grown useless or noxious to the plant, is thrown out for the greatest part by the excretory ducts, placed chiefly, at least in far the most part of plants, on the under side of the leaf.

Is there not some probability that the under part of the leaves may have been chiefly destined for this purpose; because in this way the dephlogisticated air, gushing continually out of this surface, is inclined to fall rather downwards, as a beneficial shower for the use of the animals who all breathe in a region of the air inferior to the leaves of trees? Does not this conjecture get some weight, if we consider that dephlogisticated air is in reality specifically heavier than common air, and thus tends rather to fall downwards?

If we add to these reflexions another of no less importance, *viz.* that most sorts of foul air are specifically lighter than common air, we shall be inclined to believe that the difference of the specifical gravity of that beneficial air of which I treat, and that which is become hurtful to our constitution by corruption, breathing, and other causes, indicates one of those special blessings designed by the hand of God: for by this arrangement we get soon rid, in a great measure, of that air which is become hurtful to us, as it rises soon up out of our reach; whereas the dephlogisticated air, being heavier than common air, is rather inclined to settle on the surface of the earth among the animal creation.

But, as animals spoil equally as much air in the winter as in the summer by the act of respiration, it might seem somewhat surprizing, that this great laboratory ceases entirely by the decay of the leaves. Is this defect supplied by some other means equally powerful? Though we are very far from being able to trace all the active causes which contribute their share in keeping up the wholesomeness of our atmosphere, yet we have already traced some of them, and therefore must not despair of discovering some more. The shaking of foul air in water will in great measure correct it. Water itself has a power of yielding dephlogisticated air, as Dr. Priestley discovered. Plants have a power to correct bad air, and to improve good air. Winds will blow away the noxious particles of the air, and bring on air corrected by the waters of the seas, lakes, rivers, and forests. All these causes exist equally in the winter as in the summer, or at least nearly so. The influence of the vegetable creation alone ceases in the winter: but the loss of this influence is, perhaps, more than amply counterbalanced by the diminution of the general promoting cause of corruption, *viz.* heat. Every body knows, that warm weather hastens in a great degree putrefaction. In the summer time numberless insects are produced, which did not exist in the winter: these insects infect the air by the corruption of their bodies. That immense quantity of animal substances, and many others, which undergo a putrefaction by the warmth of the weather, seems to require an additional power or agent to counter-act it; and this office is destined to the leaves. In frosty weather no animal substance is subject to putrefaction, which cannot go on without a proper degree of heat. The perspiration of animals is less offensive in the winter than in the summer, and of consequence must corrupt the atmosphere less. It seems therefore probable, that, if we are deprived of one way by which air is corrected in the winter, we have also at that time less causes which tend to contaminate our element.

SECTION II.

On the Manner in Which the Dephlogisticated Air Is Obtained from the Leaves of Plants.

As the leaves of plants yield dephlogisticated air only in the clear daylight, or in the sun-shine, and begin their operation only after they have been in a certain manner prepared, by the influence of the same light, for beginning it; they are to be put in a very transparent glass vessel, or jar, filled with fresh pump water (which seems the most adapted to promote this operation of the leaves, or at least not to obstruct it); which, being inverted in a tub full of the same water, is to be immediately exposed to the open air, or rather to the sun-shine: thus the leaves continuing to live, continue also to perform the office they performed out of the water, as far as the water does not obstruct it. The water prevents only new atmospheric air being absorbed by the leaves, but does not prevent that air, which already existed in the leaves, from oozing out. This air, prepared in the leaves by the influence of the light of the sun, appears soon upon the surface of the leaves in different forms, most generally in the form of round bubbles, which, increasing gradually in size, and detaching themselves from the leaves, rise up and settle at the inverted bottom of the jar: they are succeeded by new bubbles, till the leaves, not being in the way of supplying themselves with new atmospheric air, become exhausted. This air, gathered in this manner, is really dephlogisticated air, of a more or less good quality, according to the nature of the plant from which the leaves are taken, and the clearness of the day-light to which they were exposed.

It is not very rare to see these bubbles so quickly succeeding one another, that they rise from the same spot almost in a continual stream: I saw this more than once, principally in the *nymphaea alba.* . . .

THE DEPHLOGISTICATED AIR OOZING OUT OF THE LEAVES IN THE WATER
IS NOT AIR FROM THE WATER ITSELF.

The reverend Dr. Priestley found, that water, chiefly pump water,
standing some days by itself, forms at the bottom and sides of the vessel
a kind of green matter, seemingly vegetable, from which air bubbles rise
continually to the top of the jar, if exposed to the sunshine: that this air
is fine dephlogisticated air, which shews that there is a faculty in water to
produce by itself this beneficial fluid; and thus, that the mass of the
waters of the seas, lakes, and rivers, have their share in purifying the
atmosphere.

But as this dephlogisticated air is not produced immediately from the
pump water, but only when this green matter is formed, it is clear, that
the air obtained from the leaves, as soon as they are put in the water, is
by no means air from the water, but air continuing to be produced by a
special operation carried on in a living leaf exposed to the day-light, and
forming bubbles, because the surrounding water prevents this air from
being diffused through the atmosphere.

It is true, that pump water, placed in the sun-shine, will soon yield
some small air bubbles, settling at the bottom of the jar, and every where
at the sides; but this air is very far from being the same as that contained
in the air bubbles of the leaves.

I placed, in a warm sun-shine, a great number of inverted jars, full of
pump water, and collected carefully from them all the air yielded by
these bubbles, which proved to be much worse than the common air.

I boiled some pump water in a pot, in which I had placed a long cylindrical jar, quite full of the same water: a good deal of air was collected at
the top of the inverted jar, which was by the heat disengaged from the
water. This air proved to be much worse than common air, and entirely
unfit for respiration.

Abbé Fontana has made, some years ago, a great many experiments,
tending to investigate the nature of air contained in different waters.

THE DEPHLOGISTICATED AIR OOZING OUT OF THE LEAVES IN THE
WATER IS NOT EXISTING IN THE SUBSTANCE OF THE LEAVES IN
THIS PURE STATE, BUT IS ONLY SECRETED OUT OF THE LEAVES
WHEN IT HAS UNDERGONE A PURIFICATION, OR A
KIND OF TRANSMUTATION.

If the dephlogisticated air collected from the leaves in the sun existed in
them in its pure state, it must appear as such when squeezed out of the

leaves under water; or, at least, if the leaves are only shook gently under water, without hurting their organization, or when they are put in warm or in boiling water.

I squeezed a handful or two of potatoe leaves under water, and kept an inverted jar full of water above it, to receive the air. A great deal of it was instantly obtained, which proved to be nearly as good as common air.

I squeezed, in the same way, some air out of leaves of sage, *salvia*, which proved to be somewhat worse than the former.

A potatoe plant was shook under water, so as not to hurt it: a good deal of air was immediately disengaged, which, by the nitrous test, proved to be worse than common air.

A plant of *lamium album* was treated in the same way, and in like manner a good deal of air was obtained, which was nearly of the same quality with the former.

Some leaves of an apple tree were put in a cylindrical jar full of pump water. The jar was then inverted in a vessel full of the same water, and placed upon the fire. As soon as the water grew warm, the leaves were covered with air bubbles, just as in the sun. After the water had boiled a little while, it was put by to cool. A great deal of air was obtained, which proved to be so bad as to extinguish flame.

Some of the same leaves were put into a jar, inverted in a pot full of water, and only placed near the fire: a great deal of air was obtained, but as poisonous as the former.

SECTION VI.

THE PRODUCTION OF THE DEPHLOGISTICATED AIR FROM THE LEAVES IS NOT OWING TO THE WARMTH OF THE SUN, BUT CHIEFLY, IF NOT ONLY, TO THE LIGHT.

If the sun caused this air to ooze out of the leaves by rarifying the air in heating the water, it would follow that, if a leaf, warmed in the middle of the sun-shine upon the tree, was immediately placed in water drawn directly from the pump, and thus being very cold, the air bubbles would not appear till, at least, some degree of warmth was communicated to the water; but quite the contrary happens. The leaves taken from trees or plants the midst of a warm day, and plunged immediately into cold water, are remarkably quick in forming air bubbles, and yielding the best dephlogisticated air.

If it was the warmth of the sun, and not its light, that produced this operation, it would follow, that, by warming the water near the fire about as much as it would have been in the sun, this very air would be produced; but this is far from being the case.

I placed some leaves in pump water, inverted the jar, and kept it near the fire as was required to received a moderate warmth, near as much as a similar jar, filled with leaves of the same plant, and placed in the open air, at the same time received from the sun. The result was, that the air obtained by the fire was very bad, and that obtained in the sun was dephlogisticated air.

A jar full of walnut tree leaves was placed under the shade of other plants, and near a wall, so that no rays of the sun could reach it. It stood there the whole day, so that the water in the jar had received there about the same degree of warmth as the surrounding air (the thermometer being then at 76°); the air obtained was worse than common air, whereas the air obtained from other jars kept in the sun-shine during such a little time that the water had by no means received a degree of warmth approaching that of the atmosphere, was fine dephlogisticated air.

No dephlogisticated air is obtained in a warm room, if the sun does not shine upon the jar containing the leaves. . . .

SECTION VII.

REFLECTIONS.

It might, perhaps, be objected, that the leaves of the plants are never in a natural state when surrounded by pump water; and that thus there may, perhaps, remain some degree of doubt, whether the same operation of the leaves in their natural situation takes place.

I cannot consider the plants kept thus under water to be in a situation so contrary to their nature as to derange their usual operation. Water, even more than they want, is not hurtful to plants, if it is not applied too considerable a time. The water only cuts off the communication with the external air; and we know, that plants may live a long while without this free communication. Besides, water plants, as *persicaria urens, becabunga*, and others, which I have employed in my experiments, are often found a long while quite covered by the water in which they grow.

By bending a living plant (the root remaining in its own earth) in an inverted jar full of water, you only surprize nature upon the fact in the middle of its operation, by shutting at once all communication with the free air. In such a situation no air can be absorbed by the leaves, or by any parts of the plant under water; but any air may freely come out of it.

Without covering the leaves or the plant entirely with water, it is impossible to know what quantity of air oozes out of the plant, and of what quality this air is; for any air issuing out of a plant incorporates immediately with the surrounding air, and makes a compound whose constituent parts are an intimate mixture of air from the plant and common air; and it would be as difficult to judge accurately how much dephlogisticated air such a plant has communicated to the ordinary air which was already in the jar, as it would be for a chymist to judge accurately what quantity of distilled water was mixed with a certain quantity of common water, if some of it was really added to it on purpose to puzzle him. It may, however, be ascertained, in an inaccurate way, what quantity of this beneficial air a plant, placed in a jar full of common air, has communicated to it, by computing the degree of superior goodness the air is found to possess.

As plants yield in a few hours such a considerable quantity of dephlogisticated air, though their situation seems rather unfavourable for it when they are kept under water; may it not with some degree of probability be conjectured, that they yield much more of it when remaining in their natural situation; for then, being continually supplied by new common air, their stock of dephlogisticated air cannot be exhausted. It is an unfavourable circumstance, that air is not an object of our sight; if it was, we should perhaps see that plants have a kind of respiration as animals have; that leaves are the organs of it; that, perhaps, they have pores which absorb air, and others which throw it out by way of excretion, as are the excretory ducts of animals; that the air secreted, being dephlogisticated air, is thrown out as noxious to the plant (which article is clearly demonstrated by Dr. Priestley and Mr. Scheele); that in the most part of plants, principally trees, the greatest part of inhaling pores are placed upon the upper side of the leaf, and the excretory ducts principally on the under side.

If these conjectures were well grounded, it would throw a great deal of new light upon the arrangement of the different parts of the globe, and the harmony between all its parts would become more conspicuous. We might find, that partial tempests and hurricanes, by shaking the air and the waters, produce some partial evils for the universal benefit of nature; that, by these powerful agitations, the septic and noxious particles of the air are blown away, and rendered of no effect, by being thus diluted with the body of air, and partly buried in the waters. We might conceive a little more of the deep designs of the Supreme Wisdom in the different arrangement of sublunary beings. The stubborn atheist would, perhaps, find reason to humiliate himself before that Almighty Being, whose existence he denies because his limited senses represent to him nothing but a confused chaos of miseries and disorders in this world.

Henry Cavendish

(1731–1810)

ONE of the names most closely attached to the chemistry of gases is that of Henry Cavendish. He was a thorough scholar who made valuable contributions to physics as well as chemistry.[1] His works were published in the *Philosophical Transactions* of the Royal Society.[2] Cavendish's first important contribution, entitled, "Three Papers, containing Experiments on Factitious Air," was published in 1766.[3] In the first paper he discusses "inflammable air" or hydrogen, and for the first time differentiates between it and various other kinds of gases by carefully measured specific-gravity determinations. He was, however, a phlogistonist and supposed the gas to be a compound of phlogiston—this somewhat obscures the significance of his results. The specific gravities of inflammable air, fixed air, and other gases showed them to be distinct entities, an achievement of quantitative methods. His values are not far from those accepted today. The following selection from his work on hydrogen and carbon dioxide is characterized by an accurate and careful approach.

XIX. THREE PAPERS, CONTAINING EXPERIMENTS ON FACTITIOUS AIR, BY THE HON. HENRY CAVENDISH, F.R.S.

Read May 29, Nov. 6 and Nov. 13, 1766.

By factitious air, I mean in general any kind of air which is contained in other bodies in an unelastic state, and is produced from thence by art.

By fixed air, I mean that particular species of factitious air, which is separated from alcaline substances by solution in acids or by calcination; and to which Dr. Black has given that name in his treatise on quick lime.

As fixed air makes a considerable part of the subject of the following papers, and as the name might incline one to think, that it signified any sort of air which is contained in other bodies in an unelastic form; I thought it best to give this explanation before I went any farther. . . .

---

[1] W. F. Magie, "A Source Book in Physics," New York, 1935, pp. 105–111; K. F. Mather and S. L. Mason, "A Source Book in Geology," New York, 1939, pp. 103–107.

"Electrical Researches, (of Henry Cavendish), written between 1771 and 1781, ed. from the Original MSS. by James Clerk Maxwell," Cambridge, 1879.

[2] These, together with a number of unpublished manuscripts, have been edited by Edward Thorpe, "The Scientific Papers of the Honourable Henry Cavendish, F.R.S.," Cambridge, 1921, 2 vols.

[3] *Philosophical Transactions*, **56**: 141–184 (1766); Thorpe, *op. cit.*, vol. 2, pp. 77–101.

Experiments on Factitious Air

Part I

CONTAINING EXPERIMENTS ON INFLAMMABLE AIR

I know of only three metallic substances, namely, zinc, iron and tin, that generate inflammable air by solution in acids; and those only by solution in the diluted vitriolic acid, or spirit of salt.

Zinc dissolves with great rapidity in both these acids; and, unless they are very much diluted, generates a considerable heat. One ounce of zinc produces about 356 ounce measures of air: the quantity seems just the same whichsoever of these acids it is dissolved in. Iron dissolves readily in the diluted vitriolic acid, but not near so readily as zinc. One ounce of iron wire produces about 412 ounce measures of air: the quantity was just the same, whether the oil of vitriol was diluted with 1½, or 7 times its weight of water: so that the quantity of air produced seems not at all to depend on the strength of acid.

Iron dissolves but slowly in spirit of salt while cold: with the assistance of heat it dissolves moderately fast. The air produced thereby is inflammable, but I have not tried how much it produces.

Tin was found to dissolve scarce at all in oil of vitriol diluted with an equal weight of water, while cold: with the assistance of a moderate heat it dissolved slowly, and generated air, which was inflammable: the quantity was not ascertained.

Tin dissolves slowly in strong spirit of salt while cold: with the assistance of heat it dissolves moderately fast. One ounce of tinfoil yields 202 ounce measures of inflammable air.

These experiments were made, when the thermometer was at 50° and the barometer at 30 inches.

All these three metallic substances dissolve readily in the nitrous acid, and generate air; but the air is not at all inflammable. They also unite readily, with the assistance of heat, to the undiluted acid of vitriol; but very little of the salt, formed by their union with the acid, dissolves in the fluid. They all unite to the acid with a considerable effervescence, and discharge plenty of vapours, which smell strongly of the volatile sulphureous acid, and which are not at all inflammable. Iron is not sensibly acted on by this acid, without the assistance of heat; but zinc and tin are in some measure acted on by it, while cold.

It seems likely from hence, that, when either of the above-mentioned metallic substances are dissolved in spirit of salt, or the diluted vitriolic acid, their phlogiston flies off, without having its nature changed by the acid, and forms the inflammable air; but that, when they are dissolved in the nitrous acid, or united by heat to the vitriolic acid, their phlogiston unites to part of the acid used for their solution, and flies off with it in fumes, the phlogiston losing its inflammable property by the union. The volatile sulphureous fumes, produced by uniting these metallic substances by heat to the undiluted vitriolic acid, shew plainly, that in this case their phlogiston unites to the acid; for it is well known, that the vitriolic sulphureous acid consists of the plain vitriolic acid united to phlogiston.[4] It is highly probable too, that the same thing happens in dissolving these metallic substances in the nitrous acid; as the fumes produced during the solution appear plainly to consist in great measure of the nitrous acid, and yet it appears, from their more penetrating smell and other reasons, that the acid must have undergone some change in its nature, which can hardly be attributed to anything else than its union with the phlogiston. As to the inflammable air, produced by dissolving these substances in spirit of salt or the diluted vitriolic acid, there is great reason to think, that it does not contain any of the acid in its composition; not only because it seems to be just the same whichsoever of these acids it is produced by; but also because there is an inflammable air, seemingly much of the same kind as this, produced from animal substances in putrefaction, and from vegetable substances in distillation, as will be shewen hereafter; though there can be no reason to suppose, that this kind of inflammable air owes its production to any acid. I now proceed to the experiments made on inflammable air.

I cannot find that this air has any tendency to lose its elasticity by keeping, or that it is all absorbed, either by water, or by fixed or volatile alcalies; as I have kept some by me for several weeks in a bottle inverted into a vessel of water, without any sensible decrease of bulk; and as I have also kept some for a few days, in bottles inverted into vessels of sope leys and spirit of sal ammoniac, without perceiving their bulk to be at all diminished.

It has been observed by others, that, when a piece of lighted paper is applied to the mouth of a bottle, containing a mixture of inflammable and common air, the air takes fire, and goes off with an explosion. In order to observe in what manner the effect varies according to the different proportions in which they are mixed, the following experiment was made.

Some of the inflammable air, produced by dissolving zinc in diluted oil of vitriol, was mixed with common air in several different proportions, and the inflammability of these mixtures tried one after the other in this manner. A quart bottle was filled with one of these mixtures. . . . The bottle was taken out of the water, set upright on a table, and the flame of a

---

[4] Sulphur is allowed by chymists, to consist of the plain vitriolic acid united to phlogiston. The volatile sulphureous acid appears to consist of the same acid united to a less proportion of phlogiston than what is required to form sulphur. A circumstance which I think shews the truth of this, is that if oil of vitriol be distilled, from sulphur, the liquor, which comes over, will be the volatile sulphureous acid.

lamp or piece of lighted paper applied to its mouth. But, in order to prevent the included air from mixing with the outward air, before the flame could be applied, the mouth of the bottle was covered while under water, with a cap made of a piece of wood covered with a few folds of linnen; which cap was not removed till the instant that the flame was applied. The mixtures were all tried in the same bottle; and, as they were all ready prepared, before the inflammability of any of them was tried, the time elapsed between each trial was but small: by which means I was better able to compare the loudness of the sound in each trial. The result of the experiment is as follows.

With one part of inflammable air to 9 of common air, the mixture would not take fire, on applying the lighted paper to the mouth of the bottle; but, on putting it down into the belly of the bottle, the air took fire, but made very little sound.

With 2 parts of inflammable to 8 of common air, it took fire immediately, on applying the flame to the mouth of the bottle, and went off with a moderately loud noise.

With 3 parts of inflammable air to 7 of common air, there was a very loud noise.

With 4 parts of inflammable to 6 of common air, the sound seemed very little louder.

With equal quantities of inflammable and common air, the sound seemed much the same. In the first of these trials, namely, that with one part of inflammable to 9 of common air, the mixture did not take fire all at once, on putting the lighted paper into the bottle; but one might perceive the flame to spread gradually through the bottle. In the three next trials, though they made an explosion, yet I could not perceive any light within the bottle. In all probability, the flame spread so instantly through the bottle, and was so soon over, that it had not time to make any impression on my eye. In the last mentioned trial, namely, that with equal quantities of inflammable and common air, a light was seen in the bottle, but which quickly ceased.

With 6 parts of inflammable to 4 of common air, the sound was not very loud: the mixture continued burning a short time in the bottle, after the sound was over.

With 7 parts of inflammable to 3 of common air, there was a very gentle bounce or rather puff: it continued burning for some seconds in the belly of the bottle.

A mixture of 8 parts of inflammable to 2 of common air caught fire on applying the flame, but without any noise: it continued burning for some time in the neck of the bottle, and then went out, without the flame ever extending into the belly of the bottle.

It appears from these experiments, that this air, like other inflammable substances, cannot burn without the assistance of common air. It seems too, that, unless the mixture contains more common than inflammable air, the common air therein is not sufficient to consume the whole of the inflammable air; whereby part of the inflammable air remains, and burns by means of the common air, which rushes into the bottle after the explosion.

In order to find whether there was any difference in point of inflammability between the air produced from different metals by different acids, five different sorts of air, namely, 1. Some produced from zinc by diluted oil of vitriol, and which had been kept about a fortnight; 2. Some of the same kind of air fresh made; 3. Air produced from zinc by spirit of salt; 4. Air from iron by the vitriolic acid; 5. Air from tin by spirit of salt; were each mixed separately with common air in the proportion of 2 parts of inflammable air to $7\frac{7}{10}$ of common air, and their inflammability tried in the same bottle, that was used for the former experiment, and with the same precautions. They each went off with a pretty loud noise, and without any difference in the sound that I could be sure of. Some more of each of the above parcels of air were then mixed with common air, in the proportion of 7 parts of inflammable air to $3\frac{1}{5}$ of common air, and tried in the same way as before. They each of them went off with a gentle bounce, and burnt some time in the bottle, without my being able to perceive any difference between them.

In order to avoid being hurt, in case the bottle should burst by the explosion, I have commonly, in making these sort of experiments, made use of an apparatus contrived in such manner, that, by pulling a string, I drew the flame of a lamp over the mouth of the bottle, and at the same time pulled off the cap, while I stood out of the reach of danger. I believe, however, that this precaution is not very necessary; as I have never known a bottle to burst in any of the trials I have made.

The specific gravity of each of the above-mentioned sorts of inflammable air, except the first, was tried in the following manner. A bladder holding about 100 ounce measures was filled with inflammable air, . . . and the air pressed out again as perfectly as possible. By this means the small quantity of air remaining in the bladder was almost intirely of the inflammable kind. 80 ounce measures of the inflammable air, produced from zinc by the vitriolic acid, were then forced into the bladder in the same manner: after which, the pewter pipe was taken out of the wooden cap of the bladder, the orifice of the cap stopt up with a bit of lute, and the bladder weighed. A hole was then made in the lute, the air pressed out as perfectly as possible, and the bladder weighed again. It was found to have increased in weight $40\frac{3}{4}$ grains. Therefore the air pressed out of the bladder weighs $40\frac{3}{4}$ grains less than an equal quantity of common air: but the quantity of air pressed out of the bladder must be nearly the same as that which was forced into it, *i.e.* 80 ounce measures: consequently 80 ounce measures of this sort of inflammable air weigh 40¾ grains less than an equal bulk of common air. The three other sorts of inflammable air were then tried in the same way, in the same bladder, immediately one after the other. In the trial with air from zinc by spirit of salt, the bladder increased 40½ grains on forcing out the air. In the trial with the air from iron, it increased 41½ grains, and in that with the air from tin, it increased 41 grains. The heat of the air, when this experiment was made, was 50°; the barometer stood at 29¾ inches.

There seems no reason to imagine, from these experiments, that there is any difference in point of specific gravity between these four sorts of inflammable air; as the small difference observed in these trials is in all probability less than what may arise from the unavoidable errors of the experiment. Taking a medium therefore of the different trials, 80 ounce measures of inflammable air weigh 41 grains less than an equal bulk of common air.

Therefore, if the density of common air, at the time when this experiment was tried, was 800 times less than that of water, which, I imagine, must be near the truth, inflammable air must be 5490 times lighter than water, or near 7 times lighter than common air. But if the density of common air was 850 times less than that of water, then would inflammable air be 9200 times lighter than water, or 10⅘₀ lighter than common air.

This method of finding the density of factitious air is very convenient and sufficiently accurate, where the density of the air to be tried is not much less than that of common air, but cannot be much depended on in the present case, both on account of the uncertainty in the density of common air, and because we cannot be certain but what some common air might be mixed with the inflammable air in the bladder, notwithstanding the precautions used to prevent it; both which causes may produce a considerable error, where the density of the air to be tried is many times less than that of common air. For this reason, I made the following experiments.

I endeavoured to find the weight of the air discharged from a given quantity of zinc by solution in the vitriolic acid. . . . A is a bottle filled near full with oil of vitriol diluted with about six times its weight of water: B is a glass tube fitted into its mouth, and secured with lute: C is a glass cylinder fastened on the end of the tube, and secured also with lute. The cylinder has a small hole at its upper end to let the inflammable air escape, and is filled with dry pearl-ashes in coarse powder. The whole apparatus, together with the zinc, which was intended to be put in, and the lute which was to be used in securing the tube to the neck of the bottle, were first weighed carefully; its weight was 11930 grains. The zinc was then put in, and the tube put in its place. By this means, the inflammable air was made to pass through the dry pearl-ashes; whereby it must have been pretty effectually deprived of any acid or watery vapours that could have ascended along with it. The use of the glass tube B was to collect the minute jets of liquor, that were thrown up by the effervescence, and to prevent their touching the pearl-ashes; for which reason, a small space was left between the glass-tube and the pearl-ashes in the cylinder. When the zinc was dissolved, the whole apparatus was weighed again, and was found to have lost $11\frac{3}{4}$ grains in weight;[5] which loss is principally owing to the weight of the inflammable air discharged. But it must be observed, that, before the effervescence, that part of the bottle and cylinder, which was not occupied by other more solid matter, was filled with common air; whereas, after the effervescence, it was filled with inflammable air; so that, upon that account alone, supposing no more inflammable air to be discharged than what was sufficient to fill that space, the weight of the apparatus would have been diminished by the difference of the weight of that quantity of common air and inflammable air. The whole empty space in the bottle and cylinder was about 980 grain measures, there is no need of exactness; and the difference of the weight of that quantity of common and inflammable air is about one grain: therefore the true weight of the inflammable air discharged, is $10\frac{3}{4}$ grains. The quantity of zinc used was 254 grains, and consequently the weight of the air discharged is $\frac{1}{23}$ or $\frac{1}{24}$ of the weight of the zinc.

It was before said, that one grain of zinc yielded 356 grain measures of air: therefore 254 grains of zinc yield 90427 grain measures of air; which we have just found to weigh $10\frac{3}{4}$ grains; therefore inflammable air is about 8410 times lighter than water, or $10\frac{1}{2}$ times lighter than common air.

The quantity of moisture condensed in the pearl-ashes was found to be about $1\frac{1}{4}$ grains.

By another experiment, tried exactly in the same way, the density of inflammable air came out 8300 times less than that of water.

The specific gravity of the air, produced by dissolving zinc in spirit of salt, was tried exactly in the same manner. 244 grains of zinc being dissolved in spirit of salt diluted with about four times its weight of water, the loss in effervescence was $10\frac{3}{4}$ grains; the empty space in the bottle and cylinder was 914 grain measures; whence the weight of the inflammable air was $9\frac{3}{4}$ grains, and consequently its density was 8910 times less than that of water.

By another experiment, its specific gravity came out 9030 times lighter than water.

---

[5] As the quantity of lute used was but small, and as this kind of lute does not lose a great deal of its weight by being kept in a moderately dry room, no sensible error could arise from the drying of the lute during the experiment.

A like experiment was tried with iron. 250½ grains of iron being dissolved in oil of vitriol diluted with four times its weight of water, the loss in effervescence was 13 grains, the empty space 1420 grain measures. Therefore the weight of the inflammable air was 11⅜ grains, i.e. about ¹⁄₂₂ of the weight of the iron, and its density was 8973 times less than that of water. The moisture condensed was 1¼ grains.

A like experiment was tried with tin. 607 grains of tinfoil being dissolved in strong spirit of salt, the loss in effervescence was 14¾ grains, the empty space 873 grain measures: therefore the weight of the inflammable air was 13¾ grains, i.e. ¹⁄₄₄ of the tin, and its density 8918 times less than that of water. The quantity of moisture condensed was about three grains.

It is evident, that the truth of these determinations depend[s] on a supposition, that none of the inflammable air is absorbed by the pearl-ashes. In order to see whether this was the case or no, I dissolved 86 grains of zinc in diluted acid of vitriol, and received the air in a measuring bottle in the common way. Immediately after, I dissolved the same quantity of zinc in the same kind of acid, and made the air to pass into the same measuring bottle, through a cylinder filled with dry pearl-ashes. . . . I could not perceive any difference in their bulks.

It appears from these experiments, that there is but little, if any, difference in point of density between the different sorts of inflammable air. Whether the difference of density observed between the air procured from zinc, by the vitriolic and that by the marine acid is real, or whether it is only owing to the error of the experiment, I cannot pretend to say. By a medium of the experiments, inflammable air comes out 8760 times lighter than water, or eleven times lighter than common air.

In order to see whether inflammable air, in the state in which it is, when contained in the inverted bottles, where it is in contact with water, contains any considerable quantity of moisture dissolved in it, I forced 192 ounce measures of inflammable air, through a cylinder filled with dry pearl-ashes, by means of the same apparatus, which I used for filling the bladders with inflammable air. . . . The cylinder was weighed carefully before and after the air was forced through; whereby it was found to have increased 1 grain in weight. The empty space in the cylinder was 248 grains, the difference of weight of which quantity of common and inflammable air is ¼ of a grain. Therefore the real quantity of moisture condensed in the pearl-ashes is 1¼ grain. The weight of 192 ounce measures of inflammable air deprived of its moisture appears from the former experiments to be 10½ grains; therefore its weight when saturated with moisture would be 11¾ grains. Therefore, inflammable air, in that state in which it is in, when kept under the inverted bottles, contains near ⅑ its weight of moisture; and its specific gravity in that state is 7840 times less than that of water.

The second paper summarizes his experiments with carbon dioxide. In this paper, Cavendish found that the same weight of an acid requires different weights of different alkaline bases for neutralization. This was an early forerunner of the concept of equivalent weights.

Perhaps the most important work of Cavendish was the determination of the elementary composition of water. Although Black's work on carbon dioxide did a great deal to destroy the ancient doctrine of air as an element, it was this research of Cavendish which struck the final blow. In his experiments Cavendish determined the gases and their ratios in the composition of water. It has been difficult to assign priority for this discovery, since there have been four claimants: Watt, Cavendish, Lavoisier, and Monge. The "water controversy" is a complex subject which has been covered in detail elsewhere.[6] The recent discovery of a letter from Joseph Priestley to Sir Joseph Banks giving priority to Watt seems finally to have settled this controversy.[7] Although Cavendish did not reach his conclusions before Watt, his independent work cannot be denied. It was, perhaps, his investigation of a side reaction that delayed his presentation. On igniting the oxygen with the hydrogen, in his eudiometer, Cavendish found that he also obtained an acid. This reaction detracted from the clarity of the demonstration of the composition of water, and so he devoted a later paper to it. Here he described and explained for the first time the fixation of nitrogen and the composition of nitric acid. He also noted a small unreactive portion of the atmosphere, which a hundred years later was identified as argon. The first of these papers is here reproduced.[8]

XIII. EXPERIMENTS ON AIR. BY HENRY CAVENDISH, ESQ, F.R.S. & S.A.

Read January 15, 1784.

The following experiments were made principally with a view to find out the cause of the diminution which common air is well known to suffer by all the various ways in which it is phlogisticated, and to discover what becomes of the air thus lost or condensed; and as they seem not only to determine this point, but also to throw great light on the constitution and manner of production of dephlogisticated air, I hope they may be not unworthy the acceptance of this society.

[6] J. R. Partington, "The Composition of Water," London, 1928; G. Wilson, "The Life of the Honourable Henry Cavendish," London, 1851; J. P. Muirhead, "Correspondence of the Late James Watt," London, 1846. The papers of Cavendish on the composition of water are reprinted in full in the *Alembic Club Reprints*, No. 3, Edinburgh, 1899.

[7] S. M. Edelstein, *Chymia*, 1: 123–127 (1948).

[8] *Philosophical Transactions*, 74: 119–153 (1784); also found in Thorpe, *op. cit.*, vol. 2, pp. 161–181; and in *Alembic Club Reprints*, No. 3, "Experiments on Air. Papers published in the Philosophical Transactions by the Hon. Henry Cavendish, F.R.S. (1784–1785)," Edinburgh, 1893.

Many gentlemen have supposed that fixed air is either generated separated from atmospheric air by phlogistication, and that the observed diminution is owing to this cause; my first experiments therefore were made in order to ascertain whether any fixed air is really produced thereby.

Cavendish here rejects animal and vegetable substances as fit subjects for these experiments, since they are known to yield fixed air of themselves, while he wishes to show that fixed air is not produced from common air itself in its "diminution." Thereafter, he cites experiments to show that common air will not yield fixed air in the calcination of metals, in the burning of sulfur, of phosphorus, or inflammable air. He also shows that neither vitriolic (sulfuric) or nitrous (nitric) acids are formed from the air itself. He goes on to say,

Having now mentioned the unsuccessful attempts I made to find out what becomes of the air lost by phlogistication, I proceed to some experiments, which serve really to explain the matter.

In Dr. PRIESTLEY's last volume of experiments is related an experiment of Mr. WARLTIRE's, in which it is said that, on firing a mixture of common and inflammable air by electricity in a close copper vessel holding about three pints, a loss of weight was always perceived, on an average about two grains, though the vessel was stopped in such a manner that no air could escape by the explosion. It is also related, that on repeating the experiment in glass vessels, the inside of the glass, though clean and dry before, immediately became dewy; which confirmed an opinion he had long entertained, that common air deposits its moisture by phlogistication. As the latter experiment seemed likely to throw great light on the subject I had in view, I thought it well worth examining more closely. The first experiment also, if there was no mistake in it, would be very extraordinary and curious; but it did not succeed with me; for though the vessel I used held more than Mr. WARLTIRE's, namely, 24,000 grains of water, and though the experiment was repeated several times with different proportions of common and inflammable air, I could never perceive a loss of weight of more than one-fifth of a grain, and commonly none at all. It must be observed, however, that though there were some of the experiments in which it seemed to diminish a little in weight, there were none in which it increased.[9]

In all the experiments, the inside of the glass globe became dewy, as observed by Mr. WARLTIRE; but not the least sooty matter could be perceived. Care was taken in all of them to find how much the air was diminished by the explosion, and to observe its test. The result is as follows: the bulk of the inflammable air being expressed in decimals of the common air.

[9] Dr. PRIESTLEY, I am informed, has since found the experiment not to succeed.

Common air	Inflammable air	Diminution	Air remaining after the explosion	Test of this air in first method	Standard
	1,241	,686	1,555	,055	,0
1	1,055	,642	1,413	,063	,0
	,706	,647	1,059	,066	,0
	,423	,612	,811	,097	,03
	,331	,476	,855	,339	,27
	,206	,294	,912	,648	,58

In these experiments the inflammable air was procured from zinc, as it was in all my experiments, except where otherwise expressed: but I made two more experiments, to try whether there was any difference between the air from zinc and that from iron, the quantity of inflammable air being the same in both, namely, 0,331 of the common; but I could not find any difference to be depended on between the two kinds of air, either in the diminution which they suffered by the explosion, or the test of the burnt air.

From the fourth experiment it appears, that 423 measures of inflammable air are nearly sufficient to completely phlogisticate 1000 of common air; and that the bulk of the air remaining after the explosion is then very little more than four-fifths of the common air employed; so that as common air cannot be reduced to a much less bulk than that by any method of phlogistication, we may safely conclude, that when they are mixed in this proportion, and exploded, almost all the inflammable air, and about one-fifth part of the common air, lose their elasticity, and are condensed into the dew which lines the glass.

The better to examine the nature of this dew, 500,000 grain measures of inflammable air were burnt with about $2\frac{1}{2}$ times that quantity of common air, and the burnt air made to pass through a glass cylinder eight feet long and three-quarters of an inch in diameter, in order to deposit the dew. The two airs were conveyed slowly into this cylinder by separate copper pipes, passing through a brass plate which stopped up the end of the cylinder; and as neither inflammable nor common air can burn by themselves, there was no danger of the flame spreading into the magazines from which they were conveyed. Each of these magazines consisted of a large tin vessel, inverted into another vessel just big enough to receive it. The inner vessel communicated with the copper pipe, and the air was forced out of it by pouring water into the outer vessel; and in order that the quantity of common air expelled should be $2\frac{1}{2}$ times that of the inflammable, the water was let into the outer vessels by two holes in the bottom of the same tin pan, the hole which conveyed the water into that vessel in which the common air was confined being $2\frac{1}{2}$ times as big as the other.

In trying the experiment, the magazines being first filled with their respective airs, the glass cylinder was taken off, and water let, by the two holes, into the outer vessels, till the airs began to issue from the ends of the copper pipes; they were then set on fire by a candle, and the cylinder put on again in its place. By this means upwards of 135 grains of water were condensed in the cylinder, which had no taste nor smell, and which left no sensible sediment when evaporated to dryness; neither did it yield any pungent smell during the evaporation; in short, it seemed pure water.

In my first experiment, the cylinder near that part where the air was fired was a little tinged with sooty matter, but very slightly so; and that little seemed to proceed from the putty with which the apparatus was luted, and which was heated by the flame; for in another experiment, in which it was contrived so that the luting should not be much heated, scarce any sooty tinge could be perceived.

By the experiments with the globe it appeared, that when inflammable and common air are exploded in a proper proportion, almost all the inflammable air, and near one-fifth of the common air, lose their elasticity, and are condensed into dew. And by this experiment it appears, that this dew is plain water, and consequently that almost all the inflammable air, and about one-fifth of the common air, are turned into pure water.

In order to examine the nature of the matter condensed on firing a mixture of dephlogisticated and inflammable air, I took a glass globe, holding 8800 grain measures, furnished with a brass cock and an apparatus for firing air by electricity. This globe was well exhausted by an air-pump, and then filled with a mixture of inflammable and dephlogisticated air, by shutting the cock, fastening a bent glass tube to its mouth, and letting up the end of it into a glass jar inverted into water, and containing a mixture of 19,500 grain measures of dephlogisticated air, and 37,000 of inflammable; so that, upon opening the cock, some of this mixed air rushed through the bent tube, and filled the globe.[10] The cock was then shut, and the included air fired by electricity, by which means almost all of it lost its elasticity. The cock was then again opened, so as to let in more of the same air, to supply the place of that destroyed by the explosion, which was again fired, and the operation continued till almost the whole of the mixture was let into the globe and exploded. By this means, though the globe held not more than the sixth part of the mixture, almost the whole of it was exploded therein, without any fresh exhaustion of the globe.

As I was desirous to try the quantity and test of this burnt air, without letting any water into the globe, which would have prevented my examining the nature of the condensed matter, I took a larger globe, furnished

---

[10] In order to prevent any water from getting into this tube, while dipped under water to let it up into the glass jar, a bit of wax was stuck upon the end of it, which was rubbed off when raised above the surface of the water.

also with a stop cock, exhausted it by an air-pump, and screwed it on upon the cock of the former globe; upon which, by opening both cocks, the air rushed out of the smaller globe into the larger, till it became of equal density in both; then, by shutting the cock of the larger globe, unscrewing it again from the former, and opening it under water, I was enabled to find the quantity of burnt air in it; and consequently, as the proportion which the contents of the two globes bore to each other was known, could tell the quantity of burnt air in the small globe before the communication was made between them. By this means the whole quantity of the burnt air was found to be 2950 grain measures; its standard was 1,85.

The liquor condensed in the globe, in weight about 30 grains, was sensibly acid to the taste, and by saturation with fixed alkali, and evaporation, yielded near two grains of nitre; so that it consisted of water united to a small quantity of nitrous acid. No sooty matter was deposited in the globe. The dephlogisticated air used in this experiment was procured from red precipitate, that is, from a solution of quicksilver in spirit of nitre distilled till it acquires a red colour.

As it was suspected, that the acid contained in the condensed liquor was no essential part of the dephlogisticated air, but was owing to some acid vapour which came over in making it and had not been absorbed by the water, the experiment was repeated in the same manner, with some more of the same air, which had been previously washed with water, by keeping it a day or two in a bottle with some water, and shaking it frequently; whereas that used in the preceding experiment had never passed through water, except in preparing it. The condensed liquor was still acid.

The experiment was also repeated with dephlogisticated air, procured from red lead by means of oil of vitriol; the liquor condensed was acid, but by an accident I was prevented from determining the nature of the acid.

I also procured some dephlogisticated air from the leaves of plants, in the manner of Doctors INGENHOUSZ and PRIESTLEY, and exploded it with inflammable air as before; the condensed liquor still continued acid, and of the nitrous kind.

In all these experiments the proportion of inflammable air was such, that the burnt air was not much phlogisticated, and it was observed, that the less phlogisticated it was, the more acid was the condensed liquor. I therefore made another experiment, with some more of the same air from plants, in which the proportion of inflammable air was greater, so that the burnt air was almost completely phlogisticated, its standard being $\frac{1}{10}$. The condensed liquor was then not at all acid, but seemed pure water: so that it appears, that with this kind of dephlogisticated air, the condensed liquor is not at all acid, when the two airs are mixed in such a proportion that the burnt air is almost completely phlogisticated, but is considerably so when it is not much phlogisticated.

In order to see whether the same thing would obtain with air procured from red precipitate, I made two more experiments with that kind of air, the air in both being taken from the same bottle, and the experiment tried in the same manner, except that the proportions of inflammable air were different. In the first, in which the burnt air was almost completely phlogisticated, the condensed liquor was not at all acid. In the second, in which its standard was 1,86, that is, not much phlogisticated, it was considerably acid; so that with this air, as well as with that from plants, the condensed liquor contains, or is entirely free from, acid, according as the burnt air is less or more phlogisticated; and there can be little doubt but that the same rule obtains with any other kind of dephlogisticated air.

In order to see whether the acid, formed by the explosion of dephlogisticated air obtained by means of the vitriolic acid, would also be of the nitrous kind, I procured some air from turbith mineral [basic mercury sulfate], and exploded it with inflammable air, the proportion being such that the burnt air was not much phlogisticated. The condensed liquor manifested an acidity, which appeared, by saturation with a solution of salt of tartar [potassium carbonate], to be of the nitrous kind; and it was found, by the addition of some terra ponderosa salita [barium chloride], to contain little or no vitriolic acid.

When inflammable air was exploded with common air, in such a proportion that the standard of the burnt air was about $\frac{4}{10}$, the condensed liquor was not in the least acid. There is no difference, however, in this respect between common air, and dephlogisticated air mixed with phlogisticated in such a proportion as to reduce it to the standard of common air; for some dephlogisticated air from red precipitate, being reduced to this standard by the addition of perfectly phlogisticated air, and then exploded with the same proportion of inflammable air as the common air was in the foregoing experiment, the condensed liquor was not in the least acid.

From the foregoing experiments it appears, that when a mixture of inflammable and dephlogisticated air is exploded in such proportion that the burnt air is not much phlogisticated, the condensed liquor contains a little acid, which is always of the nitrous kind, whatever substance the dephlogisticated air is procured from: but if the proportion be such that the burnt air is almost entirely phlogisticated, the condensed liquor is not at all acid, but seems pure water, without any addition whatever; and as, when they are mixed in that proportion, very little air remains after the explosion, almost the whole being condensed, it follows, that almost the whole of the inflammable and dephlogisticated air is converted into pure water. It is not easy, indeed, to determine from these experiments what proportion the burnt air, remaining after the explosions, bore to the dephlogisticated air employed, as neither the small nor the large globe could be perfectly exhausted of air, and there was no saying with exactness what quantity was left in them; but in most of them, after allowing for this uncertainty, the true quantity of burnt air seemed not more than $\frac{1}{17}$th of the dephlogisticated air employed, or $\frac{1}{50}$th of the mixture. It seems, however, unnecessary to determine this point exactly, as the quantity is so small, that there can be little doubt but that it proceeds only from the impurities mixed with the dephlogisticated and inflammable air, and consequently that, if those airs could be obtained perfectly pure, the whole would be condensed.

With respect to common air, and dephlogisticated air reduced by the addition of phlogisticated air to the standard of common air, the case is different; as the liquor condensed in exploding them with inflammable air, I believe I may say in any proportion, is not at all acid; perhaps, because if they are mixed in such a proportion as that the burnt air is not much phlogisticated, the explosion is too weak, and not accompanied with sufficient heat.

All the foregoing experiments, on the explosion of inflammable air with common and dephlogisticated airs, except those which relate to the cause of the acid found in the water, were made in the summer of the year 1781, and were mentioned by me to Dr. PRIESTLEY, who in consequence of it made some experiments of the same kind, as he relates in a paper printed in the preceding volume of the Transactions. During the last summer also, a friend of mine gave some account of them to M. LAVOISIER, as well as of the conclusion drawn from them, that dephlogisticated air is only water deprived of phlogiston; but at that time so far was M. LAVOISIER from thinking any such opinion warranted, that, till he was prevailed upon to repeat the experiment himself, he found some difficulty in believing that nearly the whole of the two airs could be converted into water. It is remarkable, that neither of these gentlemen found any acid in the water produced by the combustion; which might proceed from the latter having burnt the two airs in a different manner from what I did; and from the former having used a different kind of inflammable air, namely, that from charcoal [*i.e.*, carbon monoxide], and perhaps having used a greater proportion of it.

Before I enter into the cause of these phaenomena, it will be proper to take notice, that phlogisticated air appears to be nothing else than the nitrous acid united to phlogiston; for when nitre is deflagrated with charcoal, the acid is almost entirely converted into this kind of air. That the acid is entirely converted into air, appears from the common process for making what is called clyssus of nitre; for if the nitre and charcoal are dry, scarce any thing is found in the vessels prepared for condensing the fumes; but if they are moist a little liquor is collected, which is nothing but the water contained in the materials, impregnated with a little volatile alkali, proceeding in all probability from the imperfectly burnt charcoal, and a little fixed alkali, consisting of some of the alkalized nitre carried over by the heat and watery vapours. As far as I can perceive too, at present, the air into which much the greatest part of the acid is converted, differs in no respect from common air phlogisticated. A small part of the acid, however, is turned into nitrous air, and the whole is mixed with a good deal of fixed, and perhaps a little inflammable air, both proceeding from the charcoal.

It is well known, that the nitrous acid is also converted by phlogistication into nitrous air, in which respect there seems a considerable analogy between that and the vitriolic acid; for the vitriolic acid, when united to a smaller proportion of phlogiston, forms the volatile sulphureous acid and vitriolic acid air, both of which, by exposure to the atmosphere, lose their phlogiston, though not very fast, and are turned back into vitriolic acid; but, when united to a greater proportion of phlogiston, it forms sulphur, which shews no signs of acidity, unless a small degree of affinity to alkalies can be called so, and in which the phlogiston is more strongly adherent, so that it does not fly off when exposed to the air, unless assisted by a heat sufficient to set it on fire. In like manner the nitrous acid, united to a certain quantity of phlogiston, forms nitrous fumes and nitrous air, which readily quit their phlogiston to common air; but when united to a different, in all probability a larger quantity, it forms phlogisticated air, which shews no signs of acidity, and is still less disposed to part with its phlogiston than sulphur.

This being premised, there seem two ways by which the phaenomena of the acid found in the condensed liquor may be explained; first, by supposing that dephlogisticated air contains a little nitrous acid which enters into it as one of its component parts, and that this acid, when the inflammable air is in a sufficient proportion, unites to the phlogiston, and is turned into phlogisticated air, but does not when the inflammable air is in too small a proportion; and, secondly, by supposing that there is no nitrous acid mixed with, or entering into the composition of, dephlogisticated air, but that, when this air is in a sufficient proportion, part of the phlogisticated air with which it is debased is, by the strong affinity of phlogiston to dephlogisticated air, deprived of its phlogiston and turned into nitrous acid; whereas, when the dephlogisticated air is not more than sufficient to consume the inflammable air, none then remains to deprive the phlogisticated air of its phlogiston, and turn it into acid.

If the latter explanation be true, I think, we must allow that dephlogisticated air is in reality nothing but dephlogisticated water, or water deprived of its phlogiston; or, in other words, that water consists of dephlogisticated air united to phlogiston; and that inflammable air is either pure phlogiston, as Dr. PRIESTLEY and Mr. KIRWAN suppose, or else water united to phlogiston;[11] since, according to this supposition, these two substances united together form pure water. On the other hand, if the first explanation be true, we must suppose that dephlogisticated air consists of water united to a little nitrous acid and deprived of its phlogiston; but still the nitrous acid in it must make only a very small part of the whole, as it is found, that the phlogisticated air, which it is converted into, is very small in comparison of the dephlogisticated air.

I think the second of these explanations seems much the most likely; as it was found, that the acid in the condensed liquor was of the nitrous kind, not only when the dephlogisticated air was prepared from red precipitate, but also when it was procured from plants or from turbith mineral: and it seems not likely, that air procured from plants, and still less likely that air procured from a solution of mercury in oil of vitriol, should contain any nitrous acid.

Another strong argument in favour of this opinion is, that dephlogisticated air yields no nitrous acid when phlogisticated by liver of sulphur; for if this air contains nitrous acid, and yields it when phlogisticated by explosion with inflammable air, it is very extraordinary that it should not do so when phlogisticated by other means.

But what forms a stronger and, I think, almost decisive argument in favour of this explanation is, that when the dephlogisticated air is very pure, the condensed liquor is made much more strongly acid by mixing the air to be exploded with a little phlogisticated air, as appears by the following experiments.

A mixture of 18,500 grain measures of inflammable air with 9750 of dephlogisticated air procured from red precipitate were exploded in the usual manner; after which, a mixture of the same quantities of the same

[11] Either of these suppositions will agree equally well with the following experiments; but the latter seems to me much the most likely. What principally makes me think so is, that common or dephlogisticated air do not absorb phlogiston from inflammable air, unless assisted by a red heat, whereas they absorb the phlogiston of nitrous air, liver of sulphur [potassium polysulfide], and many other substances, without that assistance; and it seems inexplicable, that they should refuse to unite to pure phlogiston, when they are able to extract it from substances to which it has an affinity; that is, that they should overcome the affinity of phlogiston to other substances, and extract it from them, when they will not even unite to it when presented to them. On the other hand, I know no experiment which shews inflammable air to be pure phlogiston rather than an union of it with water, unless it be Dr. PRIESTLEY's experiment of expelling inflammable air from iron by heat alone. I am not sufficiently acquainted with the circumstances of that experiment to argue with certainty about it; but I think it much more likely, that the inflammable air was formed by the union of the phlogiston of the iron filings with the water dispersed among them, or contained in the retort or other vessel in which it was heated; and in all probability this was the cause of the separation of the phlogiston, as iron seems not disposed to part with its phlogiston by heat alone, without being assisted by the air or some other substance.

dephlogisticated and inflammable air, with the addition of 2500 of air phlogisticated by iron filings and sulphur, was treated in the same manner. The condensed liquor, in both experiments, was acid, but that in the latter evidently more so, as appeared also by saturating each of them separately with marble powder, and precipitating the earth by fixed alkali, the precipitate of the second experiment weighing one-fifth of a grain, and that of the first being several times less. The standard of the burnt air in the first experiment was 1,86, and in the second only 0,9.

It must be observed, that all circumstances were the same in these two experiments, except that in the latter the air to be exploded was mixed with some phlogisticated air, and that in consequence the burnt air was more phlogisticated than in the former; and from what has been before said, it appears, that this latter circumstance ought rather to have made the condensed liquor less acid; and yet it was found to be much more so, which shews strongly that it was the phlogisticated air which furnished the acid.

As a further confirmation of this point, these two comparative experiments were repeated with a little variation, namely, in the first experiment there was first let into the globe 1500 of dephlogisticated air, and then the mixture, consisting of 12,200 of dephlogisticated air and 25,900 of inflammable, was let in at different times as usual. In the second experiment, besides the 1500 of dephlogisticated air first let in, there was also admitted 2500 of phlogisticated air, after which the mixture, consisting of the same quantities of dephlogisticated and inflammable air as before, was let in as usual. The condensed liquor of the second experiment was about three times as acid as that of the first, as it required 119 grains of a diluted solution of salt of tartar to saturate it, and the other only 37. The standard of the burnt air was 0,78 in the second experiment, and 1,96 in the first.

The intention of previously letting in some dephlogisticated air in the two last experiments was, that the condensed liquor was expected to become more acid thereby, as proved actually to be the case.

In the first of these two experiments, in order that the air to be exploded should be as free as possible from common air, the globe was first filled with a mixture of dephlogisticated and inflammable air, it was then exhausted, and the air to be exploded let in; by which means, though the globe was not perfectly exhausted, very little common air could be left in it. In the first set of experiments this circumstance was not attended to, and the purity of the dephlogisticated air was forgot to be examined in both sets.

From what has been said there seems the utmost reason to think, that dephlogisticated air is only water deprived of its phlogiston, and that inflammable air, as was before said, is either phlogisticated water, or else pure phlogiston; but in all probability the former. . . .

There are several memoirs of M. LAVOISIER published by the Academy of Sciences, in which he intirely discards phlogiston, and explains those phaenomena which have been usually attributed to the loss or attraction of that substance, by the absorption or expulsion of dephlogisticated air; and as not only the foregoing experiments, but most other phaenomena of nature, seem explicable as well, or nearly as well, upon this as upon the commonly believed principle of phlogiston, it may be proper briefly to mention in what manner I would explain them on this principle, and why I have adhered to the other. In doing this, I shall not conform strictly to his theory, but shall make such additions and alterations as seem to suit it best to the phaenomena; the more so, as the foregoing experiments may, perhaps, induce the author himself to think some such additions proper.

According to this hypothesis, we must suppose, that water consists of inflammable air united to dephlogisticated air; that nitrous air, vitriolic acid air, and the phosphoric acid, are also combinations of phlogisticated air, sulphur, and phosphorus, with dephlogisticated air; and that the two former, by a further addition of the same substance, are reduced to the common nitrous and vitriolic acids; that the metallic calces consist of the metals themselves united to the same substance, commonly, however, with a mixture of fixed air; that on exposing the calces of the perfect metals to a sufficient heat, all the dephlogisticated air is driven off, and the calces are restored to their metallic form; but as the calces of the imperfect metals are vitrified by heat, instead of recovering the metallic form, it should seem as if all the dephlogisticated air could not be driven off from them by heat alone. In like manner, according to this hypothesis, the rationale of the production of dephlogisticated air from red precipitate is, that during the solution of the quicksilver in the acid and the subsequent calcination, the acid is decompounded, and quits part of its dephlogisticated air to the quicksilver, whereby it comes over in the form of nitrous air, and leaves the quicksilver behind united to dephlogisticated air, which, by a further increase of heat, is driven off, while the quicksilver re-assumes its metallic form. In procuring dephlogisticated air from nitre, the acid is also decompounded; but with this difference, that it suffers some of its dephlogisticated air to escape, while it remains united to the alkali itself, in the form of phlogisticated nitrous acid. As to the production of dephlogisticated air from plants, it may be said, that vegetable substances consist chiefly of various combinations of three different bases, one of which, when united to dephlogisticated air, forms water, another fixed air, and the third phlogisticated air; and that by means of vegetation each of these substances are decomposed, and yield their dephlogisticated air; and that in burning they again acquire dephlogisticated air, and are restored to their pristine form.

It seems, therefore, from what has been said, as if the phaenomena of nature might be explained very well on this principle, without the help of phlogiston; and indeed, as adding dephlogisticated air to a body comes to the same thing as depriving it of its phlogiston and adding water to it, and as there are, perhaps, no bodies entirely destitute of water, and as I know no way by which phlogiston can be transferred from one body to another, without leaving it uncertain whether water is not at the same time transferred, it will be very difficult to determine by experiment which of these opinions is the truest; but as the commonly received principle of phlogiston explains all phaenomena, at least as well as M. LAVOISIER'S, I have adhered to that. There is one circumstance also, which though it may appear to many not to have much force, I own has some weight with me; it is, that as plants seem to draw their nourishment almost intirely from water and fixed and phlogisticated air, and are restored back to those substances by burning, it seems reasonable to conclude, that notwithstanding their infinite variety they consist almost intirely of various combinations of water and fixed and phlogisticated air, united according to one of these opinions to phlogiston, and deprived according to the other of dephlogisticated air; so that, according to the latter opinion, the substance of a plant is less compounded than a mixture of those bodies into which it is resolved by burning; and it is more reasonable to look for great variety in the more compound than in the more simple substance.

Another thing which M. LAVOISIER endeavours to prove is, that dephlogisticated air is the acidifying principle. From what has been explained it appears, that this is no more than saying, that acids lose their acidity by uniting to phlogiston, which with regard to the nitrous, vitriolic, phosphoric, and arsenical acids is certainly true. The same thing, I believe, may be said of the acid of sugar; and Mr. LAVOISIER's experiment is a strong confirmation of BERGMAN's opinion, that none of the spirit of nitre enters into the composition of the acid, but that it only serves to deprive the sugar of part of the phlogiston. But as to the marine acid and acid of tartar, it does not appear that they are capable of losing their acidity by any union with phlogiston. It is to be remarked also, that the acids of sugar and tartar, and in all probability almost all the vegetable and animal acids, are by burning reduced to fixed and phlogisticated air, and water, and therefore contain more phlogiston, or less dephlogisticated air, than those three substances.

Antoine Laurent Lavoisier

(1743–1794)

WHEN Antoine Laurent Lavoisier began his work in chemistry the phlogiston theory was still accepted and chemistry was essentially a mass of unorganized facts. The relative affinities of bodies toward one another had been investigated with some thoroughness, acids and bases had been examined systematically, chemical substances were characterized to some extent, but chemistry as a whole had hardly attained the rank of a science. Lavoisier, utilizing the work of his contemporaries, especially that of Black, Cavendish, and Priestley, in conjunction with experiments of his own, discovered the role of oxygen in combustion and overthrew with impeccable logic the doctrine of phlogiston, laying the foundations of modern chemistry. He accomplished for chemistry what Isaac Newton had done for mechanics a century earlier.

It should be emphasized that Lavoisier discovered no new substances and devised no improved apparatus; rather, he gave the first correct interpretation to facts already known. His many papers were published in Rozier's *Oberva-tions sur la physique* and in the volumes of the *Mémoires de l'Académie royale des sciences*. Lavoisier's most important book was the "Traité élémentaire de chimie," published in 1789.[1]

The phlogiston theory postulated that when substances are burned or metals calcined the "matter of fire" or phlogiston is evolved from them. However, even before the advent of this theory Robert Boyle had noted that metals gain in weight on calcination, a fact well known to the phlogistonists. To Becher and Stahl, however, phlogiston was a philosophical concept and, as such, explained the facts of combustion very well. Later it was held by the phlogistonists to be a material substance, whose existence explained so well a multitude of phenomena, that they were willing to ignore its inadequacy in elucidating the increase in weight of metals on calcination. It remained for Lavoisier to realize the true significance of this unexplained fact. Lavoisier repeated Boyle's experiments on calcining tin and demonstrated that the loss of weight in air equals the gain in weight of the metal. He published his investigation in the *Memoirs* of the Academy of Sciencies for the year 1774.[2] Lavoisier's clear logic and unprecedented quantitative precision are here evident.

---

[1] For full bibliographic details of the works of Lavoisier see D. I. Duveen and H. S. Klickstein, "A Bibliography of the Works of Antoine Laurent Lavoisier, 1743–1794," in press.

[2] At this period the publication of the *Mémoires de l'Académie royale des sciences* was several years in arrears, and the papers, especially in Lavoisier's case, were often drastically revised before publication. Thus this memoir, read in 1774, was not pub-

MEMOIR ON THE CALCINATION OF TIN IN CLOSED VESSELS AND ON THE CAUSE OF THE GAIN IN WEIGHT WHICH THIS METAL ACQUIRES IN THE OPERATION.[3]

It was shown in the experiments which I described in chapters V and VI of the work which I published at the beginning of this year under the title of "Opuscules physiques et chimiques," that when lead or tin is calcined with a burning glass under a glass bell immersed in water or mercury, the volume of the air is diminished about a twentieth by the calcination, and the weight of the metal is in weight nearly equal to that of the air destroyed or absorbed.

I thought that I could conclude from these experiments that a portion of the air itself or some material contained in an elastic state in the air combined with the metals during their calcination, and that this was the cause of the increase in weight of metallic calces.

The effervescence which consistently occurs in all revivifications of metallic calces, that is, wherever a metallic substance changes from the state of a calx to that of a metal, lends support to this theory. I think that I have proved that this effervescence is caused by the disengagement of an elastic fluid, of a species of air which can be retained and measured, and, as a result of the many experiments which I have carried out, that when this fluid is separated from metals by the addition of powdered charcoal or of any other matter containing phlogiston, it does not differ at all from the substance which has been given the name of *fixed air, mephitic gas, mephitic acid*, all of which are synonymous expressions, and that this gas was exactly the same whether it be disengaged from metallic calces by powdered charcoal, from vegetables by fermentation, or from saline or earth alkalis by solution in acids.

However decisive these experiments may have appeared, they were in contradiction with those published by Boyle in his treatise on the weight of flame and fire. That celebrated natural philosopher tried to calcine lead and tin in glass vessels closed hermetically. He succeeded, in part at least, and found the calx which he obtained weighed several grains more than the metal which he had used. From this Boyle concluded that the material of the flame and fire penetrated through the substance of the glass and that it combined with the metals and caused them to be converted into calces and increased their weight.

Such precise experiments made by a philosopher like Boyle were well able to put me on guard against my own opinion, however it was evi-

---

lished until the *Mémoires* for 1774 appeared in 1777. In the meanwhile Lavoisier had learned of Priestley's discovery of oxygen and had revised his paper accordingly.

[3] Memoir read at the public meeting of Martinmas, November 11, 1774. Submitted May 10, 1777. (*Mémoires de l'Académie royale des sciences*, **1774**: 351–367.)

denced to my eyes, and I proposed, in consequence, not only to repeat them as they were made by Boyle but, if possible, to add all the circumstances which appeared to me proper to render them even more conclusive.

This is, first, how I reasoned with myself: If the increase in weight of metals calcined in closed vessels is due, as Boyle thought, to the addition of the matter of the flame and fire which penetrates through the pores of the glass and combines with the metal, it follows that if, after having introduced a known quantity of metal in a glass vessel and having closed it hermetically and weighed it exactly, on calcining by a fire of coals, as Boyle did, and finally reweighing the same vessel after the calcination, before opening it, its weight should be found increased by the quantity of the matter of fire which is introduced during the calcination.

If on the contrary, I further said to myself, the increase in weight of the metallic calx is not due to the combination of the material of the fire nor to any exterior matter but to the fixation of a portion of the air contained in the vessel, the vessel should not weigh more after the calcination than before; it should simply be partly evacuated and only increases in weight at the moment when the vacuum is released.

After these reflections I supplied myself with very pure lead and tin, which I cast into rods or cylinders at most 3 or 4 *lignes*[4] in diameter, in order to introduce them easily into retorts with narrow openings. In order to cast them thus into cylinders I operated as follows: with scissors I cut out little bands of paper 6 to 8 *lignes* wide and I rolled these in spirals so as to form molds or hollow cylinders. To give greater strength to these molds I wound them many times with fine thread and finally I closed the end which was to form the bottom of the mold by drawing a turn of the string tight. Then, my molds being thus prepared, I poured into each of them by a funnel of cardboard the lead or tin, and when the metal was sufficiently cooled I removed the enveloping paper and cleaned the surface of the cylinders very carefully by scraping them with a knife.

This initial operation done, I collected a certain number of new white glass retorts of a convenient capacity and perfectly clean within. In each I placed 8 ounces of lead or tin weighed with scrupulous exactness and then by means of an enameler's lamp drew out the ends of their necks into a very fine capillary which I left open.

Of a large number of retorts of various capacities which I have prepared thus, more than three-quarters have broken, either over the enameler's lamp or during the fusion or cooling of the metal, and I ought to note, moreover, that this kind of experiment is not without danger and that once the vessels have been sealed hermetically one should never operate without having the face covered by a solid mask, for example, of tin plate equipped with very thick glasses for the eyes.

[4] [A *ligne* is $\frac{1}{12}$ *pouce* and is approximately 2.26 millimeters.]

These difficulties in carrying out the operations are such that I have been able to carry out well only two experiments with tin and scarcely one with lead, but aside from the precise and certain conclusions which I have been able to draw from those which were completely successful, some of the others have not been completely useless either for the purpose of this memoir or for other, less immediate, objectives.

CALCINATION OF TIN IN A GLASS RETORT OF 43 CUBIC POUCES CAPACITY

I took one of the retorts prepared as I have just described, namely, with a neck drawn down to a capillary by means of a lamp; this retort contained, like all the others, 8 *onces*[5] of very carefully weighed tin, and, having weighed it in order to find the weight of the retort, independent of the 8 *onces* of tin which it contained, I obtained the following results, namely:

	Onces	Gros	Grains
Weight of the tin............	8.	0.	0,00.
Weight of the retort..........	5.	2.	2,50.
Sum.....................	13.	2.	2,50.

The balance which served me for all the experiments contained in this memoir was constructed with particular care by Mr. Chemen, inspector of coinage; it can weigh up to 8 and 10 *livres*, and I have reason to believe that no more perfect instrument of this sort exists. I have already had occasion to speak of this same balance in a memoir on the conversion of water into earth which was published in the *Memoirs* of this Academy for 1772.

Having thus determined the weight of the retort and of the tin therein, I held it by the neck at a suitable distance over a fire of charcoal and thus heated it slowly in order to prevent its shattering. When the tin had just begun to melt I closed the capillary opening at the end of the neck of the retort by means of a blowpipe without removing the retort from above the fire, and then I cooled the vessel as slowly as I had heated it.

This precaution of driving out a portion of the air contained in the retort before closing it hermetically is essential, since without doing so, dangerous explosions are liable to occur, or else one is obliged to use retorts of very thick glass, which because of their great weight render the

---

[5] [1 *livre* = 16 *onces*; 1 *once* = 8 *gros*; 1 *gros* = 72 *grains*. A Paris *livre* was equivalent to 30.59 grams.]

balance less sensitive and give rise to a new source of uncertainty and error.

When the retort was thus rid of a part of the air which it contained and sealed hermetically, I returned it to the balance and found for its weight,

	Onces	Gros	Grains	Average weight		
				Onces	Gros	Grains
In the pans:						
No. 1......................	13.	1.	67,0.	13.	1.	68,75.
No. 2......................	13.	1.	70,50.			
I repeated the same weighing three days afterwards, and I had						
In the pans:						
No. 1......................	13.	1.	68,00.	13.	1.	69,00.
No. 2......................	13.	1.	70,00.			
Sum of the two averages........	...	..	......	26.	3.	65,75.
And for the average which I regarded as the effective weight	...	..	......	13.	1.	68,87.

No matter how exact the balances which one may use, this manner of weighing by changing pans and taking the average is the sole one yielding rigorously exact results.

	Onces	Gros	Grains
The weight before dispelling the air and closing the retort hermetically..	13.	2.	2,50.
It is thereafter found to be.............................	13.	1.	68,87.
The difference being the weight of the air dispelled by the heat...	0.	0.	5,63.

This weight being nearly equivalent to 12 cubic *pouces* and the capacity of the retort being about 43 cubic *pouces*, it follows that before the retort was closed hermetically, I expelled by heat about two-sevenths of the total quantity of air contained in it.

These various preliminary operations being done, I proceeded to the calcination, and for this I will transcribe what is recorded in my laboratory journal for February 14 of this year, 1774.

The retort was placed on the fire at 10:45 in the morning but the tin was not melted completely until 10:52, that is to say, after seven minutes. Soon the surface lost the brilliance which it had at first and became covered with a pellicle which grew little by little and appeared to wrinkle, while at the same time a kind of black flake was formed. Shortly afterward I noticed that there was formed, at the bottom of the vessel beneath the tin, a black powder heavier than the melted metal. This species of calx did not appear to form on the surface of the metal, as happens in calcination in the open air, but on the contrary, on the bottom underneath the metal. At the end of a half hour the quantity of the black powder ceased to increase and the surface of the metal became clear, no longer displaying a pellicle or black flakes, but was simply a little less brilliant than the metal had been at the first moment of fusion.

The black powder, of which I have just spoken, although heavier than the melted metal, was in such a fine state of division that when the retort was agitated some of it arose and fluttered in the interior like a kind of very light soot and settled on the inside walls of the vessel.

At the end of an hour and ten minutes, seeing that no further change was taking place, I began to allow the vessel to cool. Although I had very carefully regulated the fire during the course of this operation, the bottom of the retort was nevertheless a little deformed and elongated in the form of a pear. This seemed to indicate that there had been during the course of the operation no exterior pressure tending to force it in, or at least, if so, that this pressure was more than counterbalanced by the 8 *onces* of tin which weighed on the bottom of the retort.

When the vessel had cooled sufficiently I had only to weigh it again without opening it, and even before it was entirely cooled I had the following results.

TOTAL WEIGHT BEFORE OPENING

	Onces	Gros	Grains	Average Weight		
				Onces	Gros	Grains
In the pans:						
No. 1........................	13.	1.	66,90.	13.	1.	68,60.
No. 2........................	13.	1.	70,30.			
The same retort closed hermetically before the calcination weighed	...	..	......	13.	1.	68,87.
Difference....................	...	..	......	...	..	0,27.

This difference is so small that it may be regarded as zero; moreover, it will be seen below that there exist other causes of uncertainty and error of which I did not then know and which may give rise to considerable differences.

From this first observation one may already be certain that nothing exterior to the retort combines with metals during their calcination. If we suppose, then, as will be shown later, that the metal gained in weight, we must search for the cause in the interior of the retort.

This first fact established, I then proceeded to open the flask by heating it strongly toward the middle of its belly with a glowing coal and then wetting the heated place with a little water. I succeeded in this way in making a crack which I conducted around with a glowing coal and thus divided the retort into two nearly equal portions. I took pains to carry out this operation on a large sheet of white paper in order to make certain that not the least fragment of the retort was lost.

When the retort had been opened thus and the air in the interior of the vessel had come to equilibrium with the atmosphere, I weighed anew the whole comprising the retort, the lead,[6] and the black powder or calx. I found

TOTAL WEIGHT AFTER THE ENTRANCE OF THE AIR

	Onces	Gros	Grains	Average weight		
				Onces	Gros	Grains
In the pans:						
No. 1..........................	13.	2.	6,75.	13.	2.	5,63.
No. 2..........................	13.	2.	4,50.			
This same retort, full of air before						
the calcination.................	...	..	.....	13.	2.	2,50.
Whence, the increase in weight						
during the calcination.........	...	..	.....	...	..	3,13.

It has just been seen that while the retort remained closed hermetically it suffered no increase in weight as a result of the calcination and that the increase in weight did not take place until after the entrance of the exterior air. Whence, in this operation more air is found in the retort after than before the calcination, and it is evident that this excess of air causes the increase in weight. If, then, just this increase in weight be found in the metal, it will be proved that the excess of air which entered served to replace the portion which combined with the metal during the calcination and increased its weight. Therefore I weighed separately the retort, the lead, and the calx which I obtained and obtained the results which follow, namely:

[6] [This is apparently an error. Tin is meant.]

WEIGHT OF THE TIN

	Onces	Gros	Grains	Average weight		
				Onces	Gros	Grains
In the pans:						
No. 1	7.	6.	37,75.	7.	6.	37,50.
No. 2	7.	6.	37,25.			
No. 1	7.	6.	37,50.	7.	6.	37,25.
No. 2	7.	6.	37,00.			
Sum of the two weights	..	..	......	15.	5.	2,75.
Mean or effective weight	..	..	......	7.	6.	37,37.
Weight of the black powder or calx of tin	..	..	......	...	1.	37,75.
Total of the tin and the calx	..	..	......	8.	0.	3,12.
This same tin before the calcination weighed only	..	..	......	8.	0.	0.
Increase	..	..	......	...	..	3,12.

To make the proof I weighed the two fragments of the retort and had

	Onces	Gros	Grains
Weight of the retort alone	5.	2.	2,50.
Weight of the tin	7.	6.	37,37.
Weight of the black power or calx of tin	...	1.	37,75.
Total weight after the calcination	13.	2.	5,62.
Weight before the calcination	13.	2.	2,50.
Increase	...	..	3,12.

The quantity of air contained in the retort was 43 cubic *pouces*, that is to say, about 21 *grains*. We forced out, as was seen above, 5⅔ *grains* before closing the vessel hermetically. The calcination, then, involved only 15⅓ *grains* of air, and of this about a fifth had been absorbed. The following experiment, having been made in a larger vessel, will present a more marked increase in weight and in consequence will give more satisfying results.

Lavoisier here describes a similar experiment involving a retort of 250 cubic *pouces* capacity. The conclusions are the same as those arrived at in the first experiment.

I tried to repeat with lead the experiments which I have just described, but, as I said, I succeeded well only once and then with such uncertain and extraordinary results that I am induced to postpone its publication.

To summarize the conclusions which may be drawn from the two experiments on the calcination of tin which I have just described, it appears to me that we cannot refuse to conclude that

First, only a certain quantity of tin may be calcined in a given quantity of air.

Second, this quantity of metal calcined is greater in a larger retort than in a small one, although we cannot yet be certain that the quantity of metal calcined is exactly proportional to the capacity of the vessels.

Third, retorts sealed hermetically and weighed before and after the calcination of a portion of the tin which they contain present no change in weight, proving that the increase in weight which the metal undergoes evidently does not arise from the matter of the fire nor from any material exterior to the retort.

Fourth, in all calcinations of tin, the increase in weight of the metal is practically exactly equal to the weight of the air absorbed; which proves that the portion of the air which combines with the metal during the calcination is nearly equal in specific gravity to the air of the atmosphere.

I might add that certain considerations arising from these experiments which I made on the calcination of metals in closed vessels, considerations which would be very difficult for me to explain to the reader without entering into too long detail, incline me to believe that the portion of the air which combines with metals is slightly heavier than the air of the atmosphere, and that that which remains after the calcination, on the other hand, is a little lighter. The specific gravity of the air, according to this supposition, would be the resultant mean between these two airs, but more direct evidence is needed on this matter, especially since such small differences are involved, before I can speak of it with certainty.

The reader will easily see, as I have only too well myself, that despite all the care and precision which I have tried to employ in these experiments they still leave very much to be desired. It is the fate of all those who occupy themselves with physical and chemical researches that they perceive a new step as soon as they have already made one, and they would never give anything to the public if they waited until they reached the end of the path which continually unfolds before them and continues to lengthen as they advance along it.

I know, for instance, that it would be important in order to complete this work to carry out a series of calcinations of metals in a great number of vessels of different capacities, in order to determine with some precision the law which governs the increase in weight of a metal in relation to the volume of the air in which it is calcined. It would be no less interesting to try calcinations in very small vessels and even in the vacuum of the pneumatic pump, but experiments of this kind demand so much time and attention for their proper pursuit, they are so tiresome and require so much apparatus which is cumbersome and difficult to make, th: not the courage to carry this work further.

This was not true of a new route which these experiments have to me. It has just been seen that a portion of the air is susceptible to combination with metallic substances to form calces, while another portion of this same air always refuses to combine thus. This calcination has made me suspect that the air of the atmosphere is not a simple substance at all but is composed of very different substances, and the work which I have undertaken on the calcination and revivification of the calx of mercury has singularly confirmed me in this opinion. Without anticipating the conclusions which result from this work, I think that I may announce here that all the air of the atmosphere is not in a respirable state; that it is the salubrious portion which combines with metals during their calcination; and that that which remains after the calcination is a kind of noxious gas [*mofette*], incapable of maintaining either the respiration of animals or the combustion of bodies. Not only does the air of the atmosphere appear to me to be apparently composed of two elastic fluids of very different nature, but I suspect, further, that the noxious and mephitic part is itself very compound.

One of the most famous of all Lavoisier's memoirs is that which correctly explains for the first time the composition of the atmosphere and of carbon dioxide and the mechanism of the preparation of oxygen from mercuric oxide.

Here we have the result of the stimulus of Priestley's communication to Lavoisier of his discovery of "dephlogisticated air"—oxygen (October, 1774). Lavoisier read it at the *rentrée publique* of the Academy on April 27, 1775. It was first published in Rozier's *Observations sur la physique*, **5**: 429–433 (1775), and was revised and read again on August 8, 1778. The following selection is taken from this later paper, which was finally printed in the *Mémoires de l'Académie royale des sciences*, **1775**: 520–526, published in 1778.

MEMOIR ON THE NATURE OF THE PRINCIPLE WHICH COMBINES WITH METALS DURING THEIR CALCINATION AND WHICH INCREASES THEIR WEIGHT.[7]

Are there different species of air? Is it sufficient that a body be in a durable state of expansibility [*état d'expansibilité*[8] *durable*] in order to be a

---

[7] The first experiments relative to this memoir were made more than a year ago; those on precipitated mercury *per se* were first tried with a burning glass in the month of November, 1774, and made afterwards with all necessary precaution and care conjointly with Mr. Trudaine in the laboratory at Montigny February 28 and March 1 and 2 of this year. Finally they have been repeated anew on March 31 last in the presence of the Duke of Rochefoucault, Messrs. Trudaine, de Montigny, Macquer, and Cadet.

[8] The word *expansibilité* which I will use in this memoir has today a definite meaning for physicists and chemists since a modern author has defined it in a very extensive article embodying the widest and newest viewpoints. (See *Encyclopédie*, vol. VI, p. 274.)

species of air? Finally, are the different airs which occur in nature or which we may produce separate substances or merely modifications of the air of the atmosphere? Such are the principal questions which encompass the plan which I have formed and whose successive development I propose to bring before the eyes of the Academy. But the time devoted to our public meetings does not permit me to treat any of these questions extensively, and I will confine myself today to a particular case and limit myself to showing that the principle which combines with metals during their calcination, which increases their weight and constitutes them in the state of a calx, is nothing other than the most salubrious and purest portion of the air and such that, if the air, after having engaged in a metallic combination, becomes free again, it appears in an eminently respirable state more capable than the air of the atmosphere of sustaining ignition and combustion.

The majority of metallic calces are not to be reduced, that is, returned to the metallic state, without the immediate contact of a carbonaceous material or any substance whatsoever containing what we call *phlogiston*. The charcoal which is used is completely destroyed in this operation if it be present in suitable proportion; whence it follows that the air which is evolved in metallic reductions with carbon is not a simple substance but in some manner is the result of the combination of the elastic fluid disengaged from the metal and that disengaged from the carbon. Therefore the fact that this fluid is obtained as fixed air gives us no right to conclude that it existed in this form in the metallic calx before its combination with the carbon.

These considerations showed me that in order to clear up the mystery of the reduction of metallic calces it would be necessary to experiment with those calces which are reducible without the addition of anything. The calx of iron offered me this property and actually, of all those calces, either natural or artificial, which we have exposed at the foci of the large burning glasses either of the Regent or of Mr. Trudaine, there have been none which have not been completely reduced without addition.

I tried, consequently, to reduce by means of a burning glass several species of the calx of iron under large glass bells inverted in mercury, and I succeeded in disengaging by this means a large quantity of elastic fluid. But at the same time this elastic fluid became mixed with the common air contained in the bell, and this circumstance threw much uncertainty on my results, so that none of the tests which I conducted upon this air were perfectly conclusive and it was impossible for me to be certain whether the phenomena I obtained arose from the common air, from that disengaged from the calx of iron, or from the combination of the two. The experiments having failed of fully filling my purpose, I omit their details here; they will, however, find their natural place in other memoirs.

As much as these difficulties arise from the nature of iron itself, from the refractory nature of its calces, and from the difficulty of reducing them without addition, I regarded them as insurmountable and therefore thought that I ought to direct my attention to another species of calx, more easily treatable and being, like the calces of iron, reducible without addition. Precipitated mercury per se, which is nothing else than a calx of mercury, as several authors have already advanced and as will appear even more convincingly by the reading of this memoir, precipitated mercury per se, as I said, appeared to me to be completely appropriate for the object which I had in view, for everyone knows today that this substance is reducible without addition at a very medium degree of heat. Although I have repeated a great many times the experiments which I am about to describe, I have not thought it appropriate to give the details of each of them here for fear of extending the memoir too far, and consequently I have combined into a single account the circumstances pertaining to many repetitions of the same experiment.

First, to assure myself that precipitated mercury per se was a genuine metallic calx, that it gave the same results, the same species of air on reduction according to the ordinary method (that is, to use the customary expression, with the addition of phlogiston), I mixed an *once* of this calx with 48 *grains* of powdered charcoal and introduced the mixture into a little glass retort of 2 cubic *pouces* or more capacity. This I placed in a reverberatory furnace of proportionate size. The neck of this retort was about a pied[9] and 3 to 4 *lignes* in diameter and was bent in various places by means of an enameler's lamp in such a manner that its end was disposed beneath an ample glass bell filled with water and inverted in a tub of the same. The apparatus which is here before the eyes of the Academy will suffice to illustrate its operation. This apparatus, simple as it is, is even more accurate in that it has neither joints nor lute nor any passage through which the air may enter or escape.

As soon as a fire was placed beneath the retort and the first effects of the heat felt, the common air which it contained expanded and some little of it passed into the bell. However, in view of the small volume of the empty part of the retort, this air made no sensible error, and its quantity taken at the most can scarcely amount to a cubic *pouce*. As the retort is heated further the air is evolved with much speed and rises through the water in the bell. The operation did not last for more than three-quarters of an hour, the fire being kept up during this interval. When all the calx of mercury had been reduced and the air ceased to come forth, I marked the height of the water in the bell and found that the quantity of air evolved had been 64 cubic *pouces* without counting that which was unavoidably absorbed in traversing the water.

[9] [12 *pouces* = 1 *pied*.]

I submitted this air to a large number of tests, the details of which I omit, and found that 1) it can, by shaking, combine with water and give to the water all the properties of acidulated, gaseous, or aerated waters such as those of Seltz, Pougues, Bussang, Pirmont, etc.; 2) it kills in some seconds animals which were placed in it; 3) candles and all combustible bodies in general are extinguished in an instant; 4) it precipitates lime water; 5) it combines with great ease with either fixed or volatile alkalis, depriving them of their causticity and making them capable of crystallizing. All these properties are precisely those of that species of air known under the name of *fixed air* which I obtained by the reduction of minium by powdered charcoal, which calcareous earths and effervescent alkalis evolve in combining with acids, and which vegetable materials evolve in fermenting. It was thus established that precipitated mercury per se gives the same products as other metallic calces when reduced with the addition of phlogiston, and that it belongs, therefore, in the general class of metallic calces.

It then only remained to examine this calx alone, to reduce it without adding anything, to see if some elastic fluid were evolved from it, and, supposing there were, to determine its nature. To this end I placed in a retort of 2 cubic *pouces* capacity 1 *once* of precipitated mercury per se alone, arranged the apparatus in the same manner as in the preceding experiment, and operated so that all the circumstances would be exactly the same. The reduction took place this time with a little more difficulty than when charcoal was added; more heat was required, and there was no sensible change until the retort began to become slightly red. Then the air was evolved little by little, passed into the bell, and, holding the same degree of fire during two and one-half hours, all the mercury was reduced.

The operation completed, there was found, on the one hand, partly in the neck of the retort and partly in a glass vessel which I placed beneath the water under the exit of the retort, 7 *gros* and 18 *grains* of fluid mercury, and on the other hand, the quantity of the air which had passed into the bell was found to be 78 cubic *pouces;* whence it follows that by supposing that the whole loss of weight should be attributed to the air, each cubic *pouce* should weigh a little less than two-thirds of a *grain*—a value not far removed from that for common air.

After having thus fixed the first results, I had only to submit the 78 cubic *pouces* of air which I had obtained to all the tests necessary to determine its nature, and I found with much surprise

1. That it would not combine with water on shaking
2. That it did not precipitate limewater but only gave it a nearly imperceptible turbidity
3. That it failed to unite at all with fixed or volatile alkalis

4. That it failed entirely to diminish the causticity of these
5. That it could be used again to calcine metals
6. Finally, that it had none of the properties of fixed air

In contrast to the latter, animals did not perish in it and it seemed more suitable to their respiration. Candles and inflamed materials were not only not extinguished, but the flame widened in a very remarkable manner and shed much more light and brilliancy than in common air. Charcoal burned therein with a brilliance nearly like that of phosphorus, and all combustible materials in general were consumed with astonishing rapidity. All these circumstances have fully convinced me that this air, far from being fixed air, is in a more respirable, more combustible state and in consequence is more pure even than the air which sustains us.

It appears to be proved from the above that the principle which combines with and increases the weight of metals when they are calcined is nothing other than the purest portion of the air itself which surrounds us and which we breathe—this it is which in calcination passes from the expansible state to the solid one. If, then, this principle is obtained in the form of fixed air in all metallic reductions where carbon is used, it follows that this is due to the combination of this latter with the pure portion of the air, and it is very probable that all metallic calces would, like mercury, give only eminently respirable air if we could reduce them all as we do precipitated mercury per se.

All that has been said of the air of metallic calces applies naturally to that which is obtained from niter by explosion. It is known from a number of experiments already published, and which I have in greatest part repeated, that the major part of this air is in the state of fixed air, is deadly to animals which breathe it, and has the property of uniting easily with lime and the alkalis, rendering them mild and capable of crystallizing. But since, at the same time, the explosion of niter takes place only with the addition of carbon or any substance which contains phlogiston, one can hardly doubt that, under these circumstances, eminently respirable air is converted into fixed air. From this it would follow that the air combined in niter which produces the terrible explosions of gunpowder is the respirable portion of the air of the atmosphere deprived of its expansibility and is one of the constituent principles of nitric acid.

Since charcoal disappears completely in the revivification of the calx of mercury, and since one retrieves in this operation only mercury and fixed air, one is forced to conclude that the principle to which has been given till now the name of *fixed air* is the result of the combination of the eminently respirable portion of the air with charcoal. I propose to develop this in a more satisfying manner in a series of memoirs which I shall give on the topic.

In a memoir on combustion in general, published in 1780, in the *Mémoires* for 1777, Lavoisier criticizes the pholgiston theory and proves that his hypothesis is more in agreement with the facts.[10]

MEMOIR ON COMBUSTION IN GENERAL.

September 5, 1775.

As dangerous as is the desire to systematize in the physical sciences, it is, nevertheless, to be feared that in storing without order a great multiplicity of experiments we obscure the science rather than clarify it, render it difficult of access to those desirous of entering upon it, and, finally, obtain at the price of long and tiresome work only disorder and confusion. Facts, observations, experiments—these are the materials of a great edifice, but in assembling them we must combine them into classes, distinguish which belongs to which order and to which part of the whole each pertains.

Systems in physical science, considered from this point of view, are no more than appropriate instruments to aid the weakness of our organs: they are, properly speaking, approximate methods which put us on the path to the solution of the problem; these are the hypotheses which, successively modified, corrected, and changed in proportion as they are found false, should lead us infallibly one day, by a process of exclusion, to the knowledge of the true laws of nature.

Encouraged by these reflections, I venture to propose to the Academy today a new theory of combustion, or rather, to speak with the reserve which I customarily impose upon myself, a hypothesis by the aid of which we may explain in a very satisfactory manner all the phenomena of combustion and of calcination, and in part even the phenomena which accompany the respiration of animals. I have already laid out the initial foundations of this hypothesis on pages 279 and 280 of the first volume of my "Opuscules physiques et chimiques," but I acknowledge that, having little confidence in my own ability, I did not then dare to put forward an opinion which might appear peculiar and was directly contrary to the theory of Stahl and to those of many celebrated men who have followed him.

While some of the reasons which held me back perhaps remain today, facts which appear to me to be favorable to my ideas have increased in number since and have strengthened me in my opinion. These facts, without being perhaps too strong, have made me more confident, and I

[10] *Mémoires de l'Académie royale des sciences,* **1777**: 592–600.

believe that the proof or at least the probability is sufficient so that even those who are not of my opinion will not be able to blame me for having written.

We observe in the combustion of bodies generally four recurring phenomena which would appear to be invariable laws of nature; while these phenomena are implied in other memoirs which I have presented, I must recall them here in a few words.

First Phenomenon. In all combustions the matter of fire or light is evolved.

Second Phenomenon. Materials may not burn except in a very few kinds of air, or rather, combustion may take place in only a single variety of air: that which Mr. Priestley has named *dephlogisticated air* and which I name here *pure air.* Not only do those bodies which we call *combustible* not burn either in vacuum or in any other species of air, but on the contrary, they are extinguished just as rapidly as if they had been plunged into water or any other liquid.

Third Phenomenon. In all combustion, pure air in which the combustion takes place is destroyed or decomposed and the burning body increases in weight exactly in proportion to the quantity of air destroyed or decomposed.

Fourth Phenomenon. In all combustion the body of which is burned changes into an acid[11] by the addition of the substance which increases its weight. Thus, for example, if sulfur is burned under a bell, the product of the combustion is vitriolic acid; if phosphorus be burned, the product of the combustion is phosphoric acid; if a carbonaceous substance be burned, the product of the combustion is fixed air, formerly called the acid of chalk, etc.[12]

The calcination of metals follows precisely the same laws, and it is with very good reason that Mr. Macquer considers the process as a slow combustion. Thus (1) in all metallic calcinations the matter of fire is evolved; (2) genuine calcination may take place only in pure air; (3) air combines with the calcined body, but with this difference, that instead of forming an acid with it, a particular combination results which is known by the name of *metallic calx.*

This is not the place to show the analogy which exists between the respiration of animals, combustion, and calcination. I will return to it in the sequel to this memoir.

These different phenomena of the calcination of metals and of combustion are explained in a very nice manner by the hypothesis of Stahl, but it

[11] [One of the few errors in Lavoisier's theory was the assumption that oxygen is the essential component of acids.]

[12] I will observe here in passing that the number of acids is infinitely greater than we think.

is necessary to suppose with Stahl that the material of fire, of phlogiston, is fixed in metals, in sulfur, and in all bodies which are regarded as combustible. Now if we demand of the partisans of the doctrine of Stahl that they prove the existence of the matter of fire in combustible bodies, they necessarily fall into a vicious circle and are obliged to reply that combustible bodies contain the matter of fire because they burn and that they burn because they contain the matter of fire. Now it is easy to see that in the last analysis this is explaining combustion by combustion.

The existence of the matter of fire, of phlogiston in metals, sulfur, etc., is then actually nothing but a hypothesis, a supposition which, once admitted, explains, it is true, some of the phenomena of calcination and combustion; but if I am able to show that these phenomena may be explained in just as natural a manner by an opposing hypothesis, that is to say without supposing that the matter of fire or phlogiston exists in combustible materials, the system of Stahl will be found to be shaken to its foundations.

Undoubtedly it will not be amiss to ask first what is meant by the matter of fire. I reply with Franklin, Boerhaave, and some of the philosophers of antiquity that the matter of fire or of light is a very subtle, very elastic fluid which surrounds all parts of the planet which we inhabit, which penetrates bodies composed of it with greater or less ease, and which tends when free to be in equilibrium in everything.

I will add, borrowing the language of chemistry, that this fluid is the dissolvent of a large number of bodies; that it combines with them in the same manner as water combines with salt and as acids combine with metals; and that the bodies thus combined and dissolved by the igneous fluid lose in part the properties which they had before the combination and acquire new ones which make them more like the matter of fire.

Thus, as I showed in a memoir deposited with the secretary of this Academy, all aeriform liquids, all species of air are the result of the combination of any substance whatsoever, solid or liquid, with the matter of fire or light. It is to this combination that aeriform liquids owe their elasticity, their specific lightness, their rarity, and all other properties which make them like the igneous fluid.

Pure air, according to this, that which Mr. Priestley calls *dephlogisticated air*, is an igneous combination in which the matter of fire or of light enters as a dissolvent and in which another substance enters as a base. Now if in any dissolution whatsoever we present to the base a substance with which it has more affinity, it unites instantly and the dissolvent which it has left becomes free; it regains all its properties and escapes with the characteristics by which it is known, that is to say, with flame, heat, and light.

To clarify whatever may be obscure about this theory let us apply it to several examples. When a metal is calcined in pure air the base of the air, which has less affinity with its dissolvent than with the metal, unites with the latter as soon as it is melted and converts it into a metallic calx. This combination of the base of the air with the metal is shown, (1) by the increase in weight which the latter undergoes during calcination, (2) by the nearly complete destruction of the air beneath the bell. But if the base of the air were dissolved by the matter of fire, in proportion as this base combines with the metal the matter of fire should become free and should produce, in evolving, flame and light. It is concluded that the more rapid the calcination of the metal, that is to say, the more of the base of the air is fixed in a given time, the more matter of fire will be freed at the same time and consequently the more noticeable will be the combustion.

These phenomena, which are extremely slow and difficult to perceive during the calcination of metals, are almost instantaneous in the combustion of sulfur and phosphorus. I have shown by experiments, against which it appears to me difficult to make any reasonable objection, that in these two combustions air, or rather the base of the air, was absorbed; that it combined with the sulfur and with the phosphorus to form vitriolic and phosphoric acids. However, the base of the air may not pass into a new combination without leaving its dissolvent free, and this dissolvent, which is the matter of fire itself, should evolve with light and flame.

Carbon and all carbonaceous materials have the same effect on the base of the air: they appropriate it for themselves and form with it by combustion an acid *sui generis* known under the name of *fixed air* or *acid of chalk*. The solvent of the base of the air, the material of fire, is then evolved in this operation, but in less quantity than in the combustion of sulfur and phosphorus because a portion of it combines with the mephitic acid [fixed air] to render it into the vaporous and elastic state in which we find it.

I will observe here, in passing, that the combustion of charcoal under a bell inverted in mercury does not occasion a very great diminution in the volume of the air even when pure air [oxygen] is used in the experiment, for the reason that the mephitic acid which is formed remains in an aeriform state, in contrast to vitriolic and phosphoric acids, which condense into a concrete form as they are produced.

I might apply the same theory successively to all combustions, but as I shall have frequent occasion to return to this subject I will let these general examples suffice for the moment. Thus, to continue, the air is composed, according to me, of the matter of fire as dissolvent combined with a substance which serves it as a base and in some manner neutralizes it. Whenever a substance toward which it has more affinity is presented to this base, it quits its dissolvent, and then the matter of fire regains its properties and reappears before our eyes with heat, flame, and light.

Pure air, the dephlogisticated air of Mr. Priestley, is then, from this point of view, the true combustible body and perhaps the only one in nature, and we see that there is no longer need, in explaining the phenomena of combustion, of supposing that there exists an immense quantity of fixed fire in all bodies which we call *combustible*, that on the contrary it is very probable that little of this fire exists in metals, sulfur, and phosphorus and in the majority of very solid, heavy, and compact bodies; and perhaps even that only the matter of free fire exists in these substances by virtue of the property which this matter has of coming into equilibrium with neighboring bodies.

Another striking reflection which supports the foregoing is that nearly all bodies may exist in three different states, namely, in the solid, the liquid, which is to say, melted state, or the state of air and vapor. These three states depend only on the greater or lesser quantity of the matter of fire with which these bodies are penetrated and with which they are combined. Fluidity, vaporization, and elasticity characterize the presence of fire in great abundance; solidity, compactness, on the contrary, evidence its absence. As much, then, as it is proved that aeriform substances and the air itself contain a large quantity of fire, so much is it probable that solid bodies contain little.

I would be overstepping the limits which I have prescribed and which the circumstances demand were I to undertake to show how this theory throws light on all the great phenomena of nature. However, I cannot omit remarking upon the ease with which it explains why the air is an elastic and rare fluid. Indeed, fire being the most subtle, elastic, and rare of all fluids, it should communicate a part of its properties to the substances with which it unites, and, as solutions of salts always partake of some of the properties of water, so dissolutions by fire should retain some igneous properties.

It will be seen, then, why we cannot have combustion either in a vacuum or in any aeriform combination where the matter of fire has a very great affinity with the base with which it is combined.

We are no longer obliged, following these principles, to admit the presence of a large quantity of the matter of fixed and combined fire even in the diamond itself and in a great number of substances which have no quality like that of the matter of fire or which possess properties incompatible with it. Finally, we are not at all obliged to maintain, as did Stahl, that bodies which increase in weight lose a part of their substance.

I remarked above that the theory proposed in this memoir could be applied to the explanation of a part of the phenomena of respiration, and with this I will finish.

I showed in the memoir which I read at the public meeting of last Easter that pure air, after having entered the lungs, leaves in part as fixed air, or the acid of chalk. Pure air, in passing through the lungs, undergoes then a decomposition analogous to that which takes place in the combustion of charcoal. Now in the combustion of charcoal the matter of fire is evolved, whence the matter of fire should likewise be evolved in the lungs in the interval between inhalation and exhalation, and it is this matter of fire without doubt which, distributed with the blood throughout the animal economy, maintains a constant heat of about 32½ degrees Réaumur. This idea will appear to be hazarded at first glance, but before it be rejected or condemned I beg you to consider that it is founded on two certain and incontestable facts, namely, on the decomposition of the air in the lungs and on the evolution of the matter of fire which accompanies all decompositions of pure air, that is to say, all changes of pure air to the state of fixed air. But that which further confirms that the heat of animals stems from the decomposition of the air in the lungs is that only those animals in nature which respire habitually are warm-blooded and that their warmth is the greater as respiration is more frequent; that is to say, that there is a constant relation between the warmth of an animal and the quantity of air entering, or at least converted into fixed air in, its lungs.

Furthermore, I repeat, in attacking here Stahl's doctrine my object is not to substitute a rigorously demonstrated theory but solely a hypothesis which appears to me more probable, more conformable to the laws of nature, and which appears to me to contain fewer forced explanations and fewer contradictions.

Circumstances have permitted me to give here but a general outline of the system and a glance at its consequences, but I propose to take up successively each point, to develop each in different memoirs, and I venture to assert in advance that the hypothesis which I propose explains in a very satisfactory and very simple manner the principal phenomena of physics and chemistry.

It was not until 1783 that Lavoisier attacked the phlogiston theory in force in a memoir entitled "Reflections on Phlogiston, Serving to Develop the Theory of Combustion and Calcination."[13] He describes it as a sequel to his paper published in 1777, cited above. It is a notable document, asserting that the phlogiston theory was not only unnecessary but was incorrect, for it was in conflict with all the facts. The conclusion of this paper follows.

My only object in this memoir has been to give the new development of the theory of combustion which I published in 1777 and to show that the phlogiston of Stahl is an imaginary thing whose existence has been gratuitously supposed in metals, sulfur, phosphorus, and all combustible bodies; that all the phenomena of combustion and calcination may be explained in a far simpler and easier manner without phlogiston than with it. I do not expect that my ideas will be adopted all at once; human nature bends

[13] *Mémoires de l'Académie royale des sciences*, **1783**: 505–538, published in 1786.

toward one viewpoint, and those who have envisaged nature from a certain point of view during a part of their career change only with difficulty to new ideas: it is for time, then, to confirm or destroy the opinions which I have presented. In the meanwhile I see with great satisfaction that the young people who are commencing to study the science without prejudice, the geometricians and the natural philosophers who bring fresh minds to bear on chemical truths, believe no longer in a phlogiston in the sense that Stahl presented it and regard all the doctrine as a scaffolding more encumbering than useful for continuing the edifice of chemical science.

Lavoisier carried out quantitative experiments on respiration and was the first to show the chemical nature of the process. The following paper appeared in the *Mémoires de l'Académie royale des sciences,* **1777**: 185–194, published in 1780.[14]

EXPERIMENTS ON THE RESPIRATION OF ANIMALS AND ON THE CHANGES WHICH OCCUR IN AIR AS IT PASSES THROUGH THE LUNGS.

Of all the phenomena of the animal economy, there is none more striking or more worthy of the attention of philosophers and physiologists than those which accompany respiration. Little as is our acquaintance with the object of this singular function, we know that it is essential to life, and that it cannot at any time be suspended without exposing the animal to the danger of immediate death.

As is generally known air is the agent or rather the subject of respiration, but at the same time not every sort of air, or speaking more generally not every sort of elastic fluid, is suited to maintain it. There are many kinds which animals cannot breathe without perishing at least as soon as if they did not breathe at all.

The experiments of some philosophers, and especially of Messrs. Hales and Cigna, began to throw some light on this important subject; since then Dr. Priestley by a paper published last year in London, has greatly widened the field of our knowledge, and has endeavoured to prove by ingenious, delicate and very novel experiments that the respiration of animals has the effect of phlogisticating the air just as happens in the calcination of metals and other chemical processes, and that the air ceases to be respirable only when it becomes overcharged and in some way saturated with phlogiston.

However probable the theory of this celebrated philosopher may appear at first sight, however numerous and well carried out may be the experiments on which he seeks to base it, I must confess that I have found it to be at variance with so many phenomena, that I have felt justified in doubting it. I have proceeded therefore on another plan, and I have found myself led irresistibly by the course of my experiments to conclusions

[14] Translation from C. M. Taylor, "The Discovery of the Nature of the Air and of Its Changes during Breathing," London, 1923, p. 66.

entirely opposed to those of Dr. Priestley. I shall not pause at this point to discuss separately each of these experiments, nor to show how they all help to support the opinion which I shall develop in this memoir. I shall content myself with describing my own and giving an account of the results.

Lavoisier here described the preparation and decomposition of mercuric oxide —the experiment which showed the composition of the atmosphere. As this experiment is identical with that described on page 166, it is omitted.

This is the most complete kind of proof that can be achieved in chemistry, the decomposition of the air and its recomposition, and from this it follows clearly—

First, that $5/6$ of the air which we breathe is in a mephitic condition, and is incapable of supporting the respiration of animals or the burning of material.

Second, that the residue, or only $1/6$ of the volume of atmospheric air is respirable.

Third, that in the calcination of mercury the wholesome part of the air is absorbed and the mephitic part is left.

Fourth, that by the union of the two parts of the air thus separated, the part that can be breathed and the mephitic part, air like atmospheric air is formed once more.

These preliminary truths relating to the calcination of metals lead us to simple conclusions with regard to the respiration of animals, and as the air which has been used for some time to maintain this vital function bears a close resemblance to that in which metals have been calcined, the knowledge relative to the one will naturally be applied to the other.

I put a sparrow under a glass bell jar filled with common air and standing in mercury. The glass contained 31 cubic inches of air. The animal did not seem to be at all affected for the first few moments, but at the end of 55 minutes it died. In spite of the heat of the animal which at first caused the air in the bell jar to expand, by the end of a quarter of an hour there was a loss of about $1/40$ of its volume. Then instead of increasing, the diminution became a little less by the end of half-an-hour, and then after the death of the animal, when the temperature in the bell jar had fallen again to that of the room, the decrease was found to be not more than $1/60$.

This air which had been breathed by the sparrow had become very different from the ordinary air of the atmosphere: it formed a precipitate with lime water, it extinguished lights, it could no longer be diminished by nitrous air, another bird which I introduced into it lived only a few moments. In fact it was entirely mephitic, and in this respect resembled that which remained after the calcination of mercury.

After a more thorough examination, however, I detected two very re-

markable differences between these two airs. In the first place the diminution in volume caused by the breathing of the sparrow was much less than
the diminution caused by the calcination of the mercury. In the second
place the air after the breathing produced a precipitate with lime water,
while the air after the calcination did not produce any effect with lime
water.

This difference between the two airs on the one hand, and on the other,
the great likeness which they show in some respects, led me to conclude
that during respiration there are in operation two distinct causes only one
of which I yet know. To confirm my suspicions on this point I made the
following experiment. Into a bell jar fitted with mercury and standing in
the same liquid I introduced 12 cubic inches of air vitiated by respiration,
and then introduced a thin layer of caustic alkali. I could have used lime
water for the same purpose, but the volume which would have been necessary would have been too large and would have impeded the success of the
experiment. The effect of the caustic alkali was to produce in the volume
of this air a diminution of nearly $\frac{1}{6}$. At the same time the alkali lost some
of its caustic nature and acquired the property of effervescence with acids.
It crystallised in the bell jar in the form of regular rhomboidal crystals.
These properties, as is well known, can be communicated to it only by
combining it with the kind of air or gas known as fixed air, or as I shall in
future call it, aerial chalk acid [acid crayeux aériforme]. Whence it appears
that nearly $\frac{1}{6}$ of air vitiated by respiration is an aerial acid exactly the
same as that obtained from chalk. The air which has thus been deprived
of its fixable part by the caustic alkali, so far from having been restored by
that means to the condition of common air, had become more like, or
rather it had become exactly the same as, the air remaining after the calcination of mercury. Like it, it killed animals, it extinguished lights; indeed of all the experiments which I made to compare these two airs not
one seemed to me to show the slightest difference between them.

Now air which remains after the calcination of mercury as we have seen
above is simply the mephitic residue of atmospheric air whose highly
respirable part has combined with the mercury during calcination. The
air which remains after respiration, when deprived of the aerial chalk acid
which it contains, is exactly the same mephitic residue. In fact by mixing
this last about $\frac{1}{4}$ of its volume of highly respirable air obtained from mercury calx, I restored it to its original condition and made it as suitable for
respiration and for supporting combustion as common air, just as I had
done with air vitiated by the calcination of mercury.

It follows from these experiments that to restore to its ordinary and
respirable condition, air which has been vitiated by respiration, two
effects must be produced: first the removal from the air by means of lime
or caustic alkali of the aerial chalk acid which it contains; second the

restoration to it of a quantity of highly respirable or dephlogisticated air equal to the quantity which it has lost.

Respiration therefore reverses these two effects, and I have been led in this matter to adopt one or other of two conclusions, both equally probable as far as my present experience allows me to pronounce.

After what we have seen it may be concluded that one or other of the two following occurs in respiration: either the highly respirable part contained in common air is converted into aerial chalk acid as it passes through the lungs, or else an exchange takes place in which the respirable part of the air is absorbed while the lungs give out in its place nearly the same volume of aerial chalk acid.

The first of these opinions is supported by an experiment already communicated to the Academy. For I have shown in a memoir read at the Easter Meeting in 1775 that highly respirable air may be wholly converted into aerial chalk acid by the addition of powdered charcoal. . . . It is possible therefore that respiration may possess the same property and that highly respirable air which is taken into the lungs is sent out again as aerial chalk acid. But on the other hand there are strong analogies which support the second opinion that a part of the highly respirable portion of the air remains in the lungs and combines with the blood. We know that it is a property of this air to communicate a red colour to bodies, and particularly to metallic substances with which it is combined: mercury, lead and iron are examples of this fact. These metals form with highly respirable air beautiful red calces. The same effects, the same phenomena may be observed in the calcination of metals and in the respiration of animals; all the circumstances are the same even to the colour of the residues. May we not then suppose that the red colour of blood depends on combination with highly respirable air, or to speak more precisely as I shall show in a later memoir, to combination between the basis of highly respirable air and an animal fluid, in the same manner as the red colour of mercury precipitate or of minium is due to combination between the basis of this same air and a metal? Although M. Cigna and Dr. Priestley and others who have concerned themselves with this subject have not come to this conclusion, I venture to say that there is hardly one of their experiments which does not tend to its support. In fact they have proved and Dr. Priestley in particular has shown that blood is red only in proportion as it is continually in contact with the atmosphere or its more highly respirable part; that it becomes dark in aerial chalk acid, in nitrous air, in inflammable air, in fact in all airs which cannot be breathed, as well as in the exhausted receiver of an air pump; they have proved that on the contrary it recovers its red colour in contact with air and especially in contact with highly respirable air, and that this restoration of colour is invariably accompanied by a diminution in the volume of the air. May it not then be concluded from all these facts that this part of the air is able to combine with blood, and that this combination produces the red colour? But whichever of these two opinions we embrace, whether that the respirable part of the air combines with the blood, or that it is changed into aerial chalk acid in passing through the lungs, or as I am myself inclined to believe, that both of these things happen during respiration, taking into account the facts only we may regard as proved:

First, that respiration acts only on the pure highly respirable part of the air contained in the atmosphere; that the remainder, the mephitic part, is entirely passive, and enters the lungs and leaves them again without undergoing change or alteration;

Second, that the calcination of metals in a given amount of air takes place as I have already announced several times, only until the highly respirable air which it contains has been exhausted and has combined with the metal;

Third, that in the same way if animals are shut up in a given quantity of air, they die when they have absorbed or have converted into aerial chalk acid the greater part of the respirable portion of the air, and the remainder is reduced to a mephitic condition;

Fourth, that the kind of mephitic air which remains after the calcination of metals is in no way different, according to all the experiments I have made, from that which remains after the respiration of animals, provided however that this latter has been deprived by lime or by caustic alkalis of its fixable part, the aerial chalk acid: that these two mephitic residues may be substituted for each other in all experiments, and that they can both be restored to the state of atmospheric air by a quantity of highly respirable air equal to the quantity they have lost. A new proof of this last fact is that if in a given quantity of atmospheric air the quantity of highly respirable air which it contains is increased or diminished, the quantity of metal which can be calcined in it is increased or diminished in the same proportion; and to a certain extent the time which animals can live in it is similarly increased or diminished.

The limits which I set myself in this memoir will not allow me to give an account of many other experiments which give support to the theory which I have put forward. These experiments are among those which MM. de Montigny, Trudaine and I have lately made, and there is reason to hope that they will throw still more light not only on the respiration of animals but also on combustion; operations which are much more closely related than is obvious at first sight.

Lavoisier early recognized that his new theory made possible and imperative a system of nomenclature for chemistry. The development of this system, which is essentially the modern one, fell to Guyton de Morveau, aided by Lavoisier, de Fourcroy, and Berthollet. Lavoisier began to write a textbook to illustrate and advance the new nomenclature. As the writing progressed, however, the book became more than an illustration of the new nomenclature—it became the first detailed exposition of the new theory of chemistry and stands today in

TRAITÉ
ÉLÉMENTAIRE
DE CHIMIE,
PRÉSENTÉ DANS UN ORDRE NOUVEAU
ET D'APRÈS LES DÉCOUVERTES MODERNES;

Avec Figures :

Par M. LAVOISIER, de l'Académie des Sciences, de la Société Royale de Médecine, des Sociétés d'Agriculture de Paris & d'Orléans, de la Société Royale de Londres, de l'Institut de Bologne, de la Société Helvétique de Basle, de celles de Philadelphie, Harlem, Manchester, Padoue, &c.

A PARIS,
Chez CUCHET, Libraire, rue & hôtel Serpente.

M. DCC. LXXXIX.
Sous le Privilège de l'Académie des Sciences & de la Société Royale de Médecine.

Title page of first edition of Lavoisier's "Traité élémentaire de chimie," Paris, 1789. (*Courtesy of Denis I. Duveen.*)

chemistry as Newton's "Principia" stands in mechanics. Published first in 1789 in Paris under the title of "Traité élémentaire de chimie," it is nearly as clear and easy to understand as a modern text. In it (page 140) Lavoisier stated clearly the law of conservation of mass—a law which had been only implied in his quantitive investigations. After describing the process of fermentation he states that

This operation [fermentation] is one of the most striking and extraordinary of all those which chemistry presents to us, and we must examine whence comes the disengaged carbonic gas and the inflammable spirit which is formed and how a sweet body, a vegetable oxide, can transform itself thus into two different substances, one combustible and the other highly incombustible. It will be seen that to arrive at a solution to these two questions it is first necessary to know the analysis and the nature of bodies susceptible to fermentation and the products of fermentation, for nothing is created in the operations of art or of nature, and it can be taken as an axiom that in all operations the quantity of matter before is equal to that found after the operation; that the quality and quantity of the principles is the same; and that there are only changes and modifications.

Upon this principle the whole art of making experiments in chemistry is founded: we must always suppose a true equality between the principles of the body which is examined and those which are obtained on analysis. Thus, since must of grapes gives carbonic acid gas and alcohol, I may say that *must of grapes = carbonic acid + alcohol*.[15] It follows that we may determine by two different ways what takes place in vinous fermentation first, by determining the nature and principles of fermentable bodies, and second, by observing the products which result from fermentation, and it is evident that the information obtained from one leads to accurate conclusions concerning the nature of the other.

Louis Bernard Guyton de Morveau

(1737-1816)

THE new chemistry of Antoine Lavoisier made possible and indeed imperative a new and rational nomenclature. Its development was due primarily to the efforts of Louis Bernard Guyton de Morveau, one of the early converts of Lavoisier. In 1782 he published his first concepts of a new nomenclature, "Memoir on Chemical Names, the Necessity for Perfecting the System, the Rules for Attaining it, Followed by a Table of a Chemical Nomenclature."[1] This paper put forth the need of a reformed nomenclature and laid down rules for such a change. At the time of this publication Guyton de Morveau was still an adherent of the phlogiston theory, and the phlogistonists, seeing no need for a change, received his ideas coldly. Lavoisier, however, with his insight into chemical theory, saw the need of a new nomenclature in his new antiphlogistic chemistry. He soon con-

---

[15] [This is one of the beginnings of the modern chemical equation.]

[1] Rozier, *Observations sur la physique*, **19**: 370–382 (1782).

vinced de Morveau of the truth of his system, and they entered into collaboration with C. L. Berthollet and A. F. de Fourcroy. The first result of their combined efforts was a memoir read by Lavoisier at the Academy on April 18, 1787. This was essentially an outline of their proposals. It was published with several other papers in 1787 in a volume entitled, "Méthode de nomenclature chimique."[2] The paper by Lavoisier is followed by a memoir upon the development of the principles of nomenclature by de Morveau, which was read before the Academy on May 2, 1787; a memoir by de Fourcroy explaining the tables of nomenclature; appendices with the names of some compounds; a directory of the new nomenclature; and finally the symbols adapted by Hassenfratz and Adet, which never came into wide use. The work is the most important milestone in the development of chemical nomenclature.

[2] "Méthode de Nomenclature, Proposée par MM. de Morveau, Lavoisier, Bertholet, & de Fourcroy. On y a joint Un noveau Système de Caractères Chimiques, adaptés à cette Nomenclature, par MM. Hassenfratz & Adet," Paris, 1787. The second and last edition is very rare. It has a new title but has the same text, with the exception that the two final memoirs by Hassenfratz and Adet and the tables on copper are lacking. "Nomenclature Chimique, ou Synonymie ancienne et moderne, pour servir à l'Intelligence des Autheurs, Nouvelle Édition, à laquelle on a joint differens Mémoires et Rapports de MM. Lavoisier, Fourcroy, Morveau, Cadet, Baumé, d'Arcet et Sage, sur la Necessite de réformer et de perfectionner la Nomenclature," Paris, 1789. The first English translation of the first French edition appeared in 1788, and it is the source of the second citation: "Method of Chemical Nomenclature, proposed by Messrs. de Morveau, Lavoisier, Bertholet, and de Fourcroy, with a New System of Chymical Characters, adapted to the Nomenclature of Mess. Hassenfratz and Adet, translated, and the New Chymical Names adapted to the Genius of the English Language, by James St. John, M.D.," London, 1788. The second English edition is a translation of the second French edition. Its translator, George Pearson, was one of the first English disciples of Lavoisier. In his edition he used the term *nitrogen* (from Chaptal) instead of Lavoisier's term *azote*. "A Translation of the Table of chemical nomenclature proposed by de Guyton, formerly de Morveau, Lavoisier, Bertholet, and de Fourcroy; with Additions and Alterations: to which are prefixed an Explanation of the Terms, and some Observations on the New System of Chemistry," London, 1794. A second edition of the Pearson translation was published in 1799: "Translation of the Table of Chemical Nomenclature, proposed by de Guyton, formerly de Morveau, Lavoisier, Bertholet, and de Fourcroy, with Explanations, Additions, and Alterations, also Tables of Single Elective Attractions, Tables of Chemical Symbols, Tables of the precise forces of Chemical Attractions, and Schemes and Explanations of Cases of single and double Elective Attractions, 2nd Edition, enlarged," London, 1799. A tabular presentation was made in America by Lyman Spalding, who was first to suggest the idea of a U. S. Pharmacopoeia. "A New Nomenclature of Chemistry proposed by Messrs. De Morveau, Lavoisier, Berthollet and Fourcroy, with Additions and Improvements, by Lyman Spalding, M.B. Lecturer in Chemistry in Dartmouth University. Hanover, (N.H.) Printed by Moses Davis," 1799. A facsimile reprint of this work has been made. "A New Nomenclature of Chemistry by Lyman Spalding, M.B.," Reprint of the Hanover, N.H. ed. of 1799. By the American Pharmaceutical Association, Washington, D.C. Samuel L. Mitchill published, in 1801, an essay on the nomenclature of the new chemistry, which was essentially a translation of part of the original French work. "Synopsis of Chemical Nomenclature and Arrangement," New York, 1801.

The following citation is a translation of Morveau's rules for the establishment of a new nomenclature as they appeared in the paper of 1782. The explanatory text has been omitted.

First Principle. A phrase is not a name; chemicals and chemical products should have names which denominate them on all occasions, without recourse to circumlocutions.

Second Principle. Denominations should, as far as possible, conform to the nature of things.

(Corollaries) Firstly, the substantive name preferably belongs to the simplest object, to the entire, unaltered object, and the expression which modifies it and makes it specific should be placed as an epithet, or in a similar manner.

Secondly, the denomination of a chemical compound is only clear and exact in as much as it recalls the constituent parts by names conforming to their nature.

Thirdly, the names of discoverers which cannot conform with any things, either individual or generic, should be forbidden from all important nomenclature.

Third Principle. When we have no certain understanding of the character which ought chiefly to determine the denomination, a name which expresses nothing is preferable to one which may express a false idea.

Fourth Principle. In choosing new denominations, those having roots from the most widespread dead languages should be preferred in order that the word may easily be recalled by the sense and the sense by the word.

Fifth Principle. Denominations should be matched with care with regard to the genius of the language for which they are formed.

The extract below is taken from the memoir by Guyton de Morveau in the James St. John translation (pages 19 to 38) of the "Méthode de nomenclature chimique."

The principles of which the general exposition was contained in the memoir of Mr. Lavoisier, without doubt are sufficient to justify our design of reforming the chymical nomenclature; these principles have appeared to us to carry with them such conviction as cannot fail to acquire universal approbation, after which it would seem that we had nothing more to do but present to the Academy the result of our common labor, or the synopsis formed according to those principles: but we were of opinion that it was incumbent on us to give an account to the Academy of the reasons which have directed us, and even thereby to acquire information to determine us in the choice of the principal denominations: that it especially was of importance to the success of the undertaking, to surmount the difficulties of retaining and hearing the new denominations, by reducing to a single

sheet the entire system, containing all the necessary examples for the formation of compound names; in fine, that it was necessary to add to it the
latin version of the new nomenclature, thereby to demonstrate, how this
system when once adopted would become agreeable to every idiom, and to

MÉTHODE

DE

NOMENCLATURE

CHIMIQUE,

Propofée par MM. DE MORVEAU,
LAVOISIER, BERTHOLET,
& DE FOURCROY.

ON Y A JOINT

Un nouveau Syftême de Caractères Chimiques, adaptés à cette Nomenclature,
par MM. HASSENFRATZ & ADET.

A PARIS,

Chez CUCHET, Libraire, rue & hôtel Serpente.

M. DCC. LXXXVII.

Sous le Privilége de l'Académie des Sciences.

Title page of first edition of "Méthode de nomenclature chimique," Paris, 1787.

contribute as much as possible to the regulation of that uniformity of
language which is so essentially necessary to the communication of discoveries and to the progress of the science.

Such are the subjects of the present memoir, which shall be no more than the expression of the unanimous wish, and the result of all the discussions and conferences which we have had upon the subject. When I published an essay on the chymical nomenclature in the Journal de Physique for the month of May 1782, I did not think that the simple merit of having perceived the necessity of correcting the nomenclature, would at this day have procured me the satisfaction of being occupied with some of the members of the Academy, of being charged by them to present the plan, and to be able to gain that kind attention which the Academy has always been pleased to shew.

In the order which we have proposed to ourselves, the simple substances, that is to say, such as chymists to the present time have not been able to decompose, ought chiefly to fix our attention, because the denominations of bodies which by exact analysis can be reduced to their elements, are properly expressed by the re-union of the names of those same principles.

The substances which we have not as yet been able to decompose may be divided into five classes.

The *first class* contains the principles which without presenting any remarkable analogy with each other, have notwithstanding one thing in common, that is to say, that they appear to approach the nearest to a state of simplicity, which makes them resist all farther analysis, and at the same time renders them so active in their combinations.

The *second* class includes all the acidifiable bases or radical principles of the acids.

In the *third* we place all the substances whose remarkable characteristic is to appear in a metallic form.

The *fourth* contains all the different earths.

And the *fifth* is occupied by the alkalies.

After these five classes we shall indicate in an *appendix* the more compound bodies, which, combining as simple substances or without undergoing any sensible decomposition, have appeared to us worthy of occupying a place in the methodical nomenclature for the completion of the system.

We shall here give some general notions of each of these classes.

FIRST SECTION

Of the Substances Which Approach Nearest to a State of Simplicity

The substances of the first class are five in number; *light, matter of heat, dephlogisticated or vital air, inflammable gas,* and *phlogisticated air;* this last shall be placed in the nomenclature among the acidifiable bases, because it is really the basis of nitrous acid; but it is evident that it also possesses properties of a different nature, which induce us to place it in this class.

Light and heat appear in many circumstances to be productive of the same effects; but as our knowledge is not perfect enough to be able to determine their identity or their difference, we have preserved for each its particular name: we have supposed that we ought to distinguish heat only, which is generally thought to be a sensation produced by a material principle, and we have expressed this latter by the word *caloric*. Thus we shall say that the caloric passed from one body into another without producing a sensible heat, or that the caloric produced heat, &c. This manner of expression will be as clear, and will cause less embarrassment in discourse than that of *the matter of heat*, which the necessity of speaking so as to be understood has for some time past introduced.

When the appellation of dephlogisticated air was changed into that of vital air, a choice more agreeable to reason was made, by substituting to an expression founded upon mere hypothesis, a term derived from one of the most remarkable properties of that substance, and which is so essentially characteristic of it that one should never hesitate to use it whenever it be necessary to indicate simply that portion of the atmospherical air which maintains respiration and combustion; but it is at present well demonstrated that this portion of the atmospherical fluid is not always in the state of air or gas, that it is decomposed in a great many operations, and loses, at least in part, the light and caloric which are what principally constitute it vital air; this substance should be considered and represented in that state of its greatest simplicity; the logic of the nomenclature requires even that it be named the first, that the word which would recall the idea become the model for the denominations of its compounds. We have acted agreeable to these conditions by adopting the word *oxygen*, deriving it as Mr. Lavoisier proposed, from the Greek words ὀξύς *acid*, and γείνομαι *I beget*, on account of the property of this principle, the basis of vital air, to change a great many of the substances with which it unites into the state of acid, or rather because it appears to be a principle necessary to acidity. We shall therefore say that vital air is oxygen gas, and that oxygen unites with sulphur, and with phosphorus during their combustion, and to metals in their calcination, &c. and this language will be at the same time both exact and perspicuous.

On applying the same principles to the aeriform substance called inflammable gas, the necessity of having a more explicit appellation is evident at the first view; it is true that this fluid is capable of being consumed, but this property does not exclusively belong to it, notwithstanding that it is the only substance which produces water by its combustion with oxygen gas. This is the property which appeared to us to be the most worthy of affording a name, not for the gas itself, which is a composition, but for the more fixed principle which constitutes the basis, and we have therefore called it *hydrogen*, from ὕδωρ *water* and γείνομαι *I beget;* experiments having proved that water is nothing but oxygenated hydrogen, or the immediate production of the combustion of oxygen gas with hydrogen gas, deprived of the light and caloric which disengage during the combustion.

The denomination of *phlogisticated air* has been abandoned by the greater number of chymists; who thought that it expressed more than it ought, even a long time before it was known to express an error. It is at present well known that this fluid, which makes so considerable a part of the atmospherical air, is not vitiated vital air; that it has nothing in common with respirable air but its state of elastic fluidity, which is caused by its union with caloric: in short, that in losing this state of gas it becomes an element proper to many combinations. As there are several proofs of its being a distinct substance, a particular name for it was necessary, and in searching for one we endeavoured to avoid at the same time the inconvenience of one of those perfectly insignificant words which are not connected with any known idea, and which offer no hold to the memory, and the inconvenience perhaps the more considerable of prematurely affirming what has been only foreseen.

It results from some synthetical experiments made by the Hon. Mr. Cavendish, and confirmed by a great number of analyses, that this principle is a component part of the nitrous acid. Mr. Berthollet has proved its existence in the volatile alkali, and in animal substances; it is probable that the fixed alkali also contains it, and from this it appears to deserve the appellation of alkali-gen, as was proposed by Mr. de Fourcroy. But the analysis of these compositions is not sufficiently advanced to determine positively the manner of existence of this principle in those different substances, and from thence to attribute to it a constant and uniform property; besides, it was not possible by a single word to express the double property of forming the radical of a certain acid, and assisting in the production of an alkali; there did not appear any reasons for considering the latter of these properties in preference to the former, and by admitting the one in a manner to exclude the other. In this situation we thought it were the better way to derive the denomination from its other property, which it manifests in a very great degree, viz. not to maintain the existence of animals, to be really non-vital; in short to be so in a more considerable respect than the hepatic and acid gases, which do not like it constitute an essential part of the atmospherical mass, and therefore we have denominated it *azot* from the Greek privative a and ζωή *life*. After this it may not appear difficult to remember that the air which we breathe is a composition of oxygen gas and azotic gas.

SECOND SECTION

Of the Acidifiable Bases or Radical Principles of the Acids

The class of the substances whose principle characteristic is to be capable of being transformed into the state of acid is much more extensive; but at the same time it has more uniformity, and the considering of a few substances and the following of them in their various compositions, is sufficient to give a perfect idea of all this part of the nomenclature.

In this class are to be distinguished the acids whose acidifiable bases are known, and the acids whose acidifiable bases have not as yet been separated by chymical process from the general acidifying principle.

The acidifiable bases that are known are, *azot*, the basis of the nitrous acid, which we have mentioned in the preceding section, *charcoal*, *sulphur*, and *phosphorus*. On these bases we have established the method of naming, because their combinations are the most numerous, the most familiar to us, and the most easy to follow; as to the others, the base of the marine acid, of the acid of borax, of the acid of vinegar, &c. &c. we have only expressed the simple substance of each acid which modifies the oxygen, by the expression of acidifiable base, or, for more conciseness, *radical* of the acid; thereby to continue the same analogy, and to be able to consider each of these substances in order and in an abridged manner, without hazarding any thing on their essential properties, until they shall have been discovered and proved by decisive experiments. It is probable that many of these acids have compound bases, or that they differ from one another merely by the diversity of proportion of the same principles: when their elements and the order of their descent shall be discovered by exact analyses, it will without doubt be necessary to reduce them to their proper situations, but nevertheless it therefore should not be thought useless to study their properties and attractions in their present compound state, and therefore we cannot avoid giving them a place in the system of our nomenclature.

Those things being premised, let us take for example *sulphur*, or in other words the acidifiable base of the vitriolic acid, which is the third in the class; the numerous productions of its combinations, known this long time past, will enable us to explain the rules which we have formed, and follow the application in the most advantageous manner, to shew the progress of the compositions and the general system of the table.

Sulphur by combining with oxygen produces an acid: it is evident that to preserve the idea of this oxygen, and to express clearly the first degree of composition, the name of the acid should be derived from the name of its base; but this acid presents itself in two states of saturation, and therefore manifests different properties. That they should not be confounded, a name ought to be given to each of these states, which always retaining its primitive root, would yet express this difference: and the same should be done for the salts formed by these two acids; after this the other direct combinations of sulphur with the alkalies, the earths, and the metals, should be considered: the five different states of the same principle are expressed by as many different terminations adapted to the same original word, in the manner that appeared to us least unharmonious to the ear.

Sulphur*ic* acid signifies sulphur as much as possible saturated with oxygen; which composition was formerly called vitriolic acid.

Sulphur*eous* acid means sulphur united to a less quantity of oxygen; which before was called volatile sulphureous vitriolic acid, or phlogisticated vitriolic acid.

Sulph*at* is the general name for all the salts formed by the sulphuric acid.

Sulph*ite* signifies the salts formed by the sulphureous acid.

Sulph*uret* denominates all the combinations of sulphur not advanced to the state of acid, and regularly displaces the improper and absurd appellations of liver of sulphur, hepar, pyrite, &c.

Every one must perceive, at the first glance, all the advantages of such a nomenclature, which at the same time that it indicates the different substances, defines them, points out their constituent principles, classes them in their order of composition, and indicates in a manner, even the proportions which diversify their properties.

Some persons perhaps may be astonished that we should include in this reformation the words vitriolic acid and vitriol, which custom appears to have rendered sacred; in reality, it is the most considerable innovation, and the only one of the kind to be found in the whole nomenclature: we have felt all the force of the objection, we have considered it for a long time, and we would not have hesitated to suffer these words, although improper, to remain, through respect for established custom, if we were to consider them only in respect to themselves; but it was necessary to form a system for the entire class of acids, a class the most numerous and important; and surely no person will reproach us for not having sacrificed all the advantages of this method to the preservation of the word *vitriol*. Precisely, it is because the acid formed by sulphur is that which is the most frequently employed, which enters into the greater number of compositions, and especially because it is that which learners first begin to study, that we judged it the more necessary to be submitted to the rigorous application of our rules, thereby that it might serve to facilitate the study of the other acids by an agreeable conformity. Instead of creating a new word, we had only to modify by a new termination the word sulphur, which has been for a long time admitted by every chymist. We have likewise considered that the words *vitriolic acid, vitriol of iron,* and *vitriol of zink*, are not used by artists and tradesmen, but in their place they make use of the expressions of *spirit of sulphur, green copperas, white copperas,* &c. and we take it for granted that the chymists, who already have abandoned these latter terms, will at present voluntarily surrender a few terms to render the language of chymistry clear and uniform.

As to the other acids, we had much less to do in reducing their appellations to our systematical rules, as is evident from the words *nitrous acid, tartareous acid, phosphoric acid,* &c.

There is no substance whatever which has received so many different appellations as the gas which Dr. Black has called *fixed air;* at the same time expressly reserving the liberty of changing the denomination, which he confessed was improperly applied. The disagreement of the chymists of every country, gives us, without doubt, a more perfect liberty, because it shews the necessity of motives being presented capable of making them all unanimous: and we have made use of that liberty according to our principles. As fixed air has been perceived to be produced by the direct combination of *charcoal* with *vital air,* by the assistance of combustion, the name of this gazeous acid can no longer be arbitrary, but necessarily must be derived from its radical, which is the pure carbonic matter; therefore it is *carbonic acid,* and its compositions with different bases are *carbonats;* and, for the sake of greater precision in the denomination of this radical, by distinguishing it from charcoal, according to the vulgar acceptation, in idea to isolate it from the small quantity of foreign matter which it generally contains, and which constitutes the ashes, we adapt to it the modified name of *carbon,* which indicates the pure and essential principle of charcoal, and which has the advantage of expressing it by a single word, so as to prevent all equivocation.

Plumbago, which is only iron united to charcoal, shall take the appellation of *carburet* of iron, according to the established analogy.

Muriatic acid, derived from the latin *muria, muriaticum,* has already taken the place of *marine acid* in the writings of several chymists; but it is well known that it is an acid of a particular nature, because it imbibes an excess of oxygen, and because in this state its acidity seems rather to decrease than to augment, which perhaps is occasioned by the oxygen's retaining in that combination a greater quantity of caloric. Whatever be the cause of this phenomenon, it was necessary that it should have a denomination appropriated to so particular a property, which to the present time has very falsely been expressed by the term *dephlogisticated marine acid.* The appellations of *oxygenated muriatic acid,* and *oxygenated muriats,* have appeared to us more simple and more conformable to our intention of not expressing any more than the most positive facts. Likewise according to this rule, we have formed the names of all the other combinations of the muriatic acid: thus corrosive sublimate, becomes *corrosive mercurial muriat;* the mercurius dulcis, *mild mercurial muriat;* the salt produced by the dissolution of tin in this acid, *muriat of tin;* the butter of tin, *sublimated muriat of tin;* Libavius's liquor, *smoking muriat of tin,* &c.

Analogy induces us to think that the muriatic acid has an acidifiable base, as well as the carbonic, sulphuric, and phosphoric acids, which like the bases of these latter, serves to give a distinct and particular property to the produce of a combination of oxygen. We could not express this substance otherwise than by the name muriatic *radical* or muriatic radical principle; in fine, that a name should not be given to an unknown substance, and that the expression should be limited to the simple property with which we are acquainted, and which is to produce this acid. We have had the same caution in respect to all the other acids with which we are not yet well acquainted, some of whose bases will probably be discovered in the substances which we have already named. We are obliged to include in this class even the bases of the vegetable and animal acids, of which we have not as yet any exact analysis, notwithstanding the facility with which they are reduced to their elements.

The nature of the acidifiable base being independent of the proportion in which it be united to the oxygen, it is evident that the sulphur is at the same time *sulphuric* radical, and *sulphureous* radical: but it was also necessary to render that expression uniform for all the acids; and we have gone no farther than the first termination, which signifies the most complete saturation of the acidifiable base. Thus we say *boracic radical,* and even *tartaric radical,* &c. &c. although we are acquainted only with the tartareous acid, which is the tartaric radical united to a very small portion of oxygen, if we can judge from all that has as yet been observed in the phenomena of its combustion.

The choice of the one or of the other of these terminations became very important to indicate in the combinations of the acids themselves, the different degrees of saturation. As soon as they were known we have not hesitated to make the authority of the rule prevail over that of custom, by naming for example, *nitric acid* that in which the azot is impregnated with all the oxygen it is capable of containing, and reserving the appellation of *nitrous acid* for that much weaker acid where the same base is united to a much less quantity of oxygen.

According to this analogy, phlogisticated or volatile phosphoric acid becomes *phosphorus acid;* the experiments of Mr. Berthollet upon radical vinegar having demonstrated that it was no more than the common vinegar saturated with oxygen, we thought proper to distinguish the *acetic acid,* and the *acetous acid.* This distinction being once established, has afforded us the *nitrats* and *nitrites,* the *phosphats* and *phosphites,* the *acetats,* and *acetites,* as has been shewn in the denomination of the salts formed by the acid of sulphur: the word *nitre* is the only exception, which, through respect to custom, we have retained as synonimous with *nitrat of potash.*

As to the other acids which have not as yet been obtained in two states of saturation with oxygen, and which perhaps are susceptible of only the one or the other, we ought to premise, that having only very imperfect conjectures from which to draw our choice of the termination appropriated to either of these states, we have not had, in general, any other rule than the shuning of such denominations as may sound discordant to the ear, and to deviate as little as possible from the path marked out by custom: which reasons have appeared sufficient to determine us, until new discoveries shall be made to indicate the true class of those acids, when it will be time to submit these considerations to the more real interest of the science. Moreover, we have always retained that comparative analogy which is indicated by terminations corresponsive to the two states of the acids and of the salts which they form. Therefore the *benzoic acid* must produce, *benzoats;* the *gallic acid, gallats;* the *tartareous acid, tartrites,* &c.

The acids which are obtained by distillation, from tartar, from sugar, from wood, &c. have been called by the chymists empyreumatic spirits: it has appeared to us to be necessary to include this property in their denominations; but to render the expression more commodious, we have reduced it to the dyssylllable *pyro.* In this manner the empyreumatic spirit of tartar becomes *pyro-tartareous acid,* and the salts *pyro-tartrites;* the empyreumatic spirit of wood, *pyroligneous acid,* and the salts *pyro-lignites,* &c.

As we have seen the radical of one acid present itself in different states of saturation with oxygen, in like manner many other acids are capable of uniting to the same base in different proportions; some of them have the property of retaining several bases at the same time; from which are produced, 1. salts with excess of acid, 2. salts with excess of base, and, 3. triple or sur-compound salts. Our method requires that all these salts be clearly distinguished, and we think that we have effected it in the most simple manner: for *the first* by adding the epithet *acidulous* to their names; for *the second*, by employing the word *sursaturated*, and sometimes only by preserving the word in common use; and for *the last*, by specifying both the bases and as much as possible adjectively expressing that of the base to avoid the inelegant repetition of the preposition *of.*

Cream of tartar is to be called.......	*Acidulous tartrite of potash.*
Salt of sorrel......................	*Acidulous oxalat of potash.*
Common borax....................	*Borat sur-saturated with soda,* or simply *borax*
Pearly salt........................	*Phosphat sur-saturated with soda.*
Antimoniated vegetable salt.........	*Tartrite of potash containing antimony.*
Salt of correl containing copper......	*Cuprious oxalat of potash.*

And in the same manner for all the other sur-compounds, the names of which may be easily understood from their conformity with these examples.

It would be superfluous to say more on the methodical nomenclature of the acidifiable bases or radicals of the acids and the productions of their combinations; we proceed to the other sections of the nomenclature, on which we shall be less particular, what has preceded serving to elucidate what is to follow.

Claude Louis Berthollet

(1748–1822)

THE concept of elective affinity as put foward by Geoffroy was widely accepted throughout the eighteenth century. Its inadequacy was in part recognized by Baumé, who pointed out that affinity changes with temperature and that two sets of tables were necessary in expressing affinities—one for reactions in solutions at room temperature and another at elevated temperatures. Bergman constructed such tables and further showed that it was sometimes necessary to add an excess of one substance in order to bring a reaction to completion. However, it remained for Claude Louis Berthollet, near the beginning of the ninteenth century, to perceive that affinity was not an absolute force but a relative one and that other factors besides affinity, such as solubility and volatility, play an important part in determining the course of chemical reactions. He was the first to state clearly the effect of "mass" and to realize the reversible nature of chemical reactions.

Berthollet's contributions to industrial chemistry were numerous. For a period he held the official position of director of the dyeing industry in France, and it was this industry which his researches benefited most. He introduced chlorine as a bleaching agent and performed a notable service by writing his "Éléments de l'art de la teinture," Paris, 1791. As a member of the committee for the revision of chemical nomenclature he collaborated with Guyton de Morveau, Lavoisier, and Fourcroy.

Berthollet's chief contribution to chemistry lay in his concepts of affinity. While in Egypt he presented his first paper on this subject to the Institut d'Égypte, which he had formed with his colleagues while on the Napoleonic expedition. This was published as a volume entitled "Recherches sur les lois de l'affinité," Paris, 1801. This work was expanded in 1803 in his "Essai de statique chimique."[1]

[1] "Essai de Statique Chimique, par C. L. Berthollet, Membre du Senat Conservateur, de l'Institut, ... De l'Imprimerie de Demonville et Soeurs. A Paris, Rue de Thionville, No. 116, chez Firmin Didot, Libraire pour les Mathematiques, l'Architecture, la Marine, et les Editions Stereotypes. An XI—1803," 2 vols.

The only English translation was made by R. Lambert: "Essay on Chemical Statics,

In these works Berthollet modified Geoffroy's and Bergman's fundamental principles of affinity and laid the foundation of the present understanding of the causes of chemical reactions. Unfortunately, Berthollet drew incorrect conclusions from some of his experiments, holding that the composition of certain compounds may vary within small limits. This error was quickly noted by Proust, who, in a series of researches continued until about 1808, established the law of definite proportions.

Berthollet's first work was translated into English by M. Farrell and published in Baltimore in 1804 as "Researches into the Laws of Chemical Affinity." From this translation the following citation is taken.[2]

ARTICLE I.

Object of This Treatise.

1. *A theory* of chemical affinities solidly established, and serving as the basis for the explanation of all chemical questions, ought to be a collection of, or contain, all the principles from which the causes of chemical phenomena can proceed, in every possible variety of circumstance; because observation has proved, that all these phenomena are only the various effects of that affinity, to which all the various chemical powers of bodies may be attributed.

2. It cannot be expected that a work of this nature should have attained the utmost degree of perfection within the short space of time which has elapsed since chemistry has become regularly and philosophically progressive.

Bergman has treated this subject, and with more success than any other author. His work on elective affinity is useful and meritorious, not alone by the speculations which it contains on the nature of chemical affinities, on the opposition and concurrence of their various actions, and on the circumstances which can modify or disguise these actions; but still further, by the great number of chemical facts which it contains: and although observations have been made and multiplied since that great chemist wrote, and although some very learned treatises have been published on affinity since that time; yet his doctrine is that generally adopted. I have been determined by that consideration, to make his work the basis of the principal part of the discussions which follow.

3. Let us suppose, says Bergman, the substance A completely saturated with the substance C, and that the combination be termed AC; if the addition of another substance, B, to this combination, removes C, there will result the combination AB, instead of AC. He prescribes then, for

---

with copious explanatory Notes and Appendix on Vegetable and Animal Substances," London, 1804.

[2] Also translated in Ostwald's *Klassiker*, No. 74, "Untersuchungen über die Gesetzt der Verwandtschaft. 1801. Herausgegeben von W. Ostwald," Leipzig, 1896.

determining the elective affinity of two substances, to try if one of them can remove the other from its combination with a third, and *vice versa*. He takes it for granted, that that body which has removed another from its combination, cannot, in like manner, be expelled by that other, and that both experiments will concur to prove that the first has a greater elective affinity than the second. He adds at the same time, that it may be necessary to employ six times as much of the decomposing substance as would be necessary to saturate immediately the substance with which it tends to combine.

4. The doctrine of Bergman is founded entirely on the supposition that elective affinity is an invariable force, and of such a nature, that a body which expels another from its combination, cannot possibly be separated from the same by the body which it eliminated. Such was the certainty with which elective affinity has been considered as an uniform force, that celebrated chemists have endeavoured to represent by numbers, the comparative elective affinities of different substances, independently of any difference in the proportion of their quantities.

5. It is my purpose to prove in the following sheets, that elective affinity, in general, does not act as a determinate force, by which one body separates completely another from a combination; but that, in all the compositions and decompositions produced by elective affinity, there takes place a partition of the base, or subject of the combination, between the two bodies whose actions are opposed; and that the proportions of this partition are determined, not solely by the difference of energy in the affinities, but also by the difference of the quantities of the bodies; so that an excess of quantity of the body whose affinity is the weaker, compensates for the weakness of the affinity.

If I can prove that a weaker degree of affinity can be compensated by an increase of quantity, it will follow, that the action of any body is proportionate to the quantity of it which is necessary to produce a certain degree of saturation. This quantity, which is the measure of the capacity of saturation of different bodies, I shall call *mass*.

Hence it follows, that in estimating the comparative affinities of bodies, their absolute weights are to be considered, and ought to be equal; but in comparing their actions, which depend on their affinities and mutual proportions, the mass of each is to be considered.

6. I shall prove, therefore, in resuming the supposition of No. 3, that, in opposing the body A to the combination BC, the combination AC can never take place; but that the body C will be divided between the bodies A and B, proportionally to the affinity and quantity of each; that is, to their respective masses.

For the examples and proofs to be used in the following discussion, I shall refer principally to the action of acids and alkalies, comprising under the latter denomination, the earths which are endued with alkaline properties; because their great power and activity annihilates the influence of minute incidental causes, and because they frequently produce degrees of saturation which may be compared, and afford results that can be appreciated with facility. But the conclusions which I shall draw from their properties, will be applicable to all combinations in general. I shall adduce examples, to prove that the principle which I lay down, is applicable to the chemical action of all bodies.

After having proved by direct experiments that the chemical action of bodies whose powers are opposite, does not depend upon their affinity exclusively, but also on their quantity; I shall select observations on different kinds of combinations, which will confirm this principle, and prove its universality. I shall, in the next place, examine the circumstances by which this principle is modified, or those affections of bodies which favour, or impede, their chemical action, and which alter their proportions in the combinations which they are capable of forming: I shall apply the result of these considerations to compound affinities, and to those of compound bodies: I shall, finally, endeavour to point out, and fix the basis, on which ought to be established the general and particular theories of chemical phenomena.

ARTICLE II.

EXPERIMENTS WHICH PROVE THAT IN ELECTIVE AFFINITIES, THE BODIES WHOSE POWERS ARE OPPOSED, DIVIDE BETWEEN THEM THE BODY WHICH IS THE SUBJECT OF THE COMBINATION.

1. I have kept an equal quantity of potash, and sulphate of barytes, in a small quantity of boiling water. The potash had been prepared by alcohol, and contained no carbonic acid: the same served for the following experiments. The operation was performed in a retort, and consequently in communication with the air; and it was continued until the mixture was desiccated: the residue was washed with alcohol, which dissolved the potash, and after that with water, which also produced an alkaline solution, the alkali of which I saturated with acetic acid; after which, by evaporation, the solution yielded crystals, possessing all the characters and qualities of the sulphate of potash. Whence it appears, that the sulphate of barytes was partially decomposed by the potash, and that the sulphuric acid was divided between the two bases.

2. The sulphate of potash having been submitted to a similar experiment with an equal weight of lime, and the dried residue having been treated with alcohol, an alkaline solution was produced; and a part of the residue dissolved in water, and yielded a small quantity of sulphate of lime along with the sulphate of potash.

3. One part of the oxalate of lime, and two of potash, having been kept

in ebullition in a small quantity of water until the water was totally evaporated, and washed afterwards with a sufficient quantity of alcohol, to dissolve the potash; the residue, treated with water, and evaporated, yielded crystals, bearing all the characters of the oxalate of potash.

4. One part of oxalate of lime was boiled to desiccation in two of nitric acid; a part of the residue dissolved in alcohol, which solution was precipitated abundantly by oxalic acid; a proof that nitrate of lime had been formed in the operation, and dissolved by the alcohol.

5. One part of phosphate of lime, and two of potash, were boiled together to desiccation in a small quantity of water. The alkaline parts were separated from the residue by alcohol, and the remaining part treated with water; the evaporation of which, yielded crystals of phosphate of potash. The liquid which remained after this desiccation, contained still a great excess of alkali; after the saturation of which by nitric acid, an abundant precipitate was produced, by a solution of lime and barytes; a proof of its having still contained a considerable quantity of the phosphate of potash, to the decomposition of which, the formation of the phosphates of lime and of barytes was due.

6. Equal weights of potash, and of carbonate of lime, finely pulverized, were boiled in a small quantity of water, which, after being filtered and rendered transparent, effervesced strongly with acids; and the residue, after evaporation, having been treated with alcohol, in order to dissolve the alkali, furnished a substance that had all the qualities and characters of the carbonate of potash.

7. Having boiled to desiccation equal quantities of soda, and of sulphate of potash, in a large quantity of water, and having treated the residue with alcohol, and afterwards with water, the alkali separated by the alcohol, was saturated with sulphuric acid, and the evaporation of the mixture produced sulphate of soda and potash. The solution of the residue in water, gave, by evaporation, not only a sulphate of potash, but also a considerable quantity of crystallized sulphate of soda.

8. It is evident, from the preceding experiments, that the bases which are supposed to form the strongest combinations with the acids, may be separated from them by others, whose affinities are supposed to be weaker, and that the acid divides itself between the two bases. It also appears, that acids may be partially separated from their bases by other acids, whose affinities were supposed to be weaker; in which case, the base is divided between the two acids.

If but a small quantity of the decomposing substance be employed, the effect will not be perceptible; but if, on the contrary, a large quantity be employed, as for instance: if I had treated the sulphate of barytes successively with additional quantities of potash, and removed, by repeated washing, the disengaged barytes, I should have ultimately decomposed the sulphate of barytes almost entirely. The greater then the relative quantity of the decomposing substance, the greater will be the effect produced.

Whence it appears, as remarked by Bergman, that if six times as much of the decomposing substance be employed as is necessary to saturate the base, a decomposition will be effected, which may be considered as total; because the antagonist substance retains so small a part of that with which it was combined, that it may escape the observer's notice, and be considered as an evanescent quantity. But if Bergman had carefully made the contrary experiment, as he recommends, he would have found that a similar decomposition could be produced by that means, as is evinced by the experiments just related.

In the experiment, No. 4, the nitric acid combined itself to a part of the lime of the oxalate of lime, and the oxalic acid retained the other; but after having separated the two combinations, another portion of oxalic acid, the energy of which was not diminished by any degree of saturation, was added to the nitrate of lime that had been formed, and a precipitation was effected, the lime sharing itself again between the two acids.

In the experiment, No. 5, the phosphoric acid divided itself between the lime and potash; and after the removal of the excess of potash, and the addition of the solutions of lime and barytes, the phosphoric acid was again divided between the three substances.

9. It results then from the preceding experiments, many circumstances of which I shall examine in the sequel, that when a substance acts on a combination, the subject of combination divides itself between the two others, not only in proportion to the energy of their respective affinities, but also in proportion to their quantities. The two substances which act on the combination ought to be considered as two antagonist forces, which act in opposition while they act on, and share between them the subject of the combination in proportion to the intensity of their action; which intensity depends on the quantity of the substance, and on the energy of the affinity: so that the effect increases or diminishes according as the quantity increases or diminishes. It has been already remarked, Art. I. No. 5, that the absolute weight of any body, multiplied by the degree of its affinity, constitutes its mass.

10. It follows as a consequence of the preceding observations, that the action of a substance which tends to decompose a combination, diminishes in proportion as its saturation advances; for this substance may, in such case, be considered as composed of two parts, one of which is saturated, and the other free. The former may be considered as inert, and as unconnected with the latter, the quantity of which diminishes according as the saturation advances; whilst, on the contrary, the action of that which has been eliminated, increases in proportion to the augmentation of its

quantity, until the equilibrium of the contending forces ends the operation, and limits the effect.

11. Another consequence is, that when a substance separates by precipitation, a part of the substance with which it was combined must also be precipitated along with it; because each particle of the precipitated body has yielded to the action of a particle of the precipitating, and the subject of combination must have been divided in the moment of the decomposition, in proportion to the respective masses which have acted. . . .

ARTICLE XV.

Recapitulation.

. . . 3. I have considered all the forces which can, by their concurrence with, or opposition to, the reciprocal affinity of substances acting according to the preceding principle, exert any influence on chemical combinations and phenomena. They are reducible to the following: the action of solvents; or the affinity which they exert in proportion to their quantity; the force of cohesion, which is the effect of the mutual affinity of the parts of a simple or compound substance; elasticity, whether natural or produced by caloric, which ought to be considered as an effect of the affinity of caloric;[3] efflorescence, which may be attributed to an affinity not yet determined, acts only in very rare circumstances; gravitation too exerts some influence, particularly when it produces the compression of elastic fluids; but no inconvenience can result from its being confounded with the force of cohesion.

4. I have endeavoured to find if it were possible to ascertain the relative affinity of two substances by means of a third; and I have observed that, in order to do so, it would be necessary to ascertain in what proportion that third substance would combine with a given quantity of the two former, or rather in what degree they should participate of its action. I have pointed out the insurmountable obstacles which preclude us from ascertaining and determining this participation of action, and the changes of constitution which may follow.

5. As all tables of affinity have been formed on the supposition, that substances are endued with different degrees of affinity, from which originate all the combinations and decompositions that take place, independently of proportion and other circumstances which influence the results, they must give an erroneous idea of the degrees of the chemical action of substances.

6. The very term, *elective affinity* must lead into error, as it supposes the union of the whole of one substance with another, in preference to a

[3] [Heat was at this period generally thought to be a material substance.]

third; whereas there is only a partition of action, which is itself subordinate to other chemical circumstances.

Berthollet developed his ideas in greatest detail and expressed his most controversial theories in his "Essai de statique chimique." The following selections are taken from this work.

The powers which produce chemical phenomena are all derived from the mutual attractions of the molecules of the bodies and have been given the name *affinity*, to distinguish them from astronomical attraction.

It is probable that each is only the same property; but astronomical attraction is exercised only between masses placed at a distance, where the form of the molecules, their intervals, and their particular affections have no influence; its effects, always proportional to the mass and to the inverse of the square of the distance, can be rigorously submitted to calculation: the effects of chemical attraction, or affinity, are on the contrary so altered by the particular conditions, often indeterminate, that a general principle cannot be deduced; but that it is necessary to establish them successively. Only some of the effects can be so separated from other phenomena as to give them the precision of calculation.

Thus then, it is only observations that can establish the chemical properties of the bodies, or the affinities by which they exert a reciprocal action in determined conditions; however, since it is very probable that affinity does not differ in its origin from general attraction, it should equally be subject to the laws which mechanics has determined for the phenomena due to the action of mass, and it is natural to think that the more the principles to which the chemical theories apply have generality, the more they have analogy with those of mechanics; but it is only by observation that they can reach that degree which they are already able to indicate.

The immediate effect of the affinity which a substance exerts is always a combination, so that all the effects which are produced by chemical action are a consequence of the formation of some combination.

All substances which tend to enter in combination act by reason of their affinity and their quantity. These truths are the basis of all chemical observations.

But first, the different tendencies to combination should be considered as forces which lead to a result or which are in part destroyed by their opposition; so that it is necessary to distinguish these forces to reach an explanation of the phenomena which they produce or to compare them with each other.

Second, the chemical action of a substance depends not only on the affinity which belongs to the parts which compose it and the quantity; it depends also on the state in which these parts are found, either by an actual combination which causes a greater or lesser part of their affinity to disappear, or by their dilation or condensation which causes their reciprocal distance to vary: these are the conditions which, by modifying the properties of the elementary parts of a substance, form what I call its *constitution*; to reach an analysis of chemical action it is necessary to know not only each of these conditions but also all the circumstances with which they have some relation.[4] . . .

38. If we consider what is observed in a mutual combination of two antagonistic substances, for example, an acid and an alkali, we find that the acidity diminishes as the amount of alkali increases and a degree of saturation is reached at which the acidity and alkalinity have equally disappeared and become latent; however, if we continue to add alkali, its character reappears and becomes more and more dominant.

We see then, first, that the acidity and alkalinity mutually saturate each other and can become alternately dominant, according to the proportion in which the combination is effected; there is no obstacle, no suspension in the progress of combination and the saturation which accompanies it unless the force of cohesion or elasticity should produce a separation in which the proportions are determined by one of these conditions.

Second, that the acid and alkaline properties diminish according to the degree of saturation which the acid and alkali undergo, so that we once more find in chemical action, which is exerted with the greatest energy, the same character which we have observed in weaker degree to produce solution.

39. Chemists, struck by the fact that they find definite proportions in many combinations, often consider it a general property of combinations that they are composed of definite proportions, so that, according to them, when a neutral salt receives an excess of acid or alkali, the homogeneous substance which results is a solution of neutral salt in a free portion of acid or alkali.

This is a hypothesis which has for a foundation only a distinction between solution and combination, and in which the properties which cause a separation are confused with the affinity which produces combination; but it is necessary to recognize the circumstances which can determine the separation of combinations in a certain state and which thus limit the effects of the general law of affinity.

It is not always at the end of neutralization that separation can occur: the acid tartrate of potassium separates and crystallizes more easily than the neutral tartrate: should we say that it is the latter which is held in solution by the excess acid? I believe I can limit myself for the moment to this example.

40. In consequence of what has been said, it is necessary to distinguish

[4] "Essai de statique chimique," pp. 1–3.

two types of saturation; one is the limit of chemical action which one substance can exert on another in given circumstances: for example, we say that water is saturated with a salt when it no longer dissolves it, although neither the properties of water nor the properties of the salt have undergone saturation; the other is the point at which the antagonistic properties of one substance are disguised by those of another, and there is found in the equilibrium which is produced that state of indifference which we call neutralization; this second saturation is rarely encountered at the same point as the first.

When a combination is formed, its two elements are retained in it by reason of their mutual affinity and by reason of their respective quantities, so that, conforming to the general law of chemical action, if one of the two dominates, the part which is present in excess is retained all the less by the antagonistic substance, so that the excess is more considerable; but as in the neutral state the action of each element on the antagonistic substance is still far from being exhausted, we can see how a neutral salt can undergo the solvent action of water without change in the state of combination; however, when there is a great difference in the action which water exerts on each of the two elements, and when the action which joins them is not very energetic, that of the water can produce considerable changes in combination, as I have especially observed in discussing the action of solvents.

41. The force of cohesion opposes a resistance to the energetic action which produces combinations, as is the fact in solutions; thus, if a combination cannot take place, it is not necessary to conclude that two substances have no point of mutual affinity: the most finely divided alumina cannot be dissolved directly in acetic acid: but if a solution of aluminum sulfate is mixed with the solution of a salt which contains acetic acid, combination takes place and maintains itself: it can be only the force of cohesion which joins the molecules of alumina that opposes the combination in the first case. All acids can hold silica in solution if it has first been dissolved in an alkali; but if the silica molecules are condensed by desiccation, the force of the cohesion which joins them opposes their solution in acids, except fluoric acid.

42. It follows from the preceding that chemical action, stronger as well as weaker, exerts itself by reason of the reciprocal affinity of substances and of the quantities which are found in the sphere of activity, that the action diminishes by reason of saturation, that there is no end point at which the proportions are determined; but that it is in the forces which are opposed that we must seek for the limits of the proportions of the combinations which form, and those of their power; finally, we must distinguish two effects of chemical action, that by which it produces a reciprocal saturation, and that which brings about changes of constitution.[5]

[5] *Ibid.*, pp. 61–65.

Joseph Louis Proust

(1754–1826)

ALMOST since the beginning of chemistry the constancy of composition of pure substances had been quite generally assumed as a fact. It was an axiom which chemists were forced to accept if their analyses were to have any meaning at all, but one whose justification became possible only with the development of accurate quantitative methods of analysis.

The firm establishment of the law of constant proportions came about in part as a result of the work of Berthollet. In his "Recherches sur les lois de l'affinité" (1801) and more especially in his "Essai de statique chimique" (1803), both otherwise important contributions to chemistry, he confused mixtures with pure compounds and erroneously concluded that the composition of compounds may vary within certain limits. The defense of the law of constant proportions was then vigorously taken up by Joseph Louis Proust, a Frenchman, at that time professor of chemistry at Madrid, and there ensued a famous controversy between the two men which, by about the year 1808, brought the general acceptance of Proust's views. In the same year Dalton's "A New System of Chemical Philosophy," containing the atomic theory, was published and the law received a rational basis.

Proust's researches on the law of constant proportions form his chief contribution to chemistry. However, his other work deserves mention. An accomplished experimenter, he was little interested in abstractions and devoted much of his attention to the practical examination of minerals and agricultural products. He studied starch, lichens, camphor, and the preparation of mercury from cinnabar and discovered the substance which was later found to be the amino acid, leucine. Among his most important discoveries was that of glucose, although in this he was preceded by J. T. Lowitz (1757–1804).

The first citation below includes Proust's original statement of the law of constant proportions. It is taken from a paper published in 1799, shortly before the controversy with Berthollet. In one of the many papers arising from the controversy between Proust and Berthollet occurs the passage which forms the second citation. Here Proust shows his clear understanding of the difference between compounds and mixtures.

RESEARCHES ON COPPER[1]

ON CARBONATE OF COPPER

One hundred pounds of copper, dissolved in sulfuric or nitric acids and precipitated by the carbonates of soda or potash, invariably gives 180

[1] *Ann. chim.*, **32**: 26–54 (1799).

pounds of green carbonate.[2] If this quantity be submitted to a gradual
distillation it gives 10 pounds of water, which appears as essential to the
color and composition of this carbonate as the carbonic acid itself, since
this water only passes over successively and conjointly with the acid.
Deprived of these two components the carbonate leaves 125 pounds[3] of
black oxide at the bottom of the retort. This oxide dissolves in nitric acid
with heat without decomposing the same. Likewise it dissolves in oxidized
muriatic acid,[4] from which, then, the oxygen escapes in bubbles, since
copper is unable to combine with more than 25 parts of oxygen per 100.
One may, then, in all analysis take 180 pounds of carbonate or 125 pounds
of black oxide for a quintal of copper. Native carbonates of copper are also
found in this ratio of oxidation.

Here are the components of the artificial carbonate.

Copper	100
Oxygen	25
Carbonic acid	46
Water	10
	180 [*sic*]

The color of this carbonate is as constant as its proportions when it is
not at all mixed with hydrate: it is a brilliant apple green, the shade of
tone of fine malachite. But to give it its greatest luster it is necessary to
direct some attention to the manner of its preparation. As the uniformity
of its color depends also on a certain density, it is necessary in obtaining
it to precipitate from boiling water or, in default of this, place the vessel
in the sun. By this means the molecules come together, diminish in volume, and gather in a crystalline powder which has only to be washed and
dried in a porcelain cup.

To convert the carbonate to the black oxide state in the wet way it is
necessary to boil it a minute in caustic potash, which reduces it to 125
parts for 180 parts of carbonate.

On Native Carbonate of Copper

If 100 parts of this carbonate, dissolved in nitric acid and separated by
the alkaline carbonates, gives us 100 parts of artificial carbonate, and if

[2] [The composition of green copper carbonate, or malachite, corresponds to $CuCO_3 \cdot Cu(OH)_2$. Apparently this was about what Proust obtained, since a calculation with the present atomic weights gives 174 pounds of malachite as equivalent to 100 pounds of copper. The discrepancy, certainly fortuitously small under the circumstances, is typical of the perhaps inevitable inaccuracy of Proust's work. However, since his errors were fairly constant and his work was of a comparative nature, his data led to valid conclusions.]

[3] [*Grains* is given in the original, but *livres* is certainly intended.]

[4] [At this period chlorine, recently discovered by Scheele, was still regarded as a compound of hydrochloric acid and oxygen.]

the base of these two combinations is the black oxide, we must recognize that invisible hand which holds the balance for us in the formation of compounds and fashions properties according to its will. We must conclude that nature operates not otherwise in the depths of the world than at its surface or in the hands of man. These ever-invariable proportions, these constant attributes, which characterize true compounds of art or of nature, in a word, this *pondus naturae* so well seen by Stahl; all this, I say, is no more at the power of the chemist than the law of election which presides at all combinations. From these considerations is it not right to believe that the native carbonate of copper will never differ from that which art produces in its imitation? Is there actually any difference between native [*natif*] carbonate of soda and the natural [*naturel*]? No. Why, therefore, should there be any difference between those of copper or of other metals when no other perturbing cause has disarranged the reciprocal forces of the factors of these combinations?

The malachites of Aragon in nitric acid lose carbonic acid and leave one-hundredth part of sandy clay. By precipitation we reproduce 99 parts of artificial carbonate in which we discover scarcely a grain of calcareous carbonate. This solution, made warm, never shows any nitrous gas, which proves well that copper completely refuses further oxidation.

One hundred grains of the same, calcined in a crucible at a moderate temperature leaves 71 grains of black oxide. If we now subtract from this 2 parts for 100 of foreign earth, we have 69 to express the oxide contained in the malachite; but, differing only by a small fraction, these 69 grains correspond to 99 of artificial carbonate. There is, then, no difference between these two oxides, and in nature, as in art, the degree of their oxidation is evidently the same. . . .

The second citation concerning the difference between compounds and mixtures follows.

But what difference, one may say, do you recognize between your chemical combinations and these assemblages of combinations which nature does not bind fast, according to you, in any fixed proportions? Is it that the power which makes a metal dissolve in sulfur is other than that which makes one metallic sulfide dissolve in another?

I will not hasten to respond to this question, sound as it is, for fear of wandering into a region which the science of facts has perhaps not sufficiently clarified; but one will none the less conceive my distinctions, I hope, when I say, Is the attraction which makes sugar dissolve in water the same or not the same as that which makes a determinate quantity of carbon and hydrogen dissolve in another quantity of oxygen to form the sugar of our plants? But that which we see clearly is that these two sorts of attractions are so different in their results that it is impossible to confound them.

Thus the solution of niter in water is, for me, not at all like that of azote in oxygen which produces nitric acid or that of nitric acid in potash which produces saltpeter.

The solution of ammonia in water is to my eyes not at all like that of hydrogen in azote which produces ammonia.[5]

Jeremias Benjamin Richter

(*1762–1807*)

THE law of equivalents was first deduced from experiments on the combining proportions of acids and bases. In 1699 Homberg made the earliest determinations, but his results were not accurate. Henry Cavendish was the first to recognize and name *equivalents*, and Bergman also investigated the subject. There was thus an accumulation of facts which soon led to the generalization of the law of equivalents. Its author was Jeremias Benjamin Richter, who also invented the term *stoichiometry*. Richter published his researches in "Anfangsgründe der Stöchyometrie oder Messkunst chymischer Elemente"[1] and in "Ueber die neueren Gegenstände der Chemie."[2] The investigations in these works arose from Richter's considerations of the then well-known fact that neutrality is maintained in a metathetical reaction between two neutral salts. He deduced that this neutrality implied that when a compound AB was added to another CD in such a proportion that A exactly combined with C, the remaining moieties, B and D, also combined exactly. Further, he saw that if the composition of AB and CD were known, one could calculate that of AC and BD. Richter extended this concept to the determination of the quantities of acids which would satisfy a given quantity of a base and the reverse. In effect, he was determining for the first time equivalent weights. In 1802 Ernst Gottfried Fischer (1754–1831) summarized Richter's data and published the first tables of equivalents.[3]

[5] *Journal de physique*, **63**: 369 (1806).

[1] "Anfangsgründe der Stöchyometrie oder Messkunst chymischer Elemente," Breslau and Hirschberg, 1792–1794, 3 vols.

[2] "Ueber die neueren Gegenstände der Chemie," Breslau, Hirschberg and Lissa, 1791–1802, 11 vols.

[3] This first appeared in the German translation of Berthollet's "Recherches sur les lois de l'affinité:" "Uber die Gesetze der Verwandtschaft in der Chemie, ubersetzt und mit Anmerkungen, Zusätzen und einer synthetischen Darstellung von Berthollets Theorie versehen von Ernst Gottfried Fischer," Berlin, 1802.

Fischer's table and part of the text were reproduced as a French translation in

Since Richter wrote in a very involved style, chemists, most of whom were at this time occupied with Lavoisier's new theories, found his mathematics repellent. E. G. Fischer and C. L. Berthollet, however, advocated his ideas and stimulated J. J. Berzelius to determine chemical composition with greater accuracy. Although Richter's stoichiometric principles stand independent of an atomic theory, which he lacked, they probably had some influence upon John Dalton, since they upheld his atomic hypothesis. The following passages are from Richter's "Stöchyometrie."[4]

Mathematics[5] includes all those sciences which refer to magnitude, and consequently a science lies more or less in the province of mathematics (geometry), according as it requires the determination of magnitudes. In chemical experiments this truth has often led me to the question, whether and how far chemistry is a part of applied mathematics; and especially in considering the well-known fact, that two neutral salts, when they decompose each other, form again neutral compounds. The immediate consequence, in my opinion, could only be, *that there are definite relations between the magnitude* of the component parts of neutral salts. From that time I considered how these proportions could be made out, partly by exact chemical experiments, partly combining chemical with mathematical analysis. In my inaugural dissertation, published at Königsberg, in 1789, I made a slight attempt, but was not then supplied with the requisite chemical apparatus, nor was I sufficiently ready with all requisite information, bearing on my present system, imperfect as it may be. The result, therefore, was very imperfect. I promised, however, not to let the matter rest with that imperfect essay, but to work out this branch with all the accuracy and profundity of which I was capable, as soon as I was supplied with the requisite conveniences. This promise, I hope in the present volume, to make good, although I am far from believing that what I am now going to say will not be in need of still more thorough and accurate elaboration, for who will venture to limit the extent and the power which is the destination of a young and budding science. . . .

. . . as the mathematical portion of chemistry deals in a great measure with bodies which are either elements or substances incapable of being decomposed and as it teaches also their relative magnitudes, I have been able to find no more fitting name for this scientific discipline than the word stoechiometry, from στοιχεῖον which, in the Greek language, means a

---

Berthollets' "Essai de statique chimique" (Paris, 1803), where it became generally known.

[4] Translated by R. A. Smith, "Memoir of John Dalton," London, 1856, p. 190. (This is volume 13 of the *Memoirs of the Manchester Literary and Philosophical Society,* 1856.)

[5] Vol. 1, Preface.

something which cannot be divided, and μετρεῖν which means to find out relative magnitudes. . . .

DEFINITION 1.

Stoechiometry [stoechyometria] is the science of measuring the quantitative proportions, or the proportions of the masses in which chemical elements stand in regard to each other. The mere knowledge of these relations might be called quantitative stoechiology.[6] . . .

PRINCIPLE 1.

Every infinitely small particle of the mass of an element has an infinitely small part of the chemical attractive force of affinity. . . .

EXPERIENCE 5

In order to make a neutral compound out of two elements, it is needful, as each of the elements is of the same constitution at one time as at another, to take the same quantity for the first part formed as for the second part. For example, if two parts of lime require five parts of muriatic acid for solution, six parts of lime will require fifteen of the same acid.

EXPERIENCE 6

When two neutral solutions are mixed, and a decomposition follows, the new resulting products are almost without exception neutral also, but if the solutions of one or both are not neutral before mixing, the products after mixture are also not neutral.

Corollary 1

The elements must therefore have amongst themselves a certain fixed proportion of mass. To determine which, their neutral compounds generally give the best opportunity.[7]

Corollary 2

If the weights of the masses of two neutral compounds which decompose each other are A and B, and the mass of the one element in A is a, and that of the one in B is b, then the masses of the elements in A are $A - a$, a and those in B are $B - b$, b. The proportions of the masses of the elements in the neutral compounds before decomposition are $A - a:a$ and $B - b:b$; but after decomposition the new products are $a + B - b$, and $b + A - a$, and the proportion of the masses of the elements is

---

[6] Vol. 1, pp. 121 *ff*.

[7] There is present in the Element a certain *subjectum* to which the chemical attractive power or the affinity is bound, this is the Mass of the Element.

BASES.		ACIDES,	
Alumine	525	Fluorique	427
Magnésie	615	Carbonique	577
Ammoniaque	672	Sébacique	706
Chaux	793	Muriatique	712
Soude	859	Oxalique	755
Strontiane	1329	Phosphorique	979
Potasse	1605	Formique	988
Baryte	2222	Sulfurique	1000
		Succinique	1209
		Nitrique	1405
		Acétique	1480
		Citrique	1683
		Tartareux	1694

Table of Richter's equivalents, from Berthollet's "Essai de statique chimique," Paris, 1803, Vol. 1, p. 136.

$a:B - b$, $b:A - a$. If the proportion of the masses in the compounds A and B is known, that in the new products is known also.

If $a + B - b = C$ and $b + A - a = D$ then $a = C + b - B = b + A - D$ and $C - B = A - D$, so also $D - B = A - C$. In addition $b = a + B - C = D - A + a$.

John Dalton

(1766–1844)

VARIOUS forms of the atomic theory were prevalent throughout the seventeenth and eighteenth century. Indeed, the atomic concept can be found with certain of the Greek philosophers,[1] *e.g.*, Leukippos (about 480 B.C.?), Demokritos of Abdera (468–370 B.C.), and others. Revived in the seventeenth century by Pierre Gassend (or Gassendi) (1592–1655), it was widely used by such men as Boyle, Lemery, and Isaac Newton; its mechanistic character no doubt appealed to Newton. However, the atomic theory had no practical significance for chemistry

[1] C. Bailey, "The Greek Atomists and Epicurus," Oxford, 1928.

until the work of John Dalton, in the first decade of the eighteenth century. His theory, for the first time, stated clearly that chemical elements are composed of very small indivisible particles of matter, atoms, which maintain their individuality in chemical reactions; these atoms are all identical, particularly in weight, and different elemental atoms have different weights. This latter property was utilized by Dalton in characterizing the atoms. He further explained chemical combination in terms of these atoms and thus elucidated the laws of constant, multiple, and equivalent proportions as well.

John Dalton was a meteorologist of some repute, and there is little doubt that this interest led him to speculate on the physical properties of gases, which provided the basis for his atomic theory. To confirm his observations he made an investigation on the subject of multiple proportions; this was after he had conceived the atomic theory. In 1802 Dalton presented a paper on an "Experimental Enquiry into the Proportions of the Several Gases or Elastic Fluids constituting the atmosphere," which was published in 1805.[2] Here Dalton announced the first example of the law of multiple proportions. "On the Absorption of Gases by Water"[3] was read to the Manchester Philosophical Society by Dalton in 1803 and printed in 1805. The appended table in this paper is his first list of atomic weights. Dalton, in this publication, took the law which William Henry[4] (1774–1836) had recently enunciated (that the amount of gas absorbed by a liquid is proportional to the pressure) and extended it to apply to mixtures of gases, using his own law of partial pressures.[5] The latter part of this paper, which contains the first table of atomic weights, follows.

THEORY OF THE ABSORPTION OF GASES BY WATER, &c.

From the facts developed in the preceding articles, the following theory of the absorption of gases by water seems deducible.

1. All gases that enter into water and other liquids by means of pressure, and are wholly disengaged again by the removal of that pressure, are *mechanically* mixed with the liquid, and not *chemically* combined with it.

2. Gases so mixed with water, &c. retain their elasticity or repulsive power amongst their own particles, just the same in the water as out of it, the intervening water having no other influence in this respect than a mere vacuum.

[2] *Memoirs of the Literary and Philosophical Society of Manchester*, [2], **1**: 244–258 (1805); reprinted in *Alembic Club Reprints*, No. 2, "Foundations of the Atomic Theory: Comprising Papers and Extracts by John Dalton, William Hyde Wollaston, M.D., and Thomas Thomson, M.D., (1802–1808)," Edinburgh, 1899. See also Ostwald's *Klassiker*, No. 3, "J. Dalton und W. H. Wollaston, Abhandlungen zur Atomtheorie. (1803 bis 1808). Herausgegeben von W. Ostwald," Leipzig, 1889.

[3] Read October 2, 1803. *Memoirs of the Literary and Philosophical Society of Manchester*, [2], **1**: 271–287 (1805); also reprinted in *Alembic Club Reprints*, No. 2, *op. cit.*

[4] *Nicholson's J.*, **8**: 297 (1804).

[5] "On the Constitution of Mixed Gases," read October 2, 1801. *Memoirs of the Literary and Philosophical Society of Manchester*, **5**: 535 (1802).

3. Each gas is retained in water by the pressure of gas of its own kind incumbent on its surface abstractedly considered, no other gas with which it may be mixed having any permanent influence in this respect.

4. When water has absorbed its bulk of carbonic acid gas, &c., the gas does not press on the water at all, but presses on the containing vessel just as if no water were in.— When water has absorbed its proper quantity of oxygenous gas, &c. that is, $\frac{1}{27}$ of its bulk, the exterior gas presses on the surface of the water with $\frac{26}{27}$ of its force, and on the internal gas with $\frac{1}{27}$ of its force, which force presses upon the containing vessel and not on the water. With azotic and hydrogenous gas the proportions are $\frac{63}{64}$ and $\frac{1}{64}$ respectively. When water contains no gas, its surface must support the whole pressure of any gas admitted to it, till the gas has, in part, forced its way into the water.

5. A particle of gas pressing on the surface of water is analogous to a single shot pressing upon the summit of a square pile of them. As the shot distributes pressure equally amongst all the individuals forming the lowest stratum of the pile, so the particle of gas distributes its pressure equally amongst every successive horizontal stratum of particles of water downwards till it reaches the sphere of influence of another particle of gas. For instance; let any gas press with a given force on the surface of water, and let the distance of the particles of gas from each other be to those of water as 10 to 1; then each particle of gas must divide its force equally amongst 100 particles of water, as follows:—it exerts its immediate force upon 4 particles of water; those 4 press upon 9, the 9 upon 16, and so on according to the order of square numbers, till 100 particles of water have the force distributed amongst them; and in the same stratum each square of 100, having its incumbent particle of gas, the water below this stratum is uniformly pressed by the gas, and consequently has not its equilibrium disturbed by that pressure.

6. When water has absorbed $\frac{1}{27}$ of its bulk of any gas, the stratum of gas on the surface of the water presses with $\frac{26}{27}$ of its force on the water, in the manner pointed out in the last article, and with $\frac{1}{27}$ of its force on the upper-most stratum of gas in the water: The distance of the two strata of gas must be nearly 27 times the distance of the particles in the incumbent atmosphere and 9 times the distance of the particles in the water. This comparatively great distance of the inner and outer atmosphere arises from the great repulsive power of the latter, on account of its superior density, or its presenting 9 particles of surface to the other 1. When $\frac{1}{64}$ is absorbed the distance of the atmospheres becomes 64 times the distance of two particles in the outer, or 16 times that of the inner. . . .

7. An equilibrium between the outer and inner atmospheres can be established in no other circumstance than that of the distance of the particles of one atmosphere being the same or some multiple of that of the

other; and it is probable the multiple cannot be more than 4. For in this case the distance of the inner and outer atmospheres is such as to make the perpendicular force of each particle of the former on those particles of the latter that are immediately subject to its influence, physically speaking, equal; and the same may be observed of the small lateral force.

8. The greatest difficulty attending the mechanical hypothesis, arises from different gases observing different laws. Why does water not admit its bulk of every kind of gas alike?—This question I have duly considered, and though I am not yet able to satisfy myself completely, I am nearly

TABLE OF THE RELATIVE WEIGHTS OF THE ULTIMATE PARTICLES OF GASEOUS AND OTHER BODIES

Hydrogen	1
Azot	4.2
Carbone	4.3
Ammonia	5.2
Oxygen	5.5
Water	6.5
Phosphorus	7.2
Phosphuretted hydrogen	8.2
Nitrous gas [nitric oxide]	9.3*
Ether	9.6
Gaseous oxide of carbone	9.8
Nitrous oxide	13.7*
Sulphur	14.4
Nitric acid	15.2
Sulphuretted hydrogen	15.4
Carbonic acid	15.3
Alcohol	15.1
Sulphureous acid	19.9
Sulphuric acid	25.4
Carburetted hydrogen from stag. water	6.3
Olefiant gas	5.3

* [These two values are plainly misprints for 9.7 and 13.9.]

persuaded that the circumstance depends upon the weight and number of the ultimate particles of the several gases: those whose particles are lightest and single being least absorbable, and the others more according as they increase in weight and complexity.[6] An enquiry into the relative weights of the ultimate particles of bodies is a subject, as far as I know, entirely new: I have lately been prosecuting this enquiry with remarkable success. The principle cannot be entered upon in this paper; but I shall just subjoin the results, as far as they appear to be ascertained by my experiments.

In August, 1804, Thomas Thomson (1773–1852), then lecturer in chemistry in Edinburgh, visited Dalton at Manchester and discussed with him the atomic theory. After some revision Thomson accepted Dalton's concepts and gave the

[6] Subsequent experience renders this conjecture less probable.

first published account of them in his "System of Chemistry."[7] A portion of this account is given in the following selection.

This difference between the density of the gases, while their elasticity is the same, must be owing to one of two causes: Either the *repulsive force*, or the *density* of the atoms, differs in different gases. The first supposition is by no means probable, supposing the size and density of the particles of different gases the same, and indeed would but ill agree with the analogy of nature; but the second is very likely to be the true cause. And if we suppose the size and density of the atoms of different gases to differ, this in reality includes the first cause likewise; for every variation in size and density must necessarily occasion a corresponding variation in the repulsive force, even supposing that force abstractedly considered to be the same in all.

We have no direct means of ascertaining the density of the atoms of bodies; but Mr Dalton, to whose uncommon ingenuity and sagacity the philosophic world is no stranger, has lately contrived an hypothesis which, if it prove correct, will furnish us with a very simple method of ascertaining that density with great precision. Though the author has not yet thought fit to publish his hypothesis, yet as the notions of which it consists are original and extremely interesting, and as they are intimately connected with some of the most intricate parts of the doctrine of affinity, I have ventured, with Mr Dalton's permission, to enrich this work with a short sketch of it.[8]

The hypothesis upon which the whole of Mr Dalton's notions respecting chemical elements is founded, is this: When two elements unite to form a third substance, it is to [be] presumed that *one* atom of one joins to *one* atom of the other, unless when some reason can be assigned for supposing the contrary. Thus oxygen and hydrogen unite together and form water. We are to presume that an atom of water is formed by the combination of *one* atom of oxygen with *one* atom of hydrogen. In like manner *one* atom of ammonia is formed by the combination of *one* atom of azote with *one* atom of hydrogen. If we represent an atom of oxygen, hydrogen, and azote, by the following symbols,[9]

[7] This, the first printed notice of John Dalton's atomic theory, was in the third edition of Thomson's "System," published in Edinburgh in five volumes in 1807. It is in volume 3, pages 424 to 429.

[8] In justice to Mr Dalton, I must warn the reader not to decide upon the notions of that philosopher from the sketch which I have given, derived from a few minutes' conversation, and from a short written memorandum. The mistakes, if any occur, are to be laid to my account, and not to his; as it is extremely probable that I may have misconceived his meaning in some points.

[9] [These symbols, devised by Dalton, represented a great advance over earlier symbols since they allowed the chemist to indicate the composition of compounds. They were, however, soon superseded by those of Berzelius.]

Oxygen............. ◯
Hydrogen.......... ⊙
Azote............. ⏀

Then an atom of water and of ammonia will be represented respectively by the following symbols:

Water............. ◯⊙
Ammonia.......... ⊙⏀

But if this hypothesis be allowed, it furnishes us with a ready method of ascertaining the relative density of those atoms that enter into such combinations; for it has been proved by analysis, that water is composed of $85\frac{2}{3}$ of oxygen and $14\frac{1}{3}$ of hydrogen. An atom of water of course is composed of $85\frac{2}{3}$ parts by weight of oxygen and $14\frac{1}{3}$ parts of hydrogen. Now, if it consist of one atom of oxygen united to one atom of hydrogen, it follows, that the weight of one atom of hydrogen is to that of one atom of oxygen as $14\frac{1}{3}$ to $85\frac{2}{3}$, or as 1 to 6 very nearly. In like manner an atom of ammonia has been shewn to consist of 80 parts of azote and 20 of hydrogen. Hence an atom of hydrogen is to an atom of azote as 20 to 80, or as 1 to 4. Thus we have obtained the following relative densities of these three elementary bodies.

Hydrogen.......... 1
Azote............. 4
Oxygen............ 6

We have it in our power to try how far this hypothesis is consonant to experiment, by examining the combination of azote and oxygen, on the supposition that these bodies unite, atom to atom, and that the respective densities of the atoms are as in the preceding table. But azote and oxygen unite in various proportions, forming nitrous oxide, nitrous gas, and nitric acid, besides some other compounds which need not be enumerated. The preceding hypothesis will not apply to all these compounds; Mr Dalton, therefore, extends it farther. Whenever more than one compound is formed by the combination of two elements, then the next simple combination must, he supposes, arise from the union of *one* atom of the one with *two* atoms of the other. If we suppose *nitrous gas*, for example, to be composed of *one* atom of azote, and *one* of oxygen, we shall have two new compounds, by uniting an atom of nitrous gas to an atom of azote, and to an atom of oxygen, respectively. If we suppose farther, that nitrous oxide is composed of an atom of nitrous gas and an atom of azote, while nitric acid consists of nitrous gas and oxygen, united atom to atom; then the following will be the symbols and constituents of these three bodies:

Nitrous gas............ ◯⏀
Nitrous oxide.......... ⏀◯⏀
Nitric acid............ ◯⏀◯

The first gas consists only of two atoms, or is a binary compound, but the two others consist of three atoms, or are ternary compounds; nitrous oxide contains two atoms of azote united to one of oxygen, while nitric acid consists of two atoms of oxygen united to one of azote.

When the atoms of two elastic fluids join together to form *one* atom of a new elastic fluid, the density of this new compound is always greater than the mean. Thus the density of nitrous gas, by calculation, ought only to be 1.045; but its real density is 1.094. Now as both nitrous oxide and nitric acid are specifically heavier than nitrous gas, though the one contains more of the lighter ingredient, and the other more of the heavier ingredient than that compound does, it is reasonable to conclude, that they are combinations of nitrous gas with azote and oxygen respectively, and that this is the reason of the increased specific gravity of each; whereas were not this the case, nitrous oxide ought to be specifically lighter than nitrous gas. Supposing, then, the constituents of these gases to be as represented in the preceding table, let us see how far this analysis will correspond with the densities of their elements, as above deduced from the compositions of water and ammonia.

Nitrous gas is composed of 1.00 azote and 1.36 oxygen, or of 4 azote and 5.4 oxygen.

Nitrous oxide, of 2 azote and 1.174 oxygen, or of 4 + 4 azote and 4.7 oxygen.

Nitric acid, of 1 azote and 2.36 oxygen, or of 4 azote and 4.7 + 4.7 oxygen.

These three give us the following as the relative densities of azote and oxygen:

Azote. Oxygen.
4:5.4
:4.7
:4.7

The mean of the whole is nearly 4:5; but from preceding analyses of water and ammonia, we obtained their densities 4:6. Though these results do not correspond exactly, yet the difference is certainly not very great, and indeed as little as can reasonably be expected, even supposing the hypothesis is well founded, if we consider the extreme difficulty of attaining accuracy in the analysis of gaseous compounds. If ammonia were supposed a compound of 83 azote and 17 hydrogen, instead of 80 azote and 20 hydrogen, in that case the density of azote would be five instead of four, and the different sets of experiments would coincide very nearly. Now it is needless to observe how easy it is, in analysing gaseous compounds, to commit an error of 3 *per cent.* which is all that would be necessary to make the different numbers tally.

On the supposition that the hypothesis of Mr Dalton is well founded, the following Table exhibits the density of the atoms of the simple gases, and of those which are composed of elastic fluids, together with the symbols of the composition of these compound atoms:

⊙	Hydrogen	1
◐	Azote	5
○	Oxygen	6
⊖	Muriatic acid	9

⊙○	Water	7
⊙◐	Ammonia	6
○◐	Nitrous gas	11

◐○◐	Nitrous oxide	16
○◐○	Nitric acid	17
⊖○⊖	Oxymuriatic acid	24

○⊖○	Hyperoxymuriatic acid	27

In 1808 Dalton published his own account in the first volume of his "A New System of Chemical Philosophy."[10] This great classic, which contained Dalton's first clear exposition of his theory, contributed much to the progress of chemical thought. It gave chemists the means of visualizing the mechanics of reactions, and, though many were loath to admit the actual existence of atoms, they did agree that the hypothesis illuminated chemical phenomena. Two chapters of the "New System" follow.

CHAP. II.

ON THE CONSTITUTION OF BODIES

There are three distinctions in the kinds of bodies, or three states, which have more especially claimed the attention of philosophical chemists; namely, those which are marked by the terms *elastic fluids, liquids, and solids*. A very familiar instance is exhibited to us in water, of a body, which, in certain circumstances, is capable of assuming all the three states. In steam we recognise a perfectly elastic fluid, in water a perfect liquid, and in ice a complete solid. These observations have tacitly led to the con-

[10] "A New System of Chemical Philosophy. Part I. Manchester, Printed by Sl Russell, 125 Deansgate, for R. Bickerstaff, Strand," London, 1808. "Part II. Manchester, printed by Russell & Allen, Deansgate, for R. Bickerstaff, Strand," London-1810. "Part First of Vol. II. Manchester, Printed by the Executors of S. Russel, for George Wilson, Essex Street, Strand," London, 1827. The third volume is frequently missing, for it was published seventeen years after the second.

A second edition of Part I only, which is a verbatim reprint of the first, was published in 1842 shortly before Dalton's death. It has a new preface.

A portion of the book is also included in *Alembic Club Reprints*, No. 4, "Foundations of the Molecular Theory: Comprising papers and extracts by John Dalton, Joseph-Louis Gay-Lussac, and Amadeo Avogadro (1808–1811)," Edinburgh, 1899.

clusion which seems universally adopted, that all bodies of sensible magnitude, whether liquid or solid, are constituted of a vast number of extremely small particles, or atoms of matter bound together by a force of attraction, which is more or less powerful according to circumstances, and which as it endeavours to prevent their separation, is very properly called in that view, *attraction of cohesion*; but as it collects them from a dispersed state (as from steam into water) it is called, *attraction of aggregation*, or more simply, *affinity*. Whatever names it may go by, they still signify one and the same power. It is not my design to call in question this conclusion, which appears completely satisfactory; but to shew that we have hitherto made no use of it, and that the consequence of the neglect, has been a very obscure view of chemical agency, which is daily growing more so in proportion to the new lights attempted to be thrown upon it.

The opinions I more particularly allude to, are those of Berthollet on the Laws of chemical affinity; such as that chemical agency is proportional to the mass, and that in all chemical unions, there exist insensible gradations in the proportions of the constituent principles. The inconsistence of these opinions, both with reason and observation, cannot, I think, fail to strike every one who takes a proper view of the phenomena.

Whether the ultimate particles of a body, such as water, are all alike, that is, of the same figure, weight, &c. is a question of some importance. From what is known, we have no reason to apprehend a diversity in these particulars: if it does exist in water, it must equally exist in the elements constituting water, namely, hydrogen and oxygen. Now it is scarcely possible to conceive how the aggregates of dissimilar particles should be so uniformly the same. If some of the particles of water were heavier than others, if a parcel of the liquid on any occasion were constituted principally of these heavier particles, it must be supposed to affect the specific gravity of the mass, a circumstance not known. Similar observations may be made on other substances. Therefore we may conclude that *the ultimate particles of all homogeneous bodies are perfectly alike in weight, figure, &c.* In other words, every particle of water is like every other particle of water; every particle of hydrogen is like every other particle of hydrogen, &c.   . . .

CHAP. III.

ON CHEMICAL SYNTHESIS

When any body exists in the elastic state, its ultimate particles are separated from each other to a much greater distance than in any other state; each particle occupies the centre of a comparatively large sphere, and supports its dignity by keeping all the rest, which by their gravity, or otherwise are disposed to encroach upon it, at a respectful distance. When we attempt to conceive the *number* of particles in an atmosphere, it is somewhat like attempting to conceive the number of stars in the universe; we are confounded with the thought. But if we limit the subject, by taking a given volume of any gas, we seem persuaded that, let the divisions be ever so minute, the number of particles must be finite; just as in a given space of the universe, the number of stars and planets cannot be infinite.

Chemical analysis and synthesis go no farther than to the separation of particles one from another, and to their reunion. No new creation or destruction of matter is within the reach of chemical agency. We might as well attempt to introduce a new planet into the solar system, or to annihilate one already in existence, as to create or destroy a particle of hydrogen. All the changes we can produce, consist in separating particles that are in a state of cohesion or combination, and joining those that were previously at a distance.

In all chemical investigations, it has justly been considered an important object to ascertain the relative *weights* of the simples which constitute a compound. But unfortunately the enquiry has terminated here; whereas from the relative weights in the mass, the relative weights of the ultimate particles or atoms of the bodies might have been inferred, from which their number and weight in various other compounds would appear, in order to assist and to guide future investigations, and to correct their results. Now it is one great object of this work, to shew the importance and advantage of ascertaining *the relative weights of the ultimate particles, both of simple and compound bodies, the number of simple elementary particles which constitute one compound particle, and the number of less compound particles which enter into the formation of one more compound particle.*

If there are two bodies, A and B, which are disposed to combine, the following is the order in which the combinations may take place, beginning with the most simple: namely,

1 atom of A + 1 atom of B = 1 atom of C, binary.
1 atom of A + 2 atoms of B = 1 atom of D, ternary.
2 atoms of A + 1 atom of B = 1 atom of E, ternary.
1 atom of A + 3 atoms of B = 1 atom of F, quaternary.
3 atoms of A + 1 atom of B = 1 atom of G, quaternary.
&c. &c.

The following general rules may be adopted as guides in all our investigations respecting chemical synthesis.

1st. When only one combination of two bodies can be obtained, it must be presumed to be a *binary* one, unless some cause appear to the contrary.

2d. When two combinations are observed, they must be presumed to be a *binary* and a *ternary.*

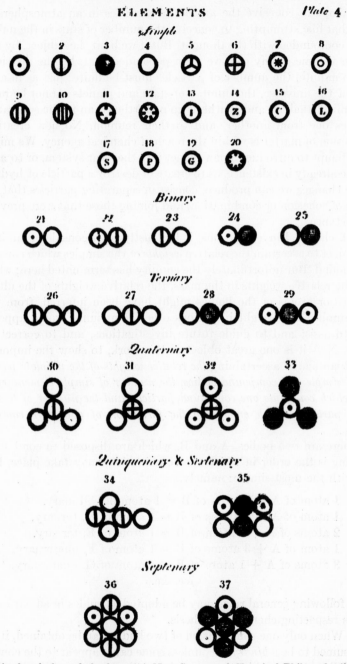

Dalton's chemical symbols, from "A New System of Chemical Philosophy," Part 1, London, 1808; Plate 4, facing page 219.

3d. When three combinations are obtained we may expect one to be a *binary*, and the other two *ternary*.

4th. When four combinations are observed, we should expect one *binary*, two *ternary*, and one *quaternary*, &c.

5th. A *binary* compound should always be specifically heavier than the mere mixture of its two ingredients.

6th. A *ternary* compound should be specifically heavier than the mixture of a binary and a simple, which would, if combined, constitute it; &c.

7th. The above rules and observations equally apply, when two bodies, such as C and D, D and E, &c. are combined.

From the application of these rules, to the chemical facts already well ascertained, we deduce the following conclusions; 1st. That water is a binary compound of hydrogen and oxygen, and the relative weights of the two elementary atoms are as 1:7, nearly; 2d. That ammonia is a binary compound of hydrogen and azote, and the relative weights of the two atoms are as 1:5, nearly; 3d. That nitrous gas is a binary compound of azote and oxygen, the atoms of which weigh 5 and 7 respectively; that nitric acid is a binary or ternary compound according as it is derived, and consists of one atom of azote and two of oxygen, together weighing 19; that nitrous oxide is a compound similar to nitric acid, and consists of one atom of oxygen and two of azote, weighing 17; that nitrous acid is a binary compound of nitric acid and nitrous gas, weighing 31; that oxynitric acid is a binary compound of nitric acid and oxygen, weighing 26; 4th. That carbonic oxide is a binary compound, consisting of one atom of charcoal, and one of oxygen, together weighing nearly 12; that carbonic acid is a ternary compound (but sometimes binary) consisting of one atom of charcoal, and two of oxygen, weighing 19; &c. &c. In all these cases the weights are expressed in atoms of hydrogen, each of which is denoted by unity. . . .

Plate IV. This plate contains the arbitrary marks or signs chosen to represent the several chemical elements or ultimate particles.

Fig.			Fig.		
1	Hydrog. its rel. weight,	1	11	Strontites,	46
2	Azote,	5	12	Barytes,	68
3	Carbone or charcoal,	5	13	Iron,	38
4	Oxygen,	7	14	Zinc,	56
5	Phosphorus,	9	15	Copper,	56
6	Sulphur,	13	16	Lead,	95
7	Magnesia,	20	17	Silver,	100
8	Lime,	23	18	Platina,	100
9	Soda,	28	19	Gold,	140
10	Potash,	42	20	Mercury,	167

21. An atom of water or steam, composed of 1 of oxygen and 1 of hydrogen, retained in physical contact by a strong affinity, and supposed to be surrounded by a common atmosphere of heat; its relative weight 8

Fig.

22. An atom of ammonia, composed of 1 of azote and 1 of hydrogen............   6
23. An atom of nitrous gas, composed of 1 of azote and 1 of oxygen............   12
24. An atom of olefiant gas, composed of 1 of carbone and one of hydrogen.....   6
25. An atom of carbonic oxide, composed of 1 of carbone and 1 of oxygen.......   12
26. An atom of nitrous oxide, 2 azote + 1 oxygen..........................   17
27. An atom of nitric acid, 1 azote + 2 oxygen.............................   19
28. An atom of carbonic acid, 1 carbone + 2 oxygen.........................   19
29. An atom of carburetted hydrogen, 1 carbone + 2 hydrogen...............   7
30. An atom of oxynitric acid, 1 azote + 3 oxygen..........................   26
31. An atom of sulphuric acid, 1 sulphur + 3 oxygen........................   34
32. An atom of sulphuretted hydrogen, 1 sulphur + 3 hydrogen...............   16
33. An atom of alcohol, 3 carbone + 1 hydrogen............................   16
34. An atom of nitrous acid, 1 nitric acid + 1 nitrous gas...................   31
35. An atom of acetous acid, 2 carbone + 2 water..........................   26
36. An atom of nitrate of ammonia, 1 nitric acid + 1 ammonia + 1 water.....   33
37. An atom of sugar, 1 alcohol + 1 carbonic acid..........................   35

Enough has been given to shew the method; it will be quite unnecessary to devise characters and combinations of them to exhibit to view in this way all the subjects that come under investigation; nor is it necessary to insist upon the accuracy of all these compounds, both in number and weight; the principle will be entered into more particularly hereafter, as far as respects the individual results. It is not to be understood that all those articles marked as simple substances, are necessarily such by the theory; they are only necessarily of such weights. Soda and potash, such as they are found in combination with acids, are 28 and 42 respectively in weight; but according to Mr Davy's very important discoveries, they are metallic oxides; the former then must be considered as composed of an atom of metal, 21, and one of oxygen, 7; and the latter, of an atom of metal, 35, and one of oxygen, 7. Or, soda contains 75 per cent. metal and 25 oxygen; potash, 83.3 metal and 16.7 oxygen. It is particularly remarkable, that according to the above-mentioned gentleman's essay on the Decomposition and Composition of the fixed alkalis, in the Philosophical Transactions (a copy of which essay he has just favoured me with) it appears that "the largest quantity of oxygen indicated by these experiments was for potash 17, and for soda, 26 parts in 100, and the smallest 13 and 19."

William Hyde Wollaston

(1766–1828)

THE law of multiple proportions constitutes strong evidence for the atomic theory, and indeed, in Dalton's time and for many years afterwards it was thought that the atomic theory was devised in an attempt to explain this law. Dalton himself clearly saw the importance of multiple proportions even before 1805 (note the values for carbon, hydrogen, carburetted hydrogen [methane] and olefiant gas [ethylene] in his first table of atomic weights, page 211), and he is sometimes called the discoverer of the law. Dalton also claimed to have shown that oxygen can combine with one or two volumes of nitric oxide. However, his experiments, carried out on gases, lacked convincing precision. Chemists were much more impressed by the analysis of series of salts of the same acid and base which Thomas Thomson and William Hyde Wollaston published in the same year that Dalton's "New System" appeared. These analyses, more particularly those of Wollaston, clearly demonstrated the law of multiple proportions and went far to influence chemists favorably toward Dalton's atomic theory.

Wollaston was a man of unusual genius and diverse accomplishments. In the course of his chemical work he investigated the metals columbium, tantalum, and titanium and discovered the elements palladium and rhodium. He indirectly performed a great service for analytical chemistry by inventing a method for rendering platinum malleable and making possible the fabrication of crucibles and other apparatus. In 1814 he draw up "A Synoptic Table of Chemical Equivalents," wherein many "equivalents" (a term apparently first used in the chemical sense by him) were arranged in a logarithmic scale. Chemists found this device of great practical assistance, and it survives today in the form of the chemical slide rule.

The paper, "On Super-acid and Sub-acid Salts," illustrative of the law of multiple proportions, is reproduced in the following.[1]

In the paper which has just been read to the Society, Dr Thomson has remarked, that oxalic acid unites to strontian as well as to potash in two different proportions, and that the quantity of acid combined with each of these bases in their super-oxalates,[2] is just double of that which is

---

[1] *Philosophical Transactions*, **98**: 96–102 (1808). The paper is also given in *Alembic Club Reprints*, No. 2, "Foundations of the Atomic Theory: Comprising Papers and Extracts by John Dalton, William Hyde Wollaston M.D., and Thomas Thomson M.D., (1802–1808)," Edinburgh, 1899; and in Ostwald's *Klassiker*, No. 3, "J. Dalton und W. H. Wollaston, Abhandlungen zur Atomtheorie. (1803 bis 1808). Herausgegeben von W. Ostwald," Leipzig, 1889.

[2] [*I.e.*, acid oxalates.]

saturated by the same quantity of base in their neutral compounds.[3]

As I had observed the same law to prevail in various other instances of super-acid and sub-acid salts, I thought it not unlikely that this law might obtain generally in such compounds, and it was my design to have pursued this subject with the hope of discovering the cause to which so regular a relation might be ascribed.

But since the publication of Mr Dalton's theory of chemical combination, as explained and illustrated by Dr Thomson, the inquiry which I had designed appears to be superfluous, as all the facts that I had observed are but particular instances of the more general observation of Mr Dalton, that in all cases the simple elements of bodies are disposed to unite atom to atom singly, or, if either is in excess, it exceeds by a ratio to be expressed by some simple multiple of the number of its atoms.[4]

However, since those who are desirous of ascertaining the justness of this observation by experiment, may be deterred by the difficulties that we meet with in attempting to determine with precision the constitution of gaseous bodies, for the explanation of which Mr Dalton's theory was first conceived, and since some persons may imagine that the results of former experiments on such bodies do not accord sufficiently to authorize the adoption of a new hypothesis, it may be worth while to describe a few experiments, each of which may be performed with the utmost facility, and each of which affords the most direct proof of the proportional redundance or deficiency of acid in the several salts employed.

SUB-CARBONATE OF POTASH[5]

Exp. 1. Sub-carbonate of potash recently prepared, is one instance of an alkali having one-half the quantity of acid necessary for its saturation, as may thus be satisfactorily proved.

Let two grains of fully saturated and well crystallized carbonate of potash[6] be wrapped in a piece of thin paper, and passed up into an inverted tube filled with mercury, and let the gas be extricated from it by a sufficient quantity of muriatic acid, so that the space it occupies may be marked upon the tube.

Next, let four grains of the same carbonate be exposed for a short time to a red heat; and it will be found to have parted with exactly half its gas; for the gas extricated from it in the same apparatus will be found to

---

[3] [This statement sums up Thomson's results in regard to the law of multiple proportions. *Philosophical Transactions,* **98**: 63 (1808).]

[4] [Dalton's "New System" did not appear until later in this year.]

[5] [Since solutions of potassium carbonate were known to absorb carbon dioxide, this salt was thought of as unsaturated and therefore called the *sub-carbonate.*]

[6] [Potassium bicarbonate.]

occupy exactly the same space, as the quantity before obtained from two grains of fully saturated carbonate.[7]

SUB-CARBONATE OF SODA

Exp. 2. A similar experiment may be made with a saturated carbonate of soda, and with the same result; for this also becomes a true semi-carbonate by being exposed for a short time to a red heat.

SUPER-SULPHATE OF POTASH[8]

By an experiment equally simple, super-sulphate of potash may be shewn to contain exactly twice as much acid as is necessary for the mere saturation of the alkali present.

Exp. 3. Let twenty grains of carbonate of potash (which would be more than neutralized by ten grains of sulphuric acid) be mixed with about twenty-five grains of that acid in a covered crucible of platina, or in a glass tube three quarters of an inch [in] diameter, and five or six inches long.

By heating this mixture till it ceases to boil, and begins to appear slightly red hot, a part of the redundant acid will be expelled, and there will remain a determinate quantity forming super-sulphate of potash, which when dissolved in water will be very nearly neutralized by an addition of twenty grains more of the same carbonate of potash; but it is generally found very slightly acid, in consequence of the small quantity of sulphuric acid which remains in the vessel in a gaseous state at a red heat.

In the preceding experiments, the acids are made to assume a determinate proportion to their base, by heat which cannot destroy them. In those which follow, the proportion which a destructible acid shall assume cannot be regulated by the same means; but the constitution of its compounds previously formed, may nevertheless be proved with equal facility.

SUPER-OXALATE OF POTASH[9]

Exp. 4. The common super-oxalate of potash is a salt that contains alkali sufficient to saturate exactly half of the acid present. Hence, if two equal quantities of salt of sorrel be taken, and if one of them be exposed to a red heat, the alkali which remains will be found exactly to saturate the redundant acid of the other portion.

In addition to the preceding compounds, selected as distinct examples

---

[7] [Wollaston omits the well-known fact that the saturated carbonate leaves the sub-carbonate when heated. He reasons thus: since the saturated carbonate loses, on heating, one-half of its gas ($KHCO_3 = \frac{1}{2}K_2CO_3 + \frac{1}{2}H_2O + \frac{1}{2}CO_2$) and gives the subcarbonate, this latter must contain half as much gas as the saturated carbonate.]

[8] [Potassium acid sulfate.]

[9] [Potassium acid oxalate.]

of binacid salts, I have observed one remarkable instance of a more extended and general prevalence of the law under consideration; for when the circumstances are such as to admit the union of a further quantity of oxalic acid with potash, I found a proportion, though different, yet analogous to the former, regularly to occur.

QUADROXALATE OF POTASH[10]

In attempting to decompose the preceding super-oxalate by means of acids, it appeared that nitric or muriatic acids, are capable of taking only half of the alkali, and that the salt which crystallizes after solution in either of these acids, has accordingly exactly four times as much acid as would saturate the alkali that remains.

Exp. 5. For the purpose of proving that the constitution of this compound has been rightly ascertained, the salt thus formed should be purified by a second crystallization in distilled water; after which the alkali of thirty grains must be obtained by exposure to a red heat, in order to neutralize the redundant acid contained in ten grains of the same salt. The quantity of unburned salt contains alkali for one part out of four of the acid present, and it requires the alkali of three equal quantities of the same salt to saturate the three remaining parts of acid.

The limit to the decomposition of super-oxalate of potash by the above acids, is analogous to that which occurs when sulphate of potash is decomposed by nitric acid; for in this case also, no quantity of that acid can take more than half the potash, and the remaining salt is converted into a definite super-sulphate, similar to that obtained by heat in the third experiment.

It is not improbable that many other changes in chemistry, supposed to be influenced by a general redundance of some one ingredient, may in fact be limited by a new order of affinities taking place at some definite proportion to be expressed by a simple multiple. And though the strong power of crystallizing in oxalic acid, renders the modifications of which its combinations are susceptible more distinct than those of other acids, it seems probable that a similar play of affinities will arise in solution, when other acids exceed their base in the same proportion.

In order to determine whether oxalic acid is capable of uniting to potash in a proportion intermediate between the double and quadruple quantity of acid, I neutralized forty-eight grains of carbonate of potash with thirty grains of oxalic acid, and added sixty grains more of acid, so that I had two parts of potash of twenty-four grains each, and six *equivalent* quantities of oxalic acid of fifteen grains each, in solution, ready to crystallize together, if disposed to unite, in the proportion of three to one; but the first portion of salt that crystallized, was the common binoxalate,

[10] [Now known as the tetroxalate, $KHC_2O_4.H_2C_2O_4$.]

or salt of sorrel, and a portion selected from the after crystals (which differed very discernibly in their form) was found to contain the quadruple proportion of acid. Hence, it is to be presumed, that if these salts could have been perfectly separated, it would have been found, that the two quantities of potash were equally divided, and combined in one instance with two, and in the other with the remaining four out of the six *equivalent* quantities of acid taken.

To account for this want of disposition to unite in the proportion of three to one by Mr Dalton's theory, I apprehend he might consider the neutral salt as consisting of

2 particles potash with 1 acid,

The binoxalate

as 1 and 1, or 2   with 2,

The quadroxalate

as 1 and 2, or 2   with 4,

in which cases the ratios which I have observed of the acids to each other in these salts would respectively obtain.

But an explanation, which admits the supposition of a double-share of potash in the neutral salt, is not altogether satisfactory; and I am further inclined to think, that when our views are sufficiently extended, to enable us to reason with precision concerning the proportions of elementary atoms, we shall find the arithmetical relation alone will not be sufficient to explain their mutual action, and that we shall be obliged to acquire a geometrical conception of their relative arrangement in all the three dimensions of solid extension.[11]

For instance, if we suppose the limit to the approach of particles to be the same in all directions, and hence their virtual extent to be spherical (which is the most simple hypothesis); in this case, when different sorts combine singly there is but one mode of union. If they unite in the proportion of two to one, the two particles will naturally arrange themselves at opposite poles of that to which they unite. If there be three, they might be arranged with regularity, at the angles of an equilateral triangle in a great circle surrounding the single spherule; but in this arrangement, for want of similar matter at the poles of this circle, the equilibrium would be unstable, and would be liable to be deranged by the slightest force of adjacent combinations; but when the number of one set of particles exceeds in the proportion of four to one, then, on the contrary, a stable equilibrium may again take place, if the four particles are situated at the angles of the four equilateral triangles composing a regular tetrahedron.

[11] [This is a remarkable prophecy. It was made sixty-six years before van't Hoff and Le Bel.]

But as this geometrical arrangement of the primary elements of matter is altogether conjectural, and must rely for its confirmation or rejection upon future inquiry, I am desirous that it should not be confounded with the results of the facts and observations related above, which are sufficiently distinct and satisfactory with respect to the existence of the law of simple multiples. It is perhaps too much to hope, that the geometrical arrangement of primary particles will ever be perfectly known; since even admitting that a very small number of these atoms combining together would have a tendency to arrange themselves in the manner I have imagined; yet, until it is ascertained how small a proportion the primary particles themselves bear to the interval between them, it may be supposed that surrounding combinations, although themselves analogous, might disturb that arrangement, and in that case, the effect of such interference must also be taken into the account, before any theory of chemical combination can be rendered complete.

In 1813 Wollaston studied *equivalent weights*, a term which he introduced. In a paper[12] read at the Royal Society on Nov. 4, 1813, he defended his use of equivalents, presenting in the concluding portions of the paper a "Numerical Table of Equivalents" and "Synoptic Scale of Chemical Equivalents," the latter not unlike the modern chemical slide rule. Portions of this paper and the "Numerical Table" follow.

A SYNOPTIC SCALE OF CHEMICAL EQUIVALENTS.

When the nature of any saline compound is proposed as the subject of inquiry to an analytic chemist, the questions that occur for his consideration are so varied and so numerous, that he will seldom be disposed to undertake a series of original experiments for the purpose of satisfying his inquiries, so long as he can rely upon the accuracy of those results that have been obtained by the labour of others, who have preceded him in this field of patient investigation.

If, for instance, the salt under examination be the common blue vitriol, or crystallized sulphate of copper, the first obvious questions are, (1) How much sulphuric acid does it contain? (2) How much oxide of copper? (3) How much water? He may not be satisfied with these first steps in the analysis, but may desire to know further the quantities (4) of sulphur, (5) of copper, (6) of oxygen, (7) of hydrogen. As means of gaining this information, he naturally considers the quantities of various reagents that may be employed for discovering the quantity of sulphuric acid, (8) how much barytes, (9) carbonate of barytes, or (10) nitrate of barytes, would be requisite for this purpose; (11) how much lead is to be used in the form of (12) nitrate of lead; and when the precipitate of (13) sulphate of barytes or (14) sulphate of lead are obtained, it will be necessary that he should

[12] *Philosophical Transactions*, **1814**: 1–22.

also know the proportion which either of them contains of dry sulphuric acid. He may also endeavour to ascertain the same point by means of (15) the quantity of pure potash, or (16) of carbonate of potash requisite for the precipitation of the copper. He might also use (17) zinc or (18) iron for the same purpose, and he may wish to know the quantities of (19) sulphate of zinc, or (20) sulphate of iron that will then remain in the solution.

These, and very many more questions of the same kind, which it would be tedious to specify, and needless to enumerate, engage the thoughts, and will occupy much of the time of every experimental chemist, unless he can have recourse to some record of former analyses on which he can depend.

The scale, which I am about to describe, is designed to answer at one view all these questions, with reference to most of the salts contained in the table, not merely expressing numerically the proportions by which the desired answers may be calculated, but directly indicating the actual weights of the several ingredients, contained in any assumed weight of the salt under consideration, and also the actual quantities of several reagents that may be used, and of the precipitates that would be obtained by each.

In the formation of this scale, it is requisite in the first place to determine the proportions in which the different known chemical bodies unite with each other, and to express these proportions in such terms that the same substance shall always be represented by the same number. . . .

Having some time since computed for private use a series of supposed atoms, I had assumed oxygen as the decimal unit of my scale, in order to facilitate the estimation of those numerous combinations which it forms with other bodies. But, though in the present table of Equivalents, I have retained the same unit, and have taken care to make oxygen equally prominent for the same reason as before, as well as on account of the important part it performs in determining the affinities of bodies by the different proportions in which it is united to them; nevertheless the real measure, by which most bodies are compared to each other, in any experiments that I have made, and to which I have, in fact, endeavoured to find equivalents, is a determinate quantity of carbonate of lime. This is a compound, that may be regarded as most distinctly neutral. It is most easy to obtain in a state of uniform purity; most easy to analyse (as a binary compound); it is a most convenient measure for the powers of acids, and affords the most distinct expression for the comparative neutralizing powers of alkalies.

The first question, consequently, to be resolved is, by what number are we to express the relative weight of carbonic acid, if oxygen be fixed at 10. It seems to be very well ascertained, that a given quantity of oxygen yields exactly an equal measure of carbonic acid by union with carbon;

and since the specific gravities of these gases are as 10 to 13,77, or as 20 to 27,54, the weight of carbon may be justly represented by 7,54, which, in this instance, is combined with 2 of oxygen forming the deutoxide, and carbonic oxide being the protoxide will be duly represented by 17,54.

Carbonic acid having consequently been assumed as 27,54, it follows from the analysis of carbonate of lime, which by heat loses 43,7 per cent. of acid, and leaves 56,3 of base, that they are combined in the proportion of 27,54 to 35,46, and consequently that lime must be represented by 35,46, and carbonate of lime by 63.

If I would proceed in the series for the purpose of estimating the reliance to be placed on preceding analyses, I might dissolve 63 of carbonate of lime in muriatic acid, and by evaporating to perfect dryness should obtain about 69,56 muriate of lime, and by deducting the weight of the lime 35,46 should learn, by means of the difference 34,1, what is to be considered as dry muriatic acid.

But since lime is now known, by the brilliant discoveries of Sir H. Davy, to be a metallic body united with oxygen, this salt may also be viewed as a binary compound in a different light as oxymuriate of calcium; in which case we must transfer the weight of 10 oxygen to the muriatic acid, making 44,1 of oxymuriatic acid combined with 25,46 calcium. Or, lastly, if with the same distinguished chemist, we regard it as chlorid of calcium, its place in the scale of equivalents is the same 69,56, and the portion of matter here added to the calcium, whether it retain its late name of oxymuriatic acid, or revert to its original one of dephlogisticated marine acid, or assume its new one of chlorine, will be rightly represented by 44,1, which expresses a bare fact without reference to any theory, and affords the means of estimating the proportion of this constituent in all muriatic compounds, without need of controversy respecting its simple or compound nature, which may never admit of any argument that will be deemed conclusive by all parties.

With the same latitude of interpretation may be understood muriate of potash or of soda in the scale of equivalents; and the relative weights of mere potash or soda may, perhaps, be determined better by means of these compounds than by any other, because they are not liable to be superacid, and are not decomposed by heat.

If to a quantity of muriatic acid, which, by previous trial, I know would dissolve 100 carbonate of lime, I add 100 grains of crystallized carbonate of potash, and after the addition find that it will dissolve only 49,8 of carbonate of lime; I hence infer that 100 of this carbonate is equivalent to 50,2 carbonate of lime, and consequently that 125,5 is the equivalent to 63 in the table.

Next, if I combine 125,5 of crystallized carbonate of potash with an excess of muriatic acid, and evaporate to dryness, I expel the whole of the water with all redundant acid, and I find 93,2 of neutral salt; and whether I call it muriate of potash, or chlorid of potassium, or by any other name, with any other views, I may deduct 34,1 as dry muriatic acid, (whether real or imaginary)[13] and infer the equivalent for potash to be 59,1, even though there should, in fact, be only 49,1 of potassium present, requiring 10 of oxygen to convert it into potash.

The next question that occurs relates to the composition of this crystallized carbonate of potash, which I am induced to call bicarbonate of potash, for the purpose of marking more decidedly the distinction between this salt and that which is commonly called a subcarbonate,[14] and in order to refer at once to the double dose of carbonic acid contained in it. With reference to carbonate of lime also, I must necessarily consider it as a supercarbonate, for if I add a solution of this salt to a neutral solution of muriate of lime, a considerable effervescence takes place, from a redundance of carbonic acid beyond what is necessary to saturate the lime. If I saturate 125,5 of this salt with nitric acid, taking due precautions not to expel any of the fluid along with the gas which escapes, it loses about 55 of carbonic acid, which is the double of 27,5. But if, previous to the saturation, I heat the salt moderately red, it loses 38,8, consisting of 27,5 carbonic acid and 11,3 water, after which the addition of an acid expels only 27,5, or a single dose of carbonic acid.

I have in this experiment made use of nitric acid, in order that the resulting compound might guide me in the selection from among former estimates which are extremely discordant with regard to the equivalent of that acid. The proportion of nitrate of potash, which I have obtained by evaporating such a solution by a heat just sufficient to fuse the residuum, gave at the lowest in three experiments 126, for the equivalent of nitrate of potash; from which, if we deduct 59,1 potash, there will remain 66,9 as the apparent equivalent of dry nitric acid. Consequently, I have no hesitation in preferring the estimate[15] to be obtained from Richter's analysis of nitrate of potash, which gives 67,45, from which if we subtract one portion of azote 17,54, there remain 49,91, so nearly 5 portions of oxygen, that I consider the truth to be 17,54 + 50, or 67,54.

From this sketch of the mode in which such an inquiry may be pursued, wherever it is necessary to make any original experiments, it will be fully understood what is meant by equivalents, and in what manner the series might be continued. I have, however, in most instances drawn my infer-

[13] Its separate existence is certainly imaginary, for it can no more be obtained uncombined than dry sulphuric acid, or dry nitric acid.

[14] I avoid using the term carbonate of potash for either of these salts, because it has been applied to both, and consequently is liable to be misunderstood when standing alone.

[15] 46,7:53,3::59.1:67,45 quoted in Mem. d'Arcueil, II, 59.

Numerical Table of Equivalents.

Hydrogen	(a)	1,32	
Oxygen		10,00	
Water		11,32	
Carbon	(b)	7,54 + 20 Oxygen = 27,54 Carbonic acid.
Sulphur	(f)	20,00 + 30 Oxyg. = 50 Sulphuric acid.
Phosphorus	(g)	17,40 + 20 Oxyg. = 37,4 Phosphoric acid.
Azote	(o)	17,54 + 50 Oxyg. = 67,54 Nitric acid (q).
Muriatic Acid (dry)	(e)	34,1 + 10 Oxyg. = 44,1 Oxymuriatic acid.
Chlorine		44,1 = Oxymur. acid + 1,32 Hydrog. = 45,42 Muriatic gas.
Oxalic acid	(b)	47,0
Ammonia	(p)	21,5
Soda	(l)	39,1 — 10 Oxyg. = 29,1 Sodium.
Potash	(m)	59,1 — 10 Oxyg. = 49,1 Potassium.
Magnesia	(n)	24,6
Lime	(c)	35,46 — 10 Oxyg. = 25,46 Calcium.
Strontia	(k)	69,
Barytes	(i)	97,
Iron	(r)	34,5 + 10 Oxyg. = 44,5 Green Oxid of Iron.
		+ 15 Oxyg. = 49,5 Red Oxid.
Copper	(t)	40, + 10 Oxyg. = 50, Black Oxid of Copper.
Zinc	(s)	41 + 10 Oxyg. = 51, Oxid of Zinc.
Mercury	(v)	125,5 + 10 Oxyg. = 135,5 Red Oxid Mercury.
		+ 125,5 ☿ = 261 Protoxid ☿.
Lead	(d)	129,5 + 10 Oxyg. = 139,5 Litharge.
Silver	(u)	135, + 10 Oxyg. = 145, Oxid Silver in Muriate.
Subcarb. of Ammonia		49,0 + 27,5 C. acid = 76,5 Bi-Carb. of Ammonia.
Subcarb. of Soda		66,6 + 27,5 C. acid + 11,3 Water = 105,5 Bi-Carb. of Soda.
Subcarb. of Potash		86, + 27,5 C. acid + 11,3 Water = 125,5 Bi-Carb. of Potash.
Carbonate of Lime		63
———— Barytes		124,5
———— Lead		167,
Sulphuric acid (dry)		50, + 1 Water 11,3 = 61,3 Oil of Vitriol (sp. gr. 1,85).
Sulphate of Soda		89,1 + 10 Water 113,2 = 202,3 Glauber Salt.
———— Potash		109,1
———— Magnesia (n)		74,6 + 7 Water 79,3 = 153,9 Epsom Salt.
———— Lime		85,5 + 2 Water 22,64 = 108,1 Selenite.
———— Strontia		119,0
———— Barytes		147,0
———— Copper		156,6 = 1 Acid + 1 Oxid. + (w) 5 Water 56,6.
———— Iron		173,8 = 1 Acid + 1 Oxid. + 7 Water 79,3.
———— Zinc		180,2 = 1 Acid + 1 Oxid. + 7 Water 79,3.
———— Lead		189,5
Nitric acid (dry)	(q)	67,54 + 2 Water 22,64 = 90,2 Liquid Nitric acid (sp. gr. 1,50).
Nitrate of Soda		106,6
———— Potash		126,6
———— Lime		103,0
———— Barytes		164,5
———— Lead		207,0
Muriate of Ammonia		66,9 = 1 Acid + 1 Amm. + 1 Water.
———— Soda		73,2
———— Potash		93,2 + 60 Oxygen = 153,2 Hyper-Oxymuriate of Potash.
———— Lime		69,6
———— Barytes		131,0 + 2 Water 22,6 (w) 153,6 Crystallized Mur. Barytes.
———— Lead		173,6
———— Silver		179,1
Corrosive Sublimate		170,1 = 1 Acid 1 Oxyg. + 1 Mercury.
Calomel		296,1 = 1 Acid + 1 Oxyg. + 2 Mercury.
Phosphate of Lead		176,9
Oxalate of Lead		186,5
Bin-Oxalate of Potash		153,0 = 2 Acid + 1 Potash

Wollaston's numerical table of equivalents.

ences from former analyses, and indeed in all, where I could find coincidences between different authorities sufficient to give confidence in their results.   . . .

With the exception of those instances that I have enumerated, there are few in which I have found it necessary to make any new experiments, as I have met with coincidences between the independent results of others sufficient to satisfy me of their correctness; and accordingly I have adopted such determinations without any pretensions to improve upon them by new experiments of my own.

It is not my design in the table which preceeds this paper, to attempt a complete enumeration of all those elements or compounds which I suppose to be well ascertained, but merely to include some of those which most frequently occur. I do not offer it as an attempt to correct the estimates that have been formed by others, but as a method in which their results may be advantageously applied in forming an easy approximation to any object of our inquiries.

Lorenzo Romano Amadeo Carlo Avogadro

(1776-1856)

DALTON conceived no distinction between the atom and the molecule of an element. This forced him to reject the assumption, that equal volumes of different gases contain the same number of ultimate particles under the same physical conditions, which he did consider for a time. He further refused to accept Gay-Lussac's law.[1] The reconciliation of Dalton's theory and Gay-Lussac's data was brought about by an Italian, Amadeo Avogadro, with a hypothesis now known as Avogadro's hypothesis. He accomplished this by distinguishing between the atom and molecule of a gas. The hypothesis, published in 1811,[2] went virtually

[1] See W. F. Magie, "A Source Book in Physics," New York, 1935, pp. 165–172; *Alembic Club Reprints*, No. 4, "Foundations of the Molecular theory: Comprising Papers and Extracts by John Dalton, Joseph Louis Gay-Lussac, and Amadeo Avogadro, (1808–1811)," Edinburgh, 1899; Ostwald's *Klassiker*, No. 44, "Das Ausdehnungsgesetz der Gase. Abhandlungen von Gay-Lussac, Dalton, Dulong und Petit, Rudberg, Magnus, Regnault (1802–1842). Herausgegeben von W. Ostwald," Leipzig, 1893; and "Les Classiques de la Découverte Scientifique. Détermination des Poids Moléculaires. Mémoires de MM. Avogadro, Ampère, Raoult, van't Hoff, D. Berthelot. Avant-Propos par M. R. Lespieau," Paris, 1938.

[2] *Journal de physique*, **73**: 58–76 (1811). The French in this paper is clumsy and occasionally obscure.

unnoticed because, for a variety of reasons, chemists were not yet ready to see its implications. A. M. Ampère (1775–1836) advanced a similar theory in 1814,[3] but it was no better received. More than half a century was to pass before Cannizzaro demonstrated the general applicability of the hypothesis and brought the atomic theory to real fruition.

The following translation of the paper, in which Avogadro announced his hypothesis, is that of the *Alembic Club Reprint*.[4]

ESSAY ON A MANNER OF DETERMINING THE RELATIVE MASSES OF THE ELEMENTARY MOLECULES OF BODIES, AND THE PROPORTIONS IN WHICH THEY ENTER INTO THESE COMPOUNDS.

I.

M. Gay-Lussac has shown in an interesting Memoir that gases always unite in a very simple proportion by volume, and that when the result of the union is a gas, its volume also is very simply related to those of its components. But the quantitative proportions of substances in compounds seem only to depend on the relative number of molecules which combine, and on the number of composite molecules which result. It must then be admitted that very simple relations also exist between the volumes of gaseous substances and the numbers of simple or compound molecules which form them. The first hypothesis to present itself in this connection, and apparently even the only admissible one, is the supposition that the number of integral molecules[5] in any gases is always the same for equal volumes, or always proportional to the volumes. Indeed, if we were to suppose that the number of molecules contained in a given volume were different for different gases, it would scarcely be possible to conceive that the law regulating the distance of molecules could give in all cases relations so simple as those which the facts just detailed compel us to acknowledge between the volume and the number of molecules. On the other hand, it is very well conceivable that the molecules of gases being at such a distance that their mutual attraction cannot be exercised, their varying attraction for caloric may be limited to condensing a greater or smaller quantity around them, without the atmosphere formed by this fluid having any greater extent in the one case than in the other, and, consequently, without the distance between the molecules varying; or, in other words, without the number of molecules contained in a given volume

[3] *Ann. chim. phys.*, **90**: 45 (1814).

[4] The Italian translation of this paper can be found in Avogadro's "Opere Scelete, publicate dalla R. Accademia delle Seienze di Torino," Torino, 1911. An enlargement of Avogadro's memoir was published in 1837, "Fisica de' Corpi Ponderbili, ossia Trattato della Constituzione Generale de' Corpi," Torino, 1837–1841.

[5] [The words "atom" and "molecule" had not yet, of course, been confined to their modern meanings. By "integral molecule" Avogadro denoted a molecule of a compound; by "constituent molecule" a molecule of an element; and by "elementary molecule" an atom.]

being different. Dalton, it is true, has proposed a hypothesis directly opposed to this, namely, that the quantity of caloric is always the same for the molecules of all bodies whatsoever in the gaseous state, and that the greater or less attraction for caloric only results in producing a greater or less condensation of this quantity around the molecules, and thus varying the distance between the molecules themselves. But in our present ignorance of the manner in which this attraction for the molecules for caloric is exerted, there is nothing to decide us *a priori* in favour of the one of these hypotheses rather than the other; and we should rather be inclined to adopt a neutral hypothesis, which would make the distance between the molecules and the quantities of caloric vary according to unknown laws, were it not that the hypothesis we have just proposed is based on that simplicity of relation between the volumes of gases on combination, which would appear to be otherwise inexplicable.

Setting out from this hypothesis, it is apparent that we have the means of determining very easily the relative masses of the molecules of substances obtainable in the gaseous state, and the relative number of these molecules in compounds; for the ratios of the masses of the molecules are then the same as those of the densities of the different gases at equal temperature and pressure, and the relative number of molecules in a compound is given at once by the ratio of the volumes of the gases that form it. For example, since the numbers 1.10359 and 0.07321 express the densities of the two gases oxygen and hydrogen compared to that of atmospheric air as unity, and the ratio of the two numbers consequently represents the ratio between the masses of equal volumes of these two gases, it will also represent on our hypothesis the ratio of the masses of their molecules. Thus the mass of the molecule of oxygen will be about 15 times that of the molecule of hydrogen, or more exactly, as 15.074 to 1. In the same way the mass of the molecule of nitrogen will be to that of hydrogen as 0.96913 to 0.07321, that is, as 13, or more exactly 13.238, to 1. On the other hand, since we know that the ratio of the volumes of hydrogen and oxygen in the formation of water is 2 to 1, it follows that water results from the union of each molecule of oxygen with two molecules of hydrogen. Similarly, according to the proportions by volume established by M. Gay-Lussac for the elements of ammonia, nitrous oxide, nitrous gas, and nitric acid, ammonia will result from the union of one molecule of nitrogen with three of hydrogen, nitrous oxide from one molecule of oxygen with two of nitrogen, nitrous gas from one molecule of nitrogen with one of oxygen, and nitric acid from one of nitrogen with two of oxygen.

II.

There is a consideration which appears at first sight to be opposed to the admission of our hypothesis with respect to compound substances. It seems that a molecule composed of two or more elementary molecules should have its mass equal to the sum of the masses of those molecules; and that in particular, if in a compound one molecule of one substance unites with two or more molecules of another substance, the number of compound molecules should remain the same as the number of molecules of the first substance. Accordingly, on our hypothesis when a gas combines with two or more times its volume of another gas, the resulting compound, if gaseous, must have a volume equal to that of the first of these gases. Now, in general, this is not actually the case. For instance, the volume of water in the gaseous state is, as M. Gay-Lussac has shown, twice as great as the volume of oxygen which enters into it, or, what comes to the same thing, equal to that of the hydrogen instead of being equal to that of the oxygen. But a means of explaining facts of this type in conformity with our hypothesis presents itself naturally enough: we suppose, namely, that the constituent molecules of any simple gas whatever (*i.e.*, the molecules which are at such a distance from each other that they cannot exercise their mutual action) are not formed of a solitary elementary molecule, but are made up of a certain number of these molecules united by attraction to form a single one; and further, that when molecules of another substance unite with the former to form a compound molecule, the integral molecule which should result splits up into two or more parts (or integral molecules) composed of half, quarter, &c., the number of elementary molecules going to form the constituent molecule of the first substance, combined with half, quarter, &c., the number of constituent molecules of the second substance that ought to enter into combination with one constituent molecule of the first substance (or, what comes to the same thing, combined with a number equal to this last of half-molecules, quarter-molecules, &c., of the second substance); so that the number of integral molecules of the compound becomes double, quadruple, &c., what it would have been if there had been no splitting-up, and exactly what is necessary to satisfy the volume of the resulting gas.[6]

On reviewing the various compound gases most generally known, I only find examples of duplication of the volume relatively to the volume of that one of the constituents which combines with one or more volumes of the other. We have already seen this for water. In the same way, we know that the volume of ammonia gas is twice that of the nitrogen which enters into it. M. Gay-Lussac has also shown that the volume of nitrous oxide is equal to that of the nitrogen which forms part of it, and consequently is twice that of the oxygen. Finally, nitrous gas, which contains equal volumes of nitrogen and oxygen, has a volume equal to the sum of the two

[6] Thus, for example, the integral molecule of water will be composed of a half-molecule of oxygen with one molecule, or, what is the same thing, two half-molecules of hydrogen.

constituent gases, that is to say, double that of each of them. Thus in all these cases there must be a division of the molecule into two; but it is possible that in other cases the division might be into four, eight, &c. The possibility of this division of compound molecules might have been conjectured *a priori;* for otherwise the integral molecules of bodies composed of several substances with a relatively large number of molecules, would come to have a mass excessive in comparison with the molecules of simple substances. We might therefore imagine that nature had some means of bringing them back to the order of the latter, and the facts have pointed out to us the existence of such means. Besides, there is another consideration which would seem to make us admit in some cases the division in question; for how could one otherwise conceive a real combination between two gaseous substances uniting in equal volumes without condensation, such as takes place in the formation of nitrous gas? Supposing the molecules to remain at such a distance that the mutual attraction of those of each gas could not be exercised, we cannot imagine that a new attraction could take place between the molecules of one gas and those of the other. But on the hypothesis of division of the molecule, it is easy to see that the combination really reduces two different molecules to one, and that there would be contraction by the whole volume of one of the gases if each compound molecule did not split up into two molecules of the same nature. M. Gay-Lussac clearly saw that, according to the facts, the diminution of volume on the combination of gases cannot represent the approximation of their elementary molecules. The division of molecules on combination explains to us how these two things may be made independent of each other.

III.

Dalton, on arbitrary suppositions as to the most likely relative number of molecules in compounds, has endeavoured to fix ratios between the masses of the molecules of simple substances. Our hypothesis, supposing it well-founded, puts us in a position to confirm or rectify his results from precise data, and, above all, to assign the magnitude of compound molecules according to the volumes of the gaseous compounds, which depend partly on the division of molecules entirely unsuspected by this physicist.

Thus Dalton supposes[7] that water is formed by the union of hydrogen and oxygen, molecule to molecule. From this, and from the ratio by weight of the two components, it would follow that the mass of the molecule of oxygen would be to that of hydrogen as $7\frac{1}{2}$ to 1 nearly, or, according to Dalton's evaluation, as 6 to 1. This ratio on our hypothesis is, as

[7] In what follows I shall make use of the exposition of Dalton's ideas given in Thomson's "System of Chemistry."

we saw, twice as great, namely, as 15 to 1. As for the molecule of water, its mass ought to be roughly expressed by $15 + 2 = 17$ (taking for unity that of hydrogen), if there were no division of the molecule into two; but on account of this division it is reduced to half, $8\frac{1}{2}$, or more exactly 8.537, as may also be found directly by dividing the density of aqueous vapour 0.625 (Gay-Lussac) by the density of hydrogen 0.0732. This mass only differs from 7, that assigned to it by Dalton, by the difference in the values for the composition of water; so that in this respect Dalton's result is approximately correct from the combination of two compensating errors,—the error in the mass of the molecule of oxygen, and his neglect of the division of the molecule.

Dalton supposes that in nitrous gas the combination of nitrogen and oxygen is molecule to molecule; we have seen on our hypothesis that this is actually the case. Thus Dalton would have found the same molecular mass for nitrogen as we have, always supposing that of hydrogen to be unity, if he had not set out from a different value for that of oxygen, and if he had taken precisely the same value for the quantities of the elements in nitrous gas by weight. But by supposing the molecule of oxygen to be less than half what we find, he has been obliged to make that of nitrogen also equal to less than half the value we have assigned to it, viz., 5 instead of 13. As regards the molecule of nitrous gas itself, his neglect of the division of the molecule again makes his result approach ours; he has made it $6 + 5 = 11$, whilst according to us it is about $\dfrac{15 + 13}{2} = 14$, or more exactly $\dfrac{15.074 + 13.238}{2} = 14.156$, as we also find by dividing 1.03636, the density of nitrous gas according to Gay-Lussac, by 0.07321. Dalton has likewise fixed in the same manner as the facts have given us, the relative number of molecules in nitrous oxide and in nitric acid, and in the first case the same circumstance has rectified his result for the magnitude of the molecule. He makes it $6 + 2 \times 5 = 16$, whilst according to our method it should be $\dfrac{15.074 + 2 \times 13.238}{2} = 20.775$, a number which is also obtained by dividing 1.52092, Gay-Lussac's value for the density of nitrous oxide, by the density of hydrogen.

In the case of ammonia, Dalton's supposition as to the relative number of molecules in its composition is on our hypothesis entirely at fault. He supposes nitrogen and hydrogen to be united in it molecule to molecule, whereas we have seen that one molecule of nitrogen unites with three molecules of hydrogen. According to him the molecule of ammonia would be $5 + 1 = 6$: according to us it should be $\dfrac{13 + 3}{2} = 8$, or more exactly

8.119, as may also be deduced directly from the density of ammonia gas. The division of the molecule, which does not enter into Dalton's calculations, partly corrects in this case also the error which would result from his other suppositions.

All the compounds we have just discussed are produced by the union of one molecule of one of the components with one or more molecules of the other. In nitrous acid we have another compound of two of the substances already spoken of, in which the terms of the ratio between the number of molecules both differ from unity. From Gay-Lussac's experiments, it appears that this acid is formed from 1 part by volume of oxygen and 3 of nitrous gas, or, what comes to the same thing, of 3 parts of nitrogen and 5 of oxygen; whence it would follow, on our hypothesis, that its molecules should be composed of 3 molecules of nitrogen and 5 of oxygen, leaving the possibility of division out of account. But this mode of combination can be referred to the preceding simpler forms by considering it as the result of the union of 1 molecule of oxygen with 3 of nitrous gas, *i.e.* with 3 molecules, each composed of a half-molecule of oxygen and a half-molecule of nitrogen, which thus already includes the division of some of the molecules of oxygen which enter into that of nitrous acid. Supposing there to be no other division, the mass of this last molecule would 57.542, that of hydrogen being taken as unity, and the density of nitrous acid gas would be 4.21267, the density of air being taken as unity. But it is probable that there is at least another division into two, and consequently a reduction of the density to half: we must wait until this density has been determined by experiment. . . .

VIII.

It will have been in general remarked on reading this Memoir that there are many points of agreement between our special results and those of Dalton, although we set out from a general principle, and Dalton has only been guided by considerations of detail. This agreement is an argument in favour of our hypothesis, which is at bottom merely Dalton's system furnished with a new means of precision from the connection we have found between it and the general fact established by M. Gay-Lussac. Dalton's system supposes that compounds are made in general in fixed proportions, and this is what experiment shows with regard to the more stable compounds and those most interesting to the chemist. It would appear that it is only combinations of this sort that can take place amongst gases, on account of the enormous size of the molecules which would result from ratios expressed by larger numbers, in spite of the division of the molecules, which is in all probability confined within narrow limits. We perceive that the close packing of the molecules in solids and in liquids, which only leaves between the integral molecules distances of the same order as those between the elementary molecules, can give rise to more complicated ratios, and even to combinations in all proportions; but these compounds will be so to speak of a different type from those with which we have been concerned, and this distinction may serve to reconcile M. Berthollet's ideas as to compounds with the theory of fixed proportions.

Alessandro Volta

(1745–1827)

IN the latter half of the eighteenth century, the study of electrical phenomena became very popular. The Leyden jar and the static machine were the only available sources of electricity, and they could furnish only small and discontinuous currents.

In 1786, Galvani (1737–1798), while studying a nerve-muscle preparation of frog legs hung on copper hooks, noticed a twitch when the hooks were hung on an iron support. He believed that the twitch was due to an electric effect arising in the muscle itself, but his countryman, Alessandro Volta, believed the electricity originated in the junction of the two metals. His experiments confirmed this, and he conceived the idea of increasing the amount of "electric fluid" by placing a number of metal junctions together. When he further found that by moistening the junctions the effect could be made to last, he had discovered the voltaic pile. Though Volta himself confined his experiments with his apparatus to those of a physiological nature, chemists quickly realized the possibilities of the new discovery, and in the hands of men like Berzelius and Davy, results of the most far-reaching theoretical and practical nature were obtained. The discovery was therefore of great importance to chemistry.

Volta described his apparatus in a letter, written in French, which he sent to Sir Joseph Banks, president of the Royal Society. This was published in the *Philosphical Transactions* for 1800.[1]

---

[1] *Philosophical Transactions*, **1800**: 403–431. A facsimile reproduction appears in *Isis*, **15**: 129–157 (1931). It is also to be found in the only collected edition of Volta's works, "Collezione dell' Opere del Alessandro Volta [publicata da Vincenzio Antinori]," Firenze, 1816, 3 vols.; and in Ostwald's *Klassiker*, No. 114, "Alessandro Volta, Untersuchungen über den Galvanismus. (1796 bis 1800). Herausgegeben von A. J. von Oettingen," Leipzig, 1900. A selection from the paper appears in W. F. Magie, "A Source Book in Physics," New York, 1935, pp. 427–431. The selection given here is taken from pages 403 to 411 and 417 of the *Philosophical Transactions*.

ON THE ELECTRICITY EXCITED BY THE MERE CONTACT OF
CONDUCTING SUBSTANCES OF DIFFERENT KINDS. IN A LETTER
FROM MR. ALEXANDER VOLTA, F.R.S. PROFESSOR OF
NATURAL PHILOSOPHY IN THE UNIVERSITY OF PAVIA, TO THE
RT. HON. SIR JOSEPH BANKS, BART. K.B. P.R.S.

Read June 26, 1800

At Como in the Milanais, March 20, 1800.
After a long silence, for which I will not seek to excuse myself, I have
the pleasure of communicating to you, Sir, and through you to the Royal
Society, some striking results at which I have arrived in pursuing my
experiments on the electricity excited by the simple mutual contact of
metals of different sorts, and even by that of other conductors, also differing among themselves, either liquids, or containing some fluid to which
they properly owe their conducting power. The principal result, and that
which comprehends nearly all the others, is the construction of an apparatus which resembles in its effects, that is to say, in the sensations which
it can cause in the arms, &c., the Leyden jars, or better yet, feebly charged
electric batteries, but which acts without ceasing, or whose charge after
each discharge is reestablished by itself; which provides, in a word, an un-
limited charge, a perpetual action or impulsion on the electrical fluid; but
which otherwise differs essentially from them, both by this continual
action which is proper to it and because in place of consisting, as do the
ordinary jars and electric batteries, of one or several insulating plates in
thin layers of those bodies thought to be only *electrics* [insulators], coated
with conductors or bodies called *nonelectrics*, this new apparatus is formed
solely of several of these latter bodies, chosen even from among the best
conductors, and therefore the most remote, according to what has always
been believed, from the electric nature. Yes, the apparatus of which I
speak, and which will no doubt astonish you, is only an assemblage of a
number of good conductors of different sorts, arranged in a certain manner. Thirty, 40, 60 pieces or more, of copper, or better of silver, each
applied to a piece of tin, or, what is much better, of zinc, and an equal
number of layers of water, or of some other fluid which is a better conductor than simple water, such as salt water, lye, &c., or pieces of cardboard, of leather, &c., well soaked in these fluids; of such layers interposed
between each couple or combination of two different metals, with such an
alternation of these three sorts of conductors always following in the same
order, that is what constitutes my new instrument; which imitates, as I
have said, the effects of Leyden jars or electric batteries, giving the same
sensations as do they; which, in truth, remains much below the activity of
these batteries charged to a high degree, as to the force and noise of the
explosions, to the spark, to the distance at which the discharge can operate, &c., equaling only the effects of a battery charged to a very feeble

degree but having an immense capacity; but what above all infinitely surpasses the virtue and the power of these same batteries is that there is no need, as in them, to be charged in advance with an external electricity, and in that it can produce its effect every time it is suitably touched, however frequently.

The apparatus, resembling fundamentally in form, as I will show and even as I construct it, the *natural electric organ* of the torpedo, the electric eel, &c., even more than the Leyden jar and the known electric batteries, I wish to call the *artificial electric organ*. And in truth is it not, like them, composed solely of conducting bodies? Is it not also active by itself, without any previous charge, without the aid of an electricity excited by any means known up to now; acting without cease, and without respite; finally, capable of giving at any moment stronger or weaker sensations, according to the circumstances, sensations which redouble at each touch and which, repeated thus with frequency or continued for a certain time, produce the same numbness of the limbs as does the torpedo, &c.

I will give here a more detailed description of this apparatus and some of its analogues, as well as some of the most remarkable experiments made with them.   . . .

I place horizontally on some table or base one of the metallic plates, for example, one of silver, and to this first I add a second of zinc; on this second I add a moistened disc; then another silver plate, followed immediately by another of zinc, to which I add another moistened disc. I thus continue in the same fashion, coupling a silver plate with one of zinc, and always in the same order, that is to say, always the silver below and the zinc above, or vice versa, according to how I began, and interposing between each of these couples a moistened disc; I continue, I say, to form from the several stages a column as high as can be sustained without falling.

Now, if it contains about 20 of these stages, or couples of metals, it will already be able not only to give the signs of the electrometer of CAR-VALLO, aided by a condenser, to charge this condenser more than 10 or 15 degrees by simply touching, at the point of making it give a spark, &c., but also to strike the fingers with which the two extremities are touched (the head and the foot of such a column) with one or several little blows, and more or less frequently, according to how these contacts are repeated; each of which blows perfectly resembles in its light sensation that produced by a feebly charged Leyden jar, or a battery charged still more feebly, or, finally, an extremely listless torpedo, which imitates the effects of my apparatus still better, from the repeated blows which it can give without cease.

To obtain such light sensations from this apparatus which I am going to describe, and which is still too small for great effects, it is necessary that the fingers with which the two extremities are touched at the same time be moistened with water at the point where the skin, which otherwise is not a good conductor, is well wetted. Again, to unite them more surely and receive considerably stronger sensations, it is necessary to connect the bottom of the column, that is to say, the bottom plate, by means of a large enough strip, or a large metal wire, to water in a dish or cup large enough so that one, two, three fingers, or the whole hand can be plunged in and that the head, or superior extremity (the last or one of the last plates of this column), be touched with the clean end of a strip, also metallic, held by the other hand, which should be very wet and hold a large surface of the strip, firmly clasped. Proceeding in this way, I can then obtain a little tingling or light sensation in both joints of a finger plunged in the water of the dish by touching with the strip held in the other hand the fourth, or even the third, pair of plates; touching then the fifth, the sixth, and successively the others, up to the last plate, which forms the head of the column, it is curious to note how the sensation gradually increases in force. . . .

Also, the effects of my apparatus (the sensations which it produces) are considerably more apparent as the temperature of the surrounding air, or that of the water, or of the moistened discs which enter the structure of the column, or even of the water in the dish, is hotter; heat renders the water a better conductor. But what makes it still much better are almost all the salts, notably common salt. This is one of the reasons, if not the only one, why it is of advantage that the water of the dish, and above all that interposed between each pair of metallic plates, the water imbibed by the discs of cardboard, &c., should be salt water, as I have already remarked.

But all these methods and all these attentions, finally, have only a limited advantage and will never permit obtaining very strong sensations, so long as the apparatus consists of only one column formed of 20 pairs of plates. . . .

Returning to the mechanical construction of my apparatus, which is susceptible of several variations, I will here not describe all those of which I have thought and have executed, either on a large or small scale, but only some which are more curious or more useful; which present some real advantage, as being easy to construct, or quicker, more certain in their effects, or keeping longer in good condition.

And to commence with one which unites nearly all these advantages, differing most in form from the *columnar apparatus* described above, but which has the disadvantage of being a much larger machine, I present to you this new apparatus, which I will call the *crown of cups* in the added figure (Fig. 1). . . .

As to the columnar apparatus, I have sought the means to lengthen it

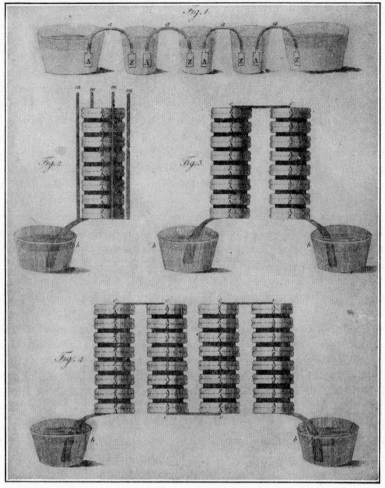

Various forms of Volta's pile.

considerably, by multiplying the metallic plates without causing them to fall; to make the instrument easy and portable, and above all, durable; and I have found, among others, the following which I show you in the figure (Fig. 2, 3, 4).

In the rest of the paper, Volta describes the sensations produced by the pile on various parts of the body.

Humphry Davy

(1778–1819)

HUMPHRY Davy was one of the most brilliant chemists of the early nineteenth century. His early study of nitrous oxide brought him his first reputation, but his later and most important investigations were devoted to electrochemistry. Following Galvani's experiments and the discovery of the voltaic pile,[1] interest in galvanic electricity had become widespread. The first electrolysis by means of the pile was carried out in 1800 by Nicholson and Carisle,[2] who obtained hydrogen and oxygen from water. Davy began to examine the chemical effects of electricity in 1800, and his numerous discoveries were presented in his Bakerian lecture to the Royal Society on November 20, 1806, "On Some Chemical Agencies of Electricity."[3] For this work the Institut de France awarded him a prize of 3,000 francs, for the most important research in electricity for the year. In these researches Davy recognized that in electricity he had an agent capable of decomposing the most stable combinations, and he therefore turned to an investigation of the electrolysis of hitherto undecomposed substances. Davy must have known of Lavoisier's suggestion that the alkali earths were probably oxides of unknown metals. On electrolyzing the alkalis he discovered potassium and sodium. The results were presented in the Bakerian lecture in November, 1807 entitled "On Some New Phenomena of Chemical Changes Produced by Electricity, Particularly the Decomposition of the Fixed Alkalies, and the Exhibition of the New Substances Which Constitute Their Bases; and on the General Nature of Alkaline Bodies."[4] Excerpts from this paper form the first selection below. By means of electrolysis Davy also prepared for the first time the metals barium, magnesium,

---

[1] See also W. F. Magie, "A Source Book in Physics," New York, 1935, pp. 420–427, 427–431.

[2] *Nicholson's J.*, July, 1800. See also Magie, *op. cit.*, pp. 431–436.

[3] *Philosophical Transactions*, **1807**: 1–56. Reprinted in "The Collected Works of Sir Humphry Davy, edited by his brother, John Davy, M.D., F.R.S.," London, 1839–1840, 9 vols. (vol. 5, pp. 1–56); Ostwald's *Klassiker*, No. 45, "Humphry Davy, Elektrochemische Untersuchungen. Vorgelesen in d. Königl. Societät zu London als Bakerian Lecture am 20, Nov. 1806 und am 19, Nov. 1807. Herausgegeben von W. Ostwald.," Leipzig, 1893; "Les Classiques de la Découverte Scientifique. Halogènes et composés oxygénés du chlore. Mémoires de Scheele, Berthollet, Gay-Lussac et Thenard, H. Davy, Balard, Courtois, H. Moissan, Millon. Avant-Propos par M. A. Damiens," Paris, 1938.

[4] *Philosophical Transactions*, **98**: 1–44, 1808. Also see "Collected Works," vol. 5, p. 57; Ostwald's *Klassiker*, No. 45; *Alembic Club Reprints*, No. 6, "The Decomposition of the Fixed Alkalies and Alkaline Earths, By Humphry Davy, (1807–1808)," Edinburgh, 1901.

calcium, and strontium.[5] He utilized the strong reducing power of potassium to prepare boron.

Davy's researches on chlorine are of an importance comparable with those on the alkali metals. Chlorine, first discovered by Scheele, was regarded by him as "dephlogisticated muriatic acid." As phlogiston was practically synonymous with hydrogen to Scheele, this view was essentially correct. Lavoisier, however, chiefly occupied with phenomena of combustion, assumed that chlorine was an oxide of an unknown "radical." Davy performed many experiments endeavoring to confirm the presence of oxygen and finally concluded that chlorine was an element. The second citation contains a portion of his work on chlorine from his papers of 1810 and 1811.[6]

II. ON THE METHODS USED FOR THE DECOMPOSITION OF THE FIXED ALKALIES.

The researches I had made on the decomposition of acids, and of alkaline and earthy neutral compounds, proved that the powers of electrical decomposition were proportional to the strength of the opposite electricities in the circuit, and to the conducting power and degree of concentration of the materials employed.

In the first attempts, that I made on the decomposition of the fixed alkalies, I acted upon aqueous solutions of potash and soda, saturated at common temperatures, by the highest electrical power I could command, and which was produced by a combination of VOLTAIC batteries belonging to the Royal Institution, containing 24 plates of copper and zinc of 12 inches square, 100 plates of 6 inches, and 150 of 4 inches square, charged with solutions of alum and nitrous acid; but in these cases, though there was a high intensity of action, the water of the solutions alone was affected, and hydrogene and oxygene disengaged with the production of much heat and violent effervescence.

The presence of water appearing thus to prevent any decomposition, I used potash in igneous fusion. By means of a stream of oxygene gas from a gasometer applied to the flame of a spirit lamp, which was thrown on a platina spoon containing potash, this alkali was kept for some minutes in a

---

[5] "Electrochemical researches on the decomposition of the earths; with observations on the metals obtained from the alkaline earths, and on the amalgam procured from ammonia," *Philosophical Transactions*, **98**: 333 (1808). See also "Collected Works," vol. 5, p. 102; *Alembic Club Reprints*, No. 6.

[6] "Researches on the Oxymuriatic Acid, its Nature and Combinations; and on the Elements of the muriatic Acid. With some Experiments on Sulphur and Phosphorus, made in the Laboratory of the Royal Institution," *Philosophical Transactions*, **100**: 231–57 (1810); see also *Alembic Club Reprints*, No. 9, "The Elementary Nature of Chlorine. Papers by Humphry Davy (1809–1818)," Edinburgh, 1902; "Collected Works," vol. 5, p. 284: "The Bakerian Lecture. On Some of the Combinations of Oxymuriatic Gas and Oxygene, and on the Chemical Relations of these Principles, to inflammable Bodies," *Philosophical Transactions*, **101**: 1–35 (1811).

strong red heat, and in a state of perfect fluidity. The spoon was preserved in communication with the positive side of the battery of the power of 100 of 6 inches, highly charged; and the connection from the negative side was made by a platina wire.

By this arrangement some brilliant phenomena were produced. The potash appeared a conductor in a high degree, and as long as the communication was preserved, a most intense light was exhibited at the negative wire, and a column of flame, which seemed to be owing to the development of combustible matter, arose from the point of contact.

When the order was changed, so that the platina spoon was made negative, a vivid and constant light appeared at the opposite point: there was no effect of inflammation round it; but aeriform globules, which inflamed in the atmosphere, rose through the potash.

The platina, as might have been expected, was considerably acted upon; and in the cases when it had been negative, in the highest degree.

The alkali was apparently dry in this experiment; and it seemed probable that the inflammable matter arose from its decomposition. The residual potash was unaltered; it contained indeed a number of dark grey metallic particles, but these proved to be derived from the platina.

I tried several experiments on the electrization of potash rendered fluid by heat, with the hopes of being able to collect the combustible matter, but without success; and I only attained my object, by employing electricity as the common agent for fusion and decomposition.

Though potash, perfectly dried by ignition, is a non-conductor, yet it is rendered a conductor, by a very slight addition of moisture, which does not perceptibly destroy its aggregation; and in this state it readily fuses and decomposes by strong electrical powers.

A small piece of pure potash, which had been exposed for a few seconds to the atmosphere, so as to give conducting power to the surface, was placed upon an insulated disc of platina, connected with the negative side of the battery of the power of 250 of 6 and 4, in a state of intense activity; and a platina wire, communicating with the positive side, was brought in contact with the upper surface of the alkali. The whole apparatus was in the open atmosphere.

Under these circumstances a vivid action was soon observed to take place. The potash began to fuse at both its points of electrization. There was a violent effervescence at the upper surface; at the lower, or negative surface, there was no liberation of elastic fluid; but small globules having a high metallic lustre, and being precisely similar in visible characters to quicksilver, appeared, some of which burnt with explosion and bright flame, as soon as they were formed, and others remained, and were merely tarnished, and finally covered by a white film which formed on their surfaces.

These globules, numerous experiments soon shewed to be the substance I was in search of, and a peculiar inflammable principle the basis of potash. I found that the platina was in no way connected with the result, except as the medium for exhibiting the electrical powers of decomposition; and a substance of the same kind was produced when pieces of copper, silver, gold, plumbago, or even charcoal were employed for compleating the circuit.

The phenomenon was independent of the presence of air; I found that it took place when the alkali was in the vacuum of an exhausted receiver.

The substance was likewise produced from potash fused by means of a lamp, in glass tubes confined by mercury, and furnished with hermetically inserted platina wires by which the electrical action was transmitted. But this operation could not be carried on for any considerable time; the glass was rapidly dissolved by the action of the alkali, and this substance soon penetrated through the body of the tube.

Soda, when acted upon in the same manner as potash, exhibited an analogous result; but the decomposition demanded greater intensity of action in the batteries, or the alkali was required to be in much thinner and smaller pieces. With the battery of 100 of 6 inches in full activity I obtained good results from pieces of potash weighing from 40 to 70 grains, and of a thickness which made the distance of the electrified metallic surfaces nearly a quarter of an inch; but with a similar power it was impossible to produce the effects of decomposition on pieces of soda of more than 15 or 20 grains in weight, and that only when the distance between the wires was about $\frac{1}{8}$ or $\frac{1}{10}$ of an inch.

The substance produced from potash remained fluid at the temperature of the atmosphere at the time of its production; that from soda, which was fluid in the degree of heat of the alkali during its formation, became solid on cooling, and appeared having the lustre of silver.

When the power of 250 was used, with a very high charge for the decomposition of soda, the globules often burnt at the moment of their formation, and sometimes violently exploded and separated into smaller globules, which flew with great velocity through the air in a state of vivid combustion, producing a beautiful effect of continued jets of fire.

III. THEORY OF THE DECOMPOSITION OF THE FIXED ALKALIES; THEIR COMPOSITION, AND PRODUCTION.

As in all decompositions of compound substances which I had previously examined, at the same time that combustible bases were developed at the negative surface in the electrical circuit, oxygen was produced, and evolved or carried into combination at the positive surface, it was reasonable to conclude that this substance was generated in a similar manner by the electrical action upon the alkalies; and a number of experiments made above mercury, with the apparatus for excluding external air, proved that this was the case.

When solid potash, or soda in its conducting state, was included in glass tubes furnished with electrified platina wires, the new substances were generated at the negative surfaces; the gas given out at the other surface proved by the most delicate examination to be pure oxygene; and unless and excess of water was present, no gas was evolved from the negative surface.

In the synthetical experiments, a perfect coincidence likewise will be found.

I mentioned that the metallic lustre of the substance from potash immediately became destroyed in the atmosphere, and that a white crust formed upon it. This crust I soon found to be pure potash, which immediately deliquesced, and new quantities were formed, which in their turn attracted moisture from the atmosphere till the whole globule disappeared, and assumed the form of a saturated solution of potash.[7]

When globules were placed in appropriate tubes containing common air or oxygene gas confined by mercury, an absorption of oxygene took place; a crust of alkali instantly formed upon the globule; but from the want of moisture for its solution, the process stopped, the interior being defended from the action of the gas.

With the substance from soda, the appearances and effects were analogous.

When the substances were strongly heated, confined in given portions of oxygene, a rapid combustion with a brilliant white flame was produced, and the metallic globules were found converted into a white and solid mass, which in the case of the substance from potash was found to be potash, and in the case of that from soda, soda.

Oxygene gas was absorbed in this operation, and nothing emitted which affected the purity of the residual air.

The alkalies produced were apparently dry, or at least contained no more moisture than might well be conceived to exist in the oxygene gas absorbed; and their weights considerably exceeded those of the combustible matters consumed.

The processes on which these conclusions are founded will be fully described hereafter, when the minute details which are necessary will be

---

[7] Water likewise is decomposed in the process. We shall hereafter see that the bases of the fixed alkalis act upon this substance with greater energy than any other known bodies. The minute theory of the oxydation of the bases of the alkalies in the free air, is this:—oxygene gas is first attracted by them, and alkali formed. This alkali speedily absorbs water. This water is again decomposed. Hence, during the conversion of a globule into alkaline solution, there is a constant and rapid disengagement of small quantities of gas.

explained, and the proportions of oxygene, and of the respective inflammable substances which enter into union to form the fixed alkalies, will be given.

It appears then, that in these facts there is the same evidence for the decomposition of potash and soda into oxygene and two peculiar substances, as there is for the decomposition of sulphuric and phosphoric acids and the metallic oxides into oxygene and their respective combustible bases.

In the analytical experiments, no substances capable of decomposition are present but the alkalies and a minute portion of moisture; which seems in no other way essential to the result, than in rendering them conductors at the surface: for the new substances are not generated till the interior, which is dry, begins to be fused; they explode when in rising through the fused alkali they come in contact with the heated moistened surface; they cannot be produced from crystallized alkalies, which contain much water; and the effect produced by the electrization of ignited potash, which contains no sensible quantity of water, confirms the opinion of their formation independently of the presence of this substance.

The combustible bases of the fixed alkalies seem to be repelled as other combustible substances, by positively electrified surfaces, and attracted by negatively electrified surfaces, and the oxygene follows the contrary order; or the oxygene being naturally possessed of the negative energy, and the bases of the positive, do not remain in combination when either of them is brought into an electrical state opposite to its natural one. In the synthesis, on the contrary, the natural energies or attractions come in equilibrium with each other; and when these are in a low state at common temperatures, a slow combination is effected; but when they are exalted by heat, a rapid union is the result; and as in other like cases with the production of fire.—A number of circumstances relating to the agencies of the bases of the alkalies will be immediately stated, and will be found to offer confirmations of these general conclusions. . . .

VII. SOME GENERAL OBSERVATIONS ON THE RELATIONS OF THE BASES OF POTASH AND SODA TO OTHER BODIES.

Should the bases of potash and soda be called metals? The greater number of philosophical persons to whom this question has been put, have answered in the affirmative. They agree with metals in opacity, lustre, malleability, conducting powers as to heat and electricity, and in their qualities of chemical combination.

Their low specific gravity does not appear a sufficient reason for making them a new class; for amongst the metals themselves there are remarkable differences in this respect, platina being nearly four times as heavy as tellurium; and in the philosophical division of the classes of bodies, the analogy between the greater number of properties must always be the foundation of arrangement.

On this idea, in naming the bases of potash and soda, it will be proper to adopt the termination which, by common consent, has been applied to other newly discovered metals, and which, though originally Latin, is now naturalized in our language.

Potasium and Sodium are the names by which I have ventured to call the two new substances: and whatever changes of theory, with regard to the composition of bodies, may hereafter take place, these terms can scarcely express an error; for they may be considered as implying simply the metals produced from potash and soda. I have consulted with many of the most eminent scientific persons in this country, upon the methods of derivation, and the one I have adopted has been the one most generally approved. It is perhaps more significant than elegant. But it was not possible to found names upon specific properties not common to both; and though a name for the basis of soda might have been borrowed from the Greek, yet an analogous one could not have been applied to that of potash, for the ancients do not seem to have distinguished between the two alkalies.

The more caution is necessary in avoiding any theoretical expression in the terms, because the new electro-chemical phenomena that are daily becoming disclosed, seem distinctly to shew that the mature time for a complete generalization of chemical facts is yet far distant; and though, in the explanations of the various results of experiments that have been detailed, the antiphlogistic solution of the phenomena has been uniformly adopted, yet the motive for employing it has been rather a sense of its beauty and precision, than a conviction of its permanency and truth.

The discovery of the agencies of the gasses destroyed the hypothesis of STAHL. The knowledge of the powers and effects of the ethereal substances may at a future time possibly act a similar part with regard to the more refined and ingenious hypothesis of LAVOISIER; but in the present state of our knowledge, it appears the best approximation that has been made to a perfect logic of chemistry.

Whatever future changes may take place in theory, there seems however every reason to believe that the metallic bases of the alkalies, and the common metals, will stand in the same arrangement of substances; and as yet we have no good reasons for assuming the compound nature of this class of bodies.

The selection describing the nature of chlorine follows (see footnote 6 above):

The illustrious discoverer of the oxymuriatic acid considered it as muriatic acid freed from hydrogene; and the common muriatic acid as a compound of hydrogene and oxymuriatic acid, and on this theory he denominated oxymuriatic acid dephlogisticated muriatic acid.

M. BERTHOLLET, a few years after the discovery of SCHEELE, made a number of important and curious experiments on this body; from which he concluded, that it was composed of muriatic acid gas and oxygene and this idea for nearly twenty years has been almost universally adopted.

Dr. HENRY, in an elaborate series of experiments, made with the view of decomposing muriatic acid gas, ascertained that hydrogene was produced from it, by electricity; and he attributed the phaenomenon to water contained in the gas.

In the Bakerian lecture for 1808, I have given an account of the action of potassium upon muriatic acid gas, by which more than one-third of its volume of hydrogene is produced; and I have stated, that muriatic acid can in no instance be procured from oxymuriatic acid, or from dry muriates, unless water or its elements be present.

In the second volume of the Memoires d'Arcueil, M.M. GAY-LUSSAC and THENARD have detailed an extensive series of facts upon muriatic acid, and oxymuriatic acid. Some of their experiments are similar to those I have detailed in the paper just referred to; others are peculiarly their own, and of a very curious kind: their general conclusion is, that muriatic acid gas contains about one quarter of its weight of water; and that oxymuriatic acid is not decomposable by any substances but hydrogene, or such as can form triple combinations with it.

One of the most singular facts that I have observed on this subject, and which I have before referred to, is, that charcoal, even when ignited to whiteness in oxymuriatic or muriatic acid gases, by the VOLTAIC battery, effects no change in them; if it has been previously freed from hydrogene and moisture by intense ignition in vacuo.

This experiment, which I have several times repeated led me to doubt of the existence of oxygene in that substance, which has been supposed to contain it above all others in a loose and active state; and to make a more rigorous investigation than had been hitherto attempted for its detection.

If oxymuriatic acid gas be introduced into a vessel exhausted of air, containing tin; and the tin be gently heated, and the gas in sufficient quantity, the tin and the gas disappear, and a limpid fluid, precisely the same as Libavius's liquor is formed;—it occured to me, that if this substance is a combination of muriatic acid and oxide of tin, oxide of tin ought to be separated from it by means of ammonia. I admitted ammoniacal gas over mercury to a small quantity of the liquor of Libavius; it was absorbed with great heat, and no gas was generated; a solid result was obtained, which was of a dull white colour; some of it was heated, to ascertain if it contained oxide of tin; but the whole volatilized, producing dense pungent fumes.[8]

Another experiment of the same kind, made with great care, and in which the ammonia was used in great excess, proved that the liquor of Libavius cannot be decompounded by ammonia; but that it forms a new combination with the substance.

I have described, on a former occasion, the nature of the operation of phosphorus on oxymuriatic acid, and I have stated that two compounds, one fluid, and the other solid, are formed in the process of combustion,[9] of which the first, on the generally received theory of the nature of oxymuriatic acid, must be considered as a compound of muriatic acid and phosphorous acid, and the other of muriatic acid and phosphoric acid. It occured to me, that if the acids of phosphorus really existed in these combinations, it would not be difficult to obtain them, and thus to gain proofs of the existence of oxygene in oxymuriatic acid.

I made a considerable quantity of the solid compound of oxymuriatic acid and phosphorus by combustion, and saturated it with ammonia, by heating it in a proper receiver filled with ammoniacal gas, on which it acted with great energy, producing much heat; and they formed a white opaque powder.[10] Supposing that this substance was composed of the dry muriates and phosphates of ammonia; as muriate of ammonia is very volatile, and as ammonia is driven off from phosphoric acid, by a heat below redness, I conceived that by igniting the product obtained, I should procure phosphoric acid; I therefore introduced some of the powder into a tube of green glass, and heated it to redness, out of the contact of air by a spirit lamp; but found, to my great surprise, that it was not at all volatile nor decomposable at this degree of heat, and that it gave off no gaseous matter.

The circumstance that a substance composed principally of oxymuriatic acid, and ammonia, should resist decomposition or change at so high a temperature, induced me to pay particular attention to the properties of this new body.

It had no taste nor smell; it did not seem to be soluble, nor did it undergo any perceptible change when digested in boiling water: it did not appear to be acted upon by sulphuric, muriatic, or nitric acid, nor by a strong lixivium of potash. The only processes by which it seemed susceptible of decomposition were by combustion, or the action of ignited hydrat of potash. When brought into the flame of a spirit lamp and made red-hot, it gave feeble indications of inflammation, and tinged the flame of a yellow

[8] [The product probably had the composition $SnCl_4.4NH_3$.]

[9] [PCl_3 and PCl_5.]

[10] [A number of compounds have since been reported as products of this reaction, and it is difficult to say which, if any, of these Davy had here.]

colour, and left a fixed acid, having the properties of phosphoric acid. When acted on by red-hot hydrat of potash, it emitted a smell of ammonia, burnt where it was in contact with air, and appeared to dissolve in the alkali. The potash which had been so acted upon gave muriatic acid, by the addition of sulphuric acid.

I heated some of the powder to whiteness, in a tube of platina; but it did not appear to alter; and after ignition gave ammonia by the action of fused hydrat of potash.

I caused ammonia, made as dry as possible, to act on the phosphuretted liquor of M.M. GAY-LUSSAC and THENARD [PCl_3]; and on the sulphuretted muriatic liquor of Dr. THOMSON [S_2Cl_2]; but no decomposition took place; nor was any muriate of ammonia formed when proper precautions were taken to exclude moisture. The results were new combinations; that from the phosphuretted liquor, was a white solid, from which a part of the phosphorus was separated by heat; but which seemed no further decomposable, even by ignition. That from the sulphuretted liquor was likewise solid, and had various shades of colour, from a bright purple to a golden yellow, according as it was more or less saturated with ammonia; but as these compounds did not present the same uniform and interesting properties, as that from the phosphoric sublimate, I did not examine them minutely: I contented myself by ascertaining that no substance known to contain oxygene could be procured from oxymuriatic acid, in this mode of operation.

It has been said, and taken for granted by many chemists, that when oxymuriatic acid and ammonia act upon each other, water is formed; I have several times made the experiment, and I am convinced that this is not the case. When about 15 or 16 parts of oxymuriatic acid gas are mixed with from 40 to 45 parts of ammoniacal gas, there is a condensation of nearly the whole of the acid and alkaline gasses, and from 5 to 6 parts of nitrogene are produced; and the result is dry muriate of ammonia.

Mr. CRUIKSHANK has shown that oxymuriatic acid and hydrogene, when mixed in proportions nearly equal, produce a matter almost entirely condensible by water; and M.M. GAY-LUSSAC and THENARD, have stated that this matter is common muriatic acid gas, and that no water is deposited in the operation. I have made a number of experiments on the action of oxymuriatic acid gas and hydrogene. When these bodies were mixed in equal volumes over water, and introduced into an exhausted vessel and fired by the electric spark, there was always a deposition of a slight vapour, and a condensation of from $\frac{1}{10}$ to $\frac{1}{20}$ of the volume; but the gas remaining was muriatic acid gas. I have attempted to make the experiment in a manner still more refined, by drying the oxymuriatic acid and the hydrogene by introducing them into vessels containing muriate of lime, and by suffering them to combine at common temperatures; but I have never been able to avoid a slight condensation; though in proportion as the gasses were free from oxygene or water, this condensation diminished.

I mixed together sulphuretted hydrogene in a high degree of purity and oxymuriatic acid gas both dried, in equal volumes: in this instance the condensation was not $\frac{1}{40}$; sulphur, which seemed to contain a little oxymuriatic acid, was formed on the sides of the vessel; no vapour was deposited; and the residual gas contained about $1\frac{9}{20}$ of muriatic acid gas, and the remainder was inflammable.

M.M. GAY-LUSSAC and THENARD have proved by a copious collection of instances, that in the usual cases where oxygene is procured from oxymuriatic acid, water is always present, and muriatic acid gas is formed; now, as it is shewn that oxymuriatic acid gas is converted into muriatic acid gas, by combining with hydrogene, it is scarcely possible to avoid the conclusion, that the oxygene is derived from the decomposition of water, and, consequently, that the idea of the existence of water in muriatic acid gas, is hypothetical, depending upon an assumption which has not yet been proved—the existence of oxygene in oxymuriatic acid gas.

M.M. GAY-LUSSAC and THENARD indeed have stated an experiment, which they consider as proving that muriatic acid gas contains one quarter of its weight of combined water. They passed this gas over litharge, and obtained so much water; but it is obvious that in this case they formed the same compound as that produced by the action of oxymuriatic acid on lead; and in this process the muriatic acid must loose its hydrogene, and the lead its oxygene; which of course would form water; these able chemists, indeed, from the conclusion of their memoir, seem aware, that such an explanation may be given, for they say that the oxymuriatic acid *may be* considered as a simple body.

I have repeated those experiments which led me first to suspect the existence of combined water in muriatic acid, with considerable care; I find that, when mercury is made to act upon 1 in volume of muriatic acid gas, by VOLTAIC electricity, all the acid disappears, calomel is formed, and about .5 of hydrogene evolved.

With potassium, in experiments made over very dry mercury, the quantity of hydrogene is always from 9 to 11, the volume of the muriatic acid gas used being 20.

And in some experiments made very carefully by my brother Mr. JOHN DAVY, on the decomposition of muriatic acid gas, by heated tin and zinc, hydrogene equal to about half its volume was disengaged, and metallic muriates, the same as those produced by the combustion by tin and zinc in oxymuriatic acid gas, resulted.

It is evident from this series of observations, that SCHEELE's view, (though obscured by terms derived from a vague and unfounded general theory,) of the nature of the oxymuriatic and muriatic acids, may be considered as an expression of facts; whilst the view adopted by the French school of chemistry, and which, till it is minutely examined, appears so beautiful and satisfactory, rests in the present state of our knowledge, upon hypothetical grounds.

When oxymuriatic acid is acted upon by nearly an equal volume of hydrogene, a combination takes place between them, and muriatic acid gas results. When muriatic acid gas is acted on by mercury, or any other metal, the oxymuriatic acid is attracted from the hydrogene, by the stronger affinity of the metal; and an oxymuriate, exactly similar to that formed by combustion, is produced.

The action of water upon those compounds, which have been usually considered as muriates, or as dry muriates, but which are properly combinations of oxymuriatic acid with inflammable bases, may be easily explained, according to these views of the subject. When water is added in certain quantities to Libavius's liquor, a solid crystallized mass is obtained from which oxide of tin and muriate of ammonia can be procured by ammonia. In this case, oxygene may be conceived to be supplied to the tin, and hydrogene to the oxymuriatic acid.

The compound formed by burning phosphorus in oxymuriatic acid, is in a similar relation to water; if that substance be added to it, it is resolved into two powerful acids; oxygene, it may be supposed, is furnished to the phosphorus to form phosphoric acid, hydrogene to the oxymuriatic acid to form common muriatic acid gas.

None of the combinations of the oxymuriatic acid with inflammable bodies, can be decomposed by dry acids; and this seems to be the test which distinguishes the oxymuriatic combinations from the muriates, though they have hitherto been confounded together. Muriate of potash for instance, if M. BERTHOLLET's estimation of its composition, approaches towards accuracy, when ignited, is a compound of oxymuriatic acid with potassium; muriate of ammonia, is a compound of muriatic acid gas and ammonia; and when acted on by potassium, it is decompounded; the oxymuriatic acid may be conceived to combine with the potassium to form muriate of potash, and the ammonia and hydrogene are set free.

The vivid combustion of bodies in oxymuriatic acid gas, at first view, appears a reason why oxygene should be admitted in it; but heat and light are merely results of the intense agency of combination. Sulphur and metals, alkaline earths and acids become ignited during their mutual agency; and such an effect might be expected in an operation so rapid, as that of oxymuriatic acid upon metals and inflammable bodies.

It may be said, that a strong argument in favour of the hypothesis, that oxymuriatic acid consists of an acid basis united to oxygene, exists in the general analogy of the compounds of oxymuriatic acid and metals, to the common neutral salts; but this analogy when strictly investigated, will be found to be very indistinct, and even allowing it, it may be applied with as much force to support an opposite doctrine, namely, that the neutral salts are compounds of bases with water; and the metals of bases with hydrogene; and that in the case of the action of oxymuriatic acid and metals, the metal furnishes hydrogene to form muriatic acid, and a basis to produce the neutral combination.

That the quantity of hydrogene evolved during the decomposition of muriatic acid gas by metals, is the same that would be produced during the decomposition of water by the same bodies, appears, at first view, an evidence in favour of the existence of water in muriatic acid gas; but as there is only one known combination of hydrogene with oxymuriatic acid, one quantity must always be separated. Hydrogene is disengaged from its oxymuriatic combination, by a metal, in the same manner as one metal is disengaged by another, from similar combinations; and of all inflammable bodies that form compounds of this kind, except perhaps phosphorus and sulphur, hydrogene is that which seems to adhere to oxymuriatic acid with the least force.

I have caused strong explosions from an electrical jar, to pass through oxymuriatic gas, by means of points of platina, for several hours in succession; but it seemed not to undergo the slightest change.

I electrized the oxymuriates of phosphorus and sulphur for some hours, by the power of the VOLTAIC apparatus of 1000 double plates; no gas separated, but a minute quantity of hydrogene, which I am inclined to attribute to the presence of moisture in the apparatus employed; for I once obtained hydrogene from Libavius's liquor by a similar operation; but I have ascertained, that this was owing to the decomposition of water, adhering to the mercury; and in some late experiments made with 2000 double plates, in which the discharge was from platina wires, and in which the mercury used for confining the liquor was carefully boiled, there was no production of any permanent elastic matter.

As there are no experimental evidences of the existence of oxygene in oxymuriatic acid gas, a natural question arises, concerning the nature of these compounds, in which the muriatic acid has been supposed to exist, combined with much more oxygene than oxymuriatic acid, in the state in which it has been named by Mr. CHENEVIX, hyperoxygenized muriatic acid [chloric acid].

Can the oxymuriatic *acid* combine either with oxygene or hydrogene, and form with each of them an acid compound; of which that with hydrogene has the strongest, and that with oxygene the weakest affinity for bases? for the able chemist to whom I have just referred, conceives that hyperoxymuriates are decomposed by muriatic acid. Or, is hyperoxymuriatic acid the basis of all this class of bodies, the most simple form of this species of matter?

The phaenomena of the composition and decomposition of the hyperoxymuriates, may be explained on either of these suppositions; but they are mere suppositions unsupported by experiment.

I have endeavoured to obtain the neutralizing acid, which has been imagined to be hyperoxygenised, from hyperoxymuriate of potash, by various modes, but uniformly without success. By distilling the salt with dry boracic acid, though a little oxymuriatic acid is generated, yet oxygene is the chief gaseous product, and a muriate of potash not decomposable is produced.

The distillation of the orange coloured fluid, produced by dissolving hyperoxymuriate of potash in sulphuric acid, affords only oxygene in great excess, and oxymuriatic acid.

When solutions of muriates, or muriatic acid are electrized in the VOLTAIC circuit, oxymuriatic acid is evolved at the positive surface, and hydrogene at the negative surface. When a solution of oxymuriatic acid in water is electrized, oxymuriatic acid and oxygene appear[11] at the positive surface, and hydrogene at the negative surface, facts which are certainly unfavourable to the idea of the existence of hyperoxygenised muriatic acid, whether it be imagined a compound of oxymuriatic acid with oxygen, or the basis of oxymuriatic acid.

If the facts respecting the hyperoxymuriate of potash, indeed, be closely reasoned upon, it must be regarded as nothing more than as a triple compound of oxymuriatic acid, potassium, and oxygene. We have no right to assume the existence of any peculiar acid in it, or of a considerable portion of combined water; and it is perhaps more conformable to the analogy of chemistry, to suppose the large quantity of oxygene combined with the potassium, which we know has an intense affinity for oxygene, and which, from some experiments, I am inclined to believe, is capable of combining directly with more oxygene than exists in potash, than with the oxymuriatic acid, which, as far as is known, has no affinity for that substance.

It is generally supposed that a mixture of oxymuriatic acid and hyperoxymuriatic acid is disengaged when hyperoxymuriate of potash is decomposed by common muriatic acid;[12] but I am satisfied, from several trials, that the gas procured in this way, when not mixed with oxygene, unites to the same quantity of hydrogene, as common oxymuriatic acid

[11] The quantity of oxymuriatic acid in the aqueous solution, is so small, that the principal products must be referred to the decomposition of water. This happens in other instances; the water only is decomposed in dilute solutions of nitric and sulphuric acids.

[12] If hyperoxymuriate of potash be decomposed by nitric or sulphuric acid, it affords oxymuriatic acid and oxygene. If it be acted upon by muriatic acid, it affords a large quantity of oxymuriatic acid gas only. In this last case, the phaenomenon seems merely to depend upon the decomposition of the muriatic acid gas, by the oxygene, loosely combined in the salt.

gas from manganese; and I find, by a careful examination, that the gas disengaged during the solution of platina, in a mixture of nitric and muriatic acids, which has been regarded as hyperoxymuriatic acid, but which I stated some years ago to possess the properties of oxymuriatic acid gas, is actually that body, owing its peculiar colour to a small quantity of nitromuriatic vapour suspended in it, and from which it is easily freed by washing.

Few substances, perhaps, have less claim to be considered as acid, than oxymuriatic acid. As yet we have no right to say that it has been decompounded; and as its tendency of combination is with pure inflammable matters, it may possibly belong to the same class of bodies as oxygene.

May it not in fact be a *peculiar* acidifying and dissolving principle, forming compounds with combustible bodies, analogous to acids containing oxygene, or oxides, in their properties and powers of combination; but differing from them, in being for the most part, decomposable by water? On this idea muriatic acid may be considered as having hydrogene for its basis, and oxymuriatic acid for its acidifying principle. And the phosphoric sublimate as having phosphorus for its basis, and oxymuriatic acid for its acidifying matter. And Libavius's liquor, and the compounds of arsenic with oxymuriatic acid, may be regarded as analogous bodies. The combinations of oxymuriatic acid with lead, silver, mercury, potassium, and sodium, in this view would be considered as a class of bodies related more to oxides than acids, in their powers of attraction.

It is needless to take up the time of this learned Society by dwelling upon the imperfection of the modern nomenclature of these substances. It is in many cases connected with false ideas of their nature and composition, and in a more advanced state of the enquiry, it will be necessary for the progress of science, that it should undergo material alterations.

In his paper in the same journal for the following year (1811) Davy summed up the conclusions from the above experiments and gave "oxymuriatic acid gas" its more appropriate modern name (see footnote 6 above).

In the last communication which I had the honour of presenting to the Royal Society, I stated a number of facts, which inclined me to believe, that the body improperly called in the modern nomenclature of chemistry, *oxymuriatic acid gas*, has not as yet been decompounded; but that it is a peculiar substance, elementary as far as our knowledge extends, and analogous in many of its properties to oxygene gas. . . .

To call a body which is not known to contain oxygen, and which cannot contain muriatic acid, oxymuriatic acid, is contrary to the principles of that nomenclature in which it is adopted; and an alteration of it seems necessary to assist the progress of discussion, and to diffuse just ideas on the subject. If the great discoverer of this substance had signified it by any simple name, it would have been proper to have recurred to it; but, dephlogisticated marine acid is a term which can hardly be adopted in the present advanced aera of the science.

After consulting some of the most eminent chemical philosophers in this country, it has been judged most proper to suggest a name founded upon one of its obvious and characteristic properties—its colour, and to call it *Chlorine*, or *Chloric* gas.[13]

Should it hereafter be discovered to be compound, and even to contain oxygene, this name can imply no error, and cannot necessarily require a change.

Jöns Jacob Berzelius

(1779–1848)

FEW chemists of the first half of the nineteenth century had a stronger and more widespread influence over chemistry than Jöns Jacob Berzelius. In general Berzelius's efforts were directed toward the consolidation and extension of the atomic theory. He improved chemical analysis and determined the composition of a large number of compounds, thus verifying the laws of constant and multiple proportions and furnishing the most accurate equivalent weights then available. By ingenious methods he arrived at the correct atomic composition of most common substances and thus was enabled to draw up (in 1826) a table of atomic weights very nearly identical with the modern one. These unfortunately attained no widespread use immediately, and chemists employed equivalent weights as having a sounder experimental basis until the late 1860's, when Cannizzaro called attention to Avogadro's hypothesis and brought light to the whole atomic-molecular theory.

One of Berzelius's earliest researches was undertaken in collaboration with a Swedish mine owner, William Hisinger (1766–1852), and had as its subject the investigation of the electrolysis of various salts. Berzelius did no more work in this field, but his brief contact with electrochemistry strongly influenced his thinking and led him to develop an electrochemical theory of chemistry which dominated the science for many years.

One of Berzelius's great contributions was his system of chemical symbols, first put forward in 1813. Dalton's symbols were much too clumsy for everyday use, and in using letters to stand for definite relative weights of elements, Berze-

[13] From χλωρός.

lius gave chemists a tool which facilitated chemical thinking along atomic lines. Berzelius's symbols remain essentially unaltered today.

Berzelius worked upon so many aspects of chemistry with such extensive results that all of them cannot be mentioned here. Suffice it to say that he discovered ceria, thorium, and selenium, and isolated silicon, titanium, and zirconium. He introduced many innovations in the laboratory, notably filter paper and rubber tubing, and developed the use of the blowpipe for mineralogical work.

He was a prolific writer, and his "Lärbok i Kemien," which first began to appear in 1808, was translated into many languages in many editions and became one of the greatest textbooks of chemistry. For many years Berzelius wrote a stimulating annual report on the progress of chemistry, which appeared in German translation as *Jahresbericht über die Fortschritte der physischen Wissenschaften.*

In 1819 Berzelius put forward his electrochemical or dualistic theory, which dominated the chemical world for many years. His ideas were expressed in a small book, "Essai sur la Théorie des Proportions chimiques et sur l'influence chimique de l'électricité," Paris, 1819. The following selection, taken from pages 70 to 76, expresses the fundamental ideas of the theory.

In many carefully made experiments, Volta has observed that two metals put in contact become electric, and that this is the cause of the phenomena of the electric pile. Davy later showed that this electrical state increases due to the force of mutual affinities of the bodies used, and that this effect can be produced, and even seen, by means of certain precautions, in all bodies which have affinity for each other. It also follows from the experiments of Davy that temperature, which, as we know, increases affinity, also increases the intensity of the electrical state in bodies which are in contact, but that this mechanical contact being followed by combination, all signs of electricity immediately cease, that is to say, at the instant when, in favorable circumstances, they burst into flame, the electrical division, or the charge which could be perceived, disappears. These facts agree well with the conjecture that the opposite electricities in the bodies which combine, mutually neutralize each other at the moment of combination, and then the fire is produced in the same manner as in the electric discharge.

But if these bodies, which are united and have ceased to be electric, should again be separated, and their elements restored to the isolated state with their original properties, they must recover the electrical state destroyed by the combination, or indeed, in other terms, if these combined bodies are restored for any reason to their original electrical state, which had vanished at their union, they must separate, and reappear with their original properties. Hisinger and I have observed that when the electric pile exerts its action on a conducting liquid, the elements of this liquid separate, oxygen and the acids are repelled from the negative pole toward the positive, and the combustible bodies as well as the salifiable bases from the positive pole toward the negative.

We believe we now know with certitude that bodies which are likely to combine show free, opposite electricities which increase in force as they approach the temperature at which combination occurs, until, at the instant of union, the electricity disappears with an elevation of temperature which is often so great that they burst into flame. On the other hand, we have the same certainty that combined bodies exposed in a suitable form to the action of the electric fluid, produced by discharge of a pile, are separated and regain their original chemical and electrical properties at the same time that the electricity which acted on them disappears.

In the actual state of our knowledge, the most probable explanation of combustion and the ignition which results from it is then: *that in all chemical combinations there is neutralization of opposing electricities, and that this neutralization produces fire in the same manner that it produces it in the discharge of the electric jar, the electric pile, and thunder, without being accompanied, in these latter phenomenon, by chemical combination.* . . .

The experiments made on the mutual electrical relations of bodies have taught us that they can be divided into two classes: *electropositive* and *electronegative.* The simple bodies which belong to the first class, as well as their oxides, always take up positive electricity when they meet simple bodies or oxides belonging to the second class; and the oxides of the first class always behave with the oxides of the other like salifiable bases with acids.

It has been believed that the electrical series of combustible bodies differs from that of their oxides; but although the different degrees of oxidation of several bodies present exceptions, the electrical order of combustible bodies agrees in general with that of their oxides, in such a way that the strongest degrees of oxidation in the affinity of different radicals are like those between the radicals themselves.

In arranging the bodies in the order of their electrical nature, there is formed an electro-chemical system which, in my opinion, is more fit than any other to give an idea of chemistry. I will speak more of this later.

Oxygen is, of all bodies, the most electronegative. As it is never positive relative to any other, and as, according to all chemical phenomena known up to the present it is not probable that any element of our globe can be more electronegative, we recognize in it an absolute negative. Also, in the electrochemical system, it is the only body whose electrical relations are invariable. The others vary in this sense, that one body can be negative with respect to a second, and positive with respect to a third: for example, sulphur and arsenic are positive relative to oxygen and negative relative to metals. The radicals of fixed alkalis and alkaline earths are, on the contrary, the most electropositive bodies; but they differ somewhat in degree;

and at the positive extreme of the electrical series, there is no body as electropositive as oxygen is electronegative.

The applications of this theory are illustrated by the following extract, taken from the French edition of Berzelius's textbook, Paris, 1831, volume 4.

The electrochemical properties of oxidised substances depend almost always exclusively on the unipolarity of their electropositive element, that is to say, of their radical. The oxide is ordinarily electronegative with regard to other oxides when its radical is negative with regard to their radicals, and *vice versa*. For example, sulfuric acid is electronegative with respect to all metallic oxides for the reason that sulfur is negative in relation to all metals. The oxides of potassium and zinc are, on the contrary, electropositive with regard to all oxidized substances, to the radicals of which, potassium and zinc are positive. This fact, the cause of which we are unable to explain, rectifies an inexact idea on the principle of acidity which in the antiphlogistic theory has been thought to be oxygen. We find now that it resides in the radical of the acid and that oxygen plays such an indifferent role that it enters equally into the strongest salifying bases, that is to say, the electropositive oxides and in the strongest acids or electronegative oxides. Sometimes it happens, however, that a positive oxide acquires by higher oxidation less electropositive properties, approaching electronegative, as, for example, stannic oxide and the acids of manganese. But in the strongest bases, such as potash and soda, an addition of oxygen may well destroy the positive reaction without, nevertheless, producing a negative; it is thus that the strongly salifying bases form peroxides. . . .

If these electrochemical views are correct it follows that all chemical combination depends solely on two opposing forces, positive and negative electricity, and that thus each combination should be composed of two parts united by the effect of their electrochemical reaction, provided that there exists no third force. Whence it follows that each compound substance, regardless of the number of its constituent principles, may be divided into two parts, of which one is electrically positive and the other negative. Thus, for example, sulfate of soda is not composed of sulfur, oxygen and sodium, but of sulfuric acid and soda[1] which both may again be divided into two elements, one positive and the other negative. Similarly alum cannot be considered as directly composed of its elements but should be regarded as the product of the reaction of sulfate of aluminum, a negative element, and sulfate of potash, a positive element. In this manner the electrochemical view equally well justifies what I have already detailed on particular compounds of the first, second and third orders, etc.

[1] [A vestige of this theory remains in the custom of reporting analysis on an oxide basis.]

The following extract explains the system of formulas developed by Berzelius.

ESSAY ON THE CAUSE OF CHEMICAL PROPORTIONS, AND ON SOME CIRCUMSTANCES RELATING TO THEM: TOGETHER WITH A SHORT AND EASY METHOD OF EXPRESSING THEM.

III. On the Chemical Signs, and the Method of Employing Them To Express Chemical Proportions.[2]

When we endeavour to express chemical proportions, we find the necessity for chemical signs. Chemistry has always possessed them, though hitherto they have been of very little utility. They owed their origin, no

Comparative Table of the Specific Weights of Elementary Bodies.

Names.	Symbols.	Weight in form of gas.	Ditto at a minimum.	Ditto at a maximum.	Sp. gr. in a solid form.
Oxygen	O	100·00	....	....	....
Sulphur	S	291·00	200·00	219·00	1·998
Phosphorus	P	167·512	167·3	....	1·714
Muriatic radicle	M	139·56	....	157·7	....
Fluoric radicle	F	60·	....	....	....
Boron	B	73·273	....	....	....
Carbon	C	75·1	73·6	75·9	3·5
Nitric radicle	N	79·54	75·51	....	....
Hydrogen	H	6·636	....	7·63	....
Arsenic	As	839·9	....	852·2	8·81
Molybdenum	Mo	601·56	....	....	8·6
Chromium	Ch	708·045	....	....	5·9 ?
Tungsten	Tn	2424·24	....	....	17·22
Antimony	Sb	1612·96	....	....	6·7
Tellurium	Te	806·48	....	819·	6·115
Columbium	Cl	....	....	....	....
Titanium	Ti	1801·	....	....	....
Zirconium	Zr	....	....	....	....
Silicium	Si	216·66	....	....	....
Osmium	Os	....	....	....	....
Iridium	I	....	....	....	....
Rhodium	Rh	1490·31	....	....	11·
Platinum	Pl	1206·7	....	....	21·65
Gold	Au	2483·8	....	....	19·361
Palladium	Pa	1407·56	....	....	11·871
Silver	Ag	2688·17	....	2718·31	10·51
Mercury	Hg	2531·6	2503·13	2536·1	13·56
Copper	Cu	806·48	800·	....	8·722
Nickel	Ni	733·8	....	....	8·666
Cobalt	Co	732·61	....	....	8·7
Bismuth	Bi	1774·	....	....	9·88
Lead	Pb	2597·4	....	2620·2	11·445

Table of atomic weights. [*From Annals of Philosophy*, **3**: 362–363 (1814).]

doubt, to the mysterious relation supposed by the alchymists, to exist between the metals and the planets, and to the desire which they had of expressing themselves in a manner incomprehensible to the public. The fellow-laborers in the antiphlogistic revolution published new signs

[2] *Annals of Philosophy*, **3**: 51–52 (1814); a preliminary note on the subject had appeared in the same journal, **2**: 359 (1813).

founded on a reasonable principle, the object of which was that the signs, like the new names, should be definitions of the composition of the substances, and that they should be more easily written than the names of the substances themselves. But, though we must acknowledge that these signs were very well contrived, and very ingenious, they were of no use; because it is easier to write an abbreviated word than to draw a figure, which has but little analogy with letters, and which, to be legible, must be made of a larger size than our ordinary writing. In proposing new chemical signs, I shall endeavour to avoid the inconveniences which rendered the old ones of little utility. I must observe here that the object of the new signs is not that, like the old ones, they should be employed to label vessels in the laboratory: they are destined solely to facilitate the expression of chemical proportions, and to enable us to indicate, without long peri-

Names.	Symbols.	Weight in form of gas.	Ditto at a minimum.	Ditto at a maximum.	Sp. gr. in a solid form.
Tin	Sn	1470·59	....	....	7·299
Iron	Fe	693·64	....	....	7·788
Zinc......................	Zn	806·45	....	....	7·215
Manganese	Ma	711·575	....	....	8·013
Uranium..................	U	....	....	....	....
Cerium	Ce	1148·8	....	....	....
Yttrium	Y	881·66	876·42	....	....
Glucinum	Gl	....	....	....	....
Aluminum	Al	228 025	....	342·	....
Magnesium...............	Ms	315·46	301·63	321·93	....
Strontium	Sr	1418·14	....	....	....
Barytium	Ba	1709·1	....	....	....
Calcium	Ca	510·2	....	....	....
Sodium	So	579·32	....	....	0·9348
Potassium	Po	978·0	....	....	0·8.

Table of atomic weights (*continued*).

phrases, the relative number of volumes of the different constituents contained in each compound body. By determining the weight of the elementary volumes, these figures will enable us to express the numeric result of an analysis as simply, and in a manner as easily remembered, as the algebraic formulas in mechanical philosophy.

The chemical signs ought to be letters, for the greater facility of writing, and not to disfigure a printed book. Though this last circumstance may not appear of any great importance, it ought to be avoided whenever it can be done. I shall take, therefore, for the chemical sign, the *initial letter of the Latin name of each elementary substance:* but as several have the same initial letter, I shall distinguish them in the following manner:—1. In the class which I call *metalloids*, I shall employ the initial letter only, even when this letter is common to the metalloid and some metal. 2. In the class of metals, I shall distinguish those that have the same initials with another metal, or a metalloid, by writing the first two letters of the word. 3. If the first two letters be common to two metals, I shall, in that case, add to the initial letter the first consonant which they have not in common: for example, S = sulphur, Si = silicium, St = stibium (antimony), Sn = stannum (tin), C = carbonicum, Co = cobaltum (cobalt), Cu = cuprum (copper), O = oxygen, Os = osmium, &c.

The chemical sign expresses always one volume of the substance. When it is necessary to indicate several volumes, it is done by adding the number of volumes: for example, the *oxidum cuprosum* (protoxide of copper) is composed of a volume of oxygen and a volume of metal; therefore its sign is $Cu + O$. The *oxidum cupricum* (peroxide of copper) is composed of 1 volume of metal and 2 volumes of oxygen; therefore its sign is $Cu + 2O$. In like manner, the sign for sulphuric acid is $S + 3O$; for carbonic acid, $C + 2O$; for water $2H + O$, &c.

When we express a compound volume of the first order, we throw away the $+$, and place the number of volumes above the letter: for example, $Cu\overset{3}{O} + SO$ = sulphate of copper, $Cu\overset{2}{O} + 2\overset{3}{S}O$ = persulphate of copper. These formulas have the advantage, that if we take away the oxygen, we see at once the ratio between the combustible radicals. As to the volumes of the second order, it is but rarely of any advantage to express them by formulas as one volume; but if we wish to express them in that way, we may do it by using the parenthesis, as is done in algebraic formulas: for example, alum is composed of 3 volumes of sulphate of aluminia and 1 volume of sulphate of potash. Its symbol is $3(Al\overset{2}{O} + 2\overset{3}{S}O) + (Po\overset{2}{} + 2\overset{3}{S}O)$ As to the organic volumes it is at present very uncertain how far figures can be successfully employed to express their composition. We shall have occasion only in the following pages to express the volume of ammonia. It is $6H + N + O$ or $H\overset{6}{N}O$.

In his later years Berzelius occupied a dominant position among European chemists and through his *Jahresbericht* engaged in numerous controversies and made many valuable theoretical contributions. Among these was his recognition of isomerism as a general phenomenon. In 1824 Liebig published an analysis of fulminic acid, and in another paper, the same year, Wöhler gave an analysis of cyanic acid. Gay-Lussac immediately noticed that the two acids had the same composition, but chemists generally were incredulous, and several years passed before the analyses were adequately confirmed and accepted.

Meanwhile Faraday had discovered a somewhat similar situation with butylene, which has the same composition (but twice the density) of ethylene. In the *Jahresbericht* for 1832[3] Berzelius drew attention to these cases and explained them correctly. The existence of such groups of compounds was, incidently, the strongest proof of the atomic theory that had then appeared.

In physical chemistry it was long taken as axiomatic that substances of similar composition, having the same constituents in the same propor-

[3] Vol. 11, p. 44–48, of the German translation by Wöhler.

tions, necessarily must also have the same chemical properties. The investigations of Faraday (*Jahresbericht*, 1827) appear to indicate that there may be an exception to this if two similarly composed substances differ in that the composition of one contains twice as many elementary atoms as occur in the other, although the proportions between the elements remain the same. It is thus with the two gaseous hydrocarbons, olefiant gas, which is C̄H,* and the other more compressible gas described by Faraday [butylene] which is C²H² and accordingly has twice as great a specific gravity as the former. Here, therefore, the similarity in composition is only apparent, for the compound atoms are still definitely different, the relative numbers of elementary atoms being equal but the absolute numbers unequal. Recent researches have now shown that the absolute as well as the relative numbers of elementary atoms may be the same, their combination taking place in such a dissimilar way that the properties of equally composed bodies may be different. We have, however, been led only gradually to such a result. Thus, for instance, I had already demonstrated several years ago that there are two oxides of tin of similar composition, but dissimilar properties. Not long afterwards, it was discovered that *Liebig's* fulminic acid and *Wöhler's* cyanic acid have completely identical compositions and saturation capacities. Almost each of the previous volumes of the *Jahresbericht* contains an attempt to discover a possible, hitherto unobserved, dissimilarity in their compositions, without, however, any actually being found. . . .

Since it is necessary for specific ideas to have definite and consequently as far as possible selected terms, I have proposed to call substances of similar composition and dissimilar properties *isomeric*, from the Greek ἰσομερης (composed of equal parts). . . .

The great ability of Berzelius to generalize a number of apparently unrelated facts into a unified picture is well illustrated by his review which led to the introduction of the term *catalysis*. As he himself indicates in the following extract, he did not discover the facts of catalysis, but not until he had presented a comprehensive survey of this phenomenon and proposed a fitting name for it did the concept become generally useful to chemists.

SOME IDEAS ON A NEW FORCE WHICH ACTS IN ORGANIC COMPOUNDS[4]

In inorganic nature, new compounds form between different bodies which occur because these bodies have a greater tendency to combine among themselves than with other bodies. The bodies which have a great affinity for each other combine with each other while avoiding those for which they have a weaker affinity and with which they were combined before, and these latter equally combine with each other. Until the year

---

* [Berzelius indicated two atoms or a "double atom" by a bar through the symbol of the atom.]

[4] *Annales chimie physique,* **61**: 146–151 (1836).

1800, there were known, besides this tendency of bodies to unite, only heat, and in some cases light, which could cause bodies to combine. Later it was recognized that electricity had an influence, but it was soon seen that chemical affinity and electricity were the same thing, and that heat and light had no other action than to increase or diminish these affinities. Passing to the study of organic chemistry, bodies were found differing greatly from one another but arising from the same source through the action of different organs. In animals this source, which is blood, flows in continuous vessels and gives birth to all the different secretions, such as milk, bile, urine, etc., without the presence of any foreign body which could serve to form new combinations.

Kirchhof discovered that starch dissolved in acids diluted with water is changed at a certain temperature to a gum, then to grape sugar; however, there is no combination between the elements of the acid and those of starch, for he never found any evolution of gas. When he treated the solution with bases, he again recovered all the acid used; the solution contained only sugar, whose weight exceeded slightly that of the starch used. Some time later, Thenard discovered a new substance, the peroxide of hydrogen, whose elements are held together by only a very feeble affinity. Under the influence of acids this body is not decomposed, but under the influence of alkalis there is a tendency for its elements to separate; a slow fermentation occurs with evolution of oxygen, and there is formation of water. It was soon seen that this effect was produced in this substance not only by soluble bodies but also even by other organic and inorganic bodies such as manganese, silver, platinum, gold, fibrin, etc., acting in the same manner on this substance. This decomposition occurs only in the presence of foreign bodies by virtue of a force which is still unknown to us, without these bodies entering in any way into the new combination, for the most careful studies cannot discover the slightest alteration in them.

Edm. Davy recognized that if exceedingly finely divided platinum is moistened with alcohol, this, by burning, renders the platinum incandescent, and the alcohol is transformed into acetic acid if it contains water. All this led to the great discovery of Döbereiner that platinum sponge has the property of igniting a current of hydrogen directed on it. This discovery was closely followed by that of Dulong and Thenard, who found that not only platinum possesses this property; that other bodies, such as gold, silver, and glass, act the same, but only when they are exposed to a very high temperature, while for platinum, iridium, and the other metals which accompany platinum, this effect occurs even more below the temperature of melting ice. They recognized the analogy between the phenomenon of transformation of sugar into alcohol by the presence of an insoluble foreign body and that of the decomposition of peroxide of hydrogen into water and oxygen by the presence of platinum, of silver, of fibrin, and of several other equally insoluble bodies. They did not know of any case analogous to that of the decomposition of peroxide of hydrogen by the presence of alkalis dissolved in this substance, for at this time they still had not recognized the analogy of this phenomenon with that of the formation of sugar by means of starch and sulfuric acid. They recognized something similar in a hypothesis on the formation of ether. Following this hypothesis, sulfuric acid takes up part of the water contained in the alcohol, and this forms ether, but they could not explain why other bodies such as potash, chloride of calcium, quicklime, etc., which have a great affinity for water, do not produce the same effect. Mitscherlich showed that if he added the alcohol to the sulfuric acid at a temperature higher than that of boiling water, water and ether distilled together and formed a mixture whose weight was exactly equal to that of the alcohol used. Thus sulfuric acid does not act by virtue of its affinity for water; its action is analogous to that of alkalis on peroxide of hydrogen; it is similarly analogous to that of sulfuric acid on starch in the formation of sugar.

It is, then, proved that several simple or compound bodies, soluble and insoluble, have the property of exercising on other bodies an action very different from chemical affinity. By means of this action they produce in these bodies decomposition of their elements and different recombinations of the same elements, to which they remain strangers.

This new force, which was unknown until now, is common to organic and inorganic nature. I do not believe that it is a force entirely independent of the electrochemical affinities of matter; I believe, on the contrary, that it is only a new manifestation, but since we cannot see their connection and mutual dependence, it will be easier to designate it by a separate name. I will call this force *catalytic force.* Similarly I will call the decomposition of bodies by this force *catalysis,* as one designates the decomposition of bodies by chemical affinity *analysis.* At first glance these questions present themselves, relative to this catalytic force:

Does this catalytic force produce differences in catalytic products depending on whether it is more or less intense?

Do different bodies endowed with catalytic force engender different catalytic products at the expense of the same compound body?

Do bodies endowed with catalytic force exert their action on a great number of different compound bodies, or is this action confined to a small number of bodies?

These questions can be answered only by later studies; it is enough for the moment to have established the existence of this force by a sufficient number of examples. This force offers opportunity for numerous applications in organic nature; thus it is only around the *eyes* of potatoes that diastase is found; it is by means of catalytic force of diastase that starch, which is insoluble, is transformed into sugar and gum, which, being soluble, form the sap which appears in the germ of the potato. This very obvious example of the action of catalytic force in an organic secretion holds not only in the animal and vegetable kingdoms. It can, perhaps, be found, by following it up, that it is by an action analogous to catalytic force that there occurs secretion of very different bodies which are, however, all drawn from one material: sap in plants and blood in animals.

Johann Wolfgang Döbereiner

(1780–1849)

THE work of Berzelius on atomic weights for the first time gave a set of values which were approximately accurate. At the same period, enough facts had accumulated to give a clear idea of the chemical properties of a number of elements. J. W. Döbereiner was the first of a long series of chemists who recognized a relation between atomic weights and chemical properties. He observed that, in a set of three elements whose chemical properties were similar, the atomic weight of the second member of the "triad" was almost exactly the mean of the atomic weights of the first and third elements. This striking observation attracted much attention, for it seemed to show a numerical law governing chemical behavior. A number of investigators, including J. B. Dumas and William Odling, extended the number of triads to other groups of elements. In time this type of study tended to become a purely arithmetical exercise. Döbereiner, however, deserves the credit for initiating the study of the relation between atomic weight and chemical properties which culminated in the discovery of the periodic law by Lothar Meyer and D. I. Mendeleev. Döbereiner first expressed his ideas as early as in 1817,[1] but the first published explanation of his system of triads appeared in the paper, "An Attempt to Group Elementary Substances according to Their Analogies," in 1829.[2]

The work of Berzelius on the determination of the atomic weights of bromine and iodine has interested me greatly, since it has established the idea, which I expressed earlier in my lectures, that perhaps the atomic weight of bromine might be the arithmetical mean of the atomic weights

[1] See *Gilbert's Annalen der Physik*, n.s., **26**: 332 (1817).

[2] Poggendorf's *Annalen der Physik und Chemie*, **15**: 301–307 (1829); reprinted in Ostwald's *Klassiker*, No. 66, "J. W. Doebereiner und Max Pettenkofer, Die Anfänge des natürlichen Systems der chemischen Elemente. (1829, 1850). Nebst einer geschichtlichen Uebersicht der Weiterentwicklungen der Lehre von den Triaden der Elemente. Herausgegeben von Lothar Meyer," Leipzig, 1895.

of chlorine and iodine. This mean is $\dfrac{35.470 + 126.470}{2} = 80.470$ [*sic*].
This number is not much greater than that found by Berzelius (78.383);
however, it comes so close that it may almost be hoped that the difference
will vanish entirely after repeated careful and exact determinations of the
atomic weights of these three salt-forming elements. This idea was the
motive for an attempt which I made twelve years ago to group substances
by their analogies. At that time I found that the specific gravity and
atomic weight of strontia are very close to the arithmetic mean of the
specific gravities and atomic weights of lime and baryta, since

$$\frac{356.019(= \dot{C}a) + 956.880(= \dot{B}a)}{2} = 656.449(= \dot{S}r)^*$$

and the actual value for strontia is 647.285.

In the alkali group, according to this view, soda stands in the middle,
since if we take the value for the atomic weight of lithia, determined by
Gmelin, = 195.310, and the value for potash = 589.916, then the arithmetic mean of these numbers,

$$\frac{195.310 + 589.916}{2} = 392.613,$$

which comes very close to the atomic value for soda, which Berzelius
determined as = 390.897.

For the group including phosphorus and arsenic, the third member is
missing. Mitscherlich, the discoverer of isomorphology, will know how to
find this if it exists.

If sulfur, selenium, and tellurium belong to one group, which can well
be assumed, since the specific gravity of selenium is exactly the arithmetic
mean of the specific gravities of sulfur and tellurium, and all three substances combine with hydrogn to form characteristic hydrogen acids, then
selenium forms the middle member, since

$$\frac{32.239(= S) + 129.243(= Te)}{2} = 80.741$$

and the empirically found atomic value for selenium is 79.263.†

Fluorine indeed belongs to the salt-forming elements, but certainly not
to the group of chlorine, bromine, and iodine; rather to another class of

---

* [Each dot above the symbol of an element signifies an oxygen atom.]

† Tellurium certainly has a still higher degree of oxidation than $\dot{T}$e. Perhaps it can
be converted to $\ddot{T}$e under the same conditions in which Mitscherlich has formed $\ddot{S}$e
from Se.

salt-forming substances which perhaps are related to the first as the alkaline earths are to the alkalies. Since it has a very small value, it apparently forms the first member of this assumed group, and in this case there would still be two more members to discover, if triads are actually a law for all groups of chemical substances. If the values shown by the atomic weights of the substances which are here grouped together are compared with the intensity of the chemical affinity which these substances possess, then we find that in the alkalies and alkaline earths the first is *directly* proportional to the last, but in the salt-forming elements they are *inversely* proportional. Thus potash, which has the largest value among the alkalies, is the strongest, while lithia, which has the smallest value, is the weakest, and soda, which holds the middle value between potash and lithia, is weaker than potash and stronger than lithia. Baryta, lime, and strontia behave in the same way. However, chlorine, which has the smallest value, is the most powerful, and iodine, which possesses the greatest value, is the weakest in salt formation, and bromine lies between both. If we express the intensity of the chemical affinity of the grouped substances by the numbers 1, 2, and 3, then these considerations can clearly be arranged in the following way:

(*a*) Salt-forming elements and their acids.

			Intensity of Chemical Affinity
$221.325 = $ Cl.	$455.129 = $ HCl.	$942.650 = \ddot{\overset{\cdot}{C}}$l	3
$789.145 = $ I.	$1590.770 = $ HI.	$2078.290 = \ddot{\overset{\cdot}{I}}$	1
$\dfrac{1010.470}{2} = $ Br.	$\dfrac{2045.899}{2} = $ HBr.	$\dfrac{3020.940}{2} = \ddot{\overset{\cdot}{B}}$r	2

(*b*) Acid-forming elements and acids.

$201.165 = $ S.	$213.644 = $ HS.	$501.165 = \ddot{S}$	3
$806.452 = $ Te.	$831.412 = $ HTe.	$1106.452 = \dot{\ddot{T}}$e?	1
$\dfrac{1007.617}{2} = $ Se.	$\dfrac{1045.056}{2} = $ HSe.	$\dfrac{1607.617}{2} = \ddot{S}$e	2

(*c*) Alkali-forming elements and alkalies.

$95.310 = $ L.	$195.310 = \dot{L}$	1
$489.916 = $ K.	$589.916 = \dot{K}$	3
$\dfrac{585.226}{2} = $ Na.	$\dfrac{785.226}{2} = \dot{N}$a	2

(*d*) Alkaline-earth-forming elements and alkaline earths.

$256.019 = $ Ca.	$356.019 = \dot{C}$a	1
$856.880 = $ Ba.	$956.880 = \dot{B}$a	3
$\dfrac{1112.899}{2} = $ Sr.	$\dfrac{1312.899}{2} = \dot{S}$r	2

Hydrogen, oxygen, nitrogen, and carbon appear to stand isolated from the substances which form bases, acids, and salts. The fact that the arithmetical mean of the atomic weights of oxygen = 16.026 and carbon = 12.256 expresses the atomic weight of nitrogen = 14.138 cannot be considered here, because no analogies occur between these three substances.

The earth metals and the earths themselves belong together, according to their similarities, but I have not yet placed them successfully. It is true that they form boron and silicon, as well as B̈ and S̈l; aluminum and beryllium, and also Äl and B̈e; yttrium and cerium, and also Ẏ and Ċe, which are special groups, but each of them lacks a third member. Magnesium stands entirely alone, and zirconium belongs with titanium and tin.

The group of heavy metal alum-forming substances is fully filled. Its factors are iron oxide F̈e, manganese oxide M̈n, and chromium oxide Ër; the last apparently forms the middle member, since

$$\frac{979.426 \text{ F̈e} + 1011.574 \text{ M̈n}}{2} = 995.000 \text{ Ër } [sic]$$

According to Mitscherlich, Ḟe, Ṁn, Ṅi, Ċo, Żn, and Ċu are isomorphic with magnesia. This is a highly interesting series of substances, since, first, they all belong to the magnetic metals, and second, they are the best conductors of electricity. But how shall we arrange them if the triad is to be taken as a principle of grouping? In nature, Fe, Mn, and Co occur as oxides which are frequently found together, and the oxides of Ni, Zn, and Cu, as an Englishman says, occur together in an ore from which the Chinese prepare their white copper, which the Germans call *Argentan*. If this is so, then in the first group manganese forms the third member, since

$$\frac{439.213 \text{ Ḟe} + 468.991 \text{ Ċo}}{2} = 454.102 \text{ Ṁn}$$

and in the second group it is copper which occupies this position, since

$$\frac{469.675 \text{ Ṅi} + 503.226 \text{ Żn}}{2} = 486.450 \text{ Ċu.}$$

However, the atomic weight of Ċu is 495.695, and the specific gravity of copper is not the arithmetical mean of the specific gravities of nickle and zinc, and I therefore believe that these six oxides must be grouped in another way. A rigorous experimental revision of the specific gravities and atomic weights will perhaps remove this doubt.

The most interesting series of analogous metals are those which occur in platinum ores, where platinum, palladium, rhodium, iridium, osmium, and pluranium belong. They fall into two groups according to their specific gravities and atomic weights. Platinum, iridium, and osmium belong in the first group, and in the second, palladium, rhodium, and pluranium. (The latter represents osmium, while rhodium corresponds to iridium and palladium to platinum.) For the members of the first group, the atomic weights, according to the most recent work of Berzelius, are as follows: for platinum, 1233.260; for iridium, 1233.260; for osmium, 1244.210. Now, since the specific gravity of iridium is very near the arithmetical mean of the specific gravities of platinum and osmium (the last, according to Berzelius, = 10), then iridium must be considered the middle member of its group. In this case, its atomic weight must be

$$\frac{1233.260 + 1244.210}{2} = 1238.735$$

The atomic weights for the members of the second group, according to the same admirable scientist, are, for palladium, 665.840; for rhodium, 651.400. Thus we get, for pluranium, 636.960, if the atomic weight of the latter stands so near the atomic weights of platinum and iridium, and if rhodium is placed in the middle of this group.[3]

The specific gravity and atomic weight of lead are fairly near the arithmetical mean of the specific gravities and atomic weights of silver and mercury, and I therefore believe that these three metals can be placed together.

Whether tin and cadmium, antimony and bismuth, gold and tungsten, or tungsten and tantalum, etc., belong together, and which may be the missing analogous members, I will not venture to decide.

Pierre Louis Dulong

(1785-1838)

TO MOST chemists, the name of Dulong brings to mind the law of Dulong and Petit, but he contributed to chemistry in many other ways. He discovered nitrogen trichloride (1813), losing an eye and two fingers in the hazardous investigation. He studied the oxides of nitrogen and hypophosphorous acid, and, independently of Davy, he proposed a hydrogen theory of acids. Much of his work concerned the measurement of physical quantities, such as the refractive index and the specific heat of gases or the heats of combustion of numerous sub-

[3] The existence of pluranium still remains in some doubt. P[oggendorf].

stances. One of his most important researches was made in collaboration with Alexis Thérèse Petit (1791–1820), with whom he announced the law that the product of atomic weight and specific heat is constant (1819). It rendered a distinct service in fixing atomic weights, especially when these were in question, and enabled Berzelius and later Cannizzaro to arrive at correct atomic weights and the correct number of atoms in molecules. This law, purely empirical and now known to be only an approximation, is cited in part from the paper entitled "Recherches sur quelques points importans de la théorie de la chaleur," which appeared in 1819.[1]

	Specific heats*	Relative weights of the atoms†	Product of the weight of each atom times the corresponding capacity
Bismuth.............	0.0288	13.30	0.3830
Lead................	0.0293	12.95	0.3794
Gold................	0.0298	12.43	0.3704
Platinum............	0.0314	11.16‡	0.3740
Tin.................	0.0514	7.35	0.3779
Silver..............	0.0557	6.75	0.3759
Zinc................	0.0927	4.03	0.3736
Tellurium...........	0.0912	4.03	0.3675
Copper..............	0.0949	3.957	0.3755
Nickel..............	0.1035	3.69	0.3819
Iron................	0.1100	3.392	0.3731
Cobalt..............	0.1498	2.46	0.3685
Sulfur..............	0.1880	2.011	0.3780

* The specific heat of water is taken as unity.
† The weight of the oxygen atom is assumed to be equal to 1.
‡ [Apparently a misprint for 11.91.]

To make clear the law which we are about to announce, in the preceding table we have added to the specific heats of various elementary substances the relative weights of their atoms. These weights are derived, as is well known, from the proportions in which weighable quantities of elementary substances combine together. The care which has for some years been devoted to the determination of the proportions of the constituents in the majority of chemical compounds leaves very slight uncertainty in the values which we have used. However, as there exists no rigorous means of ascertaining the actual number of atoms of each species which enter into a combination, it is to be concluded that there is always some arbitrariness in fixing the specific weight of elementary molecules; but the resulting uncertainty at most concerns only two or three numbers which stand in

[1] *Ann. chim.*, **10**: 395–413 (1819); see also W. F. Magie, "A Source Book in Physics," New York, 1935, pp. 178–181; and Ostwald's *Klassiker*, No. 44, "Gay-Lussac, Dalton, Dulong und Petit, Rudberg, Magnus, Regnault. Abhandlungen uber das Ausdehnungsgesetz der Gase. (1802–1842). Herausgegeben von W. Ostwald," Leipzig, 1893.

the simplest proportion to one another. The reasons which have guided us in our choice will be sufficiently explained by what follows. For the moment we will confine ourselves to saying that none of the determinations we have arrived at are out of accord with the best established chemical analogies.

We can, by means of the figures contained in the preceding tables, now easily calculate the proportions which exist between the capacities of different atoms. Let us note, therefore, that to proceed from the specific heats furnished by observation to the specific heats of the particles themselves it is but necessary to divide the former by the number of particles contained in equal weights of the substances compared. Now it is obvious that these numbers of particles are, for equal weights of matter, reciprocally proportional to the densities of the atoms. We arrive, then, at the desired result by multiplying each capacity obtained by experiment by the weight of the corresponding atom. It is these different products which have been arranged in the last column of the table.

The very inspection of these numbers shows a comparison too remarkably simple not to indicate immediately the existence of a physical law susceptible of being generalized and extended to all elementary substances. In effect, the products in question, which express the capacities of different atoms, approach equality to such a degree that it is impossible that the very slight differences which are noticed are due to anything other than inevitable errors either in the measurement of the capacities or in the chemical analyses, especially if it is noticed that in certain cases the errors arising from these two sources may be in the same direction and consequently may be found multiplied in the result. The number and diversity of the substances on which we have worked forbids considering the relation we have just indicated as simply fortuitous, and the following law may be justly concluded: Atoms of all simple substances have the same capacity for heat.

In recalling what we have said previously concerning the kind of uncertainty which is still attached to the fixation of the specific weights of atoms, it will easily be perceived that the law which we have just established would, if adopted, change the statement concerning the density of particles, a supposition different from that which we have admitted. But this law is comprised in all cases of the expression of a simple relation between the weights and the specific heats of elementary atoms, and it is felt that, having to choose between two equally probable hypotheses, we ought to decide in favor of that which establishes the simplest relationship between the elements compared.

Whatever the opinion adopted on this relation, moreover, it may henceforth serve as a control on the results of chemical analysis and, in certain cases, even offer the most exact means of arriving at a knowledge of the proportions of certain combinations. But if, in the continuation of our work, no fact arises to weaken the probability of the opinion which we now prefer, it will be found to much advantage to fix in a definite and uniform manner the specific weights of the atoms of all simple substances which may be submitted to direct observation.

The law which we have just enunciated appears to be independent of the form of the substances, provided, however, that they are considered in the same circumstances.

William Prout

(1785–1850)

THE concept of a primary substance as the basis of all matter has a tempting simplicity which has appealed to thinkers from the classic Greek age to our own day. The idea was revived in a new garb in 1815–1816 by a London physician, William Prout, who observed that with few exceptions the specific gravities of elementary gases (*i.e.*, their atomic weights) were even multiples of that of hydrogen. The experimental errors in the data then available were such as to make the hypothesis appear plausible. Prout concluded, therefore, that hydrogen is the fundamental constituent from which all other elements are compounded. Prout's hypothesis underwent many vicissitudes during the nineteenth century. As analytical data progressively increased in accuracy, some chemists supported it, others denounced it. Nevertheless the idea of a fundamental building material in matter tantalized chemists and stimulated more accurate atomic-weight determination—notably by Stas. The twentieth-century elucidation of the structure of the atom, together with more accurate atomic weights and the advent of the theory of relativity, again, for the time being, make Prout's hypothesis untenable, yet his idea that all matter is composed of the same material is now established.

Prout was also one of the founders of biochemistry, discovering that the acidity of gastric juice was due to hydrochloric acid (1803). He developed methods of wine analysis and organic analysis by means of oxygen (1815 to 1827), but it is his work concerning atomic weights that is of greatest interest. The hypothesis which came to bear his name was published anonymously in two papers, which appeared in Thomas Thomson's *Annals of Philosophy*. The first was entitled "On the Relation between the Specific Gravities of Bodies in their Gaseous State and the Weights of their Atoms."[1] Prout in this paper compared the

[1] *Annals of Philosophy*, **6**: 321–330 (1815). The term *atom* as used here refers to the smallest unit of any substance, for although Avogadro had already defined (1811) the difference between *atom* and *molecule*, the distinction was not appreciated.

"atomic weights" of some elements and compounds and the densities, relative to hydrogen, of these substances in gaseous form. The agreement between the "atomic weights" and the weights of equal volumes of gas was noted. In a second paper, the next year, Prout corrected the few apparent discrepancies of the first publication—"Correction of a Mistake in the Essay on the Relation between the Specific Gravities of Bodies in Their Gaseous State and the Weights of Their Atoms."[2] Although Prout discusses the regularity in atomic weights of certain elements in the first paper, the clear statement of his hypothesis is made in the second paper. Shortly after the publication of the last paper Thomas Thomson, apparently given permission, revealed the identity of the anonymous author as William Prout.[3] Thomson was greatly attracted to the theory, and in 1819 he commenced a series of experiments to confirm the idea that the atomic weights of all elements were multiples of the atomic weight of hydrogen. The results, which he published in 1825,[4] were severely criticized by Berzelius. Although Prout and Thomson did not realize it, the essential value of the hypothesis lay in its verification of Avogadro's theory that under the same physical conditions, equal volumes of gases contain the same number of molecules. Even though the implications of this result were not appreciated, the hypothesis as a whole stimulated experimental work on the accurate determination of atomic weights, with a view to testing the theory.

The following citations are drawn from Prout's two articles in Thomson's *Annals of Philosophy*.[5]

ON THE RELATION BETWEEN THE SPECIFIC GRAVITIES OF BODIES IN THEIR GASEOUS STATE AND THE WEIGHTS OF THEIR ATOMS.

. . . 2. *Hydrogen.* The specific gravity of hydrogen, on account of its great levity, and the obstinacy with which it retains water, has always been considered as the most difficult to take of any other gas. These obstacles made me (to speak in the first person) despair of arriving at a more just conclusion than had been before obtained by the usual process of weighing; and it occurred to me that its specific gravity might be much more accurately obtained by calculation from the specific gravity of a denser compound into which it entered in a known proportion. Ammoniacal gas appeared to be the best suited to my purpose, as its specific gravity had been taken with great care by Sir H. Davy, and the chance of error had been much diminished from the slight difference between its sp. gr. and that of steam. Moreover, Biot and Arrago had obtained almost

---

[2] *Annals of Philosophy*, **7**: 111–113 (1816).

[3] *Annals of Philosophy*, **7**: 343–346 (1816).

[4] "An Attempt to establish the First Principles of Chemistry," London, 1825, 2 vols.

[5] Also reprinted in *Alembic Club Reprints*, No. 20, "Prout's Hypothesis. Papers by William Prout, M.D. (1815–16), J. S. Stas (1860) and C. Marginac (1860)," Edinburgh, 1932.

precisely the same result as Sir H. Davy. The sp. gr. of ammonia, according to Sir H. Davy, is .590164, atmospheric air being 1.000. We shall consider it as .5902; and this we are authorized in doing, as Biot and Arrago state it somewhat higher than Sir H. Davy. Now ammonia consists of three volumes of hydrogen and one volume of azote condensed into two volumes. Hence the sp. gr. of hydrogen will be found to be .0694, atmospheric air being 1.0000. It will be also observed that the sp. gr. of oxygen as obtained above is just 16 times that of hydrogen as now ascertained, and the sp. gr. of azote just 14 times.

3. *Chlorine.* The specific gravity of muriatic acid, according to Sir H. Davy's experiments, which coincide exactly with those of Biot and Arrago, is 1.278. Now if we suppose this sp. gr. to be erroneous in the same proportion that we found the sp. gr. of oxygen and azote to be above, (which, though not rigidly accurate, may yet be fairly done, since the experiments were conducted in a similar manner), the sp. gr. of this gas will come out about 1.2845; and since it is a compound of one volume chlorine and one volume hydrogen, the specific gravity of chlorine will be found by calculation to be 2.5. Dr. Thomson states, that he has found 2.483 to be near the truth, and Gay-Lussac almost coincides with him. Hence there is every reason for concluding that the sp. gr. of chlorine does not differ much from 2.5. On this supposition, the sp. gr. of chlorine will be found exactly 36 times that of hydrogen.

ON THE SPECIFIC GRAVITIES OF ELEMENTARY SUBSTANCES IN A GASEOUS STATE THAT DO NOT AT ORDINARY TEMPERATURE EXIST IN THAT STATE.

1. *Iodine.* I had some reason to suspect that M. Gay-Lussac had in his excellent memoir rated the weight of an atom of this substance somewhat too high; and in order to prove this 50 grains of iodine, which had been distilled from lime, were digested with 30 grs. of very pure lamellated zinc. The solution formed was transparent and colourless; and it was found that 12.9 grains of zinc had been dissolved. 100 parts of iodine, therefore, according to this experiment, will combine with 25.8 parts of zinc, and the weight of an atom of iodine will be 155,[6] zinc being supposed to be 40. From these data, the sp. gr. of iodine in a state of gas will be found by calculation to be 8.611111, or exactly 124 times that of hydrogen. . . .

2. *Carbon.* I assume the weight of an atom of carbon at 7.5. Hence the sp. gr. of a volume of it in a state of gas will be found by calculation to be .4166, or exactly 12 times that of hydrogen.

[6] As 25.8:100::40:155. According to experiment 8th, stated below, the weight of an atom of zinc is 40. Dr. Thomson makes it 40.9, which differs very little. See *Annals of Philosophy*, vol. iv, p. 94.

3. *Sulphur.* The weight of an atom of sulphur is 20. Hence the specific gravity of its gas is the same as that of oxygen, or 1.1111, and consequently just 16 times that of hydrogen. . . .

With respect to the above experiments, I may add, that they were made with the greatest possible attention to accuracy, and most of them were many times repeated with almost precisely the same results.

The following tables exhibit a general view of the above results, and at the same time the proportions, both in volume and weight, in which they unite with oxygen and hydrogen: also the weights of other substances, which have not been rigidly examined, are here stated from analogy. . . .

Name.	Sp. gr. hydr. being 1.	Wt. of atom, 2 vols. hydr. being 1.	Wt. of atom, oxygen being 10.	Wt. of atom, oxygen being 10, from experiment.	Sp. gr. atmospheric air being 1.	Sp. gr. atmospheric air being 1, from experiment.	Wt. in grs. of 100 cub. inches. Barom. 30, Therm. 60.	Wt. in grs. of 100 cub. in. from exper.
Hydrogen ..	1	1	1·25	1·32	·06944	·073 [1]	2·118	2·23
Carbon	6	6	7·5	7·54 [2]	·4166	—	12·708	—
Azote	14	14	17·5	17·54	·9722	·969 [3]	29·652	29·56
Phosphorus..	14	14	17·5	17·4 [4]	·9722	—	29·652	—
Oxygen......	16	8	10	10	1·1111	1·104 [5]	33·888	33·672
Sulphur......	16	16	20	20 [6]	1·1111	—	33·888	—
Calcium	20	20	25	25·46 [7]	1·3888	—	42·36	—
Sodium	24	24	30	29·1 [8]	1·6666	—	50·832	—
Iron	28	28	35	34·5 [9]	1·9444	—	59·302	—
Zinc	32	32	40	41 [10]	2·222	—	67·777	—
Chlorine	36	36	45	44·1 [11]	2·5	2·483 [12]	76·248	—
Potassium ...	40	40	50	49·1 [13]	2·7777	—	84·72	—
Barytium ...	70	70	87·5	87 [14]	4·8611	—	148·26	—
Iodine	124	124	155	156·21 [15]	8·6111	—	262·632	—

[The heading of the third column is in error. The table was calculated upon the supposition that one volume of hydrogen is equal to one atom.]

On a general review of the tables, we may notice,

1. That all the elementary numbers, hydrogen being considered as 1, are divisible by 4, except carbon, azote, and barytium, and these are divisible by 2, appearing therefore to indicate that they are modified by a higher number than that of unity or hydrogen. Is the other number 16, or oxygen? And are all substances compounded of these two elements?

2. That oxygen does not appear to enter into a compound in the ratio of two volumes or four atoms.

3. That all the gases, after having been dried as much as possible, still contain water, the quantity of which, supposing that present views are correct, may be ascertained with the greatest accuracy.

Others might doubtless be mentioned; but I submit the matter for the present to the consideration of the chemical world.

The following selection is taken from the second paper.

There is an advantage in considering the volume of hydrogen equal to the atom, as in this case the specific gravities of most, or perhaps all, elementary substances (hydrogen being 1) will either exactly coincide with, or be some multiple of, the weights of their atoms; whereas if we make the volume of oxygen unity, the weights of the atoms of most elementary substances, except oxygen, will be double that of their specific gravities with respect to hydrogen. The assumption of the volume of hydrogen being equal to the atom will also enable us to find more readily the specific gravities of bodies in their gaseous state (either with respect to hydrogen or atmospheric air), by means of Dr. Wollaston's logometric scale.

If the views we have ventured to advance be correct, we may almost consider the πρώτη ὕλη of the ancients to be realised in hydrogen; an opinion, by the by, not altogether new. If we actually consider this to be the case, and further consider the specific gravities of bodies in their gaseous state to represent the number of volumes condensed into one; or, in other words, the number of the absolute weight of a single volume of the first matter (πρώτη ὕλη) which they contain, which is extremely probable, multiples in weight must always indicate multiples in volume, and *vice versâ;* and the specific gravities, or absolute weights of all bodies in a gaseous state, must be multiples of the specific gravity or absolute weight of the first matter (πρώτη ὕλη), because all bodies in a gaseous state which unite with one another unite with reference to their volume.

Michael Faraday

(1791–1867)

MICHAEL Faraday's researches largely concerned physics, particularly electricity.[1] His work in chemistry, although less extensive, was important.[2] Included here is his discovery of benzene (1825), butylene, hexachloroethane, tetrachloroethylene, and the two isomeric napthalenesulfonic acids. He studied the liquefaction of gases by means of cold and pressure and succeeded in obtaining many common gases, notably chlorine, in the liquid state for the first time. In 1845 Faraday made the discovery of the rotation of polarized light in magnetic fields.[3]

Chemistry is chiefly indebted to Faraday for the discovery of the laws of electrochemistry which today bear his name. The first of these, that the quantity of electrochemical change is proportional to the quantity of electricity involved, was announced in a paper which appeared in the *Philosophical Transactions* for 1833[4] under the title "Identity of Electricities Derived from Different Sources." The relevant passages are reprinted below. In 1834 Faraday published more of his electrochemical researches in the same journal.[5] It was characteristic of the man that he was particularly cautious in his statements and objected to the loose terminology which was then current in electrochemistry, and the preliminary section of this paper of 1834 was devoted to the introduction of new terms with limited and precise meanings. These words, devised with the assistance of the scholar William Whewell (1794–1866), are now familiar to all chemists—electrode, anode, cathode, ion, anion, and cation. This section is reprinted in the "Source

---

[1] W. F. Magie, "A Source Book in Physics," New York, 1935, pp. 473 *ff*.

The many papers of Faraday in electricity are collected in his "Experimental Researches in Electricity. Reprinted from the Philosophical Transactions of 1831–52, with other Electrical Papers from the Proceedings of the Royal Institution, the Quarterly Journal of Science, and the Philosophical Magazine," 3 vols., London, 1839–55; vol. I, 1831–1838; vol. II, 1838–1843; vol. III, 1846–1852.

A modern selected edition is in the Everyman's Library Series, No. 576, "Experimental Researches in Electricity," London, 1914, reprinted 1922, 1931, 1938, and 1940; also Ostwald's *Klassiker*, Nos. 81, 86, 87, 126, 128, 131, 134, 136, and 140, Leipzig.

[2] Faraday's researches in chemistry are collected in his "Experimental Researches in Chemistry and Physics. Reprinted from the Philosophical Transactions of 1821–1857; The Journal of the Royal Institution; The Philosophical Magazine, and other publications," London, 1859.

[3] Magie, *op. cit.*, pp. 352–354.

[4] *Philosophical Transactions*, **1833**: 23–52; "Experimental Researches in Electricity," 1859, pp. 106–107.

[5] *Philosophical Transactions*, **1834**: 77–122. Also in "Experimental Researches in Electricity," vol. 1, 1859, p. 195; the selection given is taken from p. 230.

Book in Physics."[6] Another section of the paper is devoted to a closer examination of the law of constant electrochemical action with respect to water and to the development of a gas electrometer to measure quantities of electricity.[7] Faraday's "Volta-electrometer" provided the first practical means for the quantitative measurement of electricity.

After assuring himself that the quantity of gas evolved in the electrometer was proportional only to the quantity of electricity which had passed, he attempted to establish the law for substances other than water. This naturally led him to compare the quantities of different substances evolved by the same amount of electricity, and so he arrived at the law of electrochemical equivalents. The description of the first successful experiment forms the second passage below.[8] Faraday's summary of his conclusions may be found in the "Source Book in Physics."[9]

373.[10] The following arrangements and results are selected from many that were made and obtained relative to chemical action. A platina wire one twelfth of an inch in diameter, weighing two hundred and sixty grains, had the extremity rendered plane, so as to offer a definite surface equal to a circle of the same diameter as the wire; it was then connected in turn with the conductor of the machine,[11] or with the voltaic apparatus (369.), so as always to form the positive pole, and at the same time retain a perpendicular position, that it might rest, with its whole weight, upon the test paper to be employed. The test paper itself was supported upon a platina spatula, connected either with the discharging train (292.), or with the negative wire of the voltaic apparatus, and it consisted of four thicknesses, moistened at all times to an equal degree in a standard solution of hydriodate of potassa (316.).

374. When the platina wire was connected with the prime conductor of the machine, and the spatula with the discharging train, ten turns of the machine had such decomposing power as to produce a pale round spot of iodine of the diameter of the wire; twenty turns made a much darker mark, and thirty turns made a dark brown spot penetrating to the second thickness of the paper. The difference in effect produced by two or three turns, more or less, could be distinguished with facility.

375. The wire and spatula were then connected with the voltaic apparatus (369.), the galvanometer being also included in the arrangement; and, a stronger acid having been prepared consisting of nitric acid and water, the voltaic apparatus was immersed so far as to give a permanent deflection of the needle to the 5⅓ division (372.), the fourfold moistened paper inter-

---

[6] Magie, *op. cit.*, pp. 492–495.

[7] *Ibid.*, pp. 495–496.

[8] *Ibid.*, pp. 495–496.

[9] *Ibid.*, pp. 497–498.

[10] [The paragraphs of all Faraday's papers were consecutively numbered, a device which, of course, greatly facilitated cross-referencing.]

[11] [A static electrical generator.]

vening as before.[12] Then by shifting the end of the wire from place to place upon the test paper, the effect of the current for five, six, seven, or any number of the beats of the watch (369.) was observed, and compared with that of the machine. After alternating and repeating the experiments of comparison many times, it was constantly found that this standard current of voltaic electricity, continued for eight beats of the watch,[13] was equal, in chemical effect, to thirty turns of the machine; twenty-eight revolutions of the machine were sensibly too few.

376. Hence it results that both in *magnetic deflection* (371.) and in *chemical force*, the current of electricity of the standard voltaic battery for eight beats of the watch was equal to that of the machine evolved by thirty revolutions.

377. It also follows that for this case of electro-chemical decomposition, and it is probable for all cases, that the *chemical power, like the magnetic force* (366.), *is in direct proportion to the quantity of electricity* which passes.

The following is from the paper of 1834 (see footnote 5 above).

ON THE DEFINITE NATURE AND EXTENT OF ELECTRO-CHEMICAL DECOMPOSITION

. . . 783. In the third series of these Researches, after proving the identity of electricities derived from different sources, and showing, by actual measurement, the extraordinary quantity of electricity evolved by a very feeble voltaic arrangement (371. 376.), I announced a law, derived from experiment, which seemed to me of the utmost importance to the science of electricity in general, and that branch of it denominated electrochemistry in particular. The law was expressed thus: *The chemical power of a current of electricity is in direct proportion to the absolute quantity of electricity which passes* (377.).

784. In the further progress of the successive investigations, I have had frequent occasion to refer to the same law, sometimes in circumstances offering powerful corroboration of its truth (456. 504. 505.); and the present series already supplies numerous new cases in which it holds good (704. 722. 726. 732.). It is now my object to consider this great principle more closely, and to develop some of the consequences to which it leads. That the evidence for it may be the more distinct and applicable, I shall quote cases of decomposition subject to as few interferences from secondary results as possible, effected upon bodies very simple, yet very definite in their nature.

785. In the first place, I consider the law as so fully established with respect to the decomposition of *water*, and under so many circumstances

[12] Of course the heightened power of the voltaic battery was necessary to compensate for the bad conductor now interposed.

[13] [The watch gave 150 beats in a minute.]

which might be supposed, if anything could, to exert an influence over it, that I may be excused entering into further detail respecting that substance, or even summing up the results here (732.). I refer, therefore, to the whole of the subdivision of this series of Researches which contains the account of the *volta-electrometer* (704. &c.).

786. In the next place, I also consider the law as established with respect to *muriatic acid* by the experiments and reasoning already advanced, when speaking of that substance, in the subdivision respecting primary and secondary results (758. &c.).

787. I consider the law as established also with regard to *hydriodic acid* by the experiments and considerations already advanced in the preceding division of this series of Researches (767. 768.).

788. Without speaking with the same confidence, yet from the experiments described, and many others not described, relating to hydro-fluoric, hydro-cyanic, ferro-cyanic, and sulpho-cyanic acids (770. 771. 772.), and from the close analogy which holds between these bodies and the hydracids of chlorine, iodine, bromine, &c., I consider these also as coming under subjection to the law, and assisting to prove its truth.

789. In the preceding cases, except the first, the water is believed to be inactive; but to avoid any ambiguity arising from its presence, I sought for substances from which it should be absent altogether; and, taking advantage of the law of conduction already developed (380. &c.), I soon found abundance, amongst which *protochloride of tin* [$SnCl_2$] was first subjected to decomposition in the following manner. A piece of platina wire had one extremity coiled up into a small knob, and having been carefully weighed, was sealed hermetically into a piece of bottle-glass tube, so that the knob should be at the bottom of the tube within. The tube was suspended by a piece of platina wire, so that the heat of a spirit-lamp could be applied to it. Recently fused protochloride of tin was introduced in sufficient quantity to occupy, when melted, about one-half of the tube; the wire of the tube was connected with a volta-electro-meter (711.), which was itself connected with the negative end of a voltaic battery; and a platina wire connected with the positive end of the same battery was dipped into the fused chloride in the tube; being, however, so bent, that it could not by any shake of the hand or apparatus touch the negative electrode at the bottom of the vessel. . . .

790. Under these circumstances the chloride of tin was decomposed: the chlorine evolved at the positive electrode formed bichloride of tin (779.) [$SnCl_4$], which passed away in fumes, and the tin evolved at the negative electrode combined with the platina, forming an alloy, fusible at the temperature to which the tube was subjected, and therefore never occasioning metallic communication through the decomposing chloride. When the experiment had been continued so long as to yield a reasonable quan-

tity of gas in the volta-electrometer, the battery connexion was broken, the positive electrode removed, and the tube and remaining chloride allowed to cool. When cold, the tube was broken open, the rest of the chloride and the glass being easily separable from the platina wire and its button of alloy. The latter when washed was then reweighed, and the increase gave the weight of the tin reduced.

791. I will give the particular results of one experiment, in illustration of the mode adopted in this and others, the results of which I shall have occasion to quote. The negative electrode weighed at first 20 grains; after the experiment, it, with its button of alloy, weighed 23.2 grains. The tin evolved by the electric current at the *cathode* weighed, therefore, 3.2 grains. The quantity of oxygen and hydrogen collected in the volta-electrometer = 3.85 cubic inches. As 100 cubic inches of oxygen and hydrogen, in the proportions to form water, may be considered as weighing 12.92 grains, the 3.85 cubic inches would weigh 0.49742 of a grain; that being, therefore, the weight of water decomposed by the same electric current as was able to decompose such weight of protochloride of tin as could yield 3.2 grains of metal. Now 0.49742:3.2::9 the equivalent of water is to 57.9, which should therefore be the equivalent of tin, if the experiment had been made without error, and if the electro-chemical decomposition *is in this case also definite*. In some chemical works 58 is given as the chemical equivalent of tin, in other 57.9. Both are so near to the result of the experiment, and the experiment itself is so subject to slight causes of variation (as from the absorption of gas in the volta-electrometer (716.) &c.), that the numbers leave little doubt of the applicability of the *law of definite action*[14] in this and all similar cases of electro-decomposition.

The first important work on the liquefaction of gases was done by Michael Faraday. His experiments, which began in 1823, showed that the ability to be liquefied was common to almost all gases. One of the first important papers published by Faraday contains the discovery of the liquefaction of chlorine, the first gas he liquefied: "On Fluid Chlorine, with Note on the Condensation of Muriatic Acid Gas into the liquid Form, by Sir Humphry Davy, P.R.S."[15] This initial work disproved the permanency of gases and clearly demonstrated that the state of aggregation is a function of temperature and pressure. The paper is reproduced in its entirety, with the omission of Davy's concluding note.[16]

[14] [In the same sense as law of definite proportion.]

[Faraday thought that only compounds formed of two atoms were capable of conducting the electric current and therefore electroyzable. Thus his law, as first developed here, rested on a false hypothesis.]

[15] *Philosophical Transactions*, **113**: 160–165 (1823).

[16] Also in the *Alembic Club Reprints*, No. 12, "The Liquefaction of Gases, Papers by Michael Faraday, F.R.S. (1823–1845) With an Appendix consisting of Papers by Thomas Northmore On the Compression of Gases (1805–1806)," Edinburgh, 1904.

I. ON FLUID CHLORINE

It is well known that before the year 1810, the solid substance obtained by exposing chlorine, as usually procured, to a low temperature, was considered as the gas itself reduced into that form; and that Sir Humphry Davy first showed it to be a hydrate, the pure dry gas not being condensible even at a temperature of −40°F.

I took advantage of the late cold weather to procure crystals of this substance for the purpose of analysis. The results are contained in a short paper in the Quarterly Journal of Science, Vol. XV. Its composition is very nearly 27.7 chlorine, 72.3 water, or 1 proportional of chlorine, and 10 of water.

The President of the Royal Society having honoured me by looking at these conclusions, suggested, that an exposure of the substance to heat under pressure, would probably lead to interesting results; the following experiments were commenced at his request. Some hydrate of chlorine was prepared, and being dried as well as could be by pressure in bibulous paper, was introduced into a sealed glass tube, the upper end of which was then hermetically closed. Being placed in water at 60°, it underwent no change; but when put into water at 100°, the substance fused, the tube became filled with a bright yellow atmosphere, and, on examination, was found to contain two fluid substances: the one, about three-fourths of the whole, was of a faint yellow colour, having very much the appearance of water; the remaining fourth was a heavy bright yellow fluid, lying at the bottom of the former, without any apparent tendency to mix with it. As the tube cooled, the yellow atmosphere condensed into more of the yellow fluid, which floated in a film on the pale fluid, looking very like chloride of nitrogen; and at 70° the pale portion congealed, although even at 32° the yellow portion did not solidify. Heated up to 100° the yellow fluid appeared to boil, and again produced the bright coloured atmosphere.

By putting the hydrate into a bent tube, afterwards hermetically sealed, I found it easy, after decomposing it by a heat of 100°, to distil the yellow fluid to one end of the tube, and so separate it from the remaining portion. In this way a more complete decomposition of the hydrate was effected, and, when the whole was allowed to cool, neither of the fluids solidified at temperatures above 34°, and the yellow portion not even at 0°. When the two were mixed together they gradually combined at temperatures below 60°, and formed the same solid substance as that first introduced. If, when the fluids were separated, the tube was cut in the middle, the parts flew asunder as if with an explosion, the whole of the yellow portion disappeared, and there was a powerful atmosphere of chlorine produced; the pale portion on the contrary remained, and when examined, proved to be a weak solution of chlorine in water, with a little muriatic acid, probably from the impurity of the hydrate used. When that end of the tube in which the yellow fluid lay was broken under a jar of water, there was an immediate production of chlorine gas.

I first thought that muriatic acid and euchlorine had been formed; then, that two new hydrates of chlorine had been produced; but at last I suspected that the chlorine had been entirely separated from the water by the heat, and condensed into a dry fluid by the mere pressure of its own abundant vapour. If that were true, it followed, that chlorine gas, when compressed, should be condensed into the same fluid, and, as the atmosphere in the tube in which the fluid lay was not very yellow at 50° or 60°, it seemed probable that the pressure required was not beyond what could readily be obtained by a condensing syringe. A long tube was therefore furnished with a cap and stop-cock, then exhausted of air and filled with chlorine, and being held vertically with the syringe upwards, air was forced in, which thrust the chlorine to the bottom of the tube, and gave a pressure of about 4 atmospheres. Being now cooled, there was an immediate deposit in films, which appeared to be hydrate, formed by water contained in the gas and vessels, but some of the yellow fluid was also produced. As this however might also contain a portion of the water present, a perfectly dry tube and apparatus were taken, and the chlorine left for some time over a bath of sulphuric acid before it was introduced. Upon throwing in air and giving pressure, there was now no solid film formed, but the clear yellow fluid was deposited, and more abundantly still upon cooling. After remaining some time it disappeared, having gradually mixed with the atmosphere above it, but every repetition of the experiment produced the same results.

Presuming that I had now a right to consider the yellow fluid as pure chlorine in the liquid state, I proceeded to examine its properties, as well as I could when obtained by heat from the hydrate. However obtained, it always appears very limpid and fluid, and excessively volatile at common pressure. A portion was cooled in its tube to 0°: it remained fluid. The tube was then opened, when a part immediately flew off, leaving the rest so cooled by the evaporation as to remain a fluid under the atmospheric pressure. The temperature could not have been higher than −40° in this case; as Sir Humphry Davy has shown that dry chlorine does not condense at that temperature under common pressure. Another tube was opened at a temperature of 50°; a part of the chlorine volatilised, and cooled the tube so much as to condense the atmospheric vapour on it as ice.

A tube having the water at one end and the chlorine at the other was weighed, and then cut in two; the chlorine immediately flew off, and the loss being ascertained was found to be 1.6 grains: the water left was examined and found to contain some chlorine: its weight was ascertained to be 5.4 grains. These proportions, however, must not be considered as indicative of the true composition of hydrate of chlorine; for, from the mildness of the weather during the time when these experiments were made, it was impossible to collect the crystals of hydrate, press, and transfer them, without losing much chlorine; and it is also impossible to separate the chlorine and water in the tube perfectly, or keep them separate, as the atmosphere within will combine with the water, and gradually reform the hydrate.

Before cutting the tube, another tube had been prepared exactly like it in form and size, and a portion of water introduced into it, as near as the eye could judge, of the same bulk as the fluid chlorine: this water was found to weigh 1.2 grains; a result, which, if it may be trusted, would give the specific gravity of fluid chlorine as 1.33; and from its appearance in, and on water, this cannot be far wrong.

Michel Eugène Chevreul

(1786–1889)

IN 1813, when Chevreul began his work on fats, chemists were busy with the problems of inorganic chemistry and the new elements and compounds which were being discovered almost daily. The substances formed in the plant and animal kingdoms, the "organic" compounds, were both complex and unstable, as compared to the inorganic salts. The methods for analysis of carbon and hydrogen were unsatisfactory. There was even doubt that organic compounds obeyed the same chemical laws as inorganic substances, since a "vital force" was supposed to give them a peculiar character. As a result very few chemists undertook the difficult and unrewarding task of studying such compounds. Chief among those who refused to be daunted was M. E. Chevreul. During his long life he studied dyes and many other organic compounds, but his chief fame has always rested on his studies of the composition of fats. His work in this field was carried on by purely chemical means and shows a remarkable understanding of the nature of organic compounds. He identified organic acids in mixtures of considerable complexity, and by a masterly interpretation of reactions he unraveled the whole problem of the nature of saponification. When it is remembered that practically nothing was known of any of the substances involved in these reactions, and when the difficulty of purifying mixtures of closely related fatty acids is recalled, the work seems the more remarkable. The sciences of organic chemistry and biochemistry owe much to the work of Chevreul. He described his experiments and conclusions in 1823 in a book[1] from which the following selection is taken.[2]

CONJECTURES ON THE COMPOSITION OF SEVERAL KINDS OF FATTY BODIES

. . . 1187. In all which has been said up to now, I have tried to establish the greatest possible agreement with the facts, I have striven, in the small number of explanations which I have given, to keep myself within the limits of experience; it now seems useful to venture some conjectures on the nature of the several kinds of fats, since these occur so naturally to the mind that it would be surprising not to find them in this work.

1188. The products of saponification of 100 parts of stearine [the fat of various animals, man, pig, beef, sheep, etc.] and of 100 parts of oleine from human fat are:

	Stearine	Oleine
Glycerine...........................	8.5	9.80
Margaric acid, melting at 55°...........	80.0	22.08
Oleic acid, liquid at 0°................	16.4	73.92

These are the same products, with this difference, that the stearine gives a little less glycerine, and with respect to oleic acid, much more margaric acid than the oleine. On the other hand, we have seen (1121) that it is very probable that the stearine on which I worked retains oleine, just as oleine retains stearine (1122). *From these considerations, it is permissible to believe that these substances, in the pure state, would give* 1) *from stearine, glycerine and margaric acid;*[3] 2), *from oleine, glycerine and oleic acid.*

1189. *For the same reason, pure sheep stearine would give glycerine and stearic acid.*

1190. Phocenine [fat of the porpoise, delphinus phocoena] and butirine [fat from butter] have given, by saponification, from 100 parts,

Phocenine		Butirine	
Glycerine.....................	15.00	Glycerine.....................	12.5
Dry phocenic acid..............	32.82	Volatile acids....	13.68
Oleic acid....................	59.00	Margaric acid, melting at 55°....	16.90
		Oleic acid, liquid at 0°..........	63.60

1191. It will conform to analogy to consider these in the manner previously described.

First, *phocenine*, as it has been described, is composed of *oleine* and

---

[1] "Recherches chimiques sur les Corps gras d'origine animale," Paris, 1823.

[2] *Ibid.*, Book VI, Sec. 7, pp. 442–451.

[3] If margaric acid is really distinct from stearic acid, it is necessary to name the stearine which furnishes it *margarine*, and to keep the name stearine for sheep stearine.

another substance which is characterized by the property of changing under alkaline influence into glycerine and phocenic acid, which would then be *pure phocenine*.

Second, *butirine*, as it has been described is formed from five immediate principles: 1) *oleine;* 2) *stearine;* 3) a substance which is converted by alkaline action into glycerine and butyric acid, which would be pure *butirine;* 4) a substance which is converted by the same action into glycerine and caproic acid, which would be *caproine;* 5) a substance which is converted by the same action into glycerine and capric acid, which would be *caprine*.

1192. Finally, always by the same hypothesis, we could consider cetine [spermaceti] as formed from two immediate principles, of which one is characterized by the property of being converted in saponification into margaric acid and ethal [cetyl alcohol]; while the other will be characterized by the property of being converted into oleic acid and ethal. Moreover, for the purification of cetine there exist the same difficulties as for that of stearine and oleine (1121).

1193. The previous conjectures are of a kind to be confirmed by experience; because it is not absurd to think that someday among organized bodies stearine, oleine, cetine, etc., will be found absolutely pure, or that one can foresee obtaining these substances in this condition by means of chemical processes. But the following conjectures, relative to the arrangement of elements which constitute several types of fatty bodies are, I admit, hypotheses which can hardly be demonstrated completely; in spite of this, I present them in the persuasion that they can suggest new studies.

1194. We have seen that phocenine and butirine, which are not acids, give, when they are treated with potash, acids and glycerine; that, exposed to the simultaneous action of air and heat, they acquire an odor and are able to give the principles of the odor to magnesia. Vegetable ethers and nitrous ether, which are considered to be combinations of acids and alcohol, show analogous properties. They are not acid at all; when they are treated with potash they are reduced into alcohol and acids; exposed to the action of air and heat, a part of their acid is liberated. From these analogies, is there not some reason to consider phocenine and butirine as combinations of odorous acids and anhydrous glycerine, or rather, of a substance formed from oxygen, carbon, and hydrogen, which, fixing water, forms glycerine?

1195. If we admit the agreement which I have shown between the immediate composition of vegetable ethers and that of phocenine and butirine, we cannot avoid extending it to stearine and oleine; for these have the greatest analogy with phocenine and butirine in the manner in which they behave, not only when they are exposed to the action of alkalis but even when they are submitted to the action of oxygen and to that of concentrated sulfuric acid. Thus,

(*a*) Stearines and oleine, under alkaline influence, change to glycerine and fixed fat acids, as phocenine and butirine are changed to glycerine and volatile fat acids.

(*b*) Stearines and oleine, exposed to the action of oxygen, become acid; and if then they produce volatile acids and a nonacid aromatic product, they behave as fixed fat acids, as do phocenic and butyric acids when phocenine and butirine are exposed to the action of oxygen. . . .

(*c*) When stearines and oleine are put with concentrated sulfuric acid, they show themselves to be fixed fat acids, and perhaps some glycerine . . . ; in the same way, when phocenine and butirine are exposed to the action of concentrated sulfuric acid, they show themselves to be phocenic and butyric acids and perhaps some glycerine. . . .

1196. In truth, it is possible to oppose to this opinion several objections, which I am the less disposed to suppress since in 1814, in my third memoir on the fatty bodies, where I treated the same subject [*Ann. chim.*, **94**: 113] these objections seemed then so strong to me that I thought it would be more natural to consider glycerine and the fixed fat acids, products of saponification of stearines and oleines, as newly formed substances, rather than to consider them as the immediate principles of the stearines and oleine; but at this time I knew neither phocenine nor butirine, I was ignorant of the analogy between the results of the action of oxygen on the saponifiable fat bodies and the results of the action of alkalis on the same bodies. Besides, I am going to quote the objections which I have made to the opinion which seems to me today to be most probable, with the replies which appear to me to weaken their force.

(*a*) Stearic, margaric, and oleic acids are insoluble in water; glycerine dissolves very well in it; how is it that water does not remove this principle from the acids which are supposed to combine with it? It is for the same reason that cold water does not remove potash from the bistearate and the supersilicate of this base.

(*b*) Why do stearic, margaric, and oleic acids, etc., which are soluble in all proportions in boiling alcohol with a density of 0.821, form with anhydrous glycerine, which is soluble in the same liquid (at least when hydrated), combinations which are not very soluble? This is for the same reason that sulfuric acid and potash form a neutral salt, little soluble in water; that acetic acid and alcohol form an ether little soluble in the same liquid, although sulfuric acid and potash, acetic acid and alcohol, are very soluble in water.

(*c*) Stearic, margaric, oleic acids, etc., have an energetic action on tournesole. Why does glycerine, which has a sensible affinity for potash and which seems to be acid rather than alkaline, neutralize the action of fat acids on tournesole? It is for the same reason that alcohol forms ethers which are not acids with nitrous, acetic, and citric acids.

(d) How is it that stearic, margaric, and oleic acids, etc., put into contact with glycerine, do not reproduce stearines, oleine, etc.? This is because, in presenting these bodies to each other, they are in the state of hydrates, and at that time their mutual affinity is not strong enough, as it is when they are deprived of the proportions of water which are foreign to the composition of stearines, oleine, etc. Besides, acetic acid, benzoic acid, etc., put in contact with alcohol, either heated or cold, never produce an ether so long as they are not under the influence of a mineral acid.

(e) Why does not saponification occur instantly when the saponifiable materials are presented to the alkaline base? Without pretending to reply to this objection in a manner which will demolish it, yet it is possible to consider a very powerful obstacle to saponification the difficulty of establishing a sufficiently prolonged, intimate contact between two liquids which mix with difficulty.

1197. Finally, I will add that the properties of anhydrous glycerine can be very different from those we know after it has been fixed by water; for organic materials are capable of uniting with water in definite proportions in two ways: (1) keeping more or less their principal properties, like an anhydrous mineral salt, which fixes water of crystallization; (2) acquiring absolutely distinct properties from those which it had before it combined with this liquid, like starch, which under the influence of weak sulfuric acid fixes water and is converted into sugar of grapes.

1198. At any rate, whichever of the two opinions may be preferred, I shall summarize the explanation of saponification (a) on the hypothesis that saponifiable fatty bodies are considered as immediately formed from oxygen, carbon, and hydrogen; (b) on the hypothesis that they are considered as immediately formed from fat acids and a compound which, by fixing water, forms glycerine or ethal.

Saponification on the First Hypothesis

1199. The stearines, oleine, phocenine, butirine, and hircine [found in goat and sheep fat], are formed of oxygen, carbon, and hydrogen in such proportions that a part of their elements represents a fixed or volatile fat acid and the other part plus water represents glycerine. Cetine is formed of the same elements in such proportions that one part represents a fixed fat acid material and the other part consists of carbon and hydrogen (in the proportion of the elements of percarburetted hydrogen) plus water to represent ethal. Now if this saponifiable body is submitted to the action of a sufficiently energetic salifiable base, the equilibrium of the elements is broken, the alkaline force determines the acidity in a part of the mass of the saponifiable substance, and the rest of this mass, by fixing water,

forms glycerine or ethal. On this hypothesis, saponification is a phenomenon of the same type as that shown by the metals when they dissolve in an
acid, oxidizing at the expense of the water; there is a difference only in the
nature of the force which is developed: in saponification, it is the alkaline
force which determines the development of the acid force; and in the solution of metals, it is the acid force which determines the development of the
alkaline force: in the two cases, salts are formed with materials which
contain, already formed, only one of the immediate principles of the salts
produced.

SAPONIFICATION ON THE SECOND HYPOTHESIS

1200. Stearines, oleine, phocenine, and butirine are types of salts
formed from an anhydrous fat acid, fixed or volatile, and anhydrous
glycerine; cetine is equally a type of salt, but the base which neutralizes
this acid part, instead of glycerine, is the percarburetted hydrogen; this
composition brings together cetine and the ethers which are considered to
be compounds of an acid and percarburetted hydrogen. In this hypothesis,
saponification is only the decomposition of a fatty salt by a salifiable base
which takes the place of the anhydrous glycerine or the percarburetted
hydrogen, while these latter bodies, by fixing water, give syrupy glycerine
or ethal.

Joseph Louis Gay-Lussac

(1778-1850)

THE extensive researches of Joseph Louis Gay-Lussac in physics and chemistry
are far too numerous even to list here. He discovered new compounds and methods;
his physicochemical measurements vastly enriched chemistry. The majority of his
early investigations were concerned with gases. In 1802 he enunciated, independently of Dalton, the law governing the expansion of gases by heat.[1] In 1805,
with Alexander von Humboldt (1769-1854) he observed the already known fact
that hydrogen and oxygen combine in the ratio of 2 to 1 by volume. Stimulated by
this work he studied the reactions of other gases to see whether there were other
simple relationships, and in 1808 he announced the law of combining volumes,
which is now known as *Gay-Lussac's law*. This generalization, obviously connected
with some fundamental property of matter, was in part responsible for Avogadro's
hypothesis.

[1] W. F. Magie, "A Source Book in Physics," New York, 1935, pp. 165-172.

Gay-Lussac collaborated in many researches with Louis Jacques Thenard (1777–1857). Together they devised the first practical method of organic analysis, one which, modified by Liebig, was to make possible the burgeoning of organic chemistry later in the century. In 1814 Gay-Lussac published his investigations on iodine (discovered in 1811 by J. B. Courtois [1777–1838]), in which he showed that the new substance was an element analogous to chlorine.[2]

One of the most important contributions of Gay-Lussac was his work on hydrocyanic acid and its compounds. In the course of his investigation on the combining volumes of gases he had prepared gaseous hydrogen cyanide. This led him to the study of related compounds, and in 1815 he published a paper, *Recherche sur l'acide prussique*,[3] wherein he announced the discovery of cyanogen and chlorcyanogen and the composition of hydrocyanic acid. His demonstration that hydrogen cyanide contains no oxygen added another oxygen-free acid to those already known (hydrogen halides and sulfide) and contributed to the overthrow of Lavoisier's oxygen theory of acids. Gay-Lussac found that the cyano radical, the first organic radical clearly recognized, could act as an element analogous to chlorine, passing unchanged through various reactions. This concept of an organic radical was important to organic chemistry.

The first of the following citations contains Gay-Lussac's famous law, which was originally published in the *Mémoires de la Société d'Arcueil*.[4] It appears here in the translation of the Alembic Club.

The second citation consists of excerpts from the paper on prussic acid, from the Thomson translation.

MEMOIR ON THE COMBINATION OF GASEOUS SUBSTANCES WITH EACH OTHER.

Substances, whether in the solid, liquid, or gaseous state, possess properties which are independent of the force of cohesion; but they also possess others which appear to be modified by this force (so variable in its intensity), and which no longer follow any regular law. The same pressure applied to all solid or liquid substances would produce a diminution of volume differing in each case, while it would be equal for all elastic fluids. Similarly, heat expands all substances; but the dilations of liquids and solids have hitherto presented no regularity, and it is only those of elastic fluids which are equal and independent of the nature of each gas. The attraction of the molecules in solids and liquids is, therefore, the cause

[2] *Ann. chim.*, **91**: 5–160 (1814); Ostwald's *Klassiker*, No. 4, "Untersuchungen uber das Jod. (1814). Herausgegeben von W. Ostwald," Leipzig, 1889.

Gay-Lussac's and Davy's researches on iodine were carried out simultaneously, which makes it difficult to assign priority. Gay-Lussac was annoyed at Davy's intrusion. His work, however, is considered as a model of experimental research.

[3] *Ann. chim.*, **95**: 136–231 (1815). English translation in Thomas Thomson's *Annals of Philosophy*, **7**: 350–64 (1816); **8**: 37–52, 108–15 (1816).

[4] *Mémoires de la Société d'Arcueil*, **2**: 207–234 (1809); translated into English in the *Alembic Club Reprints*, No. 4, "Foundations of the Molecular Theory: comprising Paper and Extracts by John Dalton, Joseph-Louis Gay-Lussac, and Amadeo Avogadro, (1808–1811)," Edinburgh, 1899.

which modifies their special properties; and it appears that it is only when the attraction is entirely destroyed, as in gases, that bodies under similar conditions obey simple and regular laws. At least, it is my intention to make known some new properties in gases, the effects of which are regular, by showing that these substances combine amongst themselves in very simple proportions, and that the contraction of volume which they experience on combination also follows a regular law. I hope by this means to give a proof of an idea advanced by several very distinguished chemists— that we are perhaps not far removed from the time when we shall be able to submit the bulk of chemical phenomena to calculation.

It is a very important question in itself, and one much discussed amongst chemists, to ascertain if compounds are formed in all sorts of proportions. M. Proust, who appears first to have fixed his attention on this subject, is of opinion that the metals are susceptible of only two degrees of oxidation, a *minimum* and a *maximum;* but led away by this seductive theory, he has seen himself forced to entertain principles contrary to physics in order to reduce to two oxides all those which the same metal sometimes presents. M. Berthollet thinks, on the other hand— reasoning from general considerations and his own experiments—that compounds are always formed in very variable proportions, unless they are determined by special causes, such as crystallisation, insolubility, or elasticity. Lastly, Dalton has advanced the idea that compounds of two bodies are formed in such a way that one atom of the one unites with one, two, three, or more atoms of the other.[5] It would follow from this mode of looking at compounds that they are formed in constant proportions, the existence of intermediate bodies being excluded, and in this respect Dalton's theory would resemble that of M. Proust; but M. Berthollet has already strongly opposed it in the Introduction he has written to Thomson's Chemistry, and we shall see that in reality it is not entirely exact. Such is the state of the question now under discussion; it is still very far from receiving its solution, but I hope that the facts which I now proceed to set forth, facts which had entirely escaped the notice of chemists, will contribute to its elucidation.

Suspecting, from the exact ratio of 100 of oxygen to 200 of hydrogen, which M. Humboldt and I had determined for the proportions of water, that other gases might also combine in simple ratios, I have made the following experiments. I prepared fluoboric,[6] muriatic, and carbonic

[5] Dalton has been led to this idea by systematic considerations; and one may see from his work, *A New System of Chemical Philosophy*, p. 213, and from that of Thomson, Vol. 6, that his researches have no connection with mine.

[6] M. Thenard and I have given the name of fluoboric gas to that particular gas which we obtained by distilling pure fluoride of lime with vitreous boracic acid [boron trifluoride].

gases, and made them combine successively with ammonia gas. 100 parts of muriatic gas saturate precisely 100 parts of ammonia gas, and the salt which is formed from them is perfectly neutral, whether one or other of the gases is in excess. Fluoboric gas, on the contrary, unites in two proportions with ammonia gas. When the acid[7] gas is put first into the graduated tube, and the other gas is then passed in, it is found that equal volumes of the two condense, and that the salt formed is neutral. But if we begin by first putting the ammonia gas into the tube, and then admitting the fluoboric gas in single bubbles, the first gas will then be in excess with regard to the second, and there will result a salt with excess of base, composed of 100 of fluoboric gas and 200 of ammonia gas. If carbonic gas is brought into contact with ammonia gas, by passing it sometimes first, sometimes second into the tube, there is always formed a sub-carbonate [ammonium carbamate] composed of 100 parts of carbonic gas and 200 of ammonia gas. It may, however, be proved that neutral carbonate of ammonia would be composed of equal volumes of each of these components. M. Berthollet, who has analysed this salt, obtained by passing carbonic gas into the sub-carbonate [ammonium carbonate], found that it was composed of 73.34 parts by weight of carbonic gas and 26.66 of ammonia gas. Now, if we suppose it to be composed of equal volumes of its components, we find from their known specific gravity, that it contains by weight

$$\begin{array}{l} 71.81 \text{ of carbonic acid,} \\ \underline{28.19} \text{ of ammonia,} \\ 100.0 \end{array}$$

a proportion differing only slightly from the preceding.

If the neutral carbonate of ammonia could be formed by the mixture of carbonic gas and ammonia gas, as much of one gas as of the other would be absorbed; and since we can only obtain it through the intervention of water, we must conclude that it is the affinity of this liquid which competes with that of the ammonia to overcome the elasticity of the carbonic acid, and that the neutral carbonate of ammonia can only exist through the medium of water.

Thus we may conclude that muriatic, fluoboric, and carbonic acids take exactly their own volume of ammonia gas to form neutral salts, and that the last two take twice as much to form *sub-salts*. It is very remarkable to see acids so different from one another neutralise a volume of ammonia gas equal to their own; and from this we may suspect that if all acids and all alkalis could be obtained in the gaseous state, neutrality would result from the combination of equal volumes of acid and alkali.

It is not less remarkable that, whether we obtain a neutral salt or a *sub-*

---

[7] ["alkaline" in the original.]

salt, their elements combine in simple ratios which may be considered as limits to their proportions. Accordingly, if we accept the specific gravity of muriatic acid determined by M. Biot and myself,[8] and those of carbonic gas and ammonia given by MM. Biot and Arago, we find that dry muriate of ammonia is composed of

Ammonia.............. 100.0   or   38.35
Muriatic acid......... 160.7   61.65
                                     ‾‾‾‾‾‾‾
                                     100.00

a proportion very far from that of M. Berthollet—

100 of ammonia,
213 of acid.

In the same way, we find that sub-carbonate of ammonia contains

Ammonia.............. 100.0   or   43.98
Carbonic acid......... 127.3   56.02
                                     ‾‾‾‾‾‾‾
                                     100.00

and the neutral carbonate

Ammonia.............. 100.0   or   28.19
Carbonic acid......... 254.6   71.81
                                     ‾‾‾‾‾‾‾
                                     100.00

It is easy from the preceding results to ascertain the ratios of the capacity of fluoboric, muriatic, and carbonic acids; for since these three gases saturate the same volume of ammonia gas, their relative capacities will be inversely as their densities, allowance having been made for the water contained in muriatic acid.

We might even now conclude that gases combine with each other in very simple ratios; but I shall still give some fresh proofs.

According to the experiments of M. Amédée Berthollet,[9] ammonia is composed of

100 of nitrogen,
300 of hydrogen,

by volume.

I have found (1st vol. of the Société d'Arcueil) that sulphuric acid is composed of

100 of sulphurous gas,
50 of oxygen gas.

When a mixture of 50 parts of oxygen and 100 of carbonic oxide [carbon monoxide] (formed by the distillation of oxide of zinc with strongly cal-

---

[8] As muriatic gas contains one-fourth its weight of water, we must only take three-fourths of the density for that of real muriatic acid.

[9] [(1783–1811), the son of Claude Louis Berthollet.]

cined charcoal) is inflamed, these two gases are destroyed and their place taken by 100 parts of carbonic acid gas. Consequently carbonic acid may be considered as being composed of

100 of carbonic oxide gas,
50 of oxygen gas.

Davy, from the analysis of various compounds of nitrogen with oxygen, has found the following proportions by weight:—

	Nitrogen.	Oxygen.
Nitrous oxide......................	63.30	36.70
Nitrous gas [nitric oxide].............	44.05	55.95
Nitric acid [nitrogen dioxide].........	29.50	70.50

Reducing these proportions to volumes we find—

	Nitrogen.	Oxygen.
Nitrous oxide......................	100	49.5
Nitrous gas........................	100	108.9
Nitric acid........................	100	204.7

The first and last of these proportions differ only slightly from 100 to 50, and 100 to 200; it is only the second which diverges somewhat from 100 to 100. The difference, however, is not very great, and is such as we might expect in experiments of this sort; and I have assured myself that it is actually nil. On burning the new combustible substance from potash[10] in 100 parts by volume of nitrous gas, there remained over exactly 50 parts of nitrogen, the weight of which, deducted from that of the nitrous gas (determined with great care by M. Bérard at Arcueil), yields as result that this gas is composed of equal parts by volume of nitrogen and oxygen.

We may then admit the following numbers for the proportions by volume of the compounds of nitrogen with oxygen:—

	Nitrogen.	Oxygen.
Nitrous oxide............	100	50
Nitrous gas..............	100	100
Nitric acid..............	100	200

From my experiments, which differ very little from those of M. Chenevix, oxygenated muriatic acid[11] is composed by weight of

[10] [Potassium, discovered in 1807 by Humphry Davy.]

[11] [This was two years before Davy recognized the elementary nature of chlorine.]

Oxygen................ 22.92
Muriatic acid.......... 77.08

Converting these quantities into volumes, we find that oxygenated muriatic acid is formed of

Muriatic gas........... 300.0
Oxygen gas............ 103.2

a proportion very nearly

Muriatic gas........... 300
Oxygen gas............ 100[12]

Thus it appears evident to me that gases always combine in the simplest proportions when they act on one another; and we have seen in reality in all the preceding examples that the ratio of combination is 1 to 1, 1 to 2, or 1 to 3. It is very important to observe that in considering weights there is no simple and finite relation between the elements of any one compound; it is only when there is a second compound between the same elements that the new proportion of the element that has been added is a multiple of the first quantity. Gases, on the contrary, in whatever proportions they may combine, always give rise to compounds whose elements by volume are multiples of each other. . . .

CONCLUSION.

I have shown in this Memoir that the compounds of gaseous substances with each other are always formed in very simple ratios, so that representing one of the terms by unity, the other is 1, or 2, or at most 3. These ratios by volume are not observed with solid or liquid substances, nor when we consider weights, and they form a new proof that it is only in the gaseous state that substances are in the same circumstances and obey regular laws. It is remarkable to see that ammonia gas neutralises exactly its own volume of gaseous acids; and it is probable that if all acids and alkalis were in the elastic state, they would all combine in equal volumes

[12] In the proportion by weight of oxygenated muriatic acid, the muriatic acid is supposed to be free from water, whilst in the proportion by volume it is supposed to be combined with a fourth of its weight of water, which, since the reading of this paper, M. Thenard and I have proved to be absolutely necessary for its existence in the gaseous state. But since the simple ratio of 300 of acid to 100 of oxygen cannot be due to chance, we must conclude that water by combining with dry muriatic acid to form ordinary muriatic acid does not sensibly change its specific gravity. We should be led to the same conclusion from the consideration that the specific gravity of oxygenated muriatic acid, which from our experiments contains no water, is exactly the same as that obtained by adding the density of oxygen gas to three times that of muriatic gas, and taking half of this sum. M. Thenard and I have also found that oxygenated muriatic gas contains precisely half its volume of oxygen, and that it can destroy in consequence its own volume of hydrogen.

to produce neutral salts. The capacity of saturation of acids and alkalis measured by volume would then be the same, and this might perhaps be the true manner of determining it. The apparent contraction of volume suffered by gases on combination is also very simply related to the volume of one of them, and this property likewise is peculiar to gaseous substances.

The following citation is from Gay-Lussac's paper on prussic acid.

EXPERIMENTS ON PRUSSIC ACID.[13]

. . . Thus from these analyses it appears evident that prussic acid is composed of
One volume of the vapour of carbon.
Half a volume of hydrogen.
Half a volume of azote.
condensed into one volume; or in weight of

Carbon	44.39
Azote	51.71
Hydrogen	3.90
	100.00

This acid, when compared with other animal substances, is distinguished by the great quantity of azote which it contains, by its small quantity of hydrogen, and especially by the absence of oxygen. Its acid properties cannot depend upon the hydrogen, which is very alkalifying, but upon the carbon and azote.[14] We ought to consider it as a true hydracid, in which the carbon and azote supply the place of the chlorine in muriatic acid, the iodine in hydriodic acid,[15] and the sulphur in sulphuretted hydrogen; but this assertion requires a fuller elucidation. . . .

Among the simple metallic bodies, potassium is one of those whose action is most proper to throw light on the true nature of prussic acid. When heated in prussic vapour mixed with hydrogen or azote, there is absorption without inflammation, and the metal is converted into a grey spongy substance, which melts, and assumes a yellow colour. Supposing the quantity of potassium employed capable of disengaging from water a volume of hydrogen equal to 50 parts, we find, after the action of the potassium,

1. That the gaseous mixture has experienced a diminution of volume amounting to 50 parts:

[13] The selection is taken from *Annals of Philosophy*, **7**: 357,359–361,363 (1816); **8**: 37, 39–42, 113 (1816).

[14] [Although Davy had suggested that hydrogen might be the essential constituent of acids, Gay-Lussac refused to accept the idea and thought of oxygen-free acids as belonging to a special class of *hydracids*.]

[15] [Gay-Lussac discovered hydriodic acid in 1813.]

2. On treating this mixture with potash, and analysing the residue by oxygen, that 50 parts of hydrogen have been produced:

3. And consequently that the potassium has absorbed 100 parts of prussic vapour; for there is a diminution of 50 parts, which would obviously have been twice as great had not 50 parts of hydrogen been disengaged.

When the yellow matter is put into water, it dissolves entirely, without the least effervescence, and exhibits all the characters of simple prussiate of potash obtained by combining directly the acid and alkali. If we suppose the water to be decomposed, which is very probable, but which must necessarily happen by the joint action of an acid, the potassium combines with its oxygen, and the hydrogen, which is precisely equal to that which the potassium disengaged from the prussic acid, reproduces this acid with all its properties.

Here, then, is a very great analogy between prussic acid and muriatic and hydriodic acids. Like them, it contains half its volume of hydrogen; and, like them, it contains a radical which combines with the potassium, and forms a compound quite analogous to the chloride and iodide of potassium. The only difference is, that this radical is compound, while those of the chloride and iodide are simple.

Since prussic acid contains

One volume of vapour of carbon.

Half a volume of azote.

Half a volume of hydrogen.

And since I have just proved that potassium disengages half its volume of hydrogen, it is obvious that the substance which combines with the metal, and which ought to be distinguished by the name of prussic radical, is a compound of carbon and azote, in the proportion of

One volume of vapour of carbon.

Half a volume of azotic gas.

This radical combined with potassium forms a true prusside of that metal. We ought, therefore, to consider prussic acid as a *hydracid;* and with the less hesitation, that a great number of other facts lead to the same conclusion.

The name *prussic acid*, then, will no longer suit it; but it must be called *hydro-prussic*. We must likewise invent a name for its radical, from which this may be derived. Were we to preserve the term *prussic*, which has never been adopted in Germany, and which never can be, we should be obliged to give it a meaning different from that which it has hitherto borne. These considerations have induced me to invent a new name for the radical of prussic acid. That of *cyanogen*[16] having appeared very proper to the chemists of this capital, I have adopted it, and shall use it

[16] From κύανος, blue; γεννάω, I produce.

afterwards in the course of this memoir. Common prussic acid will receive the name of *hydro-cyanic acid*, and the prussiates that of *hydrocyanates*. The combinations of cyanogen with simple bodies, when it performs the same part as chlorine in the chlorides, will be denoted by the term *cyanuret*.[17] It will be difficult to give the prussic radical a more convenient name; for it will be seen that it acts at once the part of a compound and simple body; and if we wished to denote it by the name *carburet of azote*, which would suit it as a compound body, circumlocutions would be necessary to denote its numerous compounds. . . .

The red oxide of mercury, when assisted by heat, acts so powerfully on hydrocyanic vapour, that the compound which ought to be formed is destroyed by the heat disengaged. The same thing happens when a little of the concentrated acid is poured upon the oxide. A great elevation of temperature takes place, which would occasion a dangerous explosion if the experiment were made upon considerable quantities. When the acid is diluted, the oxide dissolves rapidly, with a considerable heat, and without the disengagement of any gas. Nothing is obtained but the substance formerly called *prussiate of mercury*.

When the oxide is placed in contact with the vapour of hydro-cyanic acid, mixed with hydrogen, without applying heat, the vapour is absorbed in a few minutes. On emptying the tube of the hydrogen in order to fill it with a new mixture, that the result might be the more sensible, the absorption of the vapour was as complete as the first time, and the hydrogen remained with the volume which it ought to have had, which shows that it had no part in the phenomenon. After some similar operations, the oxide adhered to the sides of the tube. Having collected it at the bottom of the tube, and applied a gentle heat, a good deal of water was evaporated.

Hence when the peroxide of mercury acts in the cold on hydro-cyanic acid, the oxygen of the first combines with the hydrogen of the second, which by this last is reduced to its radical. We ought, therefore, to obtain, not hydro-cyanate of mercury, but cyanuret of mercury. Common prussiate of mercury, which is exactly the same, must likewise bear the same name. . . .

II. Of Cyanogen, or the Radical of Prussic Acid.

I discovered the peculiar gas called cyanogen by decomposing the cyanuret of mercury by heat. But as the cyanuret of mercury varies in its composition, and in that case does not furnish the same products, I shall begin by describing how it ought to be prepared.

By digesting red oxide of mercury with Prussian blue, we obtain a cyanuret perfectly neutral, which crystallizes in long four-sided prisms

[17] The term *cyanide* would be better.—T. [Footnote by Thomas Thomson, editor of the English translation.]

truncated obliquely. We may, by repeated evaporations and crystalliza-
tions, free it from the iron which it contains; but I think it better to boil
it, as M. Proust has prescribed, with peroxide of mercury, which completely precipitates the oxide of iron, and I then saturate the excess of
oxide of mercury with a little hydrocyanic acid, or even with muriatic
acid. It is cyanuret thus prepared that I decompose by heat, in order to
obtain the radical; but for common experiments we may dispense with
these precautions. . . .

When cyanuret of mercury is exposed to heat in a small retort or tube
shut at one extremity, it soon begins to blacken. It then appears to melt
like an animal matter, and then the cyanogen is disengaged in abundance.
This gas is pure from the beginning of the process to the end, provided
always that the heat be not very high; for if it were sufficiently intense to
melt the glass, a little azote would be disengaged. Mercury is volatilized
with a considerable quantity of cyanuret, and there remains a charry
matter of the colour of soot, and as light as lamp-black. I shall give an
account of it afterwards. The cyanuret of silver likewise gives out cyanogen when heated; but the cyanuret of mercury is preferable to every other.

Cyanogen is a permanently elastic fluid. Its smell, which it is impossible
to describe, is very strong and penetrating. Its solution in water has a very
sharp taste. It burns with a bluish flame, mixed with purple. Its specific
gravity compared to that of air is 1.8064. I obtained it by weighing at the
same temperature, and under the same pressure, a balloon of about $2\frac{1}{2}$
litres (152.56 cubic inches) of capacity, in which the vacuum was made to
the same degree, and alternately full of air and cyanogen. The data of the
experiment are as follows:—

Weight of the balloon empty..........	A + 0.086 gramme
full of air...........................	A + 2.824
cyanogen...........................	A + 5.032

On dividing the weight of the cyanogen by that of the air, we obtain the
number 1.8064. I have neglected the effect of humidity, because, not
knowing it exactly, the correction would have been uncertain. Besides, it
is so small that it may be neglected.

Cyanogen is capable of bearing a pretty high temperature without being
decomposed. Water, with which I agitated it for some minutes, at the
temperature of 68°, absorbed almost $4\frac{1}{2}$ times its volume. Pure alcohol
absorbs 23 times its volume. Sulphuric ether and oil of turpentine dissolve
at least as much as water; but I did not attempt to ascertain the quantity
exactly.

Tincture of litmus is reddened by cyanogen. On heating the solution,
the gas is disengaged, mixed with a little carbonic acid, and the blue
colour of the litmus is restored. The carbonic acid is no doubt owing to the

decomposition of a small quantity of cyanogen and of water. It deprives the red sulphate of manganese of its colour, a property which hydrocyanic acid does not possess. This is a proof that its elements have more mobility than those of the acid. By the dry way it separates their acid from the carbonates.

Among the simple bodies which I placed in contact with cyanogen, in a temperature produced by a spirit lamp, which is incapable of melting glass, I found that phosphorus, sulphur, and iodine, might be volatilized in it without undergoing any change. Its mixture with hydrogen was not altered by the same temperature, nor by passing electrical sparks through it. Copper and gold do not combine with it; but iron, when heated almost to whiteness, decomposes it in part. It is covered with a slight coating of charcoal, and becomes brittle. The undecomposed portion of gas is mixed with azote. In one trial the azote constituted 0.44 of the mixture, but in general it was less. Platinum, which had been placed beside the iron, did not undergo any alteration. Neither its surface, nor that of the tube, was covered with charcoal, like the iron.

In the cold, potassium acts only slowly on cyanogen, because a crust is formed on its surface, which presents an obstacle to the mutual action. On applying the spirit-lamp, the potassium becomes speedily incandescent; the absorption of the gas begins, the enflamed disc gradually diminishes, and when it disappears entirely, which takes place in a few seconds, the absorption is likewise at an end. Supposing we employ a quantity of potassium that would disengage 50 parts of hydrogen from water, we find that from 48 to 50 parts of gas have disappeared. On treating the residue with potash, there usually remains four or five parts of hydrogen; sometimes 10 or 12. I have made a great number of experiments to discover the origin of this gas. I think that I have at last succeeded. It is derived from the water which the cyanuret of mercury contains when it has not been sufficiently dried. Hydro-cyanic vapour is then produced, which, when decomposed by the potassium, leaves half of its volume of hydrogen. Before I was aware of this cause, I concluded, from the variation in the quantity of hydrogen, that it did not proceed from the cyanogen. But it is much more satisfactory to know to what source it is to be ascribed. From this experiment, I shall draw as a consequence that potassium absorbs a volume of cyanogen equal to that of the hydrogen which it would disengage from water.

The compound of cyanogen and potassium is yellowish. It dissolves in water without effervescence, and the solution is strongly alkaline. Its taste is the same as that of hydro-cyanate of potash, of which it possesses all the properties.

This experiment is doubtless very instructive; but it is not sufficient to make us acquainted with the true nature of cyanogen. This gas being very inflammable, I detonated it in Volta's eudiometer with about 2½ times its volume of oxygen. The detonation is very strong; the flame is bluish, like that of sulphur burning in oxygen.

Supposing us to operate on 100 parts of cyanogen, we find, after the detonation, a diminution of volume, which amounts from [*sic*] about four to nine parts. When the residue is treated with potash or barytes, it diminishes from 195 to 200 parts, which are carbonic acid gas. The new residue, analysed over water by hydrogen, gives from 94 to 98 parts of azote, and the oxygen which it contains, added to that in the carbonic acid, is equal (within four or five per cent.) to that which has been employed.

Neglecting the small differences which prevent these numbers from having simple ratios to each other, and which, like the presence of hydrogen, depend upon the presence of a variable portion of hydro-cyanic vapour in the cyanogen employed, proceeding from the water left in the cyanuret of mercury, we may admit that cyanogen contains a sufficient quantity of carbon to produce twice its volume of carbonic acid gas; that is to say, two volumes of the vapour of carbon and one volume of azote, condensed into a single volume. If that supposition is exact, the density of the radical derived from it ought to be equal to the density derived from experience; but supposing the density of air to be one,

Twice that of the vapour of carbon is.......... 0.8320
That of azote............................... 0.9691
                                              ─────
Total................................... 1.8011

The density of cyanogen, then, calculated from the preceding analysis, would be 1.8011; and as I found by experiment 1.8064, we are entitled to conclude, from the agreement of these numbers, that this analysis is correct, and that we may neglect the slight difference observed, the true cause of which appears known.[18]

On comparing the analysis of cyanogen with that of hydro-cyanic acid, it will be seen that, by adding a volume of hydrogen to a volume of cyanogen, we obtain exactly two volumes of hydro-cyanic vapour. Hence it follows that the density of this last is equal to half the sum of that of

---

[18] As I was not acquainted with the influence of water till after having taken the specific gravity of cyanogen, it is probable that this gas contained a small quantity of hydro-cyanic vapour, which ought to have diminished its density a little.

It is easy to explain the diminution of volume which we observe after the detonation of cyanogen and oxygen, as well as the deficit of carbonic acid, azote, and oxygen, by the presence of a little hydro-cyanic vapour. When this is detonated with oxygen, a diminution takes place equal to ¾ of the vapour. It produces but one volume of carbonic acid; while cyanogen produces two. It gives only half a volume of azote; and it contains hydrogen, which causes ¼ of the oxygen to disappear. On detonating cyanogen, I have not observed nitrous acid; but the formation of that acid does not depend solely on the presence of azote in the combination; it depends likewise on the mode in which it exists in it.

cyanogen and of hydrogen. This result is analogous to that which chlorine and iodine give us; for each of them combines with its own volume of hydrogen to produce two volumes of muriatic and hydriodic gases.

It is now easy to ascertain that the action of potassium on cyanogen agrees with its action on hydro-cyanic acid. We have seen that it absorbs 50 parts of the first, and likewise that it absorbs 100 parts of the second, from which it separates 50 parts of hydrogen. But 100 parts of hydro-cyanic vapour minus 50 parts of hydrogen amount exactly to 50 parts of cyanogen. Hence the two results agree perfectly, and the two compounds obtained ought to be identic, which agrees perfectly with experiment.

The analysis of cyanogen appearing to me of the greatest importance, I have attempted it likewise by other methods. Having put cyanuret of mercury into the bottom of a glass tube, I covered it with brown oxide of copper, and then raised the heat to a dull red. On heating gradually the part of the tube containing the cyanuret, the cyanogen was slowly disengaged, and passed through the oxide, which it reduced completely to the metallic state. On washing the gaseous products with potash, at different parts of the process, I obtained only from 0.19 to 0.30 of azote, instead of 0.33, which ought to have remained, according to my analysis. Presuming that some nitrous compound had been formed, I repeated the experiment, covering the oxide with a column of copper filings, which I kept at the same temperature as the oxide. With this new arrangement the results were very singular; for the smallest quantity of azote which I obtained during the whole course of the experiment was 32.7 in 100 of the gas, and the greatest was 34.4. The mean of all the trials was:—

$$\text{Azote} \dots \dots \dots \dots \dots \ 33.6$$
$$\text{Carbonic acid} \dots \dots \dots \ 66.4$$

a result which shows most clearly that cyanogen contains two volumes of the vapour of carbon and one volume of azote. . . .

We see from the observations which constituted the object of this memoir that the knowledge of cyanogen opens a new field of researches, which will not be soon exhausted. This gas, when it combines with hydrogen, shows us a remarkable example, and hitherto unique, of a body which, though compound, acts the part of a simple substance in its combinations with hydrogen and metals. It likewise fills up a gap in chemistry, by making us acquainted with a combination of carbon and azote, which was hitherto wanting.

Eilhard Mitscherlich

(1794–1863)

ONE of the principles most utilized by Berzelius in fixing the formulas of compounds was the law of isomorphism, enunciated by his student, Mitscherlich, while working in the laboratory of Berzelius. Mitscherlich enjoyed a fruitful career in crystallography, inorganic and organic chemistry, biochemistry, and geology, each of which fields he enriched with important discoveries. Besides isomorphism, he recognized dimorphism and polymorphism, discovered monoclinic sulfur, selenic acid, and numerous benzene derivatives, and explained ether formation and fermentation as catalytic processes. Mitscherlich's researches on benzene helped to open the field of aromatic chemistry.

His first paper on isomorphism (from ἴσος, equal and μορφή, form) was read on December 9, 1819, and published in summary the following year.[1] The actual enunciation of the law of isomorphism occurred in a Swedish journal in 1821, however. The paper was soon afterward reprinted in French and English, and Berzelius discussed it in his *Jahresbericht*, so that the work quickly became well known.[2]

The following selection is from the paper explaining the isomorphism of $Na_2HPO_4.12H_2O$ and $Na_2HAsO_4.12H_2O$, as well as of $NaH_2PO_4.H_2O$ and $NaH_2AsO_4.H_2O$, and gives the general formulation of the law.

The doctrine of chemical proportions and the mechanical viewpoint through which the atomic theory has acquainted us with the origin of these definite proportions (I mean the study which has been made to represent bodies as composed of atoms whose numbers show themselves in definite proportions in compounds) has spread a bright light over chemistry. This induces me to make a study of the hypothesis that different elements united with an equal number of atoms of one or more other common elements, *e.g.*, combustible bodies with oxygen and an acid, crystallize alike, and that the likeness in crystal form is determined entirely and completely by the number of atoms and not by the differences of the elements (in the example given, the combustible bodies). By chance, my first

---

[1] *Abhandl. Königl. Akad. Wissenschaft, Berlin, 1818–1819*, **1820**: 427–437.

[2] The original publication was in *Stockholm, Akad. Handl.*, **1821**: 4–79. It also appeared in *Ann. chim.*, **19**: 350–419 (1822) (misdated 1821) and in *Quart. J. Sci.*, **14**: 198–206, 415–418 (1823).

A German translation appears in Ostwald's *Klassiker*, No. 94, "Eilhard Mitscherlich, Ueber das Verhältniss zwischen der chemischen Zusammensetzung und der Kristallform arseniksaurer und phosphorsaurer Salze (1821). Herausgegeben von P. Groth," Leipzig, 1898; and also in "Gesammelte Schriften von Eilhard Mitscherlich. Herausgegeben von A. Mitscherlich," Berlin, 1896, pp. 133–173. The selection given here is taken from pages 133 to 134 and 171 to 173 of the latter work.

studies were made with a series of compounds in a great number of which this happened so completely that I thereupon nearly regarded the hypothesis as completely true. This study was carried on with different single and double sulfates of potassia, ammonia, magnesia, iron and manganese protoxides, zinc, copper, cobalt, and nickel oxides; but when later I extended the work to compounds of these bases with other acids which in the atomic view have a composition similar to that of sulfuric acid or to sulfates of other similarly composed bases, I found that this likeness in crystal form was not absolutely true. By this I was again driven to classify the compounds into groups whose composition, according to the viewpoint of the atomic theory, appears to be similar, in order to ascertain the similarity or difference which could be found in their crystal form. From this, which I might call a probing study which I then made, the result seemed to be generally that certain elements have the property, when combined with an equal number of atoms of one or more common elements, of producing together similar crystal forms, and that in this view, the elements can be divided into certain groups. For the sake of ease I have called the elements which belong to the same group *isomorphs*, in order to show by a more definite technical expression that they are similar. It has not yet, however, been possible for me to discover how many such isomorphous groups there are and to determine all the elements which belong to one or another of these groups. This is perhaps more than a single human can perform, since I believe I have found that here research has opened a new field, and since to some degree a key is given for explaining a very important question in the theory of chemistry which will exert a very definite influence on the future of mineralogy, I have believed that I must subject this idea to a general test and to further development; the more so in that my views from my research have already given so much that the idea cannot be considered entirely incorrect or be entirely rejected. . . .

I have carried out many studies and then repeated them with greater care to find a difference between these salts [dimorphous forms of $NaH_2PO_4.H_2O$], because these phenomena entirely contradicted the theory which I had previously favored, and also that which, with one exception, was favored by all the findings which the mineralogists had made up to now. I have now carried through some of these studies, and these suffice to indicate these facts. It is thus established: *that one and the same body, which is composed of the same substances in the same proportions, can assume two different forms*, which depend on still unknown conditions. According to the atomic theory this phenomenon can easily be understood. Different forms will result whenever the arrangement of the atoms with regard to each other is altered, but the number of separate forms which, according to the assumptions of such a view, can be shown to exist remains very limited.

No phenomenon stands alone in the field of physics, and the law which we have found here can be expanded to all crystal formation. The effect which is shown here by one salt must also be able to occur among the oxides, and this agrees with what I have already said at the beginning of this paper, namely, that different chemical compounds formed according to the same proportions divide themselves into several great groups of isomorphous bodies, *i.e.*, into those which have similar crystal forms. The reason why these groups always keep the form of crystallization belonging to their class is the same as the reason that the acid phosphate and the acid arsenate of soda usually assume different crystal forms. It lies, that is, in the different positions which the atoms occupy with regard to each other.

I would be doing wrong to put forth this view without being able to defend it. In my first communication on this subject I sought to show, and I intended to strengthen in the future with more examples, that lime, magnesia, manganese protoxide, iron protoxide, copper oxide, zinc oxide, cobalt oxide, and nickel oxide belong to a group, and that within it one atom of metal is united to two atoms of oxygen. This has long been accepted on chemical grounds by Professor Berzelius; the same chemical reasons made it necessary that two atoms of oxygen and one atom of metal be also assumed in lead oxide, in strontia, and in baryta. It is known that the crystallization of salts of the one class is entirely different from the salts of the other class. To be convinced of this, we need only to compare the series of carbonates and sulphates of both classes which occur in nature.

The crystallization of both classes will thus be different only in the arrangement of the two atoms of oxygen toward the one atom of metal, and that they so behave I will now indicate.

Mitscherlich then shows that the two forms of calcium carbonate, aragonite and calcite, differ crystallographically, aragonite being isomorphous with lead and strontium carbonates, calcite with magnesite and iron carbonate.

Since this, which I will show in another communication through more examples and will prove in greater detail, is applicable to all isomorphous bodies, then the general law for the relation of crystallography to chemical composition is the following:

An equal number of atoms, if they are bound in the same way, produce similar crystal forms, and the crystal form depends not on the nature of the atoms but on the number and method of combination.

Friedrich Wöhler

(1800–1882)

THE remarkable growth of chemistry during the nineteenth century owed much to the activities of Friedrich Wöhler. In the first decade of that century, the complex nature of organic compounds had fostered the concept that they differed radically from inorganic substances and were formed in nature as the result of a "vital force." One of the first assaults against this barrier between inorganic and organic chemistry was made by Wöhler in 1828, with his preparation of urea by evaporating a solution of the isomeric ammonium cyanate. It should be clearly understood that this was not a synthesis of urea as is commonly thought, for the sharp distinction between inorganic and organic compounds did not come to an end until the synthesis of acetic acid by Kolbe in 1844. Vitalism was not rejected by any one discovery but by the accumulation of contradictory evidence. The final death blow was given by Berthelot. Wöhler was one of the first to contribute to the overthrow of the concept, however.

Wöhler's analysis of cyanates appeared in 1824,[1] shortly after Liebig's analysis of fulminates.[2] Gay-Lussac, then editor of the *Annales de Chimie*, noted that the analyses of cyanic and fulminic acid were identical—the first case of isomerism. This incident brought Wöhler and Liebig together, and there followed many years of collaboration in which the two studied the chemistry of benzaldehyde and numerous other compounds. In addition Wöhler alone isolated aluminum and beryllium, devised the modern method for manufacturing phosphorus, and discovered calcium carbide, hydroquinone, and quinhydrone. His literary activity was considerable, for besides his own numerous publications, he translated several editions of Berzelius's textbook and a long run of the *Jahresbericht*.

The memoir on urea was entitled "Ueber künstliche Bildung des Harnstoffe" and is given in translation below.[3]

ON THE ARTIFICIAL PRODUCTION OF UREA

In a brief earlier communication, printed in Volume III of these Annals, I stated that by the action of cyanogen on aqueous ammonia, besides several other products, there are formed oxalic acid and a crystallizable

---

[1] *Ann. chim.*, **27**: 196–200 (1824).

[2] *Ibid.*, **24**: 294–317 (1823).

[3] Poggendorff's *Annalen der Physik und Chemie*, **12**: 253–256 (1828). Contemporary French and English versions appeared: *Ann. chim.*, **37**: 330–334 (1828); *Quart. J. Sci.*, Pt. 1 (April–June), 491–492 (1828). Also see "Classiques de la découverte scientifique. La synthèse totale en chimie organique. Mémoires de MM. Wöhler, Gerhardt, M. Berthelot, Le Bel, van't Hoff, Jungfleisch, Ladenburg, Pasteur," with preface and commentaries by Marcel Delépine, Paris, 1937.

white substance which is certainly not cyanate of ammonia, but which one nevertheless always obtains when one attempts to combine cyanic acid with ammonia for instance by so-called double decomposition. The fact that in the union of these substances they appear to change their nature, and give rise to a new body, drew my attention anew to this subject, and research gave the unexpected result that by the combination of cyanic acid with ammonia, urea is formed, a fact that is the more noteworthy inasmuch as it furnishes an example of the artificial production of an organic, indeed a so-called animal substance, from inorganic materials.

I have already stated that the above-mentioned white crystalline substance is best obtained by the decomposition of cyanate of silver with sal ammoniac solution or of cyanate of lead by aqueous ammonia. In the latter way I prepared for myself the not unimportant amounts employed in this research. I obtained it in colorless, clear crystals often more than an inch long in the form of slender four-sided, dull-pointed prisms.

With caustic potash or chalk this substance evolved no trace of ammonia; with acids it showed none of the breakdown phenomena of cyanic acid salts, namely, evolution of carbonic acid and cyanic acid; neither would it precipitate lead and silver salts as genuine cyanic acid salts do; it could, therefore, contain neither cyanic acid nor ammonia as such. Since I found that by the last-named method of preparation no other product was formed and that the lead oxide was separated in a pure form, I imagined that an organic substance might arise by the union of cyanic acid with ammonia, possibly a substance like a vegetable salifiable base [an alkaloid]. I therefore made some experiments from this point of view on the behavior of the crystalline substance with acids. It was, however, indifferent to them, nitric acid excepted; this, when added to a concentrated solution of the substance, produced at once a precipitate of glistening scales. After these had been purified by several recrystallizations, they showed a very acid character, and I was already inclined to take the compound for a peculiar acid, when I found that after neutralization with bases it gave salts of nitric acid, from which the crystallizable substance could be extracted again with alcohol, with all the characteristics it had before the addition of nitric acid. This similarity to urea in behavior induced me to carry out comparative experiments with completely pure urea isolated from urine, from which it was plainly apparent that urea and this crystalline substance, or cyanate of ammonia, if one can so call it, are completely identical compounds.

I will describe the properties of this artificial urea no further, since it coincides perfectly with that of urea from urine, according to the accounts of Proust, Prout and others, to be found in their writings, and I will mention only the fact, not specified by them, that both natural and artificial urea, on distillation evolve first large amounts of carbonate of ammonia, and then give off to a remarkable extent the sharp, acetic acid-like odor of cyanic acid, exactly as I found in the distillation of cyanate of mercury or uric acid, and especially of the mercury salt of uric acid. In the distillation of urea, another white, apparently distinct substance also appears, with the examination of which I am still occupied.

But if the combination of cyanic acid and ammonia actually gives merely urea, it must have exactly the composition allotted to cyanate of ammonia by calculation from my formula for the cyanates; and this is, in fact, the case if one atom of water is added to cyanate of ammonia, as all ammonium salts contain water, and if Prout's analysis of urea is taken as the most correct.

According to him urea consists of:

		Atoms
Nitrogen...........	46.650	4
Carbon............	19.975	2
Hydrogen..........	6.670	8
Oxygen............	26.650	2
	99.875	
	[*sic*]	

But cyanate of ammonia would consist of 56.92 cyanic acid, 28.14 ammonia, and 14.74 water, which for the separate elements gives:

		Atoms
Nitrogen...........	46.78	4
Carbon............	20.19	2
Hydrogen..........	6.59	8
Oxygen............	26.24[4]	2
	99.80	

One would have been able to reckon beforehand that cyanate of ammonia with 1 atom of water has the same composition as urea, without having discovered by experiment the formation of urea from cyanic acid and ammonia. By the combustion of cyanic acid with copper oxide one obtains 2 volumes of carbonic acid and 1 volume of nitrogen, but by the combustion of cyanate of ammonia one must obtain equal volumes of these gases, which proportion also holds for urea; as Prout actually found.

I refrain from all the considerations which so naturally offer themselves, particularly those bearing upon the composition relations of organic sub-

[4] The new atomic weights of Berzelius are used as a basis; accordingly N = 88.518, C = 76.437, H = 6.2398, O = 100.000, water ($\overset{\cdot\cdot}{H}$) = 112.479, cyanate of ammonia = $NH^3 + \overline{CN}O$ and urea = $NH^3 + \overline{CN}O + \overset{\cdot\cdot}{H}$.

stances, upon the like elementary and quantitative composition of compounds of very different properties, as for example fulminic acid and cyanic acid, a liquid hydrocarbon[5] and olefiant gas. The deduction of a general law awaits further experiment on several similar cases.

The first significant step in finding the order behind the bewildering complexity of organic compounds was made by Wöhler and Liebig in their joint research on benzaldehyde (oil of bitter almonds) and its derivatives. Here for the first time it was clearly seen that a group of atoms could remain intact throughout a series of reactions and function as a whole—as a radical. Guyton de Morveau had first used the name radical in its modern sense in 1787, and Lavoisier had suggested the existence of radicals in organic substances. Gay-Lussac's researches on cyanogen confirmed the possibility of the existence of organic radicals, but they first became really significant with this study of Wöhler and Liebig.

The research appeared in Liebig's *Annalen*[6] and was followed by a letter of Berzelius to the authors in a note at the end of the paper. In the letter Berzelius praised Wöhler and Liebig for their remarkable work and indicated how their compounds could be represented by formulas. He further applied the concept of radicals to the findings of Dumas and Boullay and named the group C_2H_4 (actually ethylene), *etherin*. Dumas and Boullay had not used the word *radical*, and so a new radical and a new theory, the etherin theory, were added to organic chemistry.

The following translation was made by James C. Booth, an American student of Wöhler's who afterward became a well-known American chemist. The translation appeared in Silliman's *American Journal of Science and Arts*.[7]

RESEARCHES RESPECTING THE RADICAL OF BENZOIC ACID

When in the dark province of organic nature, we succeed in finding a light point, appearing to be one of those inlets whereby we may attain to the examination and investigation of this province, then we have reason to congratulate ourselves, although conscious that the object before us is unexhausted. With such a view, let us examine the following experiments; which, as it regards their extent and connection, present a wide field for cultivation.

The substance with which we commence our undertaking, is the fluid oil of bitter almonds, distinguished from other similar bodies, by the property, first rightly investigated by Stange, of being converted in the air, by the absorption of oxygen, into an acid, into the benzoic acid, and which appeared to lay claim to the highest interest from the manner in which it arises from bodies apparently so different. . . .

Returning from this digression to the consideration of the oil of bitter

---

[5] [Butylene, discovered by Faraday in 1825.]

[6] *Annalen der Chemie*, **3**: 249–282 (1832).

[7] *American Journal of Science and Arts*, **26**: 261–285 (1834); also in Ostwald's *Klassiker*, No. 22, "Woehler und Liebig, Untersuchen über die Radikale der Benzoesaure (1832). Herausgegeben von Hermann Kopp," Leipzig, 1891.

almonds, and its conversion into crystallized benzoic acid, we now find this phenomenon capable of an easy explanation. The acid is formed by simple oxydation, the oil absorbing in the air or in oxygen gas, 2 atoms of this element.

The formation of benzoate of potassa from the oil, when the latter is heated with hydrate of potassa, depends upon the decomposition of the water in the hydrate, whereby the oil takes one atom of oxygen, while hydrogen escapes in the form of gas.

We have farther mentioned that the oil with a solution of potassa in alcohol, forms likewise without the access of air a benzoate of potassa, and that then by the addition of water, an oily body separates from the alcohol possessed of different properties. As far as we have examined this new body, it admits of no doubt, that in case the constituents of alcohol do not enter into its composition, it originates either from taking oxygen from the bitter almond oil, or from the decomposition of water. In the former case it would be composed according to the formula $C^{14}H^{12}O$, in the latter the formula $C^{14}H^{14}O^2$.

After the determining of this point, and a reviewing of the combining relations of bitter almond oil yet to be considered, we believe it naturally follows that this oil is in its pure state a hydrogen compound, wherein the radical of benzoic acid is combined with 2 atoms of hydrogen, instead of with oxygen as in the acid. This radical as yet unobtained insulated, is composed of $C^{14}H^{10}O^2$. We call it *benzöyl*, (the ending from ὕλη material, matter). The consequent name for the pure oil of bitter almonds is hydrobenzöyl (hydroguret of benzöyl), and for the benzoic acid, benzöylic acid, (benzöyl acid). We will however use the common names benzoic acid and bitter almond oil, except in theoretical demonstrations. We will see how easily the remaining relations, to which we now come, will be perceived and comprehended.

Chlorobenzöyl. If through the bitter almond oil we conduct dry chlorine gas, the latter is absorbed with considerable heat, and hydrochloric acid is evolved; but besides this, no other product which warrants the conclusion of a farther decomposition. As soon as the formation of hydrochloric acid begins to cease, the liquid becomes yellow from the solution of chlorine, but the overcharge of this gas is again expelled by boiling. Finally, if the liquid, be heated to boiling, in contact with chlorine, and the formation of hydrochloric acid is no longer perceived, we obtain a new compound, perfectly pure. This is the chlorobenzöyl, (chloride of benzöyl).

The chlorobenzöyl, is a transparent fluid of the sp. gr. 1.196. It possesses a peculiar odor in the highest degree penetrating; in particular, strongly affecting the eyes, and reminding us of the pungent odor of horse-radish. Its boiling point is very high: it is inflammable, burning with a bright, green-edged, sooty flame.

It sinks in water as an oil, without solution. After a considerable time, or sooner by boiling, it separates entirely into crystallized benzoic acid and hydro-chloric acid. It suffers the same change if kept in moist air for a length of time. If chlorine be conducted through a mixture of hydro-benzöyl and water, the oil disappears, and the water congeals into a crystalline mass of benzoic acid.

The chloride of benzöyl may be distilled unchanged over anhydrated baryta and lime.

Warmed with alkalies and water, this chloride forms at the same time a chloride of the metal and a benzoate of the alkali.

In all these decompositions beside the benzoic and hydro-chloric acids, no third body is formed, whence it clearly follows, that in this compound, chlorine and benzöyl must be in such proportion, that by the separation of water into its constituents, these last, exactly suffice to form on the one side hydrochloric, and on the other anhydrated benzoic acid,—the latter at the moment of its formation, taking up one atom of water. Hydro-benzöyl (bitter almond oil) consists of,

$$(14C + 10H + 2O) + 2H.$$

By the action of chlorine, two atoms of hydrogen unite with two atoms of chlorine to form hydro-chloric acid, which is evolved. But the hydrogen gives place to two atoms of chlorine according to the following formula:

$$(14C + 10H + 2O) + 2Cl.$$

With the constituents of water this body is decomposed in such a manner that two atoms of hydrogen unite with two atoms of chlorine to form hydrochloric acid, while the freed oxygen unites with benzöyl and forms benzoic acid. . . .

If chlorobenzöyl be treated with metallic bromides, iodides, sulphurets or cyanurets, such an exchange of constituents ensues, that a metallic chloride on the one hand, and a combination of benzöyl with bromine, iodine, sulphur or cyanogen on the other hand, are generated, which are composed similarly to the chlorobenzöyl. . . .

This composition clearly explains not merely the manner of the formation of benzamide, but also its behavior with acids and potassa, that is, its conversion into benzoic acid and ammonia.

If 2 atoms of ammonia be added to the composition of chloride of benzöyl, we obtain the formula:

$$\begin{array}{l} 14C + 10H + 2O + 2Cl = \text{chlorobenzöyl} \\ \underline{12H + 4N = \text{ammonia}} \\ 14C + 22H + 2O + 2Cl + 4N. \end{array}$$

Abstract from this 2 atoms muriate of ammonia,

$$14C + 22H + 2O + 2Cl + 4N$$
$$8H + 2Cl + 2N, \text{ we then obtain}$$
$$\overline{14C + 14H + 2O + 2N}$$

which is the true composition of benzamide and by adding to this last 1 atom of water, the formula becomes, $14C + 16H + 3O + 2N$ which expresses the true composition of neutral dry benzoate of ammonia. This salt consists of

$$1 \text{ atom benzoic acid, } = 14C + 10H + 3O$$
$$1 \text{ `` ammonia } = 6H + 2N$$
$$\overline{14C + 16H + 3O + 2N}$$

. . . *General Observations.* Reviewing and collecting together the relations described in the present essay, we find that they all group around one single compound, which does not change its nature and composition in all its combining relations with other bodies. This stability, this consequence of the phenomena, induced us to consider that body as a compound base and therefore to propose for it a peculiar name, i.e. benzöyl.

The composition of this radical we have expressed by the formula $14C + 10H + 2O$.

In combination with one atom of oxygen, benzöyl forms dry benzoic acid, and in combination with one atom of oxygen, one of water, the crystallized acid.

In combination with two atoms of hydrogen, it constitutes pure bitter almond oil. When this oil changes in the air into benzoic acid, it takes up two atoms of oxygen, one of which with the radical generates benzoic acid and the other with the two atoms of hydrogen forms the water of the crystallized acid.

Farther, the hydrogen of the oil or the oxygen of the acid may be replaced by chlorine, bromine, iodine, sulphur or cyanogen, and the bodies proceeding thence, comparable with the corresponding compounds of phosphorus, all form, by their decomposition with water, on the one side a hydracid, and on the other benzoic acid.

The replacement, of two atoms of hydrogen in the bitter almond oil by an acidifying base, appears to us in all cases a strong argument for adopting the opinion, that this hydrogen is in a peculiar manner combined with the other elements; this peculiar method of combination may be hinted at rather than pointed out by the idea of the radical, which is borrowed from inorganic chemistry.

Although both benzamide and benzoin were originally in connection with the radical, they are wholly without its sphere, and must be considered as peculiar bodies, bearing no nearer relation to benzöyl, than the cuttings of bone to ammonia.

Since we cannot compare the ternary base with cyanogen, because the greater number of elements must occasion far more complicated decompositions, and because they have no prevailing resemblance, we believe it not improbable, that there is more than one group of organic bodies, for example, the fluid oils, which may have this same radical as a compound basis.   . . .

Extracts from the note added by Berzelius follow.

The results consequent upon your examination of the bitter almond oil, are the most important which vegetable chemistry has thus received, and promise to diffuse an unexpected light over this part of science.   . . .

The facts proved by you give rise to such reflections, that we well may view them as the dawning of a new day in vegetable chemistry.   . . .

From the moment we know with certainty of the existence of ternary atoms of the first order, which combine after the manner of simple bodies, it will greatly facilitate expression in the language of formulas, to denote each radical by a peculiar sign, through which the idea of the combination to be expressed, instantly and clearly strikes the reader. I will illustrate this by a few examples. Thus if we put benzöyl $C^{14}H^{10}O^2$ = Bz, then we have,

$$\dot{B}z = \text{Benzöylic acid.}$$
$$BzH = \text{Bitter almond oil.}$$
$$BzCl = \text{Chlorobenzöyl.}$$
$$B'z \text{ or } BzS = \text{Sulphuret of benzöyl.}$$
$$Bz + 2NH^3 = \text{Ammoniuret of benzöyl, (benzöyl ammonia).}$$

If we put Amid = NH^2, we have

$$Bz + NH^2 = \text{Benzamid or bitter benzöylamid.}$$
$$\ddot{C} + NH^2 = \text{Oxamid.}$$
$$K + NH^2 = \text{Potassiumamid.}$$
$$N + NH^2 = \text{Sodium amid.}$$

If we further place *oil of wine*, which I propose to call etherin,

$$C^4H^8 = \text{E, we find}$$
$$E + 2\dot{H} = \text{Alcohol.}$$
$$E + \dot{H} = \text{Ether.}$$
$$E + \underline{H}\underline{C}l = \text{Muriatic ether.}$$
$$E + \ddot{N}\ddot{H} = \text{Nitric ether.}$$
$$E + \dot{B}z\dot{H} = \text{Benzöylic ether.}$$

. . . But I think it necessary to insist, that such formulas be employed only when the ideas they express, are advanced in some measure to confirm truths, else they would lead to a Babylonian confusion.

Justus von Liebig

(1803-1873)

FEW chemists of the nineteenth century produced a greater amount of work and exercised a wider influence than Justus von Liebig. One of his early investigations was on fulminic acid, in the laboratory of Gay-Lussac (1821). Liebig demonstrated the saltlike properties of silver fulminate and published an analysis of the substance. The analysis of cyanic acid salts published independently by F. Wöhler in the same year resulted in the first clear case of isomerism, for Gay-Lussac noted that the analyses of the fulminate and cyanic salts were the same. To list but few of his many important accomplishments, he discovered hippuric acid (1829), prepared chloroform and chloral (1831–1832), investigated uric acid compounds (1834–1837), alkaloids (1839), amino acids and amides (1846–1852), creatine and creatinine (1847). One of his outstanding researches was with Friedrich Wöhler on the benzoyl radical. They collaborated in other work and issued their findings in publications in which it is impossible to distinguish the hand of one from the other. Liebig recognized the full value of the radical theory in the interpretation of organic reactions and wrote, on this subject, a joint memoir with Dumas. In 1834 Liebig named a new radical *ethyl* which he recognized to be the same in alcohol, ether, and muriatic ether.[1] Another contribution that Liebig made to organic chemistry was his improvement of methods and apparatus of elementary analysis; with the new techniques it became relatively easy and rapid.

Justus Liebig also had a profound influence on the development of agricultural chemistry. He assembled and correlated the many chemical investigations of agriculture and published in 1840 (Braunschweig) a work that did more to revolutionize agricultural science than any other chemical publication ever written, "Die organische Chemie in ihrer Anwendung auf Agricultur und Physiologie." Through his many subsequent investigations he helped place agriculture on a firm scientific footing. He introduced inorganic fertilizers to the farm. Liebig also studied other life sciences. His conclusions were not always correct, as is all too well shown in his dispute over proteins with Gerardus Johannes Mulder (1802–1880). His views commanded wide attention, for his fame as a great teacher and investigator did not outshine his ability as a propagandist. An important factor in this influence was his participation in the founding of the *Annalen der Pharmazie* (1832), which was reorganized in 1840 as the *Annalen der Chemie und Pharmazie* under the editorship of Liebig and Wöhler. Liebig popularized chemistry in his *Familiar Letters on Chemistry*. (These first appeared in the columns of the *Augsburger Allgemeine Zeitung*, 1841.) Perhaps Liebig's greatest accomplishment was this infusion of a new spirit into chemistry.

In 1833, Thomas Graham investigated the arsenates and phosphates and came

[1] *Annalen der Chemie*, **9**: 1 (1834).

to the conclusion that the three phosphates (ortho-, pyro-, and meta-) were salts of three acids which may be formulated as $3H_2O.P_2O_5$, $2H_2O.P_2O_5$, and $H_2O.P_2O_5$. These were, in modern terminology tri-, di-, and monobasic acids. He considered that the first might lose one, two, or three molecules of water when treated by a base—that is, the first two were polybasic. In 1838 Liebig analyzed nine organic acids and their salts and found that there could be mono-, di-, and tribasic organic acids. On reexamining Graham's work he saw that the hydrogen theory of acids proposed earlier by Davy and Dulong was the most reasonable explanation of the facts. Thus the theory of acids and salt formation became essentially what it is today. A portion of Liebig's paper on the polybasic acids is given below.[2]

Davy's theory arose from the behavior of potassium chlorate and iodate. The decomposition of these salts at an elevated temperature into oxygen and potassium chloride without change of neutrality made it necessary, he thought, to conclude that the potassium was not present as the oxide in these salts. In connection with potassium iodate it is particularly certain that potash is not decomposed by iodine nor oxygen displaced by iodine. Davy concluded as follows: hydrochloric acid is a compound of chlorine and hydrogen $Cl_2 + H_2$.[3]

The radical of hydrochloric acid may take up one or several atoms of oxygen without changing its saturation capacity for, according to him, this faculty is dependent only upon the hydrogen of the acid which is located outside the radical.

Hydrochloric acid	Cl_2	$+ H_2$
Hypochlorous acid	Cl_2O_2	$+ H_2$
Chlorous acid	Cl_2O_4	$+ H_2$
Chloric acid	Cl_2O_6	$+ H_2$
Perchloric acid	Cl_2O_3	$+ H_2$

Acids are, according to this view, hydrogen compounds in which the hydrogen may be replaced by metals.

Neutral *salts* are compounds of the same class wherein the hydrogen has been replaced by an equivalent of a metal. Those substances which we at present call anhydrous acids generally acquire their property of forming salts with metal oxides only on treatment with water, but there are some compounds which decompose the oxides at higher temperatures.

On combining an acid with a metallic oxide hydrogen is in most cases

[2] *Annalen der Chemie*, **26**: 113–189 (1838); the selection is taken from pages 180 to 185. The paper has been reprinted in Ostwald's *Klassiker*, No. 26, "Justus Liebig, ueber die Konstitution des organischen Sauren, (1838). Herausgegeben von Hermann Kopp," Leipzig, 1891.

[3] [Liebig used the atomic weights of Berzelius, which had very nearly the modern values except that potassium and silver were considered as twice as great as they are now known to be, thus making the formulas for the salts of these elements incorrect. In company with many of his contemporaries, Liebig frequently erred in the matter of molecular weight, and thus many of his formulas are double the modern ones.]

separated in the form of water. As far as the constitution of the new compound is concerned it is a matter of indifference how we think of the formation of this water. In many cases it is formed by the reduction of the oxide; in others, maybe, at the expense of the elements of the acid—we know not which.

We only know that without water at ordinary temperatures no salt can be formed and that the constitution of salts is analogous to the hydrogen compounds that we call acids. In the examination of Davy's theory the principle which should preferably be kept in mind is, accordingly, that he makes the saturation capacity of an acid dependent on its hydrogen content or on a portion of its hydrogen so that if the remaining elements of the acid together be called its radical, the composition of the radical has not the most distant influence on this capacity. . . .

If we apply Davy's view to the phosphorus acids we find the following relations:

Phosphorus combines in several proportions with hydrogen; the best known of these compounds is composed according to the formula

$$P_2 + H_6.$$

If eight atoms of oxygen be taken up in this phosphorus hydride, ordinary phosphoric acid is formed. $P_2O_8 + H_6$. According to this, it must form salts wherein all or part of the hydrogen is replaced by equivalents of metals. Brought together with metal oxides, the hydrogen will be reduced by the oxygen of the oxide to water; those oxides in which oxygen is the most weakly attached will undergo this reaction more easily than others. Silver oxide stands above all others in this respect.

With the oxides of the alkalies which have a great affinity for oxygen this reaction proceeds with more difficulty. In proportion as the hydrogen of the acid is removed and replaced, the affinity of the radical for the remaining hydrogen increases and only by means of an increased mass of alkali can this reduction be completed. With many acids similar to phosphoric acid in composition this can only be done by silver oxide. The salts of phosphoric acid receive the following form:

$$P_2O_8 + H_6 \dots \dots \dots \text{phosphoric acid}$$
$$P_2O_8 + \left. \begin{matrix} H_2 \\ 2K \end{matrix} \right\} \dots \dots \text{so-called neutral salt}$$
$$P_2O_8 + \left. \begin{matrix} H_4 \\ K \end{matrix} \right\} \dots \dots \text{acid salt}$$
$$P_2O_8 + 3K \dots \dots \dots \text{so-called basic salt}$$
$$P_2O_8 + 3Ag \dots \dots \dots \text{silver salt.}$$

According to the composition of lead phosphite, phosphorous acid is

$$P_2O_6 + 6H$$

Of the 6 atoms of hydrogen which it contains only 4 may be replaced by metals. The lead salt is

$$P_2O_6 + \left.\begin{array}{c} H_2 \\ Pb_2 \end{array}\right\}$$

If phosphoric acid be exposed to a higher temperature a part of the hydrogen outside the radical combines with an equivalent of oxygen of the latter, water is formed and evolved and two new acids, pyro- and metaphosphoric acid, are formed.

$$P_2O_7 + H_4 \text{ pyrophosphoric acid}$$
$$P_2O_9 + H_2 \text{ metaphosphoric acid}$$

All the properties of cyanuric, meconic and citric acids indicate that they contain no water in the dry state and, from Davy's view, their composition is as follows: $Cy_6O_6 + 6H$ cyanuric acid $\quad C_{14}H_2O_{14} + 6H$ meconic acid.

The salts of these acids are composed in a manner analogous to the phosphorus acids. I have mentioned their relations to the modifications of phosphoric acid in the foregoing.

Jean Baptiste André Dumas

(1800–1884)

THE name of Jean Baptiste André Dumas is still associated with two procedures which he devised—the determination of vapor density and the combustion analysis for nitrogen. Among his contributions to organic chemistry may be mentioned his isolation of anthracene from coal tar and his investigation of the hydrolysis of nitriles to amides and acids. Perhaps Dumas's chief contribution was to the theory of organic chemistry. In 1828, in collaboration with Polydore Boullay (1806–1835), he published a research on the esters of ethyl alcohol wherein he showed that these compounds could be looked upon as salts of ethylene and acids, as reported in the first extract. On the basis of this work, Berzelius in 1832 called ethylene a radical which he named *aetherin* (page 316) and which took an important place among the growing number of organic radicals. Over six years later Dumas and E. M. Peligot (1811–1890) investigated methyl alcohol and its derivatives with the result that another radical, methyl, was acknowledged and a new general class of compounds, the alcohols, recognized. This work, together particularly with that of Wöhler and Liebig on the benzoyl radical (pages 312 to 316) established the radical theory as the guiding concept of organic chemistry, as Dumas and Liebig triumphantly announced in 1837—the fourth selection below.

However, the seeds which were to lead to a profound modification of the radical theory were sown in part by Dumas himself in 1834, when he published his investigation of the action of chlorine on alcohol. It had already been shown by Gay-Lussac that in the chlorination of wax, as much chlorine entered into the material as was liberated as hydrochloric acid. Dumas conceived from this fact and his own work the idea of *substitution*, which was a very important step toward a complete structural theory of organic chemistry. The substitution theory is illustrated in the second and third extracts which follow.

In 1838 Dumas discovered that the hydrogens in acetic acid could be substituted by chlorine without, however, altering the fundamental character of the substance. This led him, in the following year, to announce what he called the *theory of chemical types*, which stated that the type (*i.e.*, the class) of a compound remained the same despite substitution of its hydrogens by halogen atoms. The type theory is given in the fifth selection.

MEMOIR ON ESTERS

by J. Dumas and P. Boullay[1]

[After examining four ethyl esters (the nitrate, benzoate, oxalate, and acetate) and suggesting that these may be considered as derivatives of ether, the authors proceed to another interpretation.]

But there is another more general method of envisaging the composition of these substances. It consists in assigning to olefiant gas itself an alkaline character, and it is thus possible to embrace at a glance the most varied combinations of this kind. We attach some importance to this point of view, and its simplicity obliges us to prefer it to that point of view which we have just indicated.

It is a question of knowing whether olefiant gas actually possesses the alkaline character which we assign to it. Now the following proofs appear to us to leave no doubt on this point.

The salt which we have obtained by treating oxalic ester with ammonia [oxamide] contains two volumes of ammonia and two volumes of olefiant gas, which replace the two volumes of gaseous ammonia which would be necessary to complete the neutral oxalate of ammonia. Olefiant gas has, then, exactly the same saturation capacity as ammonia.

In hydrochloric and hydriodic ethers [ethyl chloride and iodide], one volume of gaseous acid is saturated by one volume of olefiant gas just as in the neutral chlorides and iodides of ammonia, the acid and base being combined volume for volume. The saturation capacity is here again the same.

One atom of nitric, acetic, benzoic, or oxalic acids saturates four volumes of ammonia: now in the esters formed by these acids, one atom of

[1] *Ann. chim. phys.*, **37**: 15–53 (1828).

each of them also saturates exactly four volumes of olefiant gas. The saturation capacity is still found to be the same in this circumstance.

In 1834, Dumas presented a long paper, "Recherches de chimie organique," to the Académie des sciences in Paris. In this he described chloroform and chloral and explained the mechanism by which chlorine acted upon ethyl alcohol. The paper was published soon afterward[2] and several years later was reprinted[3] with the addition in the theoretical part of Dumas's theory of metalepsy. The following selection is taken from pages 545 to 549 of this article.

RESEARCHES IN ORGANIC CHEMISTRY RELATIVE TO THE ACTION OF CHLORINE ON ALCOHOL. LAW OF METALEPSY.

. . . If we now return to all the preceding results, we see that it is easy to represent not only all the reactions which have been studied, but, even more, others which at first do not seem to be related.

When alcohol is submitted to the action of chlorine and the action of this gas is complete, it can be seen that the alcohol keeps its carbon intact, its oxygen complete, and that it loses 10 atoms of hydrogen of the 12, while gaining 6 atoms of chlorine. The reaction requires

$$4 \text{ volumes alcohol} = \begin{cases} 4 \text{ volumes carburetted hydrogen} = C^8H^8 \\ 4 \text{ volumes water vapor} = H^4O^2 \end{cases}$$

and it furnishes

$$2 \text{ volumes hydrochloric acid} = Ch^{10}H^{10}$$
$$4 \text{ volumes of chloral} = C^8O^2H^2Ch^6 \text{ [4]}$$

Thus, in all, each volume of alcohol gives one volume of chloral.

If we study these results attentively, we see further that the 10 volumes of hydrogen which arise from the alcohol have been replaced by only 6 volumes of chlorine. Now I know by experience of the action of chlorine on oil of turpentine that each volume of hydrogen evolved was replaced by an equal volume of chlorine; this also accords with the result obtained by M. Gay-Lussac in treating wax with chlorine. I should then expect that the 10 volumes of hydrogen lost by the alcohol would be replaced by 10 volumes of chlorine, which has not occurred.

The cause of this difference is easy to understand. Alcohol can be represented by water and carburetted hydrogen, and when we admit that chlorine acts quite differently on the hydrogen of water from the way it acts on the hydrogen of carburetted hydrogen, we hold the key to the apparent anomaly which we have noticed.

[2] *Ann. chim. phys.*, **56**: 113–150 (1834).

[3] *Mémoires de l'Académie royale des sciences et de l'Institut de France,* **15**: 519–556 (1838).

[4] [Dumas took the atomic weight of carbon as 6 and, with many of his contemporaries, used formulas double the present ones. Allowing for these facts, it will be seen that all his formulas correspond to modern ones.]

It will, then, be admitted that chlorine and alcohol here represent carburetted hydrogen, water, and chlorine. When these bodies are brought together, the chlorine determines the decomposition of water, taking the hydrogen to form hydrochloric acid, and leaves to the carburetted hydrogen the power of uniting with the oxygen of the water. Thus we have

$$C^8H^{12}O^2 + Ch^4 = C^8H^8O^2 + Ch^4H^4$$

But the formula $C^8H^8O^2$ being nothing more than that of acetic ether [acetaldehyde], it is possible to verify whether the effect of the production of this ether can occur under these conditions.

To a flask containing 3 liters of dry chlorine are added 6 grams of alcohol, which corresponds about to the proportions indicated by the formula. The flask is heated strongly, chlorine disappears in a short time, and the liquid is poured into a retort with an excess of chalk; from the first heating it separates into two layers. One of these, light, very fluid, and ethereal, distills entirely on the water bath. It is perfectly neutral and possesses in the highest degree the characteristics of acetic ether.

By adding portions of lime to the alcohol as the stream of chlorine disappears, it is possible to moderate the action at will. In this way acetic ether is obtained in greater quantity than by the previous method.

Finally, when the chloric ether is prepared and has been separated from the liquid which floats above, it is enough to saturate this liquid with chalk and to distill on the water bath to recognize the presence of acetic ether. Several chemists have already described its presence in the latter product.

However, it seems probable to me that acetic ether, first produced by the action of chlorine on alcohol, disappears as the chloric ether appears. In effect, if the alcohol treated by chlorine is taken up to where the ether begins to be evident, much acetic ether is recovered from it; but on the contrary, if alcohol treated by chlorine is taken up to where chloric ether is no longer produced, only traces of acetic ether are found, recognizable only by odor, but which cannot be separated by water nor by a solution of calcium chloride.

If this is admitted, it can be seen that under the influence of the first reaction of chlorine there can be produced in the beginning from four volumes of alcohol, two volumes of acetic ether; the alcohol loses four volumes of hydrogen and produces eight volumes of hydrochloric acid, without the chlorine uniting with other elements of the alcohol. We cannot wish to say that the portion of alcohol which changes to chloral passes by the state of acetic ether; it is little probable that this transition has occurred; we can only show that the hydrogen of water disappears without being replaced by chlorine.

Be that as it may, starting from this point, which marks the limit at which all the water of the alcohol has disappeared, the action of chlorine returns to the rule indicated above. There remains for us, in effect, a first residue, $C^8H^8O^2$, which in losing H^6 gains precisely Ch^6 to constitute the four volumes of chloral.

Thus, dividing the reaction into two stages, we have the following accounts:

$$C^8H^8 + H^4O^2 + Ch^4 = C^8H^8O^2 + Ch^4H^4$$
$$C^8H^8O^2 + Ch^{12} = C^8H^2Ch^6O^2 + Ch^6H^6$$

accounts which are precisely those which have been indicated by the theory which consists in regarding alcohol as being formed of equal volumes of water vapor and carburetted hydrogen.

When we examine these facts carefully, there remains little doubt in the mind of the true nature of alcohol.

Thus, chlorine possesses the singular power of removing the hydrogen of certain bodies, replacing it atom for atom. This law of nature, this law or theory of substitutions, has seemed worthy of a particular name. I propose to call it *metalepsy*, from μεταλήψις, which expresses well enough that the body on which it acts has taken one element in the place of another, chlorine in the place of hydrogen, for example.

Thus chloral is formed by substitution, or by *metalepsy;* it is one of the *metaleptic* products of alcohol.

Thus again, as we shall see, acetic ether, acetic acid, formic acid are metaleptic products of alcohol.

If we start from alcohol, we can then, by displacing and replacing certain of its elements according to this idea, give rise to a great number of compounds more or less easy to produce, and we will thus obtain the *metaleptic group* of alcohol, in which we will see placed very different bodies, and between them unexpected relations will often be revealed.

In the year following the appearance of the above, Dumas published the fifth volume of his "Traité de chimie," wherein he summarized the substitution theory.[5]

2967. *Theory of substitutions.* In carefully examining the action of chlorine on various substances I was led to establish the following rules:

1. When a hydrogenated substance is submitted to the dehydrogenating action of chlorine, bromine, iodine, oxygen, etc., for each atom of hydrogen which it loses it gains an atom of chlorine, bromine, iodine or a half atom of oxygen;

2. When the hydrogenated substance contains oxygen, the same rule is observed without modification;

3. When the hydrogenated substance contains water, this latter loses its hydrogen without replacement and, from this point, if a new quantity of hydrogen is removed, it is replaced as above.

[5] "Traité de chimie appliquée aux arts," Paris, 1828–1846, 8 vols. (vol. 5, p. 99).

The establishment of the radical theory in organic chemistry is set forth by Dumas and Liebig in the following citation.

NOTE ON THE PRESENT STATE OF ORGANIC CHEMISTRY
by Messrs. Dumas and Liebig.[6]

Sixty years have hardly passed since that ever-memorable epoch when, in the presence of this very assemblage, there began to appear the first essays of that so fecund chemical doctrine which we owe to the genius of Lavoisier. This short space of time has sufficed for deep examination of the most delicate questions of mineral chemistry, and everyone may easily convince himself that this branch of our knowledge possesses nearly all that it may acquire with the means of observation at its disposal.

Not only is this an incontestable fact, but it is a fact which everyone can explain. Mineral chemistry occupies itself indeed with the history of elementary substances, of their binary and saline combinations. Now elementary substances fall very naturally into several groups in such a manner that if one studies attentively the properties of one species of a group, one can nearly always forsee and divine the properties of neighboring species. The study of oxygen teaches us the history of sulfur; that of chlorine suffices to initiate us into the slightest details of the properties of iodine, etc.

Thus this task which appeared at first beyond human ability, for it was no less a matter than that of studying and analyzing thousands of substances of very diverse aspects and properties, this task has been nonetheless accomplished in less than half a century, and there remain here and there hardly any lacunae to fill.

Chemists have recognized that in mineral substances there exist bodies which act as elements; that these bodies combine among themselves; that their combinations may unite anew; and in these three orders of substances they have found the means of forming natural groups which render the study simple, easy, and at the same time broad and philosophical.

Of course, that which they have called *element*, or undecomposable substance, has been considered as such only with regard to the state of acquired experience. We have not wished to prejudice the question, but we have sought to construct the edifice of science in such a fashion that, if these elements were later decomposed, nothing would be changed in the architecture of the monument, although its foundations would be more profoundly excavated.

It is easy to see that with the 54 elements known today one may, with the aid of a very small number of laws and combinations, and forming all

---

[6] *Compt. rend.*, **5**: 567–572 (1837). Read before the Académie des sciences, October 25, 1837.

the binary compounds and salts possible, produce not only all the compounds known in the inorganic kingdom but also a great number of analogous compounds.

But how apply with some success such ideas to organic chemistry? There, there are encountered no fewer and no less diverse species than in mineral chemistry. There, however, in place of 54 elements, we encounter scarcely more than three or four in the majority of known compounds. In a word, how can we with the aid of the laws of mineral chemistry explain and classify the so varied substances obtained from living matter and which nearly all are formed solely of carbon, hydrogen, and oxygen, elements to which nitrogen is sometimes added?

That was an important and fitting question of natural philosophy, a question well calculated to excite to the highest degree the emulation of chemists; for once it was resolved, the finest triumphs were promised to the science. The mysteries of vegetation, the mysteries of animal life were going to be unveiled to our eyes; we were going to grasp the key to all the modifications of matter which transpire in animals and in plants so promptly, so suddenly, so spectacularly; further, we were going to find the means of imitating them in our laboratories.

Well, we do not fear to say it, and this is not on our part an assertion lightly made: this important and fitting question is today resolved; it remains solely to unfold all the consequences which its solution entails. And certainly, if before experiment had opened this new route one had demanded of any chemist his opinion on the nature of organic substances, however great his genius, he would have imagined nothing, one may be sure, which could be compared with these simple, regular, and so handsome laws which experiment has revealed to us for the last few years.

Actually, to produce with three or four elements combinations as varied as and perhaps more varied than those which form the mineral kingdom, nature has taken a course as simple as it was unexpected; for with the elements she has made compounds which manifest all the properties of elementary substances themselves.

And that, we are convinced, is the whole secret of organic chemistry.

Thus organic chemistry possesses its own elements which at one time play the role belonging to chlorine or to oxygen in mineral chemistry and at another time, on the contrary, play the role of metals. Cyanogen, amide, benzoyl, the radicals of ammonia, the fatty substances, the alcohols and analogous compounds—these are the true elements on which organic chemistry is founded and not at all the final elements, carbon, hydrogen, oxygen, and nitrogen—elements which appear only when all trace of organic origin has disappeared.

For us, mineral chemistry embraces all substances which result from the direct combination of the elements as such. Organic chemistry, on the contrary, should comprise all substances formed by compound bodies functioning as elements would function.

In mineral chemistry the radicals are simple; in organic chemistry the radicals are compound; that is all the difference. The laws of combination and of reaction are otherwise the same in these two branches of chemistry.

The type theory is given in the extract which follows.

NOTE ON THE CONSTITUTION OF ACETIC AND CHLOROACETIC ACIDS
by M. J. Dumas[7]

In a memoir which I had the honor of communicating to the Academy some time ago I showed that chlorine decomposes acetic acid under the influence of solar light and that it gives rise to a new acid which I have named chloroacetic acid.

I expressed on that occasion the opinion that acetic acid and chloroacetic acid belong to the same chemical type, $A^8B^8C^4$, one being represented by $C^8H^8O^4$ and the other by $C^8H^2O^4$,
$$Ch^6.$$

I have attempted to generalize this point of view and to show how these types may serve to group these organic substances in well-characterized genera.

As soon as he was acquainted with my memoir, M. Berzelius, who denies the theory of substitutions, published a refutation of the views which I gave there. This illustrious scientist regards acetic and chloracetic acid as very different from one another because they have not the same density, boiling point, nor odor, etc.

M. Berzelius has certainly not understood what I have called the *fundamental properties* of substances, for long ago I knew that in replacing the hydrogen in a compound by chlorine the compound is rendered more dense and less volatile and that at the same time its vapor density is increased.

Moreover, it is perfectly clear to me that the objections advanced by M. Berzelius do not apply at all to the views which I actually intended to express.

However, to prevent all misunderstanding I will attempt to state my idea precisely by means of an example.

By treating chloracetic acid with any alkali I have obtained a very remarkable reaction. The acid is converted into two new substances, namely, carbonic acid, which is combined with the alkali, and chloroform, which is liberated. We have thus

$$C^8H^2O^4 = C^4O^4 + C^4H^2$$
$$Ch^6 \qquad\qquad Ch^6.$$

[7] *Compt. rend.*, **9**: 813–815 (1839).

I was convinced, and I announced it after a fashion in my memoir, that acetic acid would give an analogous reaction: that is to say, that under the influence of an excess of base it would change into carbonic acid and a hydrocarbon which should have C^4H^8 for a formula.

After several inevitable trials I have completely succeeded in producing this remarkable reaction.

It sufficed to mix 10 grams of crystallized acetate of soda with 30 or 40 grams of caustic baryta and to heat the mixture very gently in a retort to effect the transformation of acetic acid into carbonic acid and a gas which has the formula C^4H^8.

Nothing could be more distinct than this decomposition: the residue remained perfectly white; not the least trace of oil or pyroacetic spirit [acetone], not the least vapor, other than the water which accompanied the gas, was evolved.

Here is the eudiometric analysis of this gas:

Gas..................................	32	31	30
Oxygen.............................	91	86	84
Residue after the explosion............	59	55.5	54
The potash left......................	27	25.5	24
We have then:			
Carbon..........................	32	30	30
Hydrogen........................	64	61	60

That is to say that the gas was formed, as we usually say, of one volume of carbon vapor for two of hydrogen.

But such is exactly the composition of a gas which chemists have never known how to produce; I mean marsh gas.

One cannot refrain from remarking on these connections which are manifest between marsh gas produced by the spontaneous decomposition of vegetable matters and the marsh gas arising from the final decomposition of acetic acid which, itself, was produced by the dry distillation of wood.

I propose to make a complete study of this gas and to make a complete examination of reactions analogous to that which furnished it.

For the present I confine myself to establishing in an exact manner that the gas C^4H^8, corresponding to chloroform C^4H^2 according to the theory of Ch^6 substitution, was produced by acetic acid, just as chloroform was by chloroacetic acid.

This is to say that acetic and chloracetic acids possess the same fundamental chemical properties, as I had established, and belong to the same *organic type*.

Germain Henri Hess

(1802–1850)

NUMEROUS men, notably Lavoisier and Laplace,[1] had measured the heats evolved in various reactions, but thermochemistry received its first important advance at the hands of Germain Henri Hess, who showed that the heat evolved in a reaction is the same regardless of whether the reaction is carried out directly or in a number of steps. This generalization, known now as *Hess's law*, makes possible the calculation of heats for many reactions where direct measurements are impracticable.

Hess analyzed and investigated numerous natural products: waters, minerals, petroleum, resins, and beeswax. He examined the catalytic properties of platinum and the action of potassium hydroxide on alcohol. During the course of a research on the action of dilute nitric acid on glucose he discovered saccharic acid. The most important of his researches, however, dealt with thermochemistry. His many thermochemical measurements led not only to the above-mentioned law but also to the so-called "law of thermoneutrality": that the combination of two neutral salts producing no precipitate causes practically no heat evolution. Hess also observed that the heat of neutralization of a particular acid by any of a number of bases is essentially constant.

The paper which is in part translated below was the first of a long series entitled "Recherches thermochimiques" and first appeared in the *Bulletin scientifique* of the *Académie impériale des sciences* of St. Petersburg, 1840.[2]

After describing his calorimeter in this paper, Hess attempts to show that the heat evolved in the formation of various hydrates of sulfuric acid ($SO_3.H_2O$, $SO_3.2H_2O$, etc.) are even multiples, a theory now disproved. The data is, however, immediately used to prove what we now call *Hess's law*.

The following are the experiments which serve to find the amount of heat developed by the sulfuric acid.

```
7. The apparatus full of water.................  7,809.7
   Glass vessels 100g. X 0.19...................      19
   Acid (ḦS̈)*.........  266.4
   Water.............   48
                       ―――――
                       314.4 (Ḧ²S̈) X 0 474 =   149.9
                          Total mass = 7,978.6
   Increase in temperature 2.1°
   Which gives.............................................................  77.17†
```

* [The symbolism is that of Berzelius, a barred letter referring to a double atom and a dot to an atom of oxygen. Thus Ħ S̈ is H_2SO_4 in modern symbols.]

† [Calories per gram SO_3. The arithmetical errors of the original have not been corrected.]

[1] *Mémoires de l'Académie royale des sciences*, **1780**: 355–408.

[2] *Bulletin scientifique, Académie impériale des sciences* (St. Petersburg), **8**: 257–272

8. The apparatus full of water.................. 7,809.7
   Glass vessels 100g. × 0.19.................. 19

   Acid ($\overset{\cdot\cdot}{\overset{\cdot}{\text{H}}}$S)........... 370
   Water.............. 71
   $\overline{441}$ × 0.474   =   210.3
   Total mass = $\overline{8,039.0}$

   Increase in temperature 2.9°
   Which gives... 77.33
   N.B.   The heat capacity was determined by direct experiment in all cases where
   the contrary is not indicated.

9. The apparatus full of water.................. 7,809.7
   Glass vessels 150g. × 0.19.................. 27.5

   Acid ($\overset{\cdot\cdot}{\overset{\cdot}{\text{H}}}$S)........... 185
   Water.............. 71
   $\overline{256}$ ($\overset{\cdot}{\text{H}}{}^3\overset{\cdot\cdot}{\text{S}}$) × 0.5   =   128.0
   $\overline{7,965.2}$

   Increase in temperature 2.2°
   These values give.. 116.7
   N.B.   The heat capacity of the acid $\overset{\cdot}{\text{H}}{}^3\overset{\cdot\cdot}{\text{S}}$ is not the result of direct experiment, but
   an approximate estimate.

10. The apparatus full of water.................. 7,809.7
    Glass vessels 150g. × 0.19.................. 27.5

    Acid ($\overset{\cdot}{\text{H}}{}^2\overset{\cdot\cdot}{\text{S}}$)........... 528g.
    Water.............. 85
    $\overline{613.2}$ [*sic*] × 0.5   =   306.6
    $\overline{8,143.8}$

    Increase in temperature 1.7°
    These figures give... 38.56

11. I also attempted to determine the quantity of heat evolved by the
anhydrous acid [SO_3]. For that it was collected in a tube and weighed with
the glass. Being unable to use the whole of the calorimeter because of the
small quantity of acid which I had at my disposal, I took only the interior
cylinder, which was carefully covered with a poor conductor. In this, well
closed and shaken, combination took place, and immediately afterward
the cylinder was opened to introduce the thermometer and observe the
temperature. The heat which was produced at the point of contact was so
great that the glass tube was completely shattered. It was then a matter
of the greatest care that not the least particle of glass be lost. All the fragments being collected, washed, and weighed, the difference from the preceding weight, 15.92 grams, indicated the quantity of anhydrous acid
used. As this manner of determining the quantity of the acid appeared
too easily susceptible to error, and as the acid obtained by the mixture
was too dilute to be determined by the aerometer, I decomposed a certain
quantity of the acid from the mixing with a perfectly neutral solution of
barium chloride and dipped therein a piece of weighed marble as recom-

(1840). Also in Poggendorf's *Annalen der Physik und Chemie*, **50**: 385–404 (1840). The
selection given here is found on pages 389 to 394 of this article. Reprinted in Ostwald's
Klassiker, No. 9, "G. H. Hess, Thermochemische Untersuchungen (1839 bis 1842).
Herausgegeben von W. Ostwald," Leipzig, 1890.

mended by M. Runge for muriatic acid. This gave me 16 grams of anhydrous acid.

Glass.............. 5.26 } both corrected for their heat capacity
Cylinder.......... 93.47 }
Acid.............. 15.97
Water............ 700.00
                  ———
                  814.70
Increase in temperature 10°.

The result was not otherwise corrected, in view of the fact that the heat capacity of the mixture was not found to differ sensibly from that of water.

These values give 510.1

12. From sections 7 and 8 it follows that an atom of water added to $\ddot{H}\ddot{S}$ evolved 77.17 and 77.33 of heat. Section 9 gives 116.7 for two atoms of water, of which $\frac{2}{3}(=77.8)$ corresponds to the first atom and 38.9 to the second. Finally, section 10 gives us directly for this same atom of water 38.56.* If we add to that the result of section 11 and those which were cited above (section 4), we have the following series:

Composition	Heat Evolved	
$\ddot{S} + \dot{H}$	310.4	8
$\dot{H}\ddot{S} + \dot{H}$	77.86	2
$\dot{H}^2\ddot{S} + \dot{H}$	38.9	1
$\dot{H}^3\ddot{S} + 3\dot{H}$	38.9	
$\dot{H}^6\ddot{S} + x\dot{H}$	38.9	
	504.96	

From these figures we should obtain by mixing with an excess of water

$\ddot{S}$	....	504.96
$\dot{H}\ddot{S}$	....	194.5
$\dot{H}^2\ddot{S}$	....	116.7
$\dot{H}^3\ddot{S}$	....	77.8
$\dot{H}^6\ddot{S}$	....	38.9

The agreement among these numbers is such that they prove perfectly the law of multiple proportions for the quantities of caloric evolved. As to the absolute value of these quantities, it is certain that they have not attained the rigor which we could want later, but for the moment I believed that it was more important to attempt to establish the fundamental laws of this part of the science rather than stop to discuss whether for agreement the value 38.9 or 39 ought to be admitted.

13. *A combination having taken place, the quantity of heat evolved is always constant whether the combination is performed directly or whether it takes place indirectly and in different steps.*

* [These results in themselves are evidence for Hess's law, although he chooses to prove the law by data from another reaction later on.]

Experiment made with aqueous ammonia.

14. The apparatus full of water.......................... 7,809.7
Glass vessel 100 × 0.19............................. 19
Acid ($\dot{\text{H}}\ddot{\text{S}}$)....................... 92.5
Ammonia (density 0.935)......... 280.5
$\overline{373.0}$ × 0.828 = $\underline{\quad 308.8}$
8,137.5

Increase in temperature........... 5.44°
Another experiment............... 5.6
mean $\overline{5.52}$
These figures give.. 595.8

15. The apparatus full of water.......................... 7,809.7
Glass vessel 100 × 0.19............................. 19
Acid ($\dot{\text{H}}^2\ddot{\text{S}}$)....................... 88
Ammonia........................ 233.75
$\overline{321.7}$ × 0.76 = $\underline{\quad 244.5}$
8,073.2

Elevation of temperature 3.92°
These figures give.. 518.9

16. Acid ($\dot{\text{H}}^3\ddot{\text{S}}$)....................... 81.5
Ammonia........................ 187.0
$\overline{268.5}$ × 0.77 = $\underline{\quad 206.7}$
19
Glass.............................
The apparatus full of water.......................... 7,809.7
8,035.4

Increase in temperature 2.9°
These numbers give....................................... 480.5

17. Acid ($\dot{\text{H}}^6\ddot{\text{S}}$)....................... 70.5
Ammonia........................ 93.5
$\overline{164.0}$ × 0.786 = $\underline{\quad 128.9}$
19
Glass..............................
The apparatus full of water.......................... 7,809.7
7,957.6

Increase in temperature 1.7°
These numbers give....................................... 446.2

18. The experiment with anhydrous acid not yet having been made, let us take for a point of departure the ordinary hydrated acid $\dot{\text{H}}\ddot{\text{S}}$ and add to each of the subsequent results the quantity of heat evolved during the combination of the acid with the water. We have, then, for the quantities of heat evolved by the saturation of a part of the acid ($\ddot{\text{S}}$) by ammonia,

| Acid | Quantity of heat evolved | | Sum |
	By ammonia	By water	
$\dot{\text{H}}\ddot{\text{S}}$	595.8	.....	595.8
$\dot{\text{H}}^2\ddot{\text{S}}$	518.9	77.8	596.7
$\dot{\text{H}}^3\ddot{\text{S}}$	480.5	116.7	597.2
$\dot{\text{H}}^6\ddot{\text{S}}$	446.2	155.6	601.8
Mean.........	.....	.....	597.9

19. Since the anhydrous acid evolves in all 510.1, and in order to have the quantity which it evolves in becoming $\dot{\text{H}}^6\ddot{\text{S}}$ it is necessary to subtract from this number 38.9, the sum of the heat evolved by the supposed anhydrous acid in combining with liquid ammonia would be 1,069.1.

Thomas Graham

(1805–1869)

THE researches of Thomas Graham lie in the present domains of inorganic and physical chemistry, those in the latter being of such importance that he may well be considered one of the chief founders of physical chemistry. Graham's major contribution to inorganic chemistry is presented in a paper entitled "Researches on the Arseniates, Phosphates, and Modifications of Phosphoric Acid" (1833),[1] which is given, in part, below. His elucidation of the differences between the three phosphoric acids and his discovery of their polybasicity provided Liebig with the clue to the modern concept of polybasic acids. In the physical aspects of chemistry, T. Graham made notable advances. With the simplest of apparatus he dealt with the adsorption of salts by charcoal (1830), the rate of diffusion of gases (1828 to 1833), the solubility of salts (1827), heats of reaction (1841 to 1845), and dialysis (1849 to 1861), the last being an outgrowth of his most important physicochemical study, colloid chemistry.

Although examples of colloidal phenomena were known for centuries, it was not until the middle of the nineteenth century that they received any serious attention. Among the earlier investigations of significance was that of Francisco Selini (1817–1888),[2] who studied colloidal solutions of silver chloride (1845), prussian blue (1847), and sulfur (with A. Sobrero) (1850) and distinguished between true solutions and pseudosolutions. In 1857 Michael Faraday worked with gold sols,[3] known for centuries to the alchemists as *aurum potabile*, or potable gold, and demonstrated the existence therein of discrete particles. It remained, however, for Thomas Graham to recognize colloids as a general state of matter and to characterize the many properties of that state, giving impetus to subsequent research in this field.

In the following citation, from Graham's classic paper on the arsenates and phosphates,[1] a valuable contribution was made to chemistry in two instances: first,

---

[1] *Philosophical Transactions*, **1833**: 253–284. Reprinted in *Alembic Club Reprints*, No. 10, "Researches on the Arseniates, Phosphates and Modifications of Phosphoric Acid by Thomas Graham, F.R.S. (1833)," Edinburgh, 1904; and "Chemical and Physical Researches of Thomas Graham; with Preface and Analytical Contents by R. Angus Smith, F.R.S.," Edinburgh, 1876, pp. 321–348. This collected edition was printed in only a limited number for presentation and is, therefore, scarce.

[2] For the papers of Selini, together with others by Faraday, Graham, Muthmann, van Bemmelen, and Carey Lea on colloids, refer to work of Emil Hatschek, "The Foundations of Colloid Chemistry," London, 1925.

[3] *Philosophical Transactions*, **147**: 154 (1857). Also Ostwald's *Klassiker*, No. 214, "Michael Faraday, Experimentelle Untersuchungen uber das Verhalten von Gold (und anderen Metallen) zum Licht. Uebersetzt und herausgegeben von F. H. von Hahn," Leipzig, 1925.

the relationship of ortho-, pyro-, and metaphosphoric acids and their salts was explained, and second, it was the foundation of the concept of the basicity of acids. The nomenclature used in this publication has the following modern equivalents: normal orthophosphate corresponds to "subphosphate" or "subsesquiphosphate"; salts of the formula $Na_2HPO_4.12H_2O$ are "phosphate" or "neutral phosphate"; and finally "biphosphate" is $NaH_2PO_4.H_2O$. The Berzelius notation is employed, with a dot above a symbol to represent an oxygen atom with which the symbolized substance is combined.

IV. OF THE MODIFICATIONS OF PHOSPHORIC ACID.

The distinctive character of phosphoric acid which exists in common phosphate of soda, as compared with the other modifications, is a disposition to form salts which contain three atoms of base to the double atom of acid. Of these salts the most remarkable is the yellow subphosphate of silver, which the soluble phosphates precipitate when added to nitrate of silver. This acid does not affect albumen; and the other modifications pass directly into the condition of this acid on keeping their aqueous solutions for some days, and more rapidly on boiling these solutions; or upon fusing the other modifications or their salts with at least three proportions of fixed base.

Pyrophosphoric acid, or the acid which exists in the fused phosphate of soda, is remarkably disposed to form salts having two atoms base, which is the constitution of the white pyrophosphate of silver, formed on testing the pyrophosphate of soda with a salt of silver. Such salts of the preceding acid as contain no more than two atoms of fixed base, pass into pyrophosphates when heated to redness. The acid under consideration, when free, does not disturb albumen, nor produce a precipitate in muriate of barytes.

The metaphosphoric acid is disposed to form salts which contain one atom of base to the double atom of acid. The other modifications pass into metaphosphoric acid when heated to redness per se, or when heated to redness in contact with no more than one atomic proportion of certain fixed bases, such as soda. This acid, when free, occasions precipitates in solutions of the salts of barytes and of most of the other earths and metallic oxides, and forms an insoluble compound with albumen. The glacial or metaphosphoric acid appears to be capable of dissolving in general only about four fifths of the quantity of carbonate of soda which it can decompose when converted into phosphoric acid. But a large quantity of the meta-acid passes into phosphoric acid on uniting with alkali, and the solution deposits phosphate of soda in tufts composed of fine crystalline plates of a silky lustre. The salt presented itself of this appearance, it will be remembered, in the case of a solution of phosphate of soda which had been boiled for a long time in a glass vessel. The liquid about the crystals, in the present case, still contained metaphosphoric acid.

Now it is a matter of certainty that if we take one combining proportion of any modification of phosphoric acid, and fuse it with soda or its carbonate, we shall form a metaphosphate, a pyrophosphate, or a phosphate, according as we employ one, two, or three proportions of base. The acid when separated from the base will possess, and retain for some time, the characters of its peculiar modification. It would appear, therefore, that the acid is impressed with a disposition to form different classes of salts by the proportion of base to which it has been united, and that it retains this disposition even when liberated from the original compound. But I suspect that the modifications of phosphoric acid, when in what we would call a free state, are still in combination with their usual proportion of base, and that that base is water. Thus the three modifications of phosphoric acid may be composed as follows:

$$\text{Phosphoric acid} \ldots \ldots \ldots \ldots \overset{\cdots}{\text{H}^3\text{P}}$$
$$\text{Pyrophosphoric acid} \ldots \ldots \ldots \overset{\cdots}{\text{H}^2\text{P}}$$
$$\text{Metaphosphoric acid} \ldots \ldots \ldots \overset{\cdots}{\text{HP}};*$$

* [*I.e.*, $3H_2O.P_2O_5$, $2H_2O.P_2O_5$, $H_2O.P_2O_5$.]

or they are respectively a terphosphate, a biphosphate, and phosphate of water. Now, when one of these compounds is treated with a strong base, the whole or a part of the water is supplanted, *but the amount of base in combination with the acid remains unaltered*. There are thus three sets of phosphates, in which the oxygen in the acid being five, the oxygen in the base is three, two, and one. The constitution of the acids and of the salts of soda which they form, is exhibited in the following Table.

	Oxygen in		
	Soda.	Water.	Acid.
First Class			
Phosphoric acid	0	3	5
Biphosphate of soda	1	2	5
Phosphate of soda	2	1	5
Subphosphate of soda	3	0	5
Second Class			
Pyrophosphoric acid	0	2	5
Bipyrophosphate of soda	1	1	5
Pyrophosphate of soda	2	0	5
Third Class			
Metaphosphoric acid	0	1	5
Metaphosphate of soda	1	0	5

The hypothetic composition of the acid hydrates may also be stated as follows:

	Acid.	Water.
Phosphoric acid...............	100	37.81 = 3 atoms
Pyrophosphoric acid...........	100	25.21 = 2 atoms
Metaphosphoric acid..........	100	12.61 = 1 atom

By a heat of 300° a dilute solution of phosphoric acid in a platinum crucible concentrates readily till the water is reduced to the proportion of three atoms, at which stage the acid assumes a dark colour, and is of the consistence of treacle when cold, but much more fluid when hot. In this condition the acid gives an unmixed yellow precipitate with silver, and is entirely phosphoric acid. By exposure for seven days over sulphuric acid in the vacuum of an air-pump, the water was reduced to 43.5 parts, and almost the whole of the acid had crystallized in thin plates, which were deliquescent in the extreme, and which there is every reason to believe were the terhydrate. By a protracted exposure to 300° or 320°, the acid continues to lose water, but much more slowly. At 460° the water was quickly reduced to 34.4 parts, or little more than $2\frac{2}{3}$ atoms, in an experiment conducted in an open crucible, and the acid now precipitated silver white with a trace of yellow; but when neutralized by carbonate of soda, it afforded crystalline plates of phosphate of soda, among which no crystals of pyrophosphate existed. But it may be deemed possible from this result that a hydrate of phosphoric acid exists, containing $2\frac{2}{3}$ atoms of water to 1 atom acid, which is 8 atoms base to 3 atoms acid, the proportion of base to acid in the salt termed by Berzelius, the phosphate of lime of bones. In another case in which the evaporation was conducted much more slowly in a platinum flask, the above compound was certainly not formed; but the evaporation at 415°, after advancing for several days, seemed to cease entirely when the water was reduced to 29.9 parts, which is very nearly $2\frac{1}{3}$ atoms of water. Acid at this degree of concentration, neutralized as usual by ammonia, gave, with silver, a chalky white precipitate without a shade of yellow, which suggests the idea that an acid hydrate of $2\frac{1}{3}$ water may exist, having a corresponding silver salt. Acid, so far concentrated, when neutralized by carbonate of soda, afforded a mixture of crystals of phosphate and pyrophosphate of soda, in which the latter predominated. For the production of metaphosphoric acid, the concentration of a much higher temperature was requisite; but this acid was observed to appear before the proportion of water had fallen under 2 atoms, namely, when it amounted to 28.05 per cent. in one experiment. By the greatest heat of the sand-bath, which was considerably above the melting point of lead, the proportion of water was reduced a little under 2 atoms, namely, to 22.99 parts; and the acid then contained abundance of metaphosphoric acid, as evinced by its power to coagulate albumen. In the glacial phosphoric acid, Dulong found 100 acid united with 20.6 water, and Rose 100 acid with only 10.42 water. The latter determination falls short of 1 atom water, and would indicate that phosphoric acid may be rendered partially anhydrous by heat. I do not enter upon the details of my experiments on the hydrates of phosphoric acid, as the subject is difficult, and requires a much more minute investigation than I have as yet had it in my power to give it.

Although of opinion that there is only one phosphoric acid, and that the modifications are entirely due to the quantity of water combined with the acid, I have still retained the names which have come into use, and even proposed a third, *meta*phosphoric acid, implying merely that the acid to which this name is applied is phosphoric acid with something else, namely, with an atom of water. As the classes of salts which the acid hydrates form are quite distinct, these trivial names are practically convenient, and may be adopted provisionally till chemists are prepared, by an extended knowledge of the salts, to innovate upon their nomenclature with more advantage than can be done at present. . . .

In 1829 Graham published his first paper on the diffusion of gases, which is entitled "A Short Account of Experimental Researches on the Diffusion of Gases through Each Other, and Their Separation by Mechanical Means."[4] Although this publication contains the essentials of his law, now know as *Graham's law*, it was in a subsequent paper, "On the Law of the Diffusion of Gases," that he definitely established the principle. It is from this memoir, first read before the Royal Society of Edinburgh (December 19, 1831) and published in 1833, that the citation below is drawn.[5]

ON THE LAW OF THE DIFFUSION OF GASES

It is the object of this paper to establish with numerical exactness the following law of the diffusion of gases:—

"The diffusion or spontaneous intermixture of two gases in contact is effected by an interchange in position of indefinitely minute volumes of the gases, which volumes are not necessarily of equal magnitude, being, in the case of each gas, inversely proportional to the square root of the density of that gas."

These replacing volumes of the gases may be named *equivalent volumes*

[4] Quart. J. Sci., **2**: 74–83 (1829); "Chemical and Physical Researches . . . ," pp. 28–35.

[5] *Philosophical Magazine*, **2**: 175–190, 269–276, 351–358 (1833); the selection is taken from "Chemical and Physical Researches . . . ," pages 44, 48, 64 to 65, and 68 to 69.

of diffusion, and are as follows:—air, 1; hydrogen, 3.7947; carburetted hydrogen, 1.3414; water-vapour, 1.2649; nitrogen, 1.0140; oxygen, 0.9487; carbonic acid, 0.8091; chlorine, 0.6325; etc.—numbers which are inversely proportional to the square roots of the densities of these gases, being the reciprocals of the square roots of the densities, the density of air being assumed as unity.

If the two gases are separated at the outset by a screen having apertures of insensible magnitude, the interchange of "equivalent volumes of diffusion" takes place through these apertures, being effected by a force of the highest intensity; and if the gases are of unequal density, there is a consequent accumulation on the side of the heavy gas, and loss on the side of the light gas. In the case of air, for instance, on one side of the screen, and hydrogen gas on the other, a process of exchanging 1 measure of air for 3.7947 measures of hydrogen, through the apertures, is commenced, and continues till the gases on both sides of the screen are in a state of uniform mixture. Experiments on this principle can be made with ease and precision, as will appear in the sequel, and afford an elegant demonstration of the law. . . .

I shall treat in succession of the escape of the different gases from a diffusion instrument into air. As the contained gas bears no proportion in quantity to the external air, the gas escapes entirely, and is wholly replaced by air. It is of the utmost importance to determine the proportion between the volume of gas diffused, and the replacing volume of air diffused, and the replacing volume of air eventually found in the instrument. We thus obtain the *equivalent diffusion-volume* of the gas, which it will be convenient to state in numbers with reference to the replacing volume of air as unity. I shall begin with hydrogen gas, although attended with peculiar difficulties, as it introduces in a distinct manner to our notice several circumstances which may slightly modify the results of diffusion. . . .

After a discussion of the *Diffusion-volume of Hydrogen Gas, Diffusion of Carbonic Acid Gas, Chlorine, Sulphureous Acid Gas, Protoxide of Nitrogen, Cyanogen, Muriatic Acid Gas, Ammoniacal Gas, Sulphuretted Hydrogen Gas, Oxygen Gas, Nitrogen, Carbonic Oxide*, and *Carburetted Hydrogen of Marshes*, Graham summarizes his results in a table before concluding the paper.

In the diffusion-volumes of oxygen, nitrogen, and carbonic oxide, the correspondence between theory and experiment is as close as could be desired. Indeed, admitting our law, I believe that the specific gravity of these gases can be determined by experiments on the principle of diffusion, with greater accuracy than by the ordinary means. But, to be of value, experiments performed with this important object in view, would require to be conducted with extreme care, in the most favourable circumstances, as regards uniformity of temperature, and to be frequently repeated. The diffusion-bulbs might also be considerably increased in size, and a greater minuteness of observation attained. Even in the most successful experiments recited in this paper, we cannot depend upon the absolute accuracy of the third decimal figure. In the case of carbonic acid gas, protoxide of nitrogen, sulphuretted hydrogen, and sulphurous acid, the process of diffusion is interfered with in a greater or lesser degree by the absorbent action which all porous bodies exercise upon gases. Fortunately, however, the absorbent power of stucco is very low in degree. . . .

TABLE OF EQUIVALENT DIFFUSION-VOLUMES OF GASES; AIR = 1

	By Experiment.	By Theory.	Spec. Gravity.
Hydrogen,.....................	3.83	3.7947	0.694
Carburetted Hydrogen,...........	1.344	1.3414	0.555
Olefiant Gas,...................	1.0191	1.0140	0.972
Carbonic Oxide,................	1.0149	1.0140	0.972
Nitrogen,......................	1.0143	1.0140	0.972
Oxygen,.......................	0.9487	0.9487	0.111
Sulphuretted Hydrogen,.........	0.95	0.9204	1.1805
Protoxide of Nitrogen,...........	0.82	0.8091	1.527
Carbonic Acid,.................	0.812	0.8091	1.527
Sulphurous Acid,...............	0.68	0.6708	2.222

In regard to the terms of the law of diffusion: "The diffusion, or spontaneous intermixture of two gases in contact, is effected by an interchange in position of *indefinitely minute volumes of the gases.*" My experiments, published on a former occasion, on the diffusion of mixed gases (*Quarterly Journal of Science*, p. 28, Sept. 1829), afford the first demonstration of the fact that diffusion takes place between the ultimate particles of gases, and not between sensible masses, and therefore that diffusion cannot be the result of accident. For, in the case of a mixture of two gases escaping from a receiver into the atmosphere, by apertures of 0.12 and 0.07 inch in diameter, it was not so much of the mixture which left the receiver in a given time, but a certain proportion of each of the mixed gases, independently of the other, corresponding to its individual diffusiveness. The same separation of mixed gases occured in diffusion through the pores of stucco, or the fissure of a cracked jar.

"Which volumes are not necessarily of equal magnitude, being, in the case of each gas, inversely proportional to the square root of the density of that gas." This may be demonstrated when different gases communicate by very narrow channels, or by very small apertures, and when inequality of pressure is guarded against. In the case of a gas communicating with the air by a wide aperture, on the other hand, although the diffusion or intermixture takes place precisely in the same way, still the result is different; for where a contraction takes place from the process of diffusion, the air flows in mechanically through the apertures, wholly unresisted, and makes up the deficiency. A gas, however, of large diffusion-volume escapes, in these circumstances, *in a shorter time* than a gas of small diffusion-volume. Indeed, it was the conclusion of the former paper, that gases diffuse more or less rapidly according to some function of their densities, "apparently inversely as the square root of their densities." The advantage, in illustrating the process of diffusion of minute apertures or channels of communication, such as we have in the stucco-plug, depends upon the circumstance that, when a contraction or expansion takes place in the gaseous contents of a diffusion-instrument, any current in an outward or inward direction is prevented by frictional resistance; so that the simple result of diffusion is exhibited, not complicated by the effect of any other force.

The law at which we have arrived (which is merely a description of the appearances, and involves, I believe, nothing hypothetic) is certainly not provided for in the corpuscular philosophy of the day, and is altogether so extraordinary that I may be excused for not speculating further upon its cause, till its various bearings, and certain collateral subjects, be fully investigated. . . .

From his study of the molecular movement of gases Thomas Graham went on to the associated study of the same phenomena in liquids. His Bakerian lecture, "On the Diffusion of Liquids,"[6] is regarded as the first paper in colloid chemistry. The culmination of his work in this field came with the paper entitled "Liquid Diffusion Applied to Analysis," which appeared in 1861.[7] It is essentially modern in its viewpoint and colloid terminology. Here he recognized colloids as representing a general state of matter, a concept which may be held to mark the formal beginning of colloid chemistry. Portions of this paper are reproduced in what follows.

LIQUID DIFFUSION APPLIED TO ANALYSIS.

The property of volatility, possessed in various degrees by so many substances, affords invaluable means of separation, as is seen in the ever-recurring processes of evaporation and distillation. So similar in character to volatility is the diffusive power possessed by all liquid substances, that we may fairly reckon upon a class of analogous analytical resources to arise from it. The range also in the degree of diffusive mobility exhibited by different substances appears to be as wide as the scale of vapour ten-

[6] *Philosophical Transactions*, **1850**: 1–46, 805–835; **1851**: 483–494; "Chemical and Physical Researches . . . ," pp. 444–544.

[7] *Philosophical Transactions*, **151**: 183–224 (1861); "Chemical and Physical Researches . . . ," pp. 552–600; the selection is taken from pages 552 to 556 and 595.

sions. Thus hydrate of potash may be said to possess double the velocity of diffusion of sulphate of potash, and sulphate of potash again double the velocity of sugar, alcohol, and sulphate of magnesia. But the substances named belong all, as regards diffusion, to the more "volatile" class. The comparatively "fixed" class, as regards diffusion, is represented by a different order of chemical substances, marked out by the absence of the power to crystallize, which are slow in the extreme. Among the latter are hydrated silicic acid, hydrated alumina, and other metallic peroxides of the aluminous class, when they exist in the soluble form; with starch, dextrin and the gums, caramel, tannin, albumen, gelatine, vegetable and animal extractive matters. Low diffusibility is not the only property which the bodies last enumerated possess in common. They are distinguished by the gelatinous character of their hydrates. Although often largely soluble in water, they are held in solution by a most feeble force. They appear singularly inert in the capacity of acids and bases, and in all the ordinary chemical relations. But, on the other hand, their peculiar physical aggregation with the chemical indifference referred to, appears to be required in substances that can intervene in the organic processes of life. The plastic elements of the animal body are found in this class. As gelatine appears to be its type, it is proposed to designate substances of the class as *colloids*, and to speak of their peculiar form of aggregation as the *colloidal condition of matter*. Opposed to the colloidal is the crystalline condition. Substances affecting the latter form will be classed as *crystalloids*. The distinction is no doubt one of intimate molecular constitution.[8]

Although chemically inert in the ordinary sense, colloids possess a compensating activity of their own arising out of their physical properties. While the rigidity of the crystalline structure shuts out external impressions, the softness of the gelatinous colloid partakes of fluidity, and enables the colloid to become a medium for liquid diffusion, like water itself. The same penetrability appears to take the form of cementation in such colloids as can exist at a high temperature. Hence a wide sensibility on the part of colloids to external agents. Another and eminently characteristic quality of colloids, is their mutability. Their existence is a continued metastasis. A colloid may be compared in this respect to water while existing liquid at a temperature under its usual freezing-point, or to a supersaturated saline solution. Fluid colloids appear to have always a *pectous*[9] modification; and they often pass under the slightest influences

---

[8] [This definition has now, of course, been broadened, since crystallizable substances may be obtained in the colloidal state.]

[9] πηκτὸς, *curdled*. As fibrin, casein, albumen. But certain liquid colloid substances are capable of forming a jelly and yet still remain liquefiable by heat and soluble in water. Such is gelatine itself, which is not pectous in the condition of animal jelly; but may be so as it exists in the gelatiferous tissues.

from the first into the second condition. The solution of hydrated silicic acid, for instance, is easily obtained in a state of purity, but it cannot be preserved. It may remain fluid for days or weeks in a sealed tube, but is sure to gelatinize and become insoluble at last. Nor does the change of this colloid appear to stop at that point. For the mineral forms of silicic acid, deposited from water, such as flint, are often found to have passed, during the geological ages of their existence, from the vitreous or colloidal into the crystalline condition (H. Rose). The colloidal is, in fact, a dynamical state of matter; the crystalloidal being the statical condition. The colloid possesses ENERGIA. It may be looked upon as the probable primary source of the force appearing in the phenomena of vitality. To the gradual manner in which colloidal changes take place (for they always demand time as an element), may the characteristic protraction of chemico-organic changes also be referred.

A simple and easily applicable mode of effecting a diffusive separation is to place the mixed substance under a column of water, contained in a cylindrical glass jar of 5 or 6 inches in depth. The mixed solution may be conducted to the bottom of the jar by the use of a fine pipette, without the occurrence of any sensible intermixture. The spontaneous diffusion, which immediately commences, is allowed to go on for a period of several days. It is then interrupted by siphoning off the water from the surface in successive strata, from the top to the bottom of the column. A species of cohobation has been the consequence of unequal diffusion, the most rapidly diffusive substance being isolated more and more as it ascended. The higher the water column, sufficient time being always given to enable the most diffusive substance to appear at the summit, the more completely does a portion of that substance free itself from such other less diffusive substances as were originally associated with it. A marked effect is produced even where the difference in diffusibility is by no means considerable, such as the separation of chloride of potassium from chloride of sodium, of which the relative diffusibilities are as 1 to 0.841. Supposing a third metal of the potassium group to exist, standing above potassium in diffusibility as potassium stands above sodium, it may be safely predicated that the new metal would admit of being separated from the other two metals by an application of the jar-diffusion above described.

A certain property of colloid substances comes into play most opportunely in assisting diffusive separations. The jelly of starch, that of animal mucus, of pectin, of the vegetable gelose of Payen, and other solid colloidal hydrates, all of which are, strictly speaking, insoluble in cold water, are themselves permeable when in mass, as water is, by the more highly diffusive class of substances. But such jellies greatly resist the passage of the less diffusive substances, and cut off entirely other colloid substances like themselves that may be in solution. They resemble animal membrane in this respect. A mere film of the jelly has the separating effect. Take for illustration the following simple experiment.

A sheet of very thin and well-sized letter-paper, of French manufacture, having no porosity, was first thoroughly wetted and then laid upon the surface of water contained in a small basin of less diameter than the width of the paper, and the latter depressed in the centre so as to form a tray or cavity capable of holding a liquid. The liquid placed upon the paper was a mixed solution of cane-sugar and gum-arabic, containing 5 per cent. of each substance. The pure water below and the mixed solution above were therefore separated only by the thickness of the wet sized paper. After twenty-four hours the upper liquid appeared to have increased sensibly in volume, through the agency of osmose. The water below was found now to contain three-fourths of the whole sugar, in a condition so pure as to crystallize when the liquid was evaporated on a water-bath. Indeed the liquid of the basin was only in the slightest degree disturbed by sub-acetate of lead, showing the absence of all but a trace of gum. Paper of the description used is sized by means of starch. The film of gelatinous starch in the wetted paper has presented no obstacle to the passage of the crystal-loid sugar, but has resisted the passage of the colloid gum. I may state at once what I believe to be the mode in which this takes place.

The sized paper has no power to act as a filter. It is mechanically impenetrable, and denies a passage to the mixed fluid as a whole. Molecules only permeate this septum, and not masses. The molecules also are moved by the force of diffusion. But the water of the gelatinous starch is not directly available as a medium for the diffusion of either the sugar or gum, being in a state of true chemical combination, feeble although the union of water with starch may be. The hydrated compound itself is solid, and also insoluble. Sugar, however, with all other crystalloids, can separate water, molecule after molecule, from any hydrated colloid, such as starch. The sugar thus obtains the liquid medium required for diffusion, and makes its way through the gelatinous septum. Gum, on the other hand, possessing as a colloid an affinity for water of the most feeble description, is unable to separate that liquid from the gelatinous starch, and so fails to open the door for its own passage outwards by diffusion.

The separation described is somewhat analogous to that observed in a soap-bubble inflated with a gaseous mixture composed of carbonic acid and hydrogen. Neither gas, as such, can penetrate the water-film. But the carbonic acid, being soluble in water, is condensed and dissolved by the water-film, and so is enabled to pass outwards and reach the atmosphere; while hydrogen, being insoluble in water, or nearly so, is retained behind within the vesicle.

It may perhaps be allowed to me to apply the convenient term *dialysis* to the method of separation by diffusion through a septum of gelatinous matter. The most suitable of all substances for the dialytic septum appears to be the commercial material known as vegetable parchment or parchment-paper, which was first produced by M. Gaine, and is now successfully manufactured by Messrs. De la Rue. This is unsized paper, altered by a short immersion in sulphuric acid, or in chloride of zinc, as proposed by Mr. T. Taylor. . . .

7. Colloidal Condition of Matter.

I may be allowed to advert again to the radical distinction assumed in this paper to exist between colloids and crystalloids in their intimate molecular constitution. Every physical and chemical property is characteristically modified in each class. They appear like different worlds of matter, and give occasion to a corresponding division of chemical science. The distinction between these kinds of matter is that subsisting between the material of a mineral and the material of an organized mass.

The colloidal character is not obliterated by liquefaction, and is therefore more than a modification of the physical condition of solid. Some colloids are soluble in water, as gelatine and gum-arabic; and some are insoluble, like gum-tragacanth. Some colloids, again, form solid compounds with water, as gelatine and gum-tragacanth, while others, like tannin, do not. In such points the colloids exhibit as great a diversity of property as the crystalloids. A certain parallelism is maintained between the two classes, notwithstanding their differences.

The phenomena of the solution of a salt or crystalloid probably all appear in the solution of a colloid, but greatly reduced in degree. The process becomes slow; time, indeed, appearing essential to all colloidal changes. The change of temperature, usually occurring in the act of solution, becomes barely perceptible. The liquid is always sensibly gummy or viscous when concentrated. The colloid, although often dissolved in a large proportion by its solvent, is held in solution by a singularly feeble force. Hence colloids are generally displaced and precipitated by the addition to their solution of any substance from the other class. Of all the properties of liquid colloids, their slow diffusion in water, and their arrest by colloidal septa, are the most serviceable in distinguishing them from crystalloids. Colloids have feeble chemical reactions, but they exhibit at the same time a very general sensibility to liquid reagents, as has already been explained.

Auguste Laurent

(1808–1853)

THE name of Laurent is closely bound up with that of Gerhardt, for the two men were rebels against the dominant theories of Liebig and Dumas and for most of their lives fought vainly for recognition and acceptance of their ideas. Of the two, Laurent was the more original, and many of his ideas were taken up and subsequently developed by Gerhardt.

Laurent was originally responsible for the theory of substitution, which Dumas, with his great prestige, introduced to the chemical world, but while Dumas was unwilling to accept the full consequences of the theory, Laurent unhesitatingly followed them to their logical conclusions, thereby winning the undying enmity of Dumas.

In his studies on derivatives of naphthalene, Laurent was impressed by the fact that the fundamental properties of these compounds remained, in spite of the various substitutions which took place in them. A certain nucleus seemed to impose its properties on all its derivatives. This nucleus theory was the basis for the unitary theory which was specifically formulated by Gerhardt.

Laurent possessed a profoundly systematic mind. He developed his nucleus theory and classified all organic compounds in terms of it, in a markedly original manner. His basic ideas are those current today, but the complex names which he gave the various classes of compounds have not survived.

His great book, in which he summarized all his ideas on structure and classification, appeared a year after his death[1] and exerted more influence than any of his efforts during his life. His method of classification, as first proposed, was taken up by L. Gmelin (1788–1853) in his "Handbook of Chemistry" and, in turn, was used by Beilstein as the basis for arranging the organic compounds in his "Handbuch der organischen Chemie."

The following selection, taken from pages 329 to 335 of the Odling translation, expresses the fundamental ideas of the nucleus theory and reveals some of the system of classification adopted by Laurent.

THEORY OF DERIVED NUCLEI (CARENIDES)

If I may be permitted to follow up the comparison which I have just instituted [to the growth of a tree], I would ask, if a botanist might not be

---

[1] "Méthode de chimie," Paris, 1854. The work was translated into English the next year and served to popularize Laurent's ideas in England: "Chemical Method, Notation, Classification, & Nomenclature by Auguste Laurent. Translated by William Odling. Printed for the Cavendish Society by Harrison and Sons, St. Martin's Lane," 1855.

able to ascertain, independently of generation, or metamorphosis, whether two isolated parts, a leaf and a petal for example, belonged to the same plant? The thing would, without doubt, be difficult in our present state of knowledge; but is it not conceivable, that by the aid of a more perfect dissection, we might some day succeed in discovering, that all the parts of the same plant contain something in common, an embryo, a mother cell,— the presence of which, in all the organs, will enable us to understand why they are all capable of transforming themselves into one another?

Be this as it may, I have endeavoured to ascertain, whether there is not in all the different parts of our chemical tree, something analogous to this mother cell; in one word, a *nucleus* common to all the compounds of the same series, a nucleus which would enable us to understand, why all these compounds can reciprocally engender one another.

On several occasions, I have insisted strongly upon the stability of the halydes,[2]—of these molecular groups, which incessantly re-appear in our reactions; and I have also called attention to the relative instability of the hyperhalydes.[3] I was always astonished at seeing naphthaline, though six, seven, or eight times chlorinated by equivalent substitution, yet resist the action of heat and alkalis, whilst this same naphthaline, once or twice chlorinated, but not by substitution, was destroyed by the action of these two reagents, and in every case a halyde produced. From considering the crystalline form, the analogy, the re-actions, and principally the stability of naphthaline, and the halydes, I conclude, that they constitute one unique group, or nucleus, which enters as such into the composition of the hyperhalydes. These latter, consequently, contain two groups; the one, formed of naphthaline or its halydes, the other, of the excess of chlorine.

It is true we might equally account for the stability of the one class, and the instability of the other, as also for the analogy which exists between the compounds of each of them, by supposing, that the hyperhalydes contain, not a *chlorinated*, but a *hydrochlorinated* group, as seen in the second members of the following equations:

$$C^{10}H^8 \quad + Cl^4 = C^{10}H^6Cl^2 + H^2Cl^2$$
$$C^{10}H^7Cl \quad + Cl^4 = C^{10}H^5Cl^3 + H^2Cl^2$$
$$C^{10}H^6Cl^2 + Cl^4 = C^{10}H^4Cl^4 + H^2Cl^2 \&c.$$

It is this latter mode of viewing these compounds that, in the first instance, I proposed; subsequently I abandoned it, and adopted in its stead, the arrangements indicated by the first members of the above equations. The compound $C^{10}H^6Cl^2 + Br^4$, heated to above 100°C., is decomposed

---

[2] [Hydrocarbons in which chlorine replaces hydrogen, replacing exactly the equivalent amount of hydrogen, are halydes.]

[3] [Hyperhalydes are those in which chlorine is simply absorbed, or which absorb more chlorine than they lose hydrogen.]

in $C^{10}H^6Cl^2$ and Br^4, which result would be impossible, if one part of the bromine were in the state of bromhydric acid, as in the formula $C^{10}H^4Cl^2Br^2 + H^2Br^2$.

If then, in the above compound, the bromine does not exist in the state of bromhydric acid, neither will the chlorine of the analogous and isomorphous compound, $C^{10}H^6Cl^2 + Cl^4$, be in the state of chlorhydric acid, nor by parity of reasoning in the compounds $C^{10}H^7Cl + Cl^4$, $C^{10}H^8 + Cl^4$.

If naphthaline and its halydes continue as such, when combined with an excess of chlorine or bromine, so likewise do they continue, when combined with oxygen to form aldehydes or acids. Consequently, $C^{10}H^8 + O$ will not give rise to $C^{20}H^{14}O + H^2O$, and $C^{10}H^8 + O^2$, will not form a hydrated acid of the formula $C^{20}H^{14}O^3 + H^2O$.

Having regard to the preceding considerations, observing moreover that in the aldehydes, and in the formic, acetic, propionic . . . margaric, and melissic acids, the carbon is to the hydrogen, in the ratio of molecule to molecule, or of one atom to two atoms, whilst these simple ratios become irregular, if we suppose that in the above compounds, a part of the hydrogen, constitutes a hydrate or hydruret, as seen in these examples: $C^5H^8O^3 + H^2O$, $C^{10}H^{18}O^3 + H^2O$, $C^{20}H^{38}O^3 + H^2O$, $C^{60}H^{118}O^3 + H^2O$, or indeed, $C^{60}H^{118}O^4 + H^2$, &c.; and lastly, recollecting the relations which exist between the forms of the halydes, and those of the hyperhalydes of naphthaline, relations somewhat obscure it is true, but still sufficient to indicate, that in the atomic arrangement of both classes there is a certain something in common; I draw the following conclusions:

1°. That the hydrocarbons and their halydes, form analogous groups or nuclei,—stable as regards the number and arrangement of the atoms, but variable as regards their nature. Thus, we may have hydrogen, chlorine, bromine, peroxide of nitrogen, or other bodies, occupying the place of hydrogen.

2°. That the hyperhalydes, and the corresponding aldehydes, and acids, all contain a hydrocarbon, or halyde, which constitutes a separate group.

In a word, I conclude, that the combinations of etherine, or bihydrocarbon, have the following arrangements:—

Halydes	Hyperhalydes	Aldehydes	Acids
. . . .	C^2H^4 $.H^2$	. . . .	. . . .
C^2H^4	C^2H^4 $.Cl^2$	C^2H^4 $.O$	C^2H^4 $.O^2$
C^2H^3Cl	$C^2H^3Cl.Cl^2$	$C^2H^3Cl.O$	$C^2H^3Cl.O^2$
$C^2H^2Cl^2$	$C^2H^2Cl^2.Cl^2$	$C^2H^2Cl^2.O$	$C^2H^2Cl^2.O^2$
$C^2H Cl^3$	$C^2H Cl^3.Cl^2$	$C^2H Cl^3.O$	$C^2H Cl^3.O^2$
$C^2 Cl^4$	$C^2 Cl^4.Cl^2$	$C^2 Cl^4.O$	. . . .

In applying the same reasoning to the combinations of methylene, propylene, butyrene, amylene . . . cetine, and melissine; to the combinations of benzene, phene, toluene, cymene, &c., in placing side by side, their halydes, hyperhalydes, aldehydes, and acids, and observing the harmony, the elegance, and the extreme simplicity of their formulas, I cannot help considering the above, to be a representation of the real arrangement of the atoms.

Following out these ideas, let us construct a tree, or a series, with any hydrocarbon whatever, taken as the nucleus, say for instance $C^{10}H^{10}$. For this purpose, let us bring together all the bodies which mutually generate one another, and contain the above nucleus, and let us then dispose them in the following manner:

$$\left.\begin{array}{l}\text{Nuclenides}\ldots\ldots\ldots\ldots\ldots\ldots\ldots\ldots\ldots\ldots\\ \text{Fundamental Nucleus}\ldots\ldots\ldots\ldots\ldots\end{array}\right\}C^{10}H^{10}$$

$$\begin{array}{ll}\begin{array}{l}\text{Dyadides}\\ \text{(Hyperhalydes)}\end{array}\left\{\begin{array}{ll}\text{Hyperhydride}\ldots\ldots\ldots & C^{10}H^{10}+H^2\\ \text{Dihalyde}\ldots\ldots\ldots\ldots & C^{10}H^{10}+Cl^2\\ \text{Tetrhalyde}\ldots\ldots\ldots\ldots & C^{10}H^{10}+Cl^4\\ \text{Hexhalyde}\ldots\ldots\ldots\ldots & C^{10}H^{10}+Cl^6\end{array}\right.\end{array}$$

$$\begin{array}{ll}\text{Monadides}\left\{\begin{array}{ll}\text{Monalide}\ldots\ldots\ldots\ldots & C^{10}H^{10}+O\\ \text{Deuteride}\ldots\ldots\ldots\ldots & C^{10}H^{10}+O^2\\ \text{Tritonide}\ldots\ldots\ldots\ldots & C^{10}H^{10}+O^3\end{array}\right.\end{array}$$

or better still

$$\begin{array}{ll}\text{Xeromonadides}\left\{\begin{array}{ll}\text{Xeride}\ldots\ldots\ldots\ldots & D-Aq^{\frac{1}{2}}\\ \text{Dixeride}\ldots\ldots\ldots\ldots & D-Aq\end{array}\right\}\\ \hphantom{\text{Xeromonadides}}\left\{\begin{array}{ll}\text{Anhydride}\ldots\ldots\ldots\ldots & T-Aq\\ \text{Dianhydride}\ldots\ldots\ldots & T-Aq^2\end{array}\right\}\end{array}$$

$$\text{Monodyadides}\ldots\text{Udolides}\ldots\ldots\ldots\ldots C^{10}H^{10}+H^2O$$

The dyadides contain dyads in addition to the nucleus.

The monadides contain monads in addition to the nucleus.

The monodyadides contain monads and dyads in addition to the nucleus.

The words monalide, deuteride, tritonide, have reference only to the composition of the monadides, and not to any predictions concerning their nature or functions. Were we to arrange all bodies in this manner, we should have too great a number of small series. But we have a very simple means for reducing this number, by augmenting that of the bodies which enter into each of the series.

Indeed, to every one of the tables, similar to the preceding, we may attach a host of different varieties. For this purpose, we shall be obliged to act in opposition to the general proceeding of chemists; we must unite what they separate, and separate what they unite. We shall imitate the botanists, who arrange in the species *Rose*, the white, the yellow, and the variegated rose, and do not attach any importance to the colours of their petals, though formed of very different chemical compounds; that is to say, that in the matter now under consideration, we shall attach more importance to the number and arrangement, than to the nature of the atoms.

Let us recollect that chlorine, iodine, bromine, fluorine, the nitric residue X, and the nitrous residue Y, may be substituted for hydrogen, and, to a certain extent, fulfill its functions. Consequently, let us take the fundamental nucleus of the preceding table, and let us effect in it various equivalent substitutions; that is to say, let us set free 1, 2, 3, . . . 10, atoms of hydrogen, and replace them by the same number of atoms of chlorine, bromine, iodine, fluorine, X and Y, we shall thus obtain a great number of compounds, which we shall call nuclenides, or *derived nuclei*, and which, we will arrange immediately after the fundamental nucleus.

Let us now introduce into the dyadides, monadides, and monodyadides, these derived nuclei, in the place of their constituent fundamental nucleus; then we shall have a host of derived dyadides, monadides, &c.

Lastly we shall augment considerably the compounds of the same series,—on the one hand, by replacing the hydrogen by metals, in those bodies which are capable of undergoing this kind of transformation, as are the deuterides and tritonides,—and on the other hand, by replacing the oxygen of the monadides and monodyadides by sulphur, selenium, or tellurium.

Our original series, in being thus enlarged, will not become more complicated; it will then present the following appearance:—

$$
\begin{array}{lll}
\multicolumn{3}{c}{\text{Carbhydride}\ldots\ldots\ldots C^{10}H^{10}}
\end{array}
$$

Nuclenides........ $\left\{ \text{Carbhydride}\ldots \left\{ \begin{array}{l} \text{halydo}\ldots\ldots \left\{ \begin{array}{l} C^{10}H^9Cl \\ C^{10}Cl^{10} \\ C^{10}Br^5Cl^5 \end{array} \right. \\ \text{nitro}\ldots\ldots\ldots\; C^{10}H^8X^2 \\ \text{nitroso}\ldots\ldots\ldots\; C^{10}H^9Y \\ \text{halydo-nitro}\ldots\ldots\; C^{10}H^6Cl^3X, \&c. \end{array} \right. \right.$

Dyadides.........
(Hyperhalydes)
$\left\{ \begin{array}{llr} \text{Hyperhydride}\ldots\ldots\ldots\ldots\ldots & C^{10}H^{10} & + H^2 \\ \text{Dihalyde}\ldots\ldots\ldots\ldots\ldots & \left\{ \begin{array}{l} C^{10}H^{10} \\ C^{10}Cl^{10} \end{array} \right. & \begin{array}{r} + Cl^2 \\ + Cl^2 \end{array} \\ \text{Tetrhalyde}\ldots\ldots\ldots\ldots & \left\{ \begin{array}{l} C^{10}H^{10} \\ C^{10}Br^{10} \end{array} \right. & \begin{array}{r} + Cl^4 \\ + Cl^4 \end{array} \\ \text{Hexhalyde}\ldots\ldots\ldots\ldots & \left\{ \begin{array}{l} C^{10}H^{10} \\ C^{10}H^5Cl^5 \\ C^{10}H^4Br^4X^2 \\ C^{10}Cl^3Br^3I^3X \end{array} \right. & \begin{array}{r} + Cl^6 \\ + Cl^6 \\ + Cl^6 \\ + Br^6 \end{array} \end{array} \right.$

Monadides	Monalide	$C^{10}H^{10}$	$+ O$
		$C^{10}Cl^{10}$	$+ O$
		$C^{10}H^{10}$	$+ S$
		$C^{10}Cl^{10}$	$+ S$
	Deuteride	$C^{10}H^{10}$	$+ O^2$
		$C^{10}H^9K$	$+ O^2$
		$C^{10}Cl^9K$	$+ O^2$
		$C^{10}H^8X^2$	$+ O^2$
		$C^{10}H^{10}$	$+ S^2$
	Tritonide	$C^{10}H^{10}$	$+ O^3$
		$C^{10}H^9K$	$+ O^3$
		$C^{10}Cl^8K^2$	$+ O^3$
		$C^{10}H^{10}$	$+ \begin{cases} S \\ O^2 \end{cases}$
		$C^{10}H^{10}$	$+ S^3$
		$C^{10}H^8K^2$	$+ S^3$
Monodyadides	Udolide	$C^{10}H^{10}$	$+ H^2O$
		$C^{10}Cl^{10}$	$+ H^2O$
		$C^{10}H^{10}$	$+ H^2S$
		$C^{10}Cl^{10}$	$+ H^2S$, &c.

This table, we perceive, does not in any way resemble those which are ordinarily employed. It contains 30 or 40 bodies, which, in the system of Berzelius, would be separated from one another, and be distributed in a dozen different classes. If we replace $C^{10}H^{10}$ by C^2H^4, we shall have the compounds of the bi-hydrocarbon series, which comprises Dutch liquid, perchloride of carbon, chloride of acetyl, aldehyde, acetic acid, chloro-acetic acid, alcohol, ether, &c.

Chemists have known, indeed, for a long time past, that the bodies I have just adduced, metamorphose themselves into one another; but, pre-occupied with the theory of radicals, they never thought of associating them in the above described manner. Thus Liebig places alcohol and ether in one class, because he supposes that they both contain the same radical ethyl; whilst aldehyde and acetic acid he places in another class, as both containing acetyl; I do not know where he places the chloro-compounds. Dumas unites in the same class, all the bodies in which he supposes the existence of the compound C^4H^8: hence he includes etherine, Dutch liquid, alcohol, and ether; but he rejects acetic acid, in which he supposes, or did suppose, the atomic arrangement $C^4H^6O^3.H^2O$. He also excludes aldehyde, perchloride of. cargon, &c.

The series $C^{10}H^{10}$, such as I have just represented it, is far from being completed. We do not perceive amides, ethers, amidic acids, nor, in one word, any diamerone; the preceding compounds constitute the *aplones* only. . . .

Charles Gerhardt

(*1816–1856*)

GERHARDT, though a less original thinker than Laurent, was a more able exponent of the ideas which the two men often worked out together. In spite of a dogmatic manner which made him many influential enemies during his life and a tendency to claim as original ideas which had first been put forth by others, Gerhardt did much through his publications to bring about a systematization of chemistry on an essentially modern basis.

His first major reform was his introduction in 1843 of the "two-volume system," in which the atomic weights of volatile compounds agreed with the weights of two volumes of hydrogen instead of four, the standard used by Liebig and other prominent chemists. This resulted in halving the formulas of most organic compounds as written by Liebig and thus producing the formulas which we use today. In essence, this was a return to the atomic weights of Berzelius, but Gerhardt applied the system too rigidly and did not think in terms of atoms. He therefore· continued to write some formulas incorrectly. The two-volume formulas were a step in clearing up the confusion which existed in the minds of the chemists of the period, but it was not until the work of Cannizzaro that this confusion was entirely eliminated.

Gerhardt adopted Laurent's nucleus, or unitary, theory and combined it with the theory of types and radicals. In 1852 he discovered the anhydrides of organic acids and explained their structure by an extension of the water type of Williamson. He further proposed that all organic compounds could be related to one of four inorganic types: water, hydrogen, hydrogen chloride, and ammonia. These types could be used to explain most organic reactions as double decompositions. Since Gerhardt felt that the formulas of organic compounds never expressed the actual structure of the molecule, but only its reactions, he was satisfied with this theory and carried it no farther. However, it was a great advance in systematization and helped to bring order into the confused field of organic reactions.

As with Laurent, Gerhardt's most important book, the fourth volume of his "Traité de chimie organique" (Paris, 1853–1856), was published after his death. In this volume he for the first time wrote organic formulas in terms of the concepts developed by Laurent and himself.

The following selection, taken from his paper on acid anhydrides[1] shows how Gerhardt used his modification of the type theory to clarify and explain the reactions of organic compounds.

To arrange organic compounds in series, that is, to determine the laws according to which the properties in a given type are modified by substi-

[1] *Ann. chim. phys.*, **37** : 285–342 (1853); the selection is taken from pages 336 to 341.

tution of an element or group of elements for other elements, this is the constant purpose of the chemist philosopher. These thousands of compounds which he produces in his laboratory are for him, however, the terms which serve him to construct his series. Today, in the imperfect state of the science, there is still need for many terms; but later, knowledge of certain series will eliminate direct study of many other terms whose properties he will be able to predict with the same certainty as he predicts today the properties of propionic or valeric alcohols, even though he has not yet obtained these alcohols.

In the state of the science, organic compounds can be related to three or four types, each capable of giving series which resemble those represented by formic and stearic acids, potash, and sulfuric acids; these types are

Water...................... H^2O
Hydrogen................ H^2
Hydrochloric acid.......... HCl
Ammonia................. H^3N

By exchanging their hydrogens among certain groups, these types give rise to acids, to alcohols, to ethers, to hydrides, to radicals, to organic chlorides, to acetones, to alkalis.

The series formed by each type has its extremes, which can be called the positive, or left, side and the negative, or right, side. An organic group, substituting for hydrogen, which places itself on the positive side will produce compounds placed on the same side; the groups ethyl CH^3, methyl C^2H^3,* amyl C^5H^{11}, for example, will give by this substitution alcohols resembling water, aldehydes or radicals resembling hydrogen, ethers resembling hydrochloric acid, alkalis resembling ammonia. The groups of which I speak resemble, in fact, potash or other reputedly electropositive metals; the oxides (the alcohols) and the alkalis to which they give rise behave like bases, in that they can combine with acids placed at the other extreme of the series.

Other organic groups, for example cyanogen CN, acetyl C^2H^3O, benzoyl C^7H^5O, on substituting for the hydrogen of the types mentioned give rise to those compounds which are farther removed than the preceding from compounds formed with hydrogen, to compounds which are placed more to the right, toward the negative extreme. The oxides formed by these groups resemble sulfuric acid more than potash. . . .

The *water* type, changing half its hydrogen for a hydrocarbon group CH^3, C^2H^5, etc., gives rise to an alcohol; changing all its hydrogen for a similar group, it produces the corresponding ether.

The same type, in changing half its hydrogen for a group containing at once carbon, hydrogen, and oxygen, produces a hydrated monobasic acid,

* [These are obviously misprints.]

resembling acetic acid. When the substitution is effected by the same group on the two atoms of hydrogen of water, the product is the corresponding acid anhydride; Mr. Williamson has already made the same comparison, and its exactitude seems to me today to be perfectly demonstrated by my experiments. Finally, when the substitution of the two hydrogen atoms of water is made half by a hydrocarbon group like ethyl or methyl and half by an oxygenated group resembling that which is found in a monobasic acid, the ester of this acid is obtained.

The *hydrogen* type can undergo the same substitutions as the water type and produce as many combinations.

The compounds resembling marsh gas, known as *hydrides*, are evidently related to hydrogen as alcohols are to water; the ethyl and methyl radicals correspond to the ethers of these alcohols. Aldehydes are to hydrogen as monobasic acids are to water; acetyl, benzoyl, and other oxygenated radicals correspond to acid anhydrides; the acetones, finally, as M. Chancel has already remarked, represent the esters of the aldehydes and consequently are to hydrogen as the esters of monobasic acids are to water.

The *hydrochloric acid* type gives rise, on the one hand, to hydrochloric ethers, that is, to chlorides resembling chloride of potassium or chlorides of electropositive elements, when the substitution is effected by hydrocarbon groups; and, on the other hand, to electronegative chlorides corresponding to monobasic acids, like acetyl chloride or benzoyl chloride, when the same substitution is effected by groups contained in these monobasic acids.

Finally, the *ammonia* type produces alkalis able to combine with acids, or amides able to combine with bases (oxide of silver, mercury, copper, etc.), according to whether the substitution on the hydrogens of the ammonia is effected by groups which give rise to bases (alcohols, organic oxides), or by groups which produce organic acids. The bodies resembling the hydrate of oxide of ammonia are represented at the other end of the series by acid amides.

It can be seen by this rapid summary how the application of the notion of series permits simplification of the general theory of organic compounds. They no longer terrify by their number and variety, for, instead of being formulated by special theories which lack any connection, as they are called ethers, amides, alkalis, or acids, they become simply terms whose properties can be predicted according to the place they occupy in the series. And what certainly adds to the advantage of such a system is the similarity of method of formation or decomposition which it expresses for all the bodies which it contains. Experiment shows, in fact, that organic compounds are almost all the result of *double decompositions* resembling those which we effect in mineral chemistry.

Robert Wilhelm Bunsen

(1811–1899)

LIKE many of the chemists of the nineteenth century, Bunsen was noted for his versatility. He began his chemical work at a time when the chief interest of most chemists lay in the field of the structure of organic compounds. His first important work lay in this field, the study of the cacodyl compounds (1837 to 1842). These investigations helped to establish the radical theory on a firm basis. Bunsen soon discovered, however, that his real interest lay not in organic chemistry but in a newly developing branch of the science, physical chemistry. His chief investigations in this field were his study with Gustav Robert Kirchhoff[1] (1824–1887) of spectra and spectrum analysis and his work on the chemical behavior of hydrogen and chlorine under the influence of light. These studies were carried out with the English chemist, Henry Enfield Roscoe (1833–1915), and laid the foundation for the science of quantitative photochemistry. The ingenuity of Bunsen in devising new laboratory apparatus was also well illustrated in this study. The photo-chemical studies of Bunsen and Roscoe appeared in the *Annalen der Physik* between 1855 and 1859[2] and were reprinted in the *Philosophical Transactions*.[3] The selection given here was taken from pages 610 to 617 of this English translation.

PHOTO-CHEMICAL RESEARCHES.

PART III. OPTICAL AND CHEMICAL EXTINCTION OF THE CHEMICAL RAYS.

Having determined these preliminary points, we may now return to the question originally proposed, viz.—

In the combination effected by the light between the particles of chlorine and hydrogen, are the chemical rays expended in a relation proportional to the quantity of hydrochloric acid formed? In order to solve this question, it was necessary to determine experimentally the coefficient of extinction of pure chlorine for a flame of coal-gas.

The chlorine used in the following experiments, prepared from bichromate of potash and hydrochloric acid, carefully washed and dried, was

---

[1] See W. F. Magie, "A Source Book in Physics," New York, 1935, p. 354.

[2] Poggendorf's *Annalen der Physik und Chemie*, **96**: 373–394 (1855); **100**:43–88, 481–516 (1857); **101**: 235–263 (1857); **108**: 193–273 (1859). They have been reprinted in "Gesammelte Abhandlungen von Robert Bunsen. Herausgegeben von Wilhelm Ostwald und Max Bodenstein." Leipzig, 1904, 3 vols. (vol. 3, pp. 1–213); and also in Ostwald's *Klassiker*, "R. Bunsen und H. E. Roscoe. Photochemische Untersuchungen (1855–1859). No. 34. Erste Hälfte. No. 38. Zweite Hälfte. Herausgegeben von W. Ostwald," Leipzig, 1892.

[3] *Philosophical Transactions*, **147**: 355–402, 601–620 (1857).

led through the transparent cylinders until all atmospheric air was expelled. Each of the measurements contained in the following Table is reduced from three series of observations, the first of which was made without interposed chlorine-cylinder, the second with chlorine-cylinder, and the third again without the cylinder. The mean of the first and third series gives I_0, or the intensity of the chemical rays before transmission through the chlorine-cylinder, whilst the second series gave I, or the intensity after transmission; h signifies the length of the interposed column of chlorine, P the pressure, and t the temperature on filling the cylinders

SERIES OF EXPERIMENTS VIII.

	Exp. 1.	Exp. 2.	Exp. 3.	Exp. 4.
I_0	13.51	10.86	11.12	11.40
I	3.79	3.25	3.23	6.39
h	83.8 mm.	83.8	83.8	27.4
P	0.7437 m.	0.7528	0.7528	0.7528
t	16°.0C.	14.3	14.3	14.3

with chlorine. The amount of light I_0 is not that which enters the column of chlorine. This amount, according to the former considerations, is that which remains after the quantity lost by passing both the enclosing plates of glass has been subtracted from I_0. I_0 must therefore be multiplied with $a_1 = 0.811$, found from several of the previous experiments, the difference between the coefficients of reflexion between glass and air and glass and chlorine being neglected as imperceptible. The value of $\frac{1}{\alpha}$, which signifies, according to formula (2.)[4], the depth of chlorine to which the chemical rays must penetrate in order to be reduced to one-tenth of their original amount, has been shown by Experiment VII. to vary proportionally with the density of the medium. For chlorine under 0.76 pressure and at 0°C., the value of $\frac{1}{\alpha}$ is found from the equation

$$\frac{1}{\alpha} = \frac{h \cdot P}{0.76(1 + 0.00366t)(\log a_1I_0 - \log I)} \qquad (9.)$$

hence we get from Experiment VIII.

$$\frac{1}{\alpha} = 168 \text{ millims.}$$
$$\text{“} = 182 \text{ millims}$$
$$\text{“} = 177 \text{ millims.}$$
$$\text{“} = 160 \text{ millims.}$$
$$\text{Mean} \ldots 171.7$$

[4][(2.), $\frac{I}{I_0} = (1 - g)^2 10^{-n\alpha}$.]

This mean value 171.7, gives a value of 0.00582 as the coefficient of extinction for chlorine at 0.76 pressure, and 0°C. for the flame of coal gas.

In order to prove experimentally that the coefficient of extinction varies, in the case of chlorine, in the inverse proportion of the dilution, another series of determinations was made in which the chlorine was mixed with varying quantities of atmospheric air. For this purpose, the caoutchouc-tubes, connected with the cylinders previously used, filled with V volumes of chlorine at t°C., and under the pressure P, were secured by screw-clamps, and into the end of one caoutchouc joining a fine capillary tube was fastened, whilst into the other was placed a chloride of calcium drying tube. On opening the screw-clamps, air was forced by the mouth through the drying tube into the chlorine cylinder, whence the gas escaped through the capillary tube into a reversed retort filled with a solution of iodide of potassium, and when sufficient chlorine had been expelled the screw-clamps were again closed. The volume of chlorine expelled, reduced to 0°C. and 0.76 pressure, was determined by volumetric analysis, and this volume subtracted from that originally contained, also reduced to 0°C. and 0.76 pressure, gave the volume V_1 remaining in the cylinder mixed with air. If H represent the depth of the cylinder, measured from the inner surface of one glass plate to the inner surface of the other, and h_1 represent the length of the column of chlorine before displacement,

$$h_1 = \frac{H \cdot P}{0.76(1 + 0.00366t)},$$

and after displacement,

$$h_2 = \frac{V_1}{V} H.$$

These various columns of chlorine, h_1 h_2, both of which were expanded to the height H in the cylinder, were placed between the source of light and the insolation-vessel, and from the diminution of the action from I_0 to I, the values of $\frac{1}{\alpha}$ were calculated as in the previous instance. Chlorine was again expelled from the cylinder into the reversed retort, the cylinder again placed between the flame and the instrument, the values of I_0 and I again determined, and this repeated until the whole of the chlorine had been displaced. The agreement of the sum of all the separate determinations of chlorine with the total quantity introduced, served as a control for the accuracy of the analyses. . . .

[Experimental data omitted.]

Hence it is seen that the sum of the quantities found in each analysis agrees with the quantity originally taken, 176.24, as nearly as could be expected, considering the number of analyses made. From these numbers the values of h are obtained, that is, the length which the columns of gas would have been, had they been unmixed with air and measured at 0°C. and 0.76 pressure.

1. Height of the total quantity of chlorine .... 77.6 millims.
2. Height after displacement of first portion .... 56.2 millims.
3. Height after displacement of second portion .... 43.6 millims.
4. Height after displacement of third portion .... 32.2 millims.

The photometric observations with these columns of chlorine, all of which were expanded to a height of 77.6 millims. by dilution with air, gave

SERIES OF EXPERIMENTS X.

	Exp. 1.	Exp. 2.	Exp. 3.	Exp. 4.	Exp. 5.	Exp. 6.
I_0	8.45	10.93	11.13	11.10	11.39	10.65
I	2.53	3.35	4.39	4.15	5.16	5.51
h	77.6	77.6	56.1	56.1	43.6	32.2

The values of $\frac{1}{\alpha}$, calculated from these experiments, are—

No. of
Expt.
1.   179 millims.
2.   184 millims.
3.   179 millims.
4.   167 millims.
5.   172 millims.
6.   165 millims.
Mean .... 174.3 millims.

This mean value agrees very closely with that found from the experiments with chlorine undiluted with air, but it is seen that the variation in the separate values is not inconsiderable. The cause of this lies not only in the unavoidable errors of experiment, but more especially in the fact that the formula used in the calculation is, strictly speaking, only applicable to homogeneous light, whilst the chemically active rays emanating from our coal-gas flame were certainly not all of the same degree of refrangibility. If the intensity I_0 of the light, measured by our instrument, were composed of the components $I_1 + I_2 + \text{----}$ of various degrees of refrangibility, the formula $I = I_0 10^{-h\alpha}$ would become $I = I_1 10^{-h\alpha_1} + I_2 10^{-h\alpha_2} +$ . . . . The values calculated according to the first formula can therefore only give a mean value for the various chemical rays in our flame, and the numbers obtained must vary more considerably amongst themselves than if homogeneous light had been employed. The mean of all the determinations in series VIII. and X. gives the value of the optical coefficient of extinction of chlorine at 0°C. and 0.76 pressure, for rays from a coal-gas flame, to be $1/173.0 = 0.00578$.

If the light is not consumed in the act of photo-chemical change, the coefficient just found must remain unaltered when the chlorine and hydrogen mixture is employed; but if, on the contrary, light is not only lost by the optical extinction, but also an amount of light proportional to the chemical action vanishes, experiment must give a larger value for the coefficient. In the first case, the light merely liberates the chemical forces, in the second it suffers a transformation into mechanical energy, effecting the combination of the chlorine and hydrogen. It would seem as if the simplest mode of arriving at a conclusion regarding these two alternatives, were to determine the coefficient of extinction for chlorine and hydrogen, by interposition of the transparent cylinders filled with the mixture: this plan, however, is accompanied by the unavoidable error arising from the impossibility of ascertaining when the mixture under examination has arrived at the point of maximum photo-chemical sensibility. We have therefore preferred to deduce the coefficient of extinction for chlorine and hydrogen directly from the chemical actions effected by a constant amount of light in columns of sensitive gas of various lengths. . . .

[Modification of apparatus described here is omitted.]

From the following considerations, it is seen that in order to obtain the value of α_1, the coefficient of extinction in the chlorine-hydrogen mixture, a determination of the chemical actions W and W_1, in two columns of gas of different lengths h and h_1, is sufficient. Let I_0 represent the intensity of the light on entrance into the gaseous mixture, I the intensity remaining after it has passed through a length z of gas, we have then, according to the former equation $I = I_0 10^{-\alpha_1 z}$, in which α_1 signifies the coefficient of extinction of the unreduced chlorine mixture. If, also, Wdz represents the chemical action effected in the unit of time in a film of gas of the thickness dz, we have $W = NI$ where N signifies a constant, and therefore $W = NI_0 10^{-\alpha_1 z}$. If h is the whole depth of the insolated column of gas, and W the total action occurring therein, we have

$$W = \frac{NI_0}{\alpha_1 \log \text{nat } 10} (1 - 10^{-\alpha_1 h});$$

or more simply

$$W = MI_0(1 - 10^{-\alpha_1 h}).$$

For W_1 and h_1 we get, similarly,

$$W_1 = MI_0(1 - 10^{-\alpha_1 h_1});$$

hence

$$\frac{W}{W_1} = \frac{1 - \dfrac{1}{\text{num. log} = \alpha_1 h}}{1 - \dfrac{1}{\text{num. log} = \alpha_1 h_1}}.$$

The value of α_1 is obtained from this equation by a method of approximation.

Experiments conducted in this manner at 23°.3 C., and under a pressure of 0.7589 millims., gave the following elements for the calculation of the values of $\dfrac{1}{\alpha_1}$ contained in the fifth column. Each value of W and W_1 is the mean of from ten to fifteen observations.

SERIES OF EXPERIMENTS XI.

W_1.	W.	h_1.	h.	$\dfrac{1}{\alpha_1}$.
				millims.
20.97	4.46	194.5	21.5	256
19.38	11.17	193.8	65.5	216
16.26	10.26	114.7	60.9	316
12.34	6.73	153.0	58.6	262
Mean.............................				262

Had the insolated chlorine and hydrogen mixture possessed the density corresponding to 0°C. and 0.76 pressure, and if it had been perfectly dry, the length $\dfrac{1}{\alpha_1} = 262$ would have diminished, for we have shown that the amount of light absorbed is proportional to the density of the absorbing medium. In a pure, dry mixture of equal volumes of chlorine and hydrogen, having a density corresponding to 0°C. and 0.76 pressure, the length of a column of gas through which the light must pass in order to be reduced by optical and chemical extinction to $\frac{1}{10}$th of its original amount, is $\dfrac{1}{\alpha_2} = 234$ millims. Supposing that the hydrogen were replaced by an equal volume of a chemically inactive gas, which, like hydrogen, does not absorb any chemical rays, we should obtain from the coefficient of extinction of pure chlorine $\frac{1}{173}$, a length of the gaseous mixture equal to 2×173 or 346 millims., through which the light would have to pass in order that it should be reduced to $\frac{1}{10}$th. Hence it is seen that for a given amount of chemical action effected in the mixture of chlorine and hydrogen, an equivalent quantity of light is absorbed. For we find that in the standard chlorine and hydrogen mixture, where, together with the thermal effect, a chemical action of light occurs, the value of the coefficient of extinction is 0.00427; whereas in a chlorine mixture of similar dilution, where the chemical action was absent, the coefficient was 0.00289, or very much smaller.

The difference between these two numbers, 0.00138, represents the coefficient of extinction due to chemical action alone. The consumption of rays from a coal-gas flame, solely employed in the act of photo-chemical combination, is hence represented by an amount of light which is reduced to $\frac{1}{10}$th by passing through 723 millims. of the standard chlorine mixture, whilst in consequence of optical extinction alone, the light is reduced to $\frac{1}{10}$th by passing through 346.6 of the same standard mixture.

Hermann Kopp

(1817–1892)

ALTHOUGH Hermann Kopp is best known for his work in the history of chemistry, he also conducted many investigations which helped to lay the foundation of physical chemistry. His work on atomic and molecular volumes, crystallography, boiling points, and specific heats was almost all directed toward the goal of finding relations between physical properties and chemical constitution in inorganic and organic compounds. This work began in 1842[1] but at this time Kopp was limited by the small amount of data available for physical properties. He therefore spent ten years in careful investigation of such properties, determining particularly boiling points and specific volumes of organic compounds. From these studies he was able to establish a number of important generalizations. His results were published in detail in 1855 and 1856[2] and his conclusions summarized in a short report to the French Academy of Sciences.[3] The following extract is taken from pages 186 and 187 of this report.

I find that the laws which I long ago formulated for the boiling points of several series of compounds have been confirmed. Thus, for example, there are the following propositions:

1. An alcohol containing x C_2H_2* more or less in its formula than vinic [ethyl] alcohol $C_4H_6O_2$, boils at a temperature greater or less than $x \times 19$ degrees from the boiling point of vinic alcohol.

---

[1] Annalen der Chemie, **41**: 79–89 (1842).
[2] Ibid., **96**: 1–36, 153–185, 303–335 (1855); **100**: 19–38 (1856).
[3] Compt. rend., **41**: 186–190 (1855).
* [I.e., CH_2. As he states later, Kopp used equivalents instead of atomic weights.]

2. The boiling point of an acid $C_nH_nO_4$ is 40 degrees higher than the boiling point of the corresponding alcohol $C_nH_{n+2}O_2$.

3. The boiling point of an ether $C_nH_nO_4$ is 82 degrees lower than the boiling point of the isomeric acid $C_nH_nO_4$.

The propositions, I say, show the boiling points of a very considerable number of liquids to be in satisfactory agreement with the observations. Today I can compare the results of experiment and the special consequences of these propositions for six alcohols (between $C_2H_4O_2$ and $C_{32}H_{34}O_2$), for the corresponding acids $C_nH_nO_4$, and for a great many ethers. I will discuss similar laws for other series of compounds; the frequent agreement of experiment with the rule that various analogous compounds with x C_2H_2 in their formulas have boiling points differing by $x \times 19$; the cases where this rule is only apparently defective and where conclusions can be drawn as to the chemical constitution of the bodies being compared; and finally, the case where the results of the experiment are really not in accord with this rule, and the causes of this anomaly.

The influence which the chemical composition exerts on the density of liquids is most clearly manifest (as I long ago showed) in the volumes occupied by chemically equivalent quantities, that is to say, specific volumes; the specific volumes should be compared at the temperatures of equal vapor pressure of the respective fluids. In what follows, the specific volumes are referred to the equivalents $C = 6$, $H = 1$, $O = 8$, $S = 16$, $Cl = 35.5$, $Br = 80$, $I = 127.1$ (the volume occupied by $H_2O_2 = 18$ parts of water is taken $= 18$ at $0°$) and, moreover, are *always at the boiling point* of the respective fluids.

By a great number of comparisons, I find the results which I had previously obtained are confirmed, notably

1. For analogous compounds, the differences of specific volumes are proportional to the differences of the formulas. Two compounds differing in their formulas by x C_2H_2 have specific volumes differing by about $x \times 22$.

2. Isomeric liquids have the same specific volume.

3. The comparison of liquids, one of which contains oxygen in the place where the other has an equivalent amount of hydrogen, has again shown that in this substitution, the volume remains nearly the same. Previously, when I could compare only a relatively limited number of substances belonging to this type, I had believed that in this case the volume did not change at all; at present, I can compare a much greater number of substances, and I believe I can conclude that the substitution of oxygen in place of hydrogen causes an increase in volume, although a very small one.

4. In comparing liquids, one of which contains carbon in place of an equivalent amount of hydrogen in the other, I find equality of volume,

and, for a great number of comparisons, the results are so concordant that there remains no doubt: carbon in liquid compounds can replace hydrogen without change of volume.

The rest of the memoir gives details for specific types of compounds.

Charles Adolphe Wurtz

(1817–1884)

WURTZ was responsible for the investigation of a number of organic reactions and the systematic study of many classes of organic compounds. His advocacy of the ideas of Gerhardt was influential in publicizing these important concepts. He is most noted for his investigation of glycols and for his discovery of the amines. The latter discovery in 1849 was very significant at the time, for it suggested the possibility of a new type, the ammonia type, which helped to explain the behavior of nitrogenous compounds. Wurtz himself recognized this possibility, but he did not carry the development of the idea very far. The studies of Hofmann explained the chemistry of the amines in detail and permitted the full recognition of the value of the ammonia type, which Gerhardt then used in his general systematization.

The following selection is taken from the paper "Sur une série d'alcalis organiques homologues avec l'ammoniaque"[1] and describes the original preparation of the amines and the significance which Wurtz attached to them.

The history of the ammoniacal compounds, so complete and so important from the point of view of chemical theory, forms in some sort a transition between mineral chemistry and organic chemistry. Certainly ammonia should be regarded as the simplest and the most powerful of organic bases; for all chemists it should be the type of this numerous class of bodies, if it were not for one characteristic, important certainly, but one to which, perhaps, an exaggerated value has been attributed. Ammonia does not contain carbon.

It seems that this difference of composition does not suffice to separate ammonia from organic bases. Actually, I have succeeded in preparing from this alkali a true organic compound by adding to it the elements of carburetted hydrogen, C^2H^2 or C^4H^4, without causing it to lose by this its character as a powerful base nor even its more outstanding properties, as, for example, its odor.

By adding to the elements of ammonia, AzH^3, the elements of an equiv-

[1] *Compt. rend.*, **28**: 223–226 (1849).

alent of methylene, we obtain the compound C^2H^5Az, which can be called methyl ammonia.

If we unite ammonia to the elements of etherine, C^4H^4, we obtain the compound C^4H^7Az, which will be ethyl ammonia.

The combinations C^2H^5Az and C^4H^7Az can be viewed as methyl ether C^2H^3O and ordinary ether C^4H^5O, in which the equivalent of oxygen will be replaced by one equivalent of amidogen AzH^2, or as ammonia, in which one equivalent of hydrogen is replaced by methylium C^2H^3 or ethylium C^4H^5. The following formulas show the relations which exist between these bodies and ammonia itself:

H^3Az, ammonia .... AzH^2,H, *hydramide*
C^2H^5Az, methyl ammonia .... AzH^2,C^2H^3, *methylamide*
C^4H^7Az, ethyl ammonia .... AzH^2,C^4H^5, *ethylamide*

To designate these new bases, I prefer the words *methylamide* and *ethylamide*.

I should limit myself today to indicating the circumstances in which these bodies are produced and to communicating the results of some analyses which establish their composition in a decisive manner. The methylamide and the ethylamide are produced in three different ways: by the action of potassia on the *cyanic ethers;* by the action of potassia on the *cyanuric ethers;* by the action of potassia on the *ureas.*

Some formulas will show these reactions in a precise manner.

$$C^2AzO,HO + 2KO + 2HO = 2CO^2,KO + H^3Az$$
cyanic acid · · · · · · · · · · · · · · · · · carbonate · ammonia
· of potash
$$C^2AzO,C^2H^3O + 2KO + 2HO = 2CO^2,KO + C^2H^5Az$$
cyanate of · · · · · · · · · · · · · · · · · · · methylamide
methylene
$$C^2AzO,C^4H^5O + 2KO + 2HO = 2CO^2,KO + C^4H^7Az$$
cyanic ether · · · · · · · · · · · · · · · · · · ethylamide

Cyanuric acid and the cyanuric ethers being isomeric with the cyanic compounds, it suffices to multiply the preceding formulas by 3 to explain the second method of formation of methylamide and ethylamide.

As to the ureas, here is how they give rise to these bases:

$$C^2H^4Az^2O^2 + 2KO + 2HO = 2CO^2,KO + H^3Az + H^3Az$$
ordinary urea
$$C^4H^6Az^2O^2 + 2KO + 2HO = 2CO^2,KO + H^3Az + C^2H^5Az$$
acetic urea
$$C^6H^8Az^2O^2 + 2KO + 2HO = 2CO^2,KO + H^3Az + C^4H^7Az$$
metacetic urea

August Wilhelm von Hofmann

(1818–1892)

HOFMANN was a brilliant organic chemist, as he showed by his important work on dyes and alkaloids; he was also an outstanding organizer (he founded the German Chemical Society) who did much by his lectures to give chemistry a higher position, both in England and in Germany. The work by which he did most to further the advancement of the theory of organic structure, however, was his demonstration of the true nature of amines. Wurtz had shown the existence of methyl and ethyl amines and had suggested that they might be regarded as derivatives of ammonia. Hofmann proved this in a detailed study, in which he showed that all the hydrogens of ammonia, and even of the ammonium radical, could be replaced by organic groups to give primary, secondary, and tertiary amines, and quarternary ammonium compounds. In the course of this work, he also cleared up the relation between ammonia and the ammonium radical which had long troubled chemists. The investigation was carried out in 1850, at a time when the type theory was foremost in the minds of organic chemists. It was therefore natural that Hofmann should formulate his new compounds as representatives of the "ammonia type." The formulas which he wrote, however, scarcely differ from those used today. These clear examples of three or five groups attached to a nitrogen atom helped Frankland in developing his theory of variable valence.

The work of Hofmann was published in the *Philosophical Transactions* of the Royal Society in 1850 and 1851, under the title, "Researches into the Molecular Constitution of the Organic Bases." The following selection is taken from the *Philosophical Transactions* for 1851, pages 392 to 397.

The preceding researches show that the action of the bromides and iodides of the alcohol radicals upon ammonia, gives rise to the formation of not less than four distinct groups of organic bases. Of these the members of three groups, corresponding to ammonia (H_3N), are volatile, while those of the fourth, corresponding to oxide of ammonium (H_4NO), cannot be volatilized without decomposition. The facility with which the members of this last class arise from those of the preceding ones, and the readiness with which their reconversion is effected, renders the former group as it were the connecting link between the volatile and the non-volatile organic alkaloids. . . .

In conclusion, it may not be out of place to consider how far the preceding researches affect the received views regarding the constitution of the ammonia-salts. Without reproducing all the arguments brought forward by the supporters of the various theories, we may remember that, irrespective of the impossibility of isolating ammonium itself, the instability of its oxide has been advanced as one of the most important objections against the assumption of the ammonium-theory as originally suggested by AMPÈRE, and subsequently elaborated by BERZELIUS. It deserves to be noticed that BERZELIUS expressly states that he considers the solution of ammonia-gas in water as a solution of the hydrated oxide of ammonium.

This idea, which is but a logical conclusion from the generalization of the facts, is discountenanced to a certain extent by the chemical and physical character of this solution. Everybody knows that, even at the common temperature, this liquid splits again into water and ammonia, while it still exhibits the character of the latter in so marked a manner, as almost to preclude the idea that it had undergone as essential a change as the transformation into oxide of ammonium necessarily must be. Under these circumstances, some interest is attached to the discovery of a series of compound bases, corresponding in their composition to hydrated oxide of ammonium, from which they differ only by containing methyl, ethyl, and amyl in the place of hydrogen, and exhibiting a deportment which agrees much better with the anticipated character of such compounds as suggested by analogy. Here we find a very marked difference between the properties of the compound ammonia, and those of the ammonium-oxide belonging to it; in the latter, we observe no longer any feature which could possibly betray the presence of the former; all their habits, volatility, odour, taste, &c. are totally changed; there is a difference between the two groups which is not inferior to that between ammonia and potassia. The solutions of the new oxides may be boiled for hours without the slightest quantity of the corresponding ammonia being disengaged; several of these oxides, containing more or less water of constitution or crystallization, may actually be obtained in the dry state. It is evident that the arguments mentioned above, as adduced in refutation of the ammonium-theory, cannot well be raised against the compound ammoniums. But who could deny the parallelism of these substances with the Berzelian type—with the oxide of ammonium?

Again, many have found it difficult to conceive, that in the combination of ammonia with hydrochloric or hydrobromic acid, the hydrogen of the latter should leave the chlorine and bromine, for which it is known to possess so powerful an affinity, in order to unite with ammonia converting it into ammonium. And they were the less inclined to admit of such a disposition of the elements, as every day's experience showed that the alleged chloride or bromide of ammonium was incapable of exchanging oxygen for chlorine or bromine, without losing the additional equivalent of hydrogen again in the form of water. In other terms, the decomposition of salammoniac, by lime, into chloride of calcium, ammonia-gas and water, induced them to consider this salt as a compound of ammonia and hydrochloric acid; for in the conception of the ammonium-theory we should have to assume in this decomposition *two* consecutive changes, the transformation of the chloride into oxide, and the subsequent splitting of the latter into ammoniacal gas and water. I readily admit that the latter view is less simple, but I am inclined to think that this slight inconvenience is altogether overruled by the general advantage of the ammonium-theory, especially for the purposes of instruction; by the facility with which it accounts for all phenomena of transposition and substitution, and by the simple explanation it gives of the isomorphism of the potassium- and ammonium-compounds, which will always be the firmest foundation of this theory. On the other hand, we have to enquire which of the two views comes nearest the truth, and here a comparative consideration of the deportment exhibited by the compound ammoniums may be of some interest. In many respects their properties are more clearly pronounced; and their behaviour is explicit and unequivocal in those very points in which the typical ammonium leaves room for speculation. In the combination of triethylamine with bromide or iodide of ethyl, it is no longer a matter of doubt whether the ethyl leaves the iodine in order to unite more intimately with the triethylamine, for we see that the new iodide thus produced is capable of exchanging its iodine for oxygen without the newly-formed oxide suffering immediate decomposition, as is the case with oxide of ammonium. On the contrary, we find this new oxide endowed with remarkable stability; although under the influence of heat it is liable to the same change which befalls the oxide of ammonium, its corresponding ammonia being reproduced. Here then, in the decomposition of iodide of triethylammonium by metallic oxides, we are obliged by irresistible evidence to acknowledge those very two stages, the assumption of which in the analogous change of iodide of ammonium appeared to us deficient in simplicity and probability.

The conception of ammonium does not in any way imply the notion that the different hydrogen-atoms united with nitrogen in the molecule of the compound metal, retain their positions in the molecular system with equal persistency. We are forced by unequivocal facts to admit that the fourth atom of hydrogen is in a peculiar state of mobility, and it is on the facility with which this fourth atom is dislodged from its position that one of the foundations of the ammonia-theory rests. In the compound ammoniums the mobility of the fourth atom of hydrogen, or the hydrocarbon replacing it, still prevails, although less so than in the type itself. The decomposition of the ammonium bases under the influence of heat is particularly instructive in this respect; oxide of tetraethylammonium loses the fourth equivalent of ethyl in the form of olefiant gas and water; and this deportment might be graphically indicated by writing the formula of this compound in accordance with the ammonia theory, namely, thus—

$$\left.\begin{array}{l} C_4H_5 \\ C_4H_5 \\ C_4H_5 \end{array}\right\} N, C_4H_5O.$$

The iodide accordingly would be represented by the formula

$$\left.\begin{array}{l} C_4H_5 \\ C_4H_5 \\ C_4H_5 \end{array}\right\} N, C_4H_5I,$$

an expression which is moreover in perfect harmony with the mode in which this compound is produced, namely, by the direct union of iodide of ethyl with triethylamine.

But now we combine the triethylamine with iodide of amyl, whereby the iodide

$$\left.\begin{array}{l} C_4H_5 \\ C_4H_5 \\ C_4H_5 \end{array}\right\} N, C_{10}H_{11}I$$

is formed, which, as we have seen in the preceding pages, may be converted without difficulty into the corresponding oxide; this oxide however, cannot possibly be considered as

$$\left.\begin{array}{l} C_4H_5 \\ C_4H_5 \\ C_4H_5 \end{array}\right\} N, C_{10}H_{11}O,$$

for the disengagement of olefiant gas under the influence of heat proves to us that it is an ethyl-atom which in the compound occupies the supplemental position, if I may so call it, as represented in the formula

$$\left.\begin{array}{l} C_4H_5 \\ C_4H_5 \\ C_{10}H_{11} \end{array}\right\} N, C_4H_5O,$$

and that the iodide, which is not likely to differ in its constitution from the oxide, has likewise to be represented by the formula

$$\left.\begin{array}{l} C_4H_5 \\ C_4H_5 \\ C_{10}H_{11} \end{array}\right\} N, C_4H_5I.$$

The preceding considerations clearly show, that, whatever the actual disposition of the molecules in ammonium or its congeners may be, the atoms rearrange themselves whenever the fourth equivalent of hydrogen, or of its substitute, joins the compound.

This re-arrangement, so evident in the ammonium-bases, containing various hydrocarbons, may be traced moreover in the lower ethyl-bases in a very obvious manner. For as long as there is any basic hydrogen present in the ammonia-skeleton, this hydrogen assumes what I have previously called the supplemental position, whenever the ammonia passes into the state of ammonium by the accession of a radical. Bromide of ethylammonium formed by the combination of ammonia with bromide of ethyl, when decomposed by a metallic oxide, yields ethylammonia, water and a metallic bromide, the oxide of ethylammonium formed in the first instance being decomposed like oxide of ammonium itself. It is this very transposition which we are in the habit of representing by the equation

$$H_3N + C_4H_5Br = C_4H_5,H_2N,HBr.$$

. . . In the preceding pages I have stated some of the reasons which induced me to adopt the idea of an ammonium for the new class of compounds which I have had the honour to place before the Royal Society in the present memoir. I need scarcely mention, that such a step involves as a matter of necessity the assumption of a similar view for all the lower bases which form part of this investigation. It would be inconsistent to speak any longer of hydrochlorate of ethylamine, of hydrobromate of diethylamine, &c.; these salts have henceforward to be called chloride of ethylammonium, bromide of diethylammonium, &c., these compounds being nothing but intermediate substitution-terms between the type and the last derivative. On considering the various chlorides from this point of view, we arrive at the following series:—

chloride of ammonium $\quad\quad\quad H_4$ N Cl.

chloride of ethylammonium $\quad\quad \begin{Bmatrix} H_3 \\ C_4H_5 \end{Bmatrix}$ N Cl.

chloride of diethylammonium $\quad \begin{Bmatrix} H_2 \\ (C_4H_5)_2 \end{Bmatrix}$ N Cl.

chloride of triethylammonium $\quad \begin{Bmatrix} H \\ (C_4H_5)_3 \end{Bmatrix}$ N Cl.

chloride of tetraethylammonium $(C_4H_5)_4$ N Cl.

Hermann Kolbe

(1818–1884)

IN 1850 the type theory of organic structure had forced the older idea of radicals into the background. At almost the same time, however, Kolbe had electrolyzed potassium acetate (1849) and produced a gas which he called "the free methyl radical" (really ethane). During the next few years, Edward Frankland isolated a number of hydrocarbons which he believed to be free radicals, although these were actually saturated hydrocarbons with twice the molecular weight of the assumed radicals. Under these circumstances, Kolbe modified the type theory by recognizing the individuality of the radicals which entered into the type (the "newer type theory"). Kolbe continued to use equivalents instead of atomic weights until 1870, and therefore he wrote methyl as C_2H_3, and in fact, wherever we now write C, he wrote C_2 as an inseparable unit. Thus his formulas at first glance appear strange, yet he gradually built up a method of writing them which embodied most of the essentials of the modern structural system and which permitted him to explain reactions and predict new compounds almost as easily as can be done today. Unfortunately, he seldom accepted the views of other investigators and bitterly criticized the much simpler formulas of Kekulé when they were introduced. Kolbe's work, however, was a great advance in explaining the true nature of organic compounds.

The selections given below illustrate three stages in the development of his ideas. The first shows his recognition of the essential nature of the acetyl group as CH_3C united to oxygen or other atoms, although he expressed this union in terms of the copula theory of Berzelius. In the second selection he shows that carboxylic acids can be considered as derivatives of carbonic acid (which he wrote $2HO,C_2O_4$) in which a hydrogen and two equivalents of oxygen are replaced by an alkyl radical. In conformity with this, he wrote acetic acid as $HO (C_2H_3) C_2O_3$. This is actually a recognition of the existence of a special group, carboxyl, in the fatty acids. Since he recognized the difference of the oxygen in the HO group from that in the C_2O_3 group, he was able to explain the occurrence of aldehydes and ketones and still later, as shown in the third selection, to explain the nature of alcohols and predict the existence and properties of secondary and tertiary alcohols. These substances were prepared soon afterward by Charles Friedel (1832–1899) and Alexander Butlerov (1828–1886).[1]

[1] See Ostwald's *Klassiker*, No. 92, "H. Kolbe, Ueber den natürlichen Zusammenhang der organischen mit den unorganischen Verbindungen, die wissenschaftliche Grundlage zu einer naturgemässen Klassifikation der organischen chemischen Körper. Herausgegeben von Ernst von Meyer," Leipzig, 1897.

THE CHEMICAL CONSTITUTION AND NATURE OF ORGANIC RADICALS[2]

If, then, we believe less firmly in the unchangeability of organic radicals, still another hypothesis of the chemical constitution of acetic acid and acetyl compounds generally, one very similar to the previous ones, may serve. It shares the advantage of the other, without at the same time being burdened with its disadvantages. This hypothesis is *that in acetyl compounds there actually exists an acetyl radical, but that this cannot, as before, be considered an atom complex composed of four equivalents of carbon and three equivalents of hydrogen, whose four carbon equivalents have equal functions, that it is much more likely to be composed of two equivalents of carbon, with methyl as the copula:*

$$acetyl = (C_2H_3)C_2,$$

in which C_2 serves exclusively as the point of attack of the binding power of oxygen, chlorine, etc.

Kolbe demonstrates in the following citation that carboxylic acids can be considered as derivatives of carbonic acid.

THE RATIONAL COMPOSITION OF FATTY AND AROMATIC ACIDS, ALDEHYDES, ACETONES, ETC., AND THEIR RELATION TO CARBONIC ACID[3]

The preceding considerations led us to the idea that in carbonic acid also, in a similar way, single oxygen atoms could be replaced by hydrogen and ether radicals. If we think that in C_2O_4 an atom of oxygen is exchanged for hydrogen, methyl, ethyl, etc., the fatty acids result. In the same way, acids of the series HO, $C_xH_{x-3}O_3$ (acrylic acid, etc.) result, and further, the so-called "aromatic acids" (benzoic acid, etc.) and other monobasic acids of composition analogous to the carbonic acids are deduced. The question of whether these acids actually stand in the same relation to carbonic acid as does methyl dithionic acid to sulfuric acid, cacodylic acid to arsenic acid, or ethyl tin oxide to tin oxide, is clearly important enough to be given a careful test.

Even if we disregard the mass of known facts concerning the structure and chemical properties of fatty and aromatic acids, which are exceedingly favorable evidence for this view, we still have indications of its correctness if we can produce these acids directly from carbonic acid. We are proceding in this direction in our studies of formation of organic compounds from carbonic acid, chlorocarbonic acid, thiocarbonic acid, and other simple inorganic substances. We have been busy for a long time carrying these out, and we hope soon to be able to communicate the results.

[2] *Annalen der Chemie*, **75**: 211–239 (1850); the selection is taken from page 216.
[3] *Ibid.*, **101**: 257–265 (1857); the selection is taken from pages 262 to 264.

We might find space here for some observations on other classes of bodies which we believe stand in the same relation to carbonic acid as the above acids. As an explanation of the following formulas I mention that we place the chemical symbols of the positive elements which substitute for an oxygen atom in inorganic oxygen compounds always on the left of the symbol for the radical of the inorganic oxide.

We write the formula of dimethyl arsenic acid $HO,(C_2H_3)_2AsO_3$ (not $HO,As \begin{cases} (C_2H_3)_2 \\ O_3 \end{cases}$) and keep, correspondingly, for methyl carbonic acid (acetic acid) the former formula $HO,(C_2H_3)C_2O_3$, since we believe that clarity is attained by this formula.

We are of the opinion that in carbonic acid C_2O_4 still a second oxygen atom can be replaced by a positive radical, by which, since it follows on the replacement of the first oxygen atom of the dibasic carbonic acid to give a monobasic acid, an indifferent body now results. If hydrogen is the second element substituting for the oxygen atom, an aldehyde results; if in the same way as before, an ether radical substitutes, the carbonic acid forms an acetone.

There derive from the dibasic

$2HO,C_2O_4$ carbonic acid

monobasic acids	aldehydes	acetones
$HO,(C_2H_3)C_2O_3$	$\left.\begin{array}{c} C_2H_3 \\ H \end{array}\right\} C_2O_2$	$\left.\begin{array}{c} C_2H_3 \\ C_2H_3 \end{array}\right\} C_2O_2$
methyl carbonic acid (acetic acid)	methyl hydrocarbon monoxide (aldehyde)	dimethyl carbon monoxide (acetone)
$HO,(C_{12}H_5)C_2O_3$	$\left.\begin{array}{c} C_{12}H_5 \\ H \end{array}\right\} C_2O_2$	$\left.\begin{array}{c} C_{12}H_5 \\ C_{12}H_5 \end{array}\right\} C_2O_2$
phenyl carbonic acid (benzoic acid) etc.	phenyl hydrocarbon monoxide (benzyl hydride) etc.	diphenylcarbon monoxide (benzophenone) etc.

In the selection below, Kolbe explains the nature of alcohols and predicts the existence and properties of secondary and tertiary alcohols.

THE NATURAL RELATION OF ORGANIC AND INORGANIC COMPOUNDS, THE SCIENTIFIC BASIS FOR A NATURAL CLASSIFICATION OF ORGANIC CHEMICAL BODIES[4]

If we consider the formula by which I have previously expressed the rational composition of acetic acid, the aldehyde related to it, and alcohol, namely,

$HO,(C_2H_3)[C_2O_2],O$ acetic acid

$\left.\begin{array}{c} C_2H_3 \\ H \end{array}\right\} [C_2O_2]$ aldehyde

$HO. \left\{\begin{array}{c} C_2H_3 \\ H_2 \end{array}\right\} C_2,O$ alcohol

[4] *Ibid.*, **113**: 293–332 (1860); the selection is taken from pages 305 to 308.

we immediately see how it happens that of the five hydrogen atoms in the ethyl oxide of the alcohol, when the latter is oxidized, only two atoms of hydrogen, and in aldehyde only one atom of hydrogen, are substituted. Only the independent hydrogen atoms in alcohol and aldehyde undergo the oxidizing effect, and they serve much more easily as the points of attack for the oxygen than do the other hydrogen atoms which are more firmly held in the methyl radical.

This explanation of the chemical constitution of alcohols opens for us the possibility of the discovery of new, still unknown alcohols, as well as a new class of bodies which, closely related to the alcohols in composition, can share many properties with them, yet in many obvious ways must have different properties.

As soon as we have the means of changing all alcohol acids into aldehydes and alcohols by direct introduction of one or two atoms of hydrogen in the place of even as much as one oxygen atom, we will obviously also succeed in obtaining from these acids aldehydes and alcohols which, like amino acetic acid, hydroxyacetic acid, etc., are simple derivatives of the primary acid. The relations in composition of the formulas concerned will best illustrate these similarities (see these *Annals*, **109**, 267).

$$\underbrace{HO.(C_2H_3)[C_2O_2],O}_{\text{acetic acid}} \qquad \underset{\substack{\text{acetic acid}\\\text{aldehyde}}}{\left.\begin{matrix}C_2H_3\\H\end{matrix}\right\}[C_2O_2]} \qquad \underbrace{HO.\left\{\begin{matrix}C_2H_3\\H_2\end{matrix}\right\}C_2,\,O}_{\text{alcohol}}$$

$$\underbrace{HO.\left(C_2\left\{\begin{matrix}H_2\\H_2N\end{matrix}\right\}\right)[C_2O_2],O}_{\text{aminoacetic acid}} \qquad \underset{\substack{\text{aldehyde of}\\\text{aminoacetic acid}}}{\left(C_2\left\{\begin{matrix}H_2\\H_2N\end{matrix}\right\}\right)\left.\begin{matrix}\\H\end{matrix}\right\}[C_2O_2]} \qquad \underbrace{HO.\left(C_2\left\{\begin{matrix}H_2\\H_2N\end{matrix}\right\}\right)C_2,\,O}_{\substack{\text{alcohol of}\\\text{aminoacetic acid}}}$$

$$\underbrace{HO.\left(C_2\left\{\begin{matrix}H_2\\HO_2\end{matrix}\right\}\right)[C_2O_2],O}_{\text{hydroxyacetic acid}} \qquad \underset{\substack{\text{aldehyde of}\\\text{hydroxyacetic acid}}}{\left(C_2\left\{\begin{matrix}H_2\\HO_2\end{matrix}\right\}\right)\left.\begin{matrix}\\H\end{matrix}\right\}[C_2O_2]} \qquad \underbrace{HO.\left(C_2\left\{\begin{matrix}H_2\\HO_2\end{matrix}\right\}\right)C_2,\,O}_{\substack{\text{alcohol of}\\\text{hydroxyacetic acid}}}$$

If, in an aldehyde, the independent hydrogen atom is replaced by a compound radical, there result acetones:

$$\left.\begin{matrix}C_2H_3\\H\end{matrix}\right\}[C_2O_2] \quad \text{aldehyde}$$

$$\text{or} \qquad \left.\begin{matrix}\left.\begin{matrix}C_2H_3\\C_2H_3\end{matrix}\right\}[C_2O_2]\\\left.\begin{matrix}C_2H_3\\C_4H_5\end{matrix}\right\}[C_2O_2]\end{matrix}\right\}\text{acetones}$$

If we consider that in a similar way one or two of the two independent hydrogen atoms in the alcohol are substituted by as many methyl, ethyl, etc., atoms, there result new alcohollike compounds of the following composition:

$$\text{HO.}\left.\begin{cases} C_2H_3 \\ H_2 \end{cases}\right\} C_2, O \qquad \text{normal alcohol}$$

$$\text{HO.}\left.\begin{cases} C_2H_3 \\ C_2H_3 \\ H \end{cases}\right\} C_2, O \qquad \text{singly methylated alcohol}$$

$$\text{HO.}\left.\begin{cases} C_2H_3 \\ C_2H_3 \\ C_2H_3 \end{cases}\right\} C_2, O \qquad \text{doubly methylated alcohol}$$

$$\text{HO.}\left.\begin{cases} C_2H_3 \\ C_2H_3 \\ C_4H_5 \end{cases}\right\} C_2, O \qquad \text{methyloethylated alcohol}$$

The singly methylated alcohol is only an isomer, not identical with propyl alcohol:

$$\text{HO.}\left.\begin{cases} C_2H_3 \\ C_2H_3 \\ H \end{cases}\right\} C_2, O \qquad \text{singly methylated alcohol}$$

$$\text{HO.}\left.\begin{cases} C_4H_5 \\ H_2 \end{cases}\right\} C_2, O \qquad \text{propyl alcohol}$$

In the same way the doubly methylated alcohol has the same number of elements as butyl alcohol:

$$\text{HO.}\left.\begin{cases} C_6H_7 \\ H_2 \end{cases}\right\} C_2, O \text{ etc.}$$

Even though none of these alcoholic compounds has been prepared up to now, I feel sure of their existence and believe that as soon as we begin experimental work in this matter, their discovery will not long be delayed. Their chemical properties can already be predicted in many ways. These bodies, like the normal alcohols, will obviously yield halogen compounds analogous to ethyl chloride with the hydrogen acids and, similarly, will give rise to sulfur compounds and mercaptans and, with sulfuric acid, to compounds analogous to ethyl sulfuric acid; but no sort of *doubly methylated* alcoholic compound bodies can be converted by means of oxidation into aldehydes and acids like normal alcohols, since they lack the two independent hydrogen atoms on which in normal alcohols oxidation occurs. The compound hydroxyhydrates analogous to *singly methylated* alcohol, which still contain one independent hydrogen atom, can as little yield an acid but can well undergo oxidation processes, by which normal alcohols are converted into aldehydes. But here not aldehyde but acetone results as an oxidation product:

$$\underbrace{\text{HO.}\left.\begin{cases} C_2H_3 \\ C_2H_3 \\ H \end{cases}\right\} C_2, O}_{\substack{\text{singly methylated} \\ \text{alcohol}}} + 2O = \underbrace{\left.\begin{matrix} C_2H_3 \\ C_2H_3 \end{matrix}\right\} [C_2O_2].}_{\text{acetone}}$$

Louis Pasteur

(1822–1895)

THE inception of stereochemistry is to be found in Biot's experiments on polarization (1815 to 1835). He observed two types of substances, those that would rotate the plane of polarized light only in crystalline form and another class which would do it in other states, particularly in solution. The latter group must, therefore, have its property inherent in the molecule; here he classified sugars, turpentine, camphor, and tartaric acid. Mitscherlich studied this last acid in 1844 and recognized that tartaric and racemic acid (paratartaric acid), while isomeric, are not both optically active. This attracted the attention of Louis Pasteur, who made an exhaustive study of the tartrates, especially the double sodium ammonium salt (1848 to 1853), and soon explained the phenomena. Pasteur demonstrated that by the slow crystallization of sodium ammonium racemate, crystals were obtained, some with facets on the right side and others on the left (dextro and levo). He further separated the optically inactive substances by fractional crystallization with an optically active acid or base (1853) and later by the use of a preferential mold growth (1860). In 1860 L. Pasteur recognized the existence of molecular dissymmetry, which provided a basis for a fuller explanation of his work. The full interpretation of his results, as applied to chemical constitution, was advanced in 1874 by van't Hoff and Le Bel, each independently. Pasteur's first researches on tartaric and racemic acid appeared in 1848[1] and are fully summarized and evaluated in two lectures given in 1860, which were later published by the Chemical Society of Paris.[2]

Pasteur investigated fermentation and provided experimental proof for the vitalistic theory (1857). He proclaimed that fermentation is the result of microscopic organisms. Another of Pasteur's important contributions was his fundamental research in bacteriology, which finally overthrew the doctrine of spontaneous generation (1862).

The following selection from Pasteur's study of tartarates and racemates is taken from the Alembic Club translation.

[1] *Compt. rend.*, **26**: 535 (1848); *Ann. chim.*, **24**: 442 (1848).

[2] "Leçons de chimie professées en 1860," Paris, 1861; translated, in part, in: *Alembic Club Reprints*, No. 14, "Researches on the Molecular Asymmetry of Natural Organic Products by Louis Pasteur, (1860)," Edinburgh, 1905; Ostwald's *Klassiker*, No. 28, "L. Pasteur., Ueber die Asymmetrie bei natürlich vorkommenden organischen Verbingungen. (1860). Uebersetzt und herausgegeben von M. und A. Ladenburg," Leipzig, 1891; the collected works of Pasteur, "Oeuvres. Réunies par Pasteur Vallery-Radot . . . ," Paris, 1922–1939, 7 vols. Volume 1 contains his publications on molecular asymmetry.

RESEARCHES ON THE MOLECULAR ASYMMETRY
OF NATURAL ORGANIC PRODUCTS

III.

When I began to devote myself to special work, I sought to strengthen myself in the knowledge of crystals, foreseeing the help that I should draw from this in my chemical researches. It seemed to me to be the simplest course, to take, as a guide, some rather extensive work on crystalline forms; to repeat all the measurements, and to compare my determinations with those of the author. In 1841, M. DE LA PROVOSTAYE, whose accuracy is well known, had published a beautiful piece of work on the crystalline forms of tartaric and paratartaric acids and of their salts. I made a study of this memoir. I crystallised tartaric acid and its salts, and investigated the forms of the crystals. But, as the work proceeded, I noticed that a very interesting fact had escaped the learned physicist. All the tartrates which I examined gave undoubted evidence of hemihedral faces.

This peculiarity in the forms of tartrates was not very obvious. This will be readily conceived, seeing that it had not been observed before. But when, in a species, its presence was doubtful, I always succeeded in making it manifest by repeating the crystallisation and slightly modifying the conditions. Sometimes the crystals bore all the faces demanded by the law of symmetry, but the hemihedry was still betrayed by an unequal development of one half of the faces. This is seen, for example in tartar emetic. It must be admitted that a circumstance which adds greatly to the difficulty in recognising hemihedry is the frequent irregularities of the crystals, which never develop quite freely. From this cause there arise deformations, arrestments of development in one direction or another, faces suppressed by accident, etc. Unless in circumstances of an almost exceptional character, the recognition of hemihedry, particularly in laboratory crystals, demands very attentive study. To this we must add the fact that, although hemihedry may be possible in a given form, and although it is a function of the internal structure of the substance, it may not be indicated externally, any more than one finds on every crystal of a cubic species all the forms compatible with the cube.

But however these things may be, I repeat that I found the tartrates hemihedral.

This observation would probably have remained sterile, without the following one.

Let *a*, *b*, *c*, be the parameters of the crystal form of any tartrate, and α, β, γ, the angles of the crystallographic axes. The latter are ordinarily perpendicular, or slightly oblique. In addition, the ratio of two parameters, such as *a* and *b*, is almost the same in the various tartrates, whatever may be their composition, their quantity of water of crystallisation, or the nature of the bases; c alone shows sensible variations. There is a kind of semi-isomorphism among all the tartrates. One would imagine that the tartaric group dominated and stamped with similarity the forms of all the various substances in spite of the difference in the other constituent elements.

The results of this are, a resemblance in the forms of all tartrates, and the possibility of parallel orientation, taking, for example, as basis of orientation the position of the axes a and b.

Now if we compare the disposition of the hemihedral faces on all the prisms of the primitive forms of the tartrates, when they are oriented in the same manner, this disposition is found to be the same.

These results, which have been the foundation of all my later work, may be summed up in two words: the tartrates are hemihedral, and that in the same sense.

Guided then on the one hand by the fact of the existence of molecular rotary polarisation, discovered by BIOT in tartaric acid and all its compounds, and on the other by HERSCHEL's ingenious correlation, and yet again by the sagacious views of M. DELAFOSSE, with whom hemihedry has always been a law of structure and not an accident of crystallisation, I believed that there might be a relation between the hemihedry of the tartrates and their property of deviating the plane of polarised light.

It is important thoroughly to grasp the development of the conceptions:—HAÜY and WEISS observe that quartz possesses hemihedral faces and that these faces incline to the right on some specimens and to the left on others. BIOT on his part finds that quartz crystals likewise separate themselves into two sets, in relation to their optical properties, the one set deviating the plane of polarised light to the right, the other to the left, according to the same laws. HERSCHEL in his turn supplies to these hitherto isolated facts the bond of union, and says:—Plagihedra of one kind deviate in the same sense; plagihedra of the other kind deviate in the opposite sense.

For my part I find that all tartrates are plagihedral, if I may so express myself, and that in the same sense; so that I might presume that here, as in the case of quartz, there was a relation between the hemihedry and the circular polarisation. At the same time the essential differences to which I have just referred between circular polarisation in quartz and in tartaric acid must not be neglected.

Thanks to the above discoveries, and to the relations which I have just enumerated, we are now in possession of a preconceived notion (for it is still nothing more than that) as to the possible inter-relation of the hemihedry and the rotative power of the tartrates.

Being very anxious to find by experiment some support for this still purely speculative view, my first thought was to see whether the very numerous crystallisable organic products which possess the molecular rotative property, have hemihedral crystalline forms, an idea which had not previously occurred to any one in spite of Herschel's correlation. This investigation met with the success which I anticipated.

I also occupied myself with the examination of the crystalline forms of paratartaric acid and its salts. These substances are isomeric with the tartaric compounds, but had all been found by BIOT to be inactive towards polarised light. None of them exhibited hemihedry.

Thus the idea of the inter-relation of the hemihedry and the molecular rotatory power of natural organic products gained ground.

I was soon enabled to establish it clearly by a wholly unexpected discovery.

After discussing Mitscherlich's work Pasteur continues.

IV.

You will now understand why, being preoccupied, for the reasons already given, with a possible relation between the hemihedry of the tartrates and their rotative property, MITSCHERLICH's note of 1844 should recur to my memory. I thought at once that MITSCHERLICH was mistaken on one point. He had not observed that his double tartrate was hemihedral while his paratartrate was not. If this is so, the results in his note are no longer extraordinary; and further, I should have, in this, the best test of my preconceived idea as to the interrelation of hemihedry and the rotatory phenomenon.

I hastened therefore to re-investigate the crystalline form of MITSCHERLICH's two salts. I found, as a matter of fact, that the tartrate was hemihedral, like all the other tartrates which I had previously studied, but, strange to say, the paratartrate was hemihedral also. Only, the hemihedral faces which in the tartrate were all turned the same way, were, in the paratartrate inclined sometimes to the right and sometimes to the left. In spite of the unexpected character of this result, I continued to follow up my idea. I carefully separated the crystals which were hemihedral to the right from those hemihedral to the left, and examined their solutions separately in the polarising apparatus. I then saw with no less surprise than pleasure that the crystals hemihedral to the right deviated the plane of polarisation to the right, and that those hemihedral to the left deviated it to the left; and when I took an equal weight of each of the two kinds of crystals, the mixed solution was indifferent towards the light in consequence of the neutralisation of the two equal and opposite individual deviations.

Thus, I start with paratartaric acid; I obtain in the usual way the double paratartrate of soda and ammonia; and the solution of this deposits, after some days, crystals all possessing exactly the same angles and the same aspect. To such a degree is this the case that MITSCHERLICH, the celebrated crystallographer, in spite of the most minute and severe study possible, was not able to recognize the smallest difference. And yet the molecular arrangement in one set is entirely different from that in the other. The rotatory power proves this, as does also the mode of asymmetry of the crystals. The two kinds of crystals are isomorphous, and isomorphous with the corresponding tartrate. But the isomorphism presents itself with a hitherto unobserved peculiarity; it is the isomorphism of an asymmetric crystal with its mirror image. This comparison expresses the fact very exactly. Indeed, if, in a crystal of each kind, I imagine the hemihedral facets produced till they meet, I obtain two symmetrical tetrahedra, inverse, and which cannot be superposed, in spite of the perfect identity of all their respective parts. From this I was justified in concluding that, by the crystallisation of the double paratartrate of soda and ammonia, I had separated two symmetrically isomorphous atomic groups, which are intimately united in paratartaric acid. Nothing is easier than to show that these two species of crystals represent two distinct salts from which two different acids can be extracted.

Using the treatment always employed in such cases, the purpose is served by precipitating each salt with a salt of lead or baryta, and then isolating the acids by means of sulphuric acid. . . .

VI.

Let us return to the two acids furnished by the two sorts of crystals deposited in so unexpected a manner in the crystallisation of the double paratartrate of soda and ammonia. I have already remarked that nothing could be more interesting than the investigation of these acids.

One of them, that which comes from crystals of the double salt hemihedral to the right, deviates to the right, and is identical with ordinary tartaric acid. The other deviates to the left, like the salt which furnishes it. The deviation of the plane of polarisation produced by these two acids is rigorously the same in absolute value. The right acid follows special laws in its deviation, which no other active substance had exhibited. The left acid exhibits them, in the opposite sense, in the most faithful manner, leaving no suspicion of the slightest difference.

That paratartaric acid is really the combination, equivalent for equivalent, of these two acids, is proved by the fact that, if somewhat concentrated solutions of equal weights of each of them are mixed, as I shall do before you, their combination takes place with disengagement of heat, and the liquid solidifies immediately on account of the abundant crystallisation of paratartaric acid, identical with the natural product.[3]

[3] [This beautiful experiment called forth applause from the audience.]

In accord with their chemical and crystallographic properties, all that can be done with one acid can be repeated with the other under the same conditions, and in each case we get identical, but not superposable products; products which resemble each other like the right and left hands. The same forms, the same faces, the same angles, hemihedry in both cases. The sole dissimilarity is in the inclination to right or left of the hemihedral facets and in the sense of the rotatory power. . . .

Alexander William Williamson

(1824–1904)

THE "water type" of Laurent was extended by Alexander William Williamson. Laurent (1846) had pictured alcohol and ether as analogous to water, potassium oxide, and potassium hydroxide: OHH, OEtH, OEtEt, OKK, OHK. Williamson's work was on the formulas of alcohol and ether and related compounds. At the time that Williamson published his theory of etherification there were three theories prevalent to explain the relationship between alcohol and ether: the first, that of Berzelius, regarded both ether and alcohol as the oxides of different radicals, $(C_4H_5)O$ and C_2H_3O; the second was held by Dumas in his etherin theory that both were hydrates of the same radical, etherin C_4H_4, giving a formulation of $C_4H_4.H_2O$ and $2C_4H_4.H_2O$; the third, which was the most popular and had replaced that of Berzelius by 1850, expressed alcohol $C_4H_5.H_2O$ as the hydrate of ether C_4H_5O. Williamson showed that Liebig's formula was incorrect, also supplying experimental proof for Gerhardt's two-volume theory, that the molecules of alcohol and ether occupied equal volumes in the vapour state. The paper is notable in that it presents a mechanism for a "contact," or catalytic, process, and thus makes much clearer the rather vague picture which Berzelius had given for catalysis. The first paper of Williamson on a "Theory of Aetherification" was read before the British Association at Edinburgh on Aug. 3, 1850, and published as both a short abstract in the *Report*[1] of the meeting and as a full presentation in *The London, Edinburgh, and Dublin Philosophical Magazine and Journal of Science.*[2] This was followed by other publications.[3] The following selection is taken from Williamson's paper of 1850.

[1] *Report of the Twentieth Meeting of the British Association for the Advancement of Science,* **2**: 65 (1850).

[2] *The London, Edinburgh, and Dublin Philosophical Magazine and Journal of Science,* **37**: 350–356 (1850).

[3] These are, with the paper in note 1, to be found in the *Alembic Club Reprints,* No. 16, "Papers on Etherification and on the Constitution of Salts by Alexander W. Williamson, LL.D., F.R.S. (1850–1856)," Edinburgh, 1902.

THEORY OF AETHERIFICATION.

When sulfuric acid is brought in contact with alcohol under certain circumstances, a new arrangement is effected in the elements of the alcohol, which divide into two groups, forming aether and water. Now it is well known that the process by which this change is effected may be represented in two ways, the difference of which consists in their respectively selecting for starting-point a different view of the constitution of alcohol. According to the one view, an atom of alcohol weighs 23, and is made up of C^2H^6O; so that to form aether, two atoms of it are needed, one of which takes C^2H^4 from the other, setting free the water with which these elements were combined; whereas, according to the other view, alcohol weighs 46, and *contains* aether and water. These are not the only points of difference which are urged; but they are the most real and tangible, and their consideration is sufficient for our present purpose. If by any direct fact we could decide which of these two expressions is the correct one, the ground would be clear for an examination of the process of aetherification itself. In order to show more clearly the true meaning of the facts I have to adduce on this point, I will bring them before you in the order in which they arose.

My object in commencing the experiments was to obtain new alcohols by substituting carburetted hydrogen for hydrogen in a known alcohol. With this view I had recourse to an expedient, which may render valuable services on similar occasions. It consisted in replacing the hydrogen first by potassium and acting upon the compound thus formed by the chloride or iodide of the carburetted hydrogen which was to be introduced in the place of that hydrogen. I commenced with common alcohol, which, after careful purification, was saturated with potassium, and as soon as the action had ceased, mixed with a portion of iodide of aethyle equivalent to the potassium used. Iodide of potassium was readily formed on the application of a gentle heat, and the desired substitution was effected; but, to my astonishment, the compound thus formed had none of the properties of an alcohol—it was nothing else than common aether, $C^4H^{10}O$.

Now this result at once struck me as being inconsistent with the higher formula of alcohol; for if that body contained twice as many atoms of oxygen as are in aether, I ought clearly to have obtained a product containing twice as much oxygen as aether does. The alternative was evident; for having obtained aether by substituting C^2H^5 for H in alcohol, the relative composition of the two bodies is represented *by expressing that fact in our formula.* Thus alcohol is $\left.{C^2H^5 \atop H}\right\}O$, and the potassium compound is $\left.{C^2H^5 \atop K}\right\}O$; and by acting upon this by iodide of aethyle, we have

$$\begin{matrix} C^2H^5 \\ K \end{matrix} O + C^2H^5I = IK + \begin{matrix} C^2H^5 \\ C^2H^5 \end{matrix} O.$$

Of course the proportion between the two bodies is the only point upon which I here enter, and the same reasoning would be applicable to any multiple of the formulae assumed. Some chemists may perhaps prefer doubling them in order to avoid the use of atoms of hydrogen, potassium, &c.; but I have not felt myself justified in doing so, because that would involve doubling the usual formula for water; for, as I will presently show, water is formed in aetherification by replacing the carburetted hydrogen of alcohol by hydrogen, which, of course, obliges us to assume the same unity of oxygen in both. Alcohol is therefore water in which half the hydrogen is replaced by carburetted hydrogen, and aether is water in which both atoms of hydrogen are replaced by carburetted hydrogen: thus,

$$\begin{matrix} H \\ H \end{matrix} O, \quad \begin{matrix} C^2H^5 \\ H \end{matrix} O, \quad \begin{matrix} C^2H^5 \\ C^2H^5 \end{matrix} O.$$

This formation of aether might however be explained after a fashion by the other theory—by supposing the potassium compound to contain aether and potash, which separate during the action of the iodide of aethyle; so that half the aether obtained would have been contained in that compound, and the other half formed by double decomposition between potash and iodide of aethyle: thus—

$$\begin{matrix} C^4H^{10}O \\ K^2O \end{matrix} + C^4H^{10}I^2 = 2 \ IK + 2(C^4H^{10}O).$$

But although the insufficiency of this explanation becomes evident on a little reflection, I devised a further and more tangible method of arriving at a conclusion. It consisted in acting upon the potassium compound by iodide of methyle, in which case I should, if that compound were aether and potash, obtain a mixture of aether and oxide of methyle; whereas in the contrary case I should obtain a body of the composition C^3H^8O. Now this substance I obtained, and neither aether nor oxide of methyle.

In this experiment the two theories cross one another, and must lead to different results; for it is evident that, in the first-mentioned decomposition by which aether was formed, the only difficulty in explaining the process decisively consisted in our inability to prove that the carburetted hydrogen introduced instead of the hydrogen did not have in the product an atom of oxygen to itself, but that, on the contrary, it was coupled with the carburetted hydrogen already contained in the alcohol—the two in combination with one atom of oxygen. It is clear that if alcohol *contain* aether and water, and the carburetted hydrogen in my first experiment formed a second atom of aether by taking the place of the hydrogen of this water, that the process being the same in the second experiment, we should then have obtained two aethers. Whereas if the formation of aether from alcohol be effected by synthesis, a new carburetted hydrogen being added to the one already contained in the alcohol, we ought to obtain the new intermediate aether which I obtained.

The complete description of this remarkable body and of its decompositions, will form the subject of a future paper. I will now merely state that its boiling point is a little above 10° Cent.; it is possessed of a very peculiar smell, distinctly different from that of common aether; and, like that body, it is only slightly soluble in water. It is not acted upon by the alkali-metals at the common atmospheric temperature.

By acting upon the potassium-alcohol in like manner by iodide of amyle, I effected a similar substitution of the elements of that carburetted hydrogen in the place of the hydrogen of alcohol, and obtained an aether boiling at 111°C., having the composition $C^7H^{16}O$. There is some reason to believe that this body is the same which Balard obtained by decomposition of chloride of amyle by an alcoholic solution of hydrated potash, and which that distinguished chemist took for oxide of amyle.

From the perfect analogy of properties between the known terms of the alcoholic series, it was to be expected that similar substitutions might be effected in the others; and I have verified this by experiment. Of course the formulae of the other alcohols must be reduced to half, for the same reasons as that of common alcohol. Methylic alcohol is therefore expressed by the formula $\begin{matrix} CH^3 \\ H \end{matrix} O$, as common alcohol is $\begin{matrix} C^2H^5 \\ H \end{matrix} O$; and in the same manner amylic alcohol is $\begin{matrix} C^5H^{11} \\ H \end{matrix} O$, and the same of the higher ones. In conformity to this fact, we must be able to obtain the same intermediate aethers by replacing hydrogen in these alcohols (methylic and amylic) by the carburetted hydrogen of iodide of aethyle, as by the inverse process described above. This I have verified in the case of the three-carbon aether, which may be obtained indifferently by replacing one-fourth of the hydrogen of methylic alcohol by C^2H^5, or by replacing one-sixth of the hydrogen of common alcohol by CH^3. Its rational formula is therefore $\begin{matrix} C^2H^5 \\ CH^3 \end{matrix} O$.

By acting upon the compound $\begin{matrix} CH^3 \\ K \end{matrix} O$ by iodide of amyle, I obtained a third aetheral compound, of which the formula is $\begin{matrix} CH^3 \\ C^5H^{11} \end{matrix} O$. This is evidently the only one of the three new aethers, which, containing an even number of carbon atoms, might be conceived to have been formed from one alcohol; but when treated with monobasic acids, as hydrochloric, it cannot be expected to act in the same manner as its homogeneous isomeric, the aether $\begin{smallmatrix} C^3H^7 \\ C^3H^7 \end{smallmatrix}O$ of the three-carbon alcohol $\begin{smallmatrix} C^3H^7 \\ H \end{smallmatrix}O$; but of this I will give an exact account in the paper above alluded to.

My task is now to explain the process of aetherification by the action of sulphuric acid (SO^4H^2) upon alcohol; and in order to accomplish that, I must show the connexion between those substances and the reagents used in the above-described experiments. With this view, I have merely to add to the above facts the acknowledged analogy of the simple and compound radicals in their compounds. I must first show how a substance analogous to my iodide of aethyle is formed, and then how by double decomposition with alcohol it produces aether. This is very easy; for sulphovinic acid is strictly analogous to iodide of aethyle plus iodide of hydrogen, which we should obtain by replacing SO^4 in its formula by an equivalent of iodine; and in order to represent the formation of this sulphovinic acid, which is well known to precede that of aether, the simplest mode is at the same time the one most free from hypothesis; it consists in stating the fact, that sulphuric acid and alcohol are transformed into sulphovinic acid and water, by half the hydrogen of the former changing places with the carburetted hydrogen of the latter: thus—

$$\frac{\begin{smallmatrix} H \\ H \end{smallmatrix}SO^4}{\begin{smallmatrix} C^2H^5 \\ H \end{smallmatrix}O} = \frac{\begin{smallmatrix} H \\ C^2H^5 \end{smallmatrix}SO^4}{\begin{smallmatrix} H \\ H \end{smallmatrix}O}$$

Now from this point it is clear that the process is the same as in the decompositions above described; for by this sulphovinic acid coming in contact with an atom of alcohol, it reacts in the same manner as the iodide did, forming of course sulphuric acid and aether:

$$\frac{\begin{smallmatrix} H \\ C^2H^5 \end{smallmatrix}SO^4}{\begin{smallmatrix} H \\ C^2H^5 \end{smallmatrix}O} = \frac{\begin{smallmatrix} H \\ H \end{smallmatrix}SO^4}{\begin{smallmatrix} C^2H^5 \\ C^2H^5 \end{smallmatrix}O}$$

The sulphuric acid thus reproduced comes again in contact with alcohol, forming sulphovinic acid, which reacts as before; and so the process goes on continuously, as found in practice.

We thus see that the formation of aether from alcohol is neither a process of simple separation, nor one of mere synthesis; but that it consists in the substitution of one molecule for another, and is effected by double decomposition between two compounds. I therefore admit the contact theory, inasmuch as I acknowledge the circumstance of contact as a necessary *condition* of the reaction of the molecules upon one another. By reducing the formulae of the alcohols to one atom of oxygen, I also retain the equality of volumes which the contact theory insists upon between the vapours of these bodies and their aethers, so that aether truly contains the elements of olefiant gas in addition to those of alcohol in one atom. But, on the other hand, I attach equal importance to all the essential facts of the chemical theory, and rest my explanation of the process as much upon them as upon those of the contact theory; for, one-sixth of the hydrogen in alcohol truly exhibits different reactions from the remaining five, and must therefore be contained in that compound in a different manner from them; and the alternate formation and decomposition of sulphovinic acid is to me, as to the partisans of the chemical theory, the key to explaining the process of aetherification.

Innovations in science frequently gain ground *only* by displacing the conceptions which preceded them, and which served more or less directly as their foundation; but, if the view which I have here presented be considered a step in our understanding of the subject, I must beg leave to disclaim for it the title of innovation; for my conclusion consists in establishing the connexion and showing the compatibility of views which have hitherto been considered contrary; and the best possible justification of the eminent philosophers who advocated either one of the two contending theories, is thus afforded by my reconciling their arguments with those of their equally illustrious opponents.

Edward Frankland

(1825–1899)

ANTOINE Lavoisier extended his oxygen theory to include organic acids, regarding these as oxides of "radicals" which contained more than one element, including in any case hydrogen and carbon. Gay-Lussac proposed a "compound radical" as the result of his work on cyanogen compounds (1815). The dualistic theory was applied in 1817 by Berzelius to organic compounds, defining organic substances as oxides of organic radicals. The concept that organic chemistry was the chemistry of "compound radicals" was supported by the investigations of Liebig and Wöhler on the radical of benzoic acid (1832). They found that oil of bitter almonds (benzaldehyde), benzoic acid, benzoyl chloride, and benzamide all contained what they called *benzoyl*, $C_{14}H_{10}O_2(C_7H_5O)$, which was therefore analogous to a single element. Berzelius at first strongly supported this radical theory, since it was a confirmation of his dualistic electrical hypothesis extended to organic substances, but he later opposed it, for he would not admit that radicals could contain oxygen. In 1838 Liebig gave a general definition of a radical. Other radicals were reported:

Dumas and Peligot, cinnamyl (1834); Piria, salicyl (1838); Bunsen, cacodyl (1837). Organic radicals were generally accepted around 1840. The radical theory, at this time, could be defined as the view that organic bodies were composed of groups of atoms or radicals which were generally maintained intact throughout a series of reactions, with a function therefore not unlike that of an element. With the radicals of benzoyl, cacodyl, and cyanogen defined, a series of researches were begun to bring into line such simple compounds as ether, acetic acid, and alcohol. Although it seemed for a time that the radical theory was firmly established, the work of Dumas and Laurent soon led to the downfall of the dualistic, and with it the radical, theory. The unitary theory, with its basis in the fact of substitution, contributed, in large measure, to this denial of the radical theory. The work of Frankland and Kolbe in 1848 led to a brief reanimation of the radical theory. They reported the production of acetic acid by heating methyl cyanide with potassium hydroxide. In the paper they announced the isolation of alcohol radicals from the electrolysis of corresponding organic acids. They thought that they had achieved the isolation of alcohol radicals; actually they had obtained hydrocarbons. Their hydrolysis of organic cyanides, however, is an important method today for the synthesis of organic acids. Both were influenced by Berzelius's concepts. The joint paper, which was one of Frankland's first pieces of original research, was published in 1848.[1] Frankland continued his investigations on organic radicals and in 1849 reported the isolation of free ethyl from the reaction of ethyl iodide with zinc (now known to be butane). His paper "On the Isolation of the Organic Radicals" describes this isolation (ethyl), and he considers it the fullest justification of his views. The following selection is taken from this publication.[2]

1. ON THE ISOLATION OF THE ORGANIC RADICALS.

Considering the importance of having positive proof of the existence of the hitherto hypothetical radicals entering, on the one hand, into the composition of the basic compounds of which alcohol is a type, and, on the other, giving rise to the acids of the series commencing with formic acid, it is somewhat remarkable that so few attempts have been made either to isolate these radicals, or at least to discover the simpler groups into which they are decomposed at the moment of their separation.

Although the method by which Bunsen succeeded in isolating cacodyl pointed out the conditions under which a similar separation of other radicals might be effected, yet, with the exception of an unsuccessful attempt made by Löwing to obtain ethyl by the action of potassium upon ethylic chloride, the subject does not seem to have received further attention until Kolbe succeeded in isolating butyl $(C_4H_9)_2$ by an entirely different method, viz. by the electrolysis of valeric acid.

The action of potassium upon ethylic cyanide induced me to hope that,

---

[1] *Annalen der Chemie*, **65**: 288 (1848).

[2] *J. Chem. Soc.*, **2**: 265 (1849). The paper was later included in Frankland's collection of his own works: "Experimental Researches in Pure, Applied and Physical Chemistry," London, 1877, pp. 67–97, from which the citation is taken.

by employing a body of less complex constitution and a metal of a less electro-positive character, the radical might be separated without being at the same time broken up into the groups (C_2H_4) and (C_2H_6).

The weak affinity possessed by iodine for the organic groups, its energetic action upon metals, and the comparatively low temperature at which its organic compounds are decomposed with the separation of free iodine, suggested the combinations of this element as being well adapted for such experiments; and although probably no metal, with the exception of potassium and sodium, has any action upon these compounds at their ordinary boiling-points, yet it appeared in the highest degree probable that, if the metal and iodide were exposed under pressure to a progressively increasing temperature, a point would be attained where the affinity of the metal for iodine, overbalancing that of the radical for the same element, would determine the decomposition of the iodide. The nature of the products would, of course, depend greatly upon the temperature, and perhaps, in some degree, upon the nature of the metal employed.

From the superior interest possessed by ethyl, the iodide of that radical was selected for my first experiments. . . .

ACTION OF ZINC UPON ETHYLIC IODIDE.

A preliminary experiment, conducted as above described, showed that the decomposition of ethylic iodide, by zinc, occurs at a temperature of about 150°C., and proceeds with tolerable rapidity when an extensive surface of the metal is exposed; white crystals gradually incrust the zinc and glass, whilst a colourless mobile liquid remains, equal in volume to only about half the ethylic iodide employed, and very different from that liquid in appearance. It was further evident, from the cessation of ebullition soon after decomposition commenced, that a gas or highly elastic vapour had been generated. Having been maintained at the above temperature for about two hours, and the decomposition appearing to be complete, the tube was removed from the bath and allowed to cool. On afterwards breaking off its capillary extremity under water, about forty times its volume of gas was evolved, whilst the whole of the mobile liquid above mentioned disappeared. The gas had a strong ethereal odour, burnt with a bright flame, and was rapidly and completely absorbed by recently boiled absolute alcohol. On cutting off the upper portion of the tube, and introducing distilled water, the white mass of crystals dissolved with brisk effervescence, occasioned by the evolution of a considerable quantity of a gas possessing properties quite similar to those just mentioned. The solution of the crystals thus obtained possessed all the properties of a solution of zincic iodide, and, with the exception of a trace of undecomposed ethylic iodide, appeared to contain no organic substance.

After a discussion of his analytical results in which he characterized one of his gaseous products as the radical ethyl, Frankland concludes,

From the foregoing facts, the decomposition of ethylic iodide by zinc may be thus expressed:—

$$2C_2H_5I \quad + Zn = ZnI_2 + (C_2H_5)_2$$
Ethylic iodide.   Ethyl.

A portion of the ethyl thus set free is at the same time decomposed into equal volumes of ethylene and ethylic hydride:—

$$(C_2H_5)_2 = \quad C_2H_4 \quad + \quad C_2H_6$$
Ethyl.   Ethylene.   Ethylic hydride.

whilst the zincic iodide combines with a small proportion of ethylic hydride, forming a white crystalline compound, probably of definite constitution.[3] . . .

It was on the study of these by-products from his experiments on radicals, a study of organometallic compounds, that the fame of Frankland was to rest. He made in one of his subsequent papers the first statement of the principles of the valence theory. His idea was to flourish when later the concepts by which an actual valence could be determined were developed. Kekulé, Couper, Cannizzaro, and others were to contribute to the whole. The discussion is found in the conclusion of his paper "On a New Series of Organic Bodies Containing Metals," which appeared in 1852,[4] one of a series. It is here reproduced.

THEORETICAL CONSIDERATIONS.

Imperfect as our knowledge of the organometallic bodies may yet appear, I am unwilling to close this memoir without directing attention to some peculiarities in the habits of these compounds, which promise to throw light upon their rational constitution, if they do not lead to extensive modifications of our views respecting chemical compounds in general, and especially that interesting class termed conjugate compounds.

That stannous ethide, zincmethyl, mercurous ethide, &c. are perfectly analogous to cacodyl there can be no reasonable doubt, inasmuch as, like that body, they combine directly with the electronegative metalloids,

---

[3] The white crystalline body was subsequently found to be ZnEtI, which, on contact with water, suffers the following decomposition—

$$ZnEtI \quad + OH_2 = \quad EtH \quad + \quad ZnHOI$$
Zincic ethiodide.   Water.   Ethylic hydride.   Zincic iodohydrate.

and by dry distillation the following change—

$$2ZnEtI \quad = \quad ZnI_2 \quad + \quad ZnEt_2$$
Zincic ethiodide.   Zincic iodide.   Zincic ethide.

[4] *Philosophical Transactions*, **142**: 417 (1852); "Experimental Researches . . . ," pp. 160–191; the selection is taken from pages 185 to 191.

forming true salts; from which, in most cases, and probably in all, the original group can be again separated unaltered; and therefore any view which may be taken of the new bodies must necessarily be extended to cacodyl. The discovery and isolation of this remarkable organic radical by Bunsen was certainly one of the most important steps in the development of organic chemistry; and its influence upon our theoretical views of the constitution of certain classes of organic compounds can scarcely be too highly estimated. It was impossible to consider the striking features in the behaviour of this body, without finding in them a most remarkable confirmation of the theory of organic radicals propounded by Berzelius and Liebig.

The formation of cacodyl, its habits, and the products of its decomposition, have for some time left no doubt of the existence of methyl ready formed in this body; and Kolbe, in developing his views on the so-called conjugate compounds, has proposed to regard it as arsenic conjugated with two semimolecules of methyl $(C_2H_3)_2As$. So long as cacodyl was an isolated example of an organometallic body, this view of its rational composition, harmonizing as it did with the facts elicited during the passage of cacodyl through its various combinations and decompositions, could scarcely be contested; but now, since we have become acquainted with the properties and reactions of a considerable number of analogous bodies, circumstances have arisen which militate greatly against this view, even if they do not render it absolutely untenable. According to the theory of conjugate radicals just alluded to, cacodyl and its congeners, so far as they are at present known, would be thus represented:—

Cacodyl... $(C_2H_3)_2As.$
Oxide of cacodyl....................................... $(C_2H_3)_2AsO.$
Cacodylic acid .... $(C_2H_3)_2AsO_3.$
Stannous methide...................................... $(C_2H_3)Sn.$
Stannous ethide....................................... $(C_4H_5)Sn.$
Oxide of stannous ethide.............................. $(C_4H_5)SnO.$
Stannous amylide..................................... $(C_{10}H_{11})Sn.$
Zincmethyl.. $(C_2H_3)Zn.$
Zincethyl... $(C_4H_5)Zn.$
Zincamyl.. $(C_{10}H_{11})Zn.$
Stibethine (stibethyl)................................ $(C_4H_5)_3Sb.$
Binoxide of stibethine................................ $(C_4H_5)_3SbO_2.$
Oxide of stibmethylium............................... $(C_2H_3)_4SbO.$
Mercurous methide.................................... $(C_2H_3)Hg.$
Iodide of mercurous methide, or mercuric methiodide.......... $(C_2H_3)HgI.$

It is generally admitted that when a body becomes conjugated, its essential chemical character is not altered by the presence of the conjunct: thus, for instance, the series of acids $C_nH_nO_4$, formed by the conjunction of the radicals $C_nH_{(n+1)}$ with oxalic acid, have the same neutralizing power as the original oxalic acid; and, therefore, if we assume the organometallic bodies above mentioned to be metals conjugated with various hydrocarbons, we might reasonably expect that the chemical relations of each metal to oxygen, chlorine, sulphur, &c. would remain unchanged; a glance at the formulae of these compounds, however, will suffice to show us that this is far from being the case. It is true that cacodyl forms protoxide of cacodyl and cacodylic acid, corresponding the one to a somewhat hypothetical protoxide of arsenic, which, if it exist, does not seem to possess any well-defined basic character, and the other to arsenious acid (*arsenious anhydride*); but no compound corresponding to arsenic acid can be formed: and yet it cannot be urged that cacodylic acid is decomposed by the powerful reagents requisite to procure further oxidation; for concentrated nitric acid may be distilled from cacodylic acid without decomposition or oxidation in the slightest degree. The same anomaly presents itself even more strikingly in the case of stannous ethide, which, if we are to regard it as a conjugate radical, ought to combine with oxygen in two proportions at least, to form compounds corresponding to protoxide and peroxide of tin: now stannous ethide rapidly oxidizes when exposed to the air, and is converted into pure protoxide; but the latter exhibits none of that powerful tendency to combine with an additional atom of oxygen which is so characteristic of protoxide of tin; nay, it may even be boiled with dilute nitric acid without evincing any signs of oxidation. I have been quite unable to form any higher oxide than that already described; it is only when the group is entirely broken up and the ethyl separated, that the tin can be induced to unite with another atom of oxygen. Stibethyl also refuses to unite with more or less than two atoms of oxygen, sulphur, iodine, &c., and thus forms compounds which are not at all represented amongst the combinations of the simple metal antimony.

When the formulae of inorganic chemical compounds are considered, even a superficial observer is impressed with the general symmetry of their construction. The compounds of nitrogen, phosphorus, antimony, and arsenic, especially, exhibit the tendency of these elements to form compounds containing 3 or 5 atoms of other elements; and it is in these proportions that their affinities are best satisfied: thus in the ternal group we have NO_3, NH_3, NI_3, NS_3, PO_3, PH_3, PCl_3, SbO_3, SbH_3, $SbCl_3$, AsO_3, AsH_3, $AsCl_3$, &c.; and in the five-atom group, NO_5, NH_4O, NH_4I, PO_5, PH_4I, &c. Without offering any hypothesis regarding the cause of this symmetrical grouping of atoms, *it is sufficiently evident, from the examples just given, that such a tendency or law prevails, and that, no matter what the character of the uniting atoms may be, the combining-power of the attracting element*, if I may be allowed the term, *is always satisfied by the same number of these atoms.* It was probably a glimpse of the operation of this law amongst the more complex organic groups which led Laurent and Dumas to the enunciation of the theory of types; and had not those distinguished chemists extended their views beyond the point to which they were well supported by then existing facts, had they not assumed that the properties of an organic compound are dependent upon the *position* and not upon the *nature* of its single atoms, that theory would undoubtedly have contributed to the development of the science to a still greater extent than it has already done. Such an assumption could only have been made at a time when the data upon which it was founded were few and imperfect; and as the study of the phenomena of substitution progressed, it gradually became untenable, and the fundamental principles of the electro-chemical theory again assumed their sway. The formation and examination of the organometallic bodies promise to effect a fusion of the two theories which have so long divided the opinions of chemists, and which have too hastily been considered irreconcilable; for, whilst it is evident that certain types of series of compounds exist, it is equally clear that the nature of the body derived from the original type is essentially dependent upon the electro-chemical character of its single atoms, and not merely upon the relative position of those atoms. Let us take, for instance, the compounds formed by zinc and antimony. By combination with one atom of oxygen the electro-positive quality of the zinc is nearly annihilated; it is only by the action of the highly oxidizing peroxide of hydrogen that the metal can be made to form a very unstable peroxide; but when zinc combines with one semimolecule of methyl or ethyl, its positive quality, so far from being neutralized, is exalted by the addition of the positive group; and the compound now exhibits such intense affinity for the electro-negative elements, as to give it the property of spontaneous inflammability. Teroxide of antimony has also little tendency to pass into a higher state of oxidation; but when its three atoms of oxygen are replaced by electro-positive ethyl, as in stibethine, its affinity for oxygen is elevated to the intense degree so remarkable in this body.

Taking this view of the so-called conjugate organic radicals, and regarding the oxygen, sulphur, or chlorine compounds of each metal as the true molecular types of the organometallic bodies derived from them by the substitution of an organic group for oxygen, sulphur, &c., the anomalies above mentioned entirely disappear, and we have the following inorganic types and organometallic derivatives:—

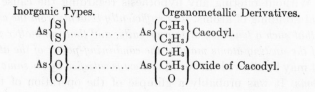

Inorganic Types.   Organometallic Derivatives.

$$As\begin{Bmatrix} S \\ S \end{Bmatrix} \ldots\ldots\ldots\ldots \quad As\begin{Bmatrix} C_2H_3 \\ C_2H_3 \end{Bmatrix} \text{Cacodyl.}$$

$$As\begin{Bmatrix} O \\ O \\ O \end{Bmatrix} \ldots\ldots\ldots\ldots \quad As\begin{Bmatrix} C_2H_3 \\ C_2H_3 \\ O \end{Bmatrix} \text{Oxide of Cacodyl.}$$

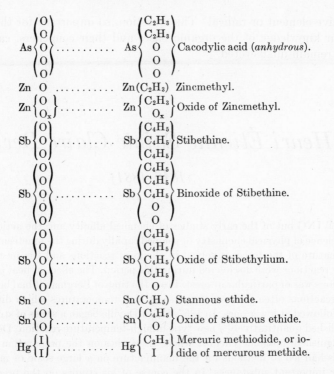

$As \begin{Bmatrix} O \\ O \\ O \\ O \\ O \end{Bmatrix}$ .... $As \begin{Bmatrix} C_2H_3 \\ C_2H_3 \\ O \\ O \\ O \end{Bmatrix}$ Cacodylic acid (*anhydrous*).

$Zn \ O$ .... $Zn(C_2H_3)$ Zincmethyl.

$Zn \begin{Bmatrix} O \\ O_x \end{Bmatrix}$ .... $Zn \begin{Bmatrix} C_2H_3 \\ O_x \end{Bmatrix}$ Oxide of Zincmethyl.

$Sb \begin{Bmatrix} O \\ O \\ O \end{Bmatrix}$ .... $Sb \begin{Bmatrix} C_4H_5 \\ C_4H_5 \\ C_4H_5 \end{Bmatrix}$ Stibethine.

$Sb \begin{Bmatrix} O \\ O \\ O \\ O \\ O \end{Bmatrix}$ .... $Sb \begin{Bmatrix} C_4H_5 \\ C_4H_5 \\ C_4H_5 \\ O \\ O \end{Bmatrix}$ Binoxide of Stibethine.

$Sb \begin{Bmatrix} O \\ O \\ O \\ O \\ O \end{Bmatrix}$ .... $Sb \begin{Bmatrix} C_4H_5 \\ C_4H_5 \\ C_4H_5 \\ C_4H_5 \\ O \end{Bmatrix}$ Oxide of Stibethylium.

$Sn \ O$ .... $Sn(C_4H_5)$ Stannous ethide.

$Sn \begin{Bmatrix} O \\ O \end{Bmatrix}$ .... $Sn \begin{Bmatrix} C_4H_5 \\ O \end{Bmatrix}$ Oxide of stannous ethide.

$Hg \begin{Bmatrix} I \\ I \end{Bmatrix}$ .... $Hg \begin{Bmatrix} C_2H_3 \\ I \end{Bmatrix}$ Mercuric methiodide, or iodide of mercurous methide.

The only compound which does not harmonize with this view is ethostibylic acid, to which Löwig assigns the formula $C_4H_5SbO_5$; but as he has not yet fully investigated this body, it is possible that further research may satisfactorily elucidate its apparently anomalous composition.

It is obvious that the establishment of this theory of the constitution of the organometallic bodies will remove them from the class of organic radicals, and place them in the most intimate relation with ammonia and the bases of Wurtz, Hofmann, and Paul Thénard; indeed the close analogy existing between stibethine and ammonia, first suggested by Gerhardt, has been most satisfactory demonstrated by the behaviour of stibethine with the haloid compounds of methyl and ethyl. Stibethine furnishes us, therefore, with a remarkable example of the operation of the law of symmetrical combination already alluded to, and shows that the formation of a five-atom group from one containing three atoms, can be effected by the assimilation of two atoms (or semimolecules), either of the same or of opposite electro-chemical character. This remarkable circumstance suggests the following question:—Is such behaviour common also to the corresponding compounds of arsenic, phosphorus, and nitrogen? and can the position of each of the five atoms, with which these elements respectively combine, be occupied indifferently by an electro-negative or electropositive element or radical? This question, so important for the advance of our knowledge of the organic bases and their congeners, cannot now long remain unanswered.

Henri Étienne Sainte-Claire Deville

(1818–1881)

GROWING out of the early studies of chemical affinity and the action of mass, the science of physical chemistry developed rapidly during the nineteenth century. The nature of the forces involved in chemical reactions and the mechanisms of many reactions were discovered during this period. The effect of heat on chemical reactions was of particular interest. From the time of Bergman it had been realized that reactions often followed a course at high temperatures which differed from that followed at lower ones. In 1857, Henri Deville began a series of studies which established quantitatively a new type of high-temperature reaction. Deville was a distinguished inorganic chemist whose researches on the preparation of various metals had led to methods for the manufacture on a large scale of many industrially important substances. In the course of his studies on the preparation of sodium and potassium and their use as reducing agents in the manufacture of other metals, Deville often used high temperatures. He was aware of the decompositions which often occurred under these conditions, and he suspected that such decompositions were of very frequent occurrence. He therefore undertook the study of reactions which occurred reversibly at high temperature. Such reactions he called *dissociations*, and by an extensive series of studies he showed the importance of dissociation as a general phenomenon in chemistry. The following selection gives his first paper on this subject.

DISSOCIATION OR SPONTANEOUS DECOMPOSITION OF A BODY UNDER THE INFLUENCE OF HEAT[1]

When heat acts on any material, it first produces a dilatation which is attributed to a force which is called the *repulsive force of heat*. If the material destined for the experiment is properly chosen and the temperature is raised sufficiently, the distance between the molecules can increase to such a point that they separate, returning to the elementary state. There is then a spontaneous decomposition in the sense that no chemical phenomenon intervenes to determine it. This is what I propose to call the *dissociation of compound bodies*. I have collected and discussed in my memoir a great number of facts which are cases of dissociation; I will show

[1] *Compt. rend.*, **45**: 857–861 (1857).

new ones, and will try to show that this phenomenon, which should be general on condition that a sufficiently high temperature is used, can be, and often is, susceptible of measurement.

Before anything else, I will cite some examples of easy dissociation: thus, the anhydride of nitric acid decomposes spontaneously at ordinary temperature. Anhydrous ammonium carbonate dissociates at about 60 degrees, ammonia is resolved into its elements at red heat. I do not make any allusion at this moment to decompositions in which another case than heat must be made to intervene, or even to relative affinities at the temperature of which I have already given a singular example[2] in studying the action of hydrogen on the oxide of zinc.

M. Grove has shown that platinum at its fusion temperature determines the decomposition of water into its elements. This experiment, which I have repeated on a large scale by pouring into water large masses of melted platinum and which then produces a considerable effect, gives, however, only a small quantity of detonating gas, relative to the quantity of heat expended. The great part recombines during cooling, however rapid, and evidently only that part of the gas escapes which has reached ordinary temperature rapidly by immediate contact with the surrounding water. This confirms an experiment which I performed a long time ago by passing the vapor of very *pure* water along a platinum tube heated nearly to its melting point and filled with fragments of lime. The vapor formed by a small generator at high pressure moves with considerable speed. In spite of these favorable conditions, I still obtained only small quantities of detonating gas, and even this experiment would have caused doubts for me if the fact discovered by M. Grove had not been known.

Not being able to measure the quantity of water thus dissociated, I decided to determine the temperature needed for the production of the phenomenon. I remembered that M. Regnault had decomposed water by means of silver raised to the melting point; the silver absorbs oxygen and liberates it on cooling at the moment of *frothing*. I have explained this important fact by the dissociation of water,[3] supposing that it is reduced to its elements while passing through the heated porcelain tube where the operation is effected, and by admitting that, without this circumstance, the affinity of silver for oxygen would be insufficient to cause decomposition of water. I wished to confirm this explanation by substituting for silver a metallic oxide which is very easily reduced by hydrogen at low temperature and consequently is completely unfit for decomposing water by itself. I chose oxide of lead, or pure litharge; I melted it in a platinum crucible and poured it into a large and long platinum boat which entered by friction a porcelain tube 40 millimeters long which it filled in two

[2] *Ann. chim. phys.*, [3], **43** : 477.

[3] See *Compt. rend.*, **42** : 894.

layers. The tube was heated to bright redness, and there was passed in a very rapid current of vapor furnished by a small retort containing distilled water and a little sulfate of aluminum (because of ammonia). A large amount of oxide of lead volatilized, and after the experiment I found signs of an evolution of oxygen given off by the litharge of the boat at the moment of its cooling, a phenomenon so well described by M. Leblanc. The tube, examined for its whole length, showed traces of vitrification by the litharge vapor at the points which had been heated most violently, then powdered oxide of lead, and finally a bluish-black deposit composed of reduced lead whose globules are easily visible under the lens and are soluble in nitric acid with evolution of nitrous vapors. Thus the water had manifestly dissociated in the porcelain tube; the oxygen liberated was dissolved in the litharge. The hydrogen, carried by the current of gas or of nondecomposed vapor, reacted on the oxide of lead, but only at the point where the dissociated water was reconstituted. It is at this precise point that the phenomenon occurs, and the temperature to which it corresponds, and which I have observed very closely, according to my estimate is the melting point of silver.

Thus no more water exists at the melting point of silver, yet hydrogen and oxygen in combining produce such a temperature that their flame melts iridium. How is it that this flame melts platinum, and that melted platinum decomposes water? If we could compare the amount of melted platinum for a given weight of detonating gas per weight of water dissociated by the platinum thus melted, we could conclude from it the probable state of this gas at the moment of development of the heat where it could not form water; but these numeric values are entirely lacking, and I will limit myself to drawing this inexplicable fact to the attention of the physicists.

I believe I will show by the following experiments that the hydrate of soda, and especially the hydrate of potassium, are dissociated with great ease at a temperature near the melting point of cast iron, so that potassium, hydrogen, and oxygen are not really combined at this temperature. I took a bottle of mercury furnished with an iron tube screwed to its upper extremity, at the place where the stopper is found, and another iron tube fitted to the lower part, perpendicular to the axis of the cylinder. The apparatus is placed on a rest near the fire bridge of a reverberatory furnace heated to white heat by a coal flame, which is kept as reducing as possible. The vault of the furnace is pierced to allow the vertical tube to pass; the interior wall gives issue to the horizontal tube. The bottle has been filled either with iron turnings entirely purified by hydrogen or with pure sponge iron. The position which the bottle occupies in the reverberatory furnace is such that the bottom is much less hot than the middle portion. When the temperature has reached white heat, monohydrated potassium is introduced by the upper tube and a receiver is placed at the end of the lower tube. It is seen that I have repeated on a large scale the experiment of MM. Gay-Lussac and Thenard. When potassium[4] has thus been obtained, the operation is quickly stopped. This is what I have observed.

1. When the passage of potassium into the vapor ceases to be very rapid, much volatilized potassium reaches the receiver; potassium forms only when much potash is introduced into the upper tube.

2. When the bottle is sawed open, the iron contained in the hottest part of the apparatus is absolutely intact, as bright as before the experiment, and without a trace of oxide melted on the surface. On the lower, less heated part, there is a slag, often spongy, of oxides of iron and potassium, and the operation quickly stops when this slag reaches the higher, violently heated part of the apparatus.[5]

3. If the entire bottle is heated to the temperature at which the slag is found to be carried in the previous experiment, no trace of potassium is obtained but only hydrogen and potash.

From this it is concluded that hydrated potash is entirely dissociated in passing across incandescent iron; that in the lower part there is really potassium, hydrogen, and oxygen. Only a part of the oxygen is absorbed by the iron, and there results potassium which is *rapidly* carried away by the current of hydrogen, so that the reconstituted potash hinders *mechanically* the giving up of oxygen by the oxide of iron to potassium or to excess hydrogen. This ulterior decomposition is without doubt effected when the current of gas is sufficiently slow, for, in this case, only hydrogen is obtained, coming from the decomposition of water, without which it produces a trace of potassium. Thus potash should be introduced into the apparatus with great rapidity if it is desired to obtain potassium, whose production is, so to speak, accidental. MM. Gay-Lussac and Thenard have well recommended this.

The most obvious proof that can be given for the dissociation of potash in these circumstances, and that which well shows that the iron in the hot part of the apparatus serves only to transmit the heat, is that when the entire apparatus is raised to the temperature at which melting of the bottle occurs, all phenomena of dissociation cease and only hydrogen and alkali vapor are obtained. The temperature of dissociation is higher for soda than for potash.

---

[4] I have used sodium more often, but the operation requires a higher temperature, as MM. Gay-Lussac and Thenard have observed. However, I have thus obtained nearly 300 grams of a very beautiful sodium.

[5] I should say here that the illustrious authors of the physicochemical studies have made, in different parts of their memoir, observations parallel to mine, and in particular, that which concerns the state of the iron in their apparatus for reducing the potash.

I will close by remarking how the rate influences chemical reactions based on dissociation when it concerns the production of alterable materials. I have shown that the oxide of zinc can be *distilled* without any alteration in a slow current of hydrogen, and yet reduction of the oxide is effected with production of metallic zinc in a rapid current of hydrogen, without using the ideas of mass given by Berthollet in the explanation of these facts. It is thus that I give an account of the useful effect produced by carbonate of lime in the mixtures from which I extracted sodium, an effect produced especially by the amount of oxide of carbon gas which is given off on contact with carbon. There would be, in experiments of this type, the elements of a chapter of chemical dynamics in which the facts where *rate* enters as a determinant of reactions would be explained.

M. Debray and I will continue to study these questions, seeking the dissociation temperature of carbonic acid and some chlorides by the methods already described and using for the required heat production in the lime kilns oxygen and illuminating gas. I hope then that in a later communication we can give some further elements for the solution of the problems which are presented in this memoir.

Ludwig Ferdinand Wilhelmy

(1812–1864)

PRIOR to 1850, almost no one had been interested in the field now known as chemical kinetics. In that year, however, Ludwig Wilhelmy took up the study of the rate of the reaction of sucrose when it was hydrolyzed by water in the presence of acid. This was a particularly easy reaction to follow, owing to the change in sign of the rotation of polarized light as the sucrose was inverted to glucose and fructose. He first deduced the mathematical law for a monomolecular reaction— $-dZ/dt = kZ$, where dZ is the loss of sucrose in the time interval dt, Z the amount of sugar present, and k a constant. He then showed that the experimental facts confirmed this formula. The work did not attract much attention at the time, but it paved the way for later generalizations in the field of reaction velocity and for the law of mass action announced by Guldberg and Waage.

THE LAW BY WHICH THE ACTION OF ACIDS ON CANE SUGAR OCCURS[1]

It is known that the action of acids on cane sugar, which rotates the plane of polarized light passing through its solution to the right, converts

[1] Poggendorf's *Annalen der Physik und Chemie*, **81**: 413–433, 499–526 (1850); the selection is taken from pages 413, 418, and 425 to 428. The paper has been reprinted

it into fruit sugar, which rotates the plane to the left. Since now with the aid of a polarization apparatus, the Soleil double plate, readings of how far this change has proceeded can be made with great ease in an instant, it seemed to me to offer the possibility of finding the laws of the process which we are discussing. It is also a problem of interest to establish in what way the chemical action depends on general conditions, at least in this special case. However, this is certainly only one member of a greater series of phenomena which all follow general laws of nature. . . .

After discussing various factors which may possibly affect the reaction, Wilhelmy shows that variations in acid concentration do not affect the process and then goes on to consider the case when the action is independent of acid concentration, as follows:

Under the final assumption, however, the formula which expresses the chemical process can be developed in the following way:

Using the symbols introduced above,[2] dZ is the sugar loss in the time interval dT, and it is assumed that this is determined by the formula

$$-\frac{dZ}{dT} = MZS$$

in which M, as before, is the mean value of the infinitely small amount of sugar units which are changed during the time element by the action of the amount of acid present.

The above equation gives by integration

$$\log Z = -\int_0^T MS \, dT$$

or since, as has already been shown, S is constant, and on the other hand, M also is independent of Z and therefore also of T, as will later be shown by experiment,

$$\log Z = -MST + C$$

For $T = 0$, $Z = Z_0$, therefore,

$$\log Z_0 - \log Z = MST, \text{ or } Z = Z_0 e^{-MST}.$$

 . . . According to the preceding work, I can therefore use the formula developed earlier

$$\log Z_0 - \log Z = MST$$

in the study now made.

---

in Ostwald's *Klassiker*, No. 29. "Ueber das Gesetz nach welchem die Einwirkung der Säuren auf den Rohrzucker stattfindet. Herausgegeben von W. Ostwald," Leipzig, 1891.

[2] Z = concentration of sugar, S = concentration of acid.

A. INFLUENCE OF TIME

A mixture of 10 grams sugar solution (rotation 46°, 8) and 2 grams nitric acid (specific gravity 1.2042) was placed in the apparatus (tube length 150 millimeters, content 13,850 milligrams distilled water at 15°), and the course of action was observed for a day. The readings gave the values for rotation which follow, and it was noted that the temperature of the room and the liquid at the beginning of the study was 15°, 5. This rose slightly at 1 hr. 30′, reached a maximum of 18°, and then at the end of the study fell slowly to 14°, 5. Correspondingly, the difference in the inversion coefficient is calculated at $\mu = 0.3966$, decreasing to 0.3846 and rising to 0.404: thus we obtain the values of the expression

$$\frac{\log Z - \log Z_0}{MS}$$

The convenient half-Briggsian logarithms could be used without disadvantage, since we are concerned only with the ratio of the numbers to each other and not with their absolute values. The figures thus obtained are collected in Table III.

TABLE III

T	Rotation	$\dfrac{\log Z_0 - \log Z^*}{MS}$	t
	46°, 75 before mixing		
8 h.	Mixing of acid with sugar solution		
8 h. 15′	+43°, 75		15°5
" 30	+41		
45	+38, 25		
9 h.	+35, 75	0.0801671	
9 h. 15	+33, 25		
" 30	+30, 75		
" 45	+28, 25		
10 h.	+26	0.1661271	
10 h. 30	+22		
11 h.	+18, 25	0.2504869	
11 h. 30	+15		
12 h.	+11, 5	0.3393678	
12 h. 30	+ 8, 25		
1 h. 30	+ 2, 75	0.4882238	18°
2 h. 30	− 1, 75	0.5859208	16°
3 h. 30	− 4, 5	0.6628879	
4 h. 30	− 7	0.7470561	15°
5 h. 30	− 8, 75	0.8173016	
6 h. 30	−10	0.8752936	14°5

* Z is found from the observed rotation; D, by the formula

$$Z = Z_0 - \frac{Z_0 - D}{1 + \mu}$$

As can be seen, the values found during the time which passed are very nearly proportional, from which the correctness of the formula $Z = Z_0 e^{-MST}$ in relation to time T is established. The small deviation from proportionality is explained by the irregularities of temperature, to which I will return later. A necessary conclusion from the equation, moreover, is that when $T = \infty$, Z can become zero, hence the inversion of the sugar, strictly speaking, is never ended, although due to the smallness of the residue, very soon a further decrease is not noticeable.

B. INFLUENCE OF THE AMOUNT OF SUGAR

It was earlier remarked that the inversion coefficient M is independent of the amount of sugar; this appears from the series of observations already reported. If we calculate M for each time interval by the formula

$$M = \frac{\log Z_0 - \log Z}{T} \cdot \frac{1}{5}$$

we get the following values

$$
\begin{aligned}
M &= 0.0204467 \cdot \tfrac{1}{5} \quad &\text{(t 15°, 5)}\\
M &= 0.0197215 \quad ``\\
M &= 0.0204460 \quad ``\\
M &= 0.0195529 \quad ``\\
M &= 0.0204748 \quad ``\\
M &= 0.0214880 \quad ``\\
M &= 0.0226069 \quad ``\\
M &= 0.0213903 \quad ``\\
M &= 0.0210030 \quad ``\\
M &= 0.0202667 \quad ``\\
M &= 0.0241737 \quad ``\\
M &= 0.0240091 \quad ``\\
M &= 0.0252094 \quad `` \quad &\text{t 18° (maximum temperature)}\\
M &= 0.0244242 \quad ``\\
M &= 0.0192418 \quad ``\\
M &= 0.0210170 \quad ``\\
M &= 0.0175614 \quad ``\\
M &= 0.0142906 \quad `` \quad &\text{t 14°, 5}
\end{aligned}
$$

The slight irregularity in value of M corresponds to the temperature, whose influence will be considered in a special section; thus M remains constant while the amount of sugar in the liquid has fallen from 46, 75 to 6, 23.

The independence of the value of M of the amount of sugar will be further indicated by a special study. This was found in each of the studies carried out simultaneously and at the same temperatures, in which, besides the amount of acid S and the amount of water W, M by the formula $\log Z_0 - \log Z = MST$ was found constant. The detailed conditions and results are given in Table IV.

TABLE IV

Z_0	Anhydrous HNO_3 S	W	T	D	M
45°	0.281 g.	7.542 g.	13 h.	+4°, 25	0.1240
36	"	"	"	+3	0.1267
27	"	"	"	+2	0.1290
18	"	"	"	+1, 25	0.1301
9	"	"	"	+1	0.1201

Z is, as always, calculated from D by the formula previously mentioned,

$$Z = Z_0 - \frac{Z_0 - D}{1 + \mu}$$

Johann Wilhelm Hittorf

(1824-1914)

In 1834, Faraday created the terms *electrolyte, ion,* and the other words relating to the phenomena of electrolysis. He believed that during electrolysis, conductors in the solution were decomposed by the current into ions. Hence electrolytes were binary compounds of elementary atoms, corresponding to their chemical equivalents. J. F. Daniell in 1839 extended these ideas and showed that salts were not compounds of acid anhydrides and metallic oxides, as Berzelius had said, but of metallic cations and elemental or compound acid anions. He initiated experiments on the transference of ions. His ideas were not in accord with the ideas which were developing from organic chemistry and did not receive much attention from the dominant organic chemists of the time.

His work was continued in a much more extensive and elaborate way by J. W. Hittorf from 1853 to 1859.[1] At this time, questions of chemical constitution were in the air. The organic chemists were solving the problem of the constitution of organic compounds, but very few investigators concerned themselves with simple

[1] Poggendorf's *Annalen der Physik und Chemie,* **89**: 177–211 (1853); **98**: 1–33 (1856); **103**: 1–56 (1858); **106**: 337–411, 513–586 (1859).

The papers are also given in Ostwald's *Klassiker,* "Ueber die Wanderungen der Ionen während der Elektrolysis. Abhandlungen von W. Hittorf (1853–1859). Herausgegeben von W. Ostwald. No. 21. Erste Hälfte. No. 23, Zweite Hälfte." Leipzig, 1891.

An English translation of the first paper in the series is given in "The Fundamental Laws of Electrolytic Conduction. Memoirs by Faraday, Hittorf and F. Kohlrausch," translated and edited by H. M. Goodwin, New York, 1899, pp. 49–80.

inorganic salts. Hittorf, however, saw that the chemical reactivity of salts was linked to their conductivity. He began a series of investigations of the transport of ions in solution. He first clearly defined the concept of the transport number, the fraction of an ion concentration (*n*) taken from the immediate vicinity of an electrode (migrating out of the cathode space in the case of an anion) when one equivalent of the cation is deposited. Using very exact methods, he measured the transport numbers of a large group of ions, showing that each ion had its own characteristic rate of migration in a solution undergoing electrolysis. From these studies he was able to discover many facts about the structure of salts. He came very close to discovering electrolytic dissociation, but his work was widely criticized, and in his later papers he was forced to devote much space to polemical matters, and he never quite reached the modern concept. Arrhenius, however, owed much to the work of Hittorf when he at length made his famous discovery (page 483).

The first selection presented below gives Hittorf's concept of ionic migration and transport numbers; the second indicates the nature of his experimental findings; and the remaining three show some of his important deductions from his work.

We usually picture the process [of electrolytic decomposition] to ourselves by means of a row of adjacent molecules, as shown in Fig. 1. It is assumed in the figure that the distance between the neighboring molecules of the electrolyte is greater than that between the chemically bound ions of each individual molecule. This assumption is certainly permissible in those cases which we shall alone have to consider later—namely, those in which the electrolyte is brought into the liquid state by means of a solvent.

The first action of the current consists in bringing the particles of the body to be decomposed into such a position that the cation of each molecule is turned toward the cathode, and the anion towards the anode. The two ions then separate from each other, move in opposite directions, and thereby meet with the neighboring ions likewise migrating (Fig. 1, *b*). By this process, however, they have arrived in a position where each anion is turned towards the cathode, and each cation towards the anode. There must therefore result a rotation of each molecule, and the reverse position be established, if the same constitutent is to be continuously liberated at the same electrode (Fig. 1, *c*).

It would certainly be of great importance if we could represent these motions, to which the smallest particles of an electrolyte are subjected during the passage of the current, more definitely than in these most general outlines. They would not only throw light on the nature of electricity, but also on the chemical constitution of bodies.

In many cases it seems possible to determine by experiment the relative distances through which the two ions move during electrolysis. As we shall be concerned only with this point in what follows, we will give prominence to it alone in the figure. For this purpose let us adopt the method of representation given by Berzelius in his works, in which the two ions are represented one below the other, and supposed to move by each other in a horizontal direction (Fig. 2). It is assumed that the electrolyte is brought into the liquid state by means of an indifferent non-conducting solvent.

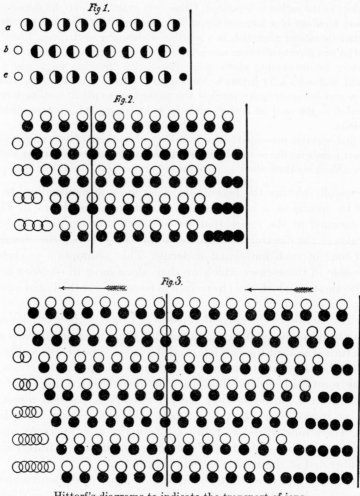

Hittorf's diagrams to indicate the transport of ions.

If we can divide the liquid at any definite place, we shall find that the ions in each portion are in a different proportion after electrolysis has taken place than before. This proportion is determined by the distance through which each ion moves during the passage of the current.

If, for example, we make the assumption, tacitly made in former presentations, that these distances are equal, in which case both migrating ions meet half way between their original positions, a glance at Fig. 2 shows, that after electrolysis, that portion of liquid which borders on the anode will contain half an equivalent less cations than before. The converse is of course true for the other portion which is in contact with the cathode. By equivalent is understood the quantity of the component liberated.

If the two ions do not move through equal distances—that is, if they do not meet each other half way—then the side of the liquid in which the more rapidly moving ion makes its appearance will be increased by more than half an equivalent of it, and diminished by less than half an equivalent of the other ion. Fig. 3 shows this for the case when the anion moves $\frac{1}{3}$, the cation $\frac{2}{3}$ of the distance. The anode side of the liquid contains $\frac{1}{3}$ of an equivalent more anions and $\frac{2}{3}$ of an equivalent less cations after the decomposition than before. The other side shows the converse relation.

This result evidently holds generally. If one ion moves through $1/n$ the distance, and the other $\frac{n-1}{n}$, then the side of the liquid in which the former appears will contain $1/n$ equivalent more of it and $\frac{n-1}{n}$ equivalent less of the other ion. The converse relation will hold for the other side of the electrolyte.[2]

Hittorf indicates the nature of his experimental results in the following citation.

1. The chemical events by which electrolytes transmit the electric current seem to occur only in the two layers which touch the electrodes directly; all the other sections seem not to be changed by electrolysis. This is the case not only if the electrolyte is liquefied by heat; the solution itself behaves in the same way. If we prevent these boundary layers from mixing with that which lies between, the latter keeps its original concentration as long as the current flows through it. In molten electrolytes the study of the decomposition products of electrolysis is limited; the relation which this bears to the current strength as well as to the nature of the electrolytes has been revealed by the classic work of Faraday. In solutions of an electrolyte another fact is found which until now has been very incompletely known. The boundary layers, in which the ions are free, undergo an alteration of their concentrations.

2. The phenomenon is best established in the salts of the electropositive metals which do not decompose the solvent. Therefore we will first consider these. In such a salt solution the layer in which the metal becomes free undergoes a dilution, while a concentration accompanies the separation of the electronegative part if we are careful that the anode enters a soluble compound with it. The last condition is most suitably fulfilled if we choose the same metal for the anode whose salts are submitted to the current. We see this process best if the cathode is placed in the upper part

---

[2] Poggendorf's *Annalen der Physik und Chemie*, **89**: 180–182 (1853); this selection is quoted from the translation of Goodwin, *loc. cit.*, pp. 51–54.

of the vessel and the anode in the lower, and we then clearly see how the layers of liquid which are not in contact with the electrodes retain their original density.

3. To obtain a closer insight into these effects we must determine quantitatively the amount of dilution or concentration. The behavior which is considered here follows automatically from the above discussion. We expose a solution with known concentration in each vertical layer to the current, separate it after electrolysis at any desired position which lies between the electrodes, so long as it is not mixed with the boundary layers, and finally determine the composition of the liquid which is contained in one of the two parts. Theoretically it makes no difference which choice is made here, since both parts combine to make up the original solution. Practical experience soon shows that one or the other pole has the preference.   . . .

5. Thus the investigation yields as a result the amount of any ion which is contained in a definite weight of the solvent when a definite amount of salt is decomposed by the current. Since the content of unaltered solution is given, the masses of ions which were found before electrolysis in any weight of solvent are known, and the differences show the weights of ions which are carried by the current to the pole concerned or have been separated from each other. But these differences are proportional to the quantities which are decomposed by the current. While they are related to the latter, the phenomenon is shown to be independent of any hypothesis.[3]

The following selection shows, in its final sentence, how close Hittorf came to the idea of the independent existence of ions in any solution, that is, the theory of electrolytic dissociation.

Clausius has recently given an explanation of electrolytic conduction in terms of the dominant theory of electricity and in this has considered transport relationships. He assumes that the electrical fluid whose ponderable atoms are inseparable is the bearer of the electrical force and accordingly considers electrolysis as a continuous process, limited by the free electricity found on the surface of the electrolytes. The conclusion to which he comes on these premises is undisputed. The Faraday law which is found to be valid for the weakest current is at variance with the position of modern chemistry as to the condition of a liquid compound body. The ions of an electrolyte cannot be combined in a stable form to whole molecules, and these cannot exist in a definite, regular arrangement.[4]

In the following selection, Hittorf not only explains the nature of complex ions, but also foreshadows the view that the behavior of solutions is analogous to that of gases.

[3] Poggendorf's *Annalen der Physik und Chemie*, **98**: 1–5 (1856).
[4] *Ibid.*, **103**: 53 (1858).

The numbers which the concentrated solutions of cadmium iodide give, numbers I, II, and III, vary noticeably from those which have previously been obtained. After electrolysis, we find here an increase of both constituents at the anode, so that, since the middle layer maintains its composition, there follows an equally great decrease at the cathode.

If we wish to explain the relations as before, both ions of iodine and cadmium have moved to the anode in such a manner that the first always travels a greater space than the distance of two salt molecules and overtakes the metal, which in this situation travels very slowly. In solution I, for example, iodine in each separation and reunion approaches the anode by about one and one-fourth of the distance of two salt molecules, the cadmium by about one-fourth. Apparently this explanation must be rejected and another sought.

In the double salt (ICd + IK) the cadmium moves with the total iodine to the anode; in the dilute solution of cadmium iodide, cadmium shows the ordinary behavior of metals and moves to the cathode while it travels about two-fifths, and iodine three-fifths, of the distance of two salt molecules.

Most chemists at present assume that in many elementary and compound gases the atoms are united two and two, in other words, they establish what to the older school seemed an absurdity, chemical compounds between substances of the same kind. Anyone who works enough with the properties of solutions is driven unwillingly to accept the analogy which exists between dissolved bodies and gaseous bodies.

The above results force me to assume that in concentrated solutions there are double salts which consist of two equivalents of ICd and which behave toward the current as if composed of two different metals. They split during electrolysis into (ICd + I) and Cd. One-half the cadmium moves to the cathode and, in the sense of the dominant theory of electricity, is electropositive; the other half goes with the total iodine to the anode. If the distance traveled, for example, is in the ratio of 2 to 3, then we obtain approximately the transport of solution II. For an equivalent of iodine which is set free on the anode, the supply of this amounts to $2 \cdot \frac{3}{5}$, or 1.2, and at the same pole there is an increase of cadmium in the amount of $\frac{3}{5} - \frac{2}{5}$ or 0.2 of the quantity which, with 1 equivalent, is set free at the cathode.

The important relation of transport number and concentration of the solution is explained in the same way as in the double salt (ICd + IK). With the addition of water the double atoms break up in continually increasing numbers into simple ones; the current therefore becomes increasingly conducted by simple ones, which alone are present with strong dilution.[5]

[5] *Ibid.*, **106**: 545–546 (1859).

The following selection gives Hittorf's views on the chemical nature of electrolytes.

All electrolytes are salts in the sense of the newer chemistry. During electrolysis there occurs the same exchange between the constituents of their molecules as in double elective affinities.[6] The same effect causes the transmission of molecular movement, which we call the *electric current*. According as this exchange goes faster or slower in different electrolytes with the same initiating cause, there will, I believe, be called forth different degrees of resistance. I hope in a supplement to my electrochemical work to be able to show this relation through a number of measurements of resistance more definitely than has yet been possible for me. The differences which exist here first make themselves evident in chemical phenomena when they are extraordinarily great.[7]

Stanislao Cannizzaro

(1826–1910)

IT IS difficult to describe the confused state of chemistry up to the middle of the nineteenth century. There was no universal system of atomic weights, and different formulas were used for the same compounds, depending on the chemist and his school. Although Dalton's atomic theory was fifty years old, it still was not completely accepted because of the confusion and doubt brought about by several presentations of numbers called atomic weights. There was, moreover, a failure to distinguish clearly between ultimate particles, especially the terms *atom* and *molecule*. Despite the work of Berzelius, Dumas, Stas, and others, the atomic weights used were, in many instances, only equivalent weights or combining proportions with, of course, no standard, none having been adopted. The investigations of Avogadro and Gay-Lussac were not understood by most chemists. True, there were some, Laurent, Gerhardt, and Frankland, who had clear concepts, but the majority were unimpressed.

The final and decisive step toward the establishment of a uniform and consistent system of chemistry was taken by an Italian chemist, Stanislao Cannizzaro, in 1858. This was the culmination of several years of teaching and thought on the basic concepts of chemistry. His plan of teaching the foundations of theoretical chemistry was first published in 1858 in the Italian journal *Il Nuovo Cimento*,[1] and entitled "Sunto di Un Corso di Filosofia Chimica fatto nella Reale Universita di

---

[6] [Cf. Bergman, page 93.]

[7] Poggendorf's *Annalen der Physik und Chemie*, **106**: 572 (1859).

[1] *Il Nuovo Cimento*, **7**: 321–366 (1858).

Genova," or "An Abridgement of a Course of Chemical Philosophy given in the Royal University of Genoa." The first word, *Sunto*, is usually translated as "outline" or "sketch," but a better interpretation is given by the word *abridgement*. It was republished the following year (1859) as a pamphlet (Pisa), again in 1880 (Rome), and it is included in a memorial volume of Cannizzaro's papers published in 1896 on his seventieth birthday.[2] The "Sunto" is available, in English, in the *Alembic Club Reprints* and, in German, in Ostwald's *Klassiker der Exacten Wissenschaften*.[3] Here Cannizzaro made three distinctive contributions. First, he recognized and clearly defined the terms *atom* and *molecules;* secondly, he used Avogadro's hypothesis in determining molecular weights; and lastly, he employed a common standard, $H = 1$, as a reference to which to refer the weights of the elements. The communication is written as a letter to S. de Luca from Cannizzaro. The acceptance and dissemination of Cannizzaro's doctrines were hastened when, at the first international chemical congress at Karlsruhe (1860), copies of the "Sunto" were distributed by Angelo Pavesi, who had accompanied Cannizzaro to the conference. Lothar Meyer, who received one of the pamphlets, was so deeply impressed with the completeness and clearness of the article in the manner in which it discussed atoms, molecules, atomic weights, and molecular weights that he incorporated and developed Cannizzaro's views in his book, "Modernen Theorien der Chemie," first published in 1864. Contrary to the widespread belief, the "Sunto" was not the only important contribution that Cannizzaro made in the period of the 1850's. The same volume (**7**) of *Il Nuovo Cimento* that contained the "Sunto" had in addition three other papers by Cannizzaro on theoretical chemistry. Cannizzaro also published a significant article entitled "Lessons on the Atomic Theory Given in the Royal University of Genoa in 1858," in an obscure journal issued in Genoa.[4] It was his "Sunto," however, that convinced chemists of his views, and they were quietly incorporated into chemical thinking. The following is taken from the English version of the "Sunto."

LETTER OF
PROFESSOR STANISLAO CANNIZZARO
TO
PROFESSOR S. DE LUCA:

SKETCH OF A COURSE OF CHEMICAL PHILOSOPHY
GIVEN IN THE ROYAL UNIVERSITY OF GENOA.

I believe that the progress of science made in these last years has confirmed the hypothesis of Avogadro, of Ampère, and of Dumas on the

---

[2] "Scritti intoro alla Teoria Molecolare ed Atomica, ed alla notazione chimica. Pubblicati nel 70° anniversario della sua nascita," Palermo, 1896.

[3] *Alembic Club Reprints*, No. 18, "Sketch of a Course of Chemical Philosophy by Stanislao Cannizzaro (1858)," Edinburgh, 1910; Ostwald's *Klassiker*, No. 30, "Abriss eines Lehrgangs der theoretische Chemie, vorgetragen an der Königlichen Universität Genua. (1858). Uebersetzt von Arthur Miolati aus Mantua. Herausgegeben von Lothar Meyer," Leipzig, 1891.

[4] *Liguria Medica, Giornale di Scienze mediche e naturali*, **1856**: Nos. 5–6. Also reprinted in "Scritti intoro alla Teoria Molecolare . . . ," pp. 58–83.

similar constitution of substances in the gaseous state; that is, that equal volumes of these substances, whether simple of compound, contain an equal number of molecules, not however an equal number of atoms, since the molecules of the different substances, or those of the same substance in its different states, may contain a different number of atoms, whether of the same or of diverse nature.

In order to lead my students to the conviction which I have reached myself, I wish to place them on the same path as that by which I have arrived at it—the path, that is, of the historical examination of chemical theories.

I commence, then, in the first lecture by showing how, from the examination of the physical properties of gaseous bodies, and from the law of Gay-Lussac on the volume relations between components and compounds, there arose almost spontaneously the hypothesis alluded to above, which was first of all enunciated by Avogadro, and shortly afterwards by Ampère. Analysing the conception of these two physicists, I show that it contains nothing contradictory to known facts, provided that we distinguish, as they did, molecules from atoms; provided that we do not confuse the criteria by which the number and the weight of the former are compared, with the criteria which serve to deduce the weight of the latter; provided that, finally, we have not fixed in our minds the prejudice that whilst the molecules of compound substances may consist of different numbers of atoms, the molecules of the various simple substances must all contain either one atom, or a least an equal number of atoms.

In the second lecture I set myself the task of investigating the reasons why this hypothesis of Avogadro and Ampère was not immediately accepted by the majority of chemists. I therefore expound rapidly the work and the ideas of those who examined the relationships of the reacting quantities of substances without concerning themselves with the volumes which these substances occupy in the gaseous state; and I pause to explain the ideas of Berzelius, by the influence of which the hypothesis above cited appeared to chemists out of harmony with the facts.

I examine the order of the ideas of Berzelius, and show how on the one hand he developed and completed the dualistic theory of Lavoisier by his own electro-chemical hypothesis, and how on the other hand, influenced by the atomic theory of Dalton (which had been confirmed by the experiments of Wollaston), he applied this theory and took it for his guide in his later researches, bringing it into agreement with the dualistic electrochemical theory, whilst at the same time he extended the laws of Richter and tried to harmonise them with the results of Proust. I bring out clearly the reason why he was led to assume that the atoms, whilst separate in simple bodies, should unite to form the atoms of a compound of the first order, and these in turn, uniting in simple proportions, should form composite atoms of the second order, and why (since he could not admit that when two substances give a single compound, a molecule of the one and a molecule of the other, instead of uniting to form a single molecule, should change into two molecules of the same nature) he could not accept the hypothesis of Avogadro and of Ampère, which in many cases leads to the conclusion just indicated.

I then show how Berzelius, being unable to escape from his own dualistic ideas, and yet wishing to explain the simple relations discovered by Gay-Lussac between the volumes of gaseous compounds and their gaseous components, was led to formulate a hypothesis very different from that of Avogadro and of Ampère, namely, that equal volumes of simple substances in the gaseous state contain the same number of atoms, which in combination unite intact; how, later, the vapour densities of many simple substances having been determined, he had to restrict this hypothesis by saying that only simple substances which are permanent gases obey this law; how, not believing that composite atoms even of the same order could be equidistant in the gaseous state under the same conditions, he was led to suppose that in the molecules of hydrochloric, hydriodic, and hydrobromic acids, and in those of water and sulphuretted hydrogen, there was contained the same quantity of hydrogen, although the different behaviour of these compounds confirmed the deductions from the hypothesis of Avogadro and of Ampère.

I conclude this lecture by showing that we have only to distinguish atoms from molecules in order to reconcile all the experimental results known to Berzelius, and have no need to assume any difference in constitution between permanent and coercible, or between simple and compound gases, in contradiction to the physical properties of all elastic fluids.

In the third lecture I pass in review the various researches of physicists on gaseous bodies, and show that all the new researches from Gay-Lussac to Clausius confirm the hypothesis of Avogadro and of Ampère that the distances between the molecules, so long as they remain in the gaseous state, do not depend on their nature, nor on their mass, nor on the number of atoms they contain, but only on their temperature and on the pressure to which they are subjected.

In the fourth lecture I pass under review the chemical theories since Berzelius: I pause to examine how Dumas, inclining to the idea of Ampère, had habituated chemists who busied themselves with *organic substances* to apply this idea in determining the molecular weights of compounds; and what were the reasons which had stopped him half way in the application of this theory. I then expound, in continuation of this, two different methods—the one due to Berzelius, the other to Ampère and Dumas—which were used to determine formulae in inorganic and in organic chemistry respectively until Laurent and Gerhardt sought to bring both parts of the science into harmony. I explain clearly how the discoveries made by Gerhardt, Williamson, Hofmann, Wurtz, Berthelot, Frankland, and others, on the constitution of organic compounds confirm the hypothesis of Avogadro and Ampère, and how that part of Gerhardt's theory which corresponds best with the facts and best explains their connection, is nothing but the extension of Ampère's theory, that is, its complete application, already begun by Dumas.

I draw attention, however, to the fact that Gerhardt did not always consistently follow the theory which had given him such fertile results; since he assumed that equal volumes of gaseous bodies contain the same number of molecules, only in the majority of cases, but not always.

I show how he was constrained by a prejudice, the reverse of that of Berzelius, frequently to distort the facts. Whilst Berzelius, on the one hand, did not admit that the molecules of simple substances could be divided in the act of combination, Gerhardt supposes that all the molecules of simple substances are divisible in chemical action. This prejudice forces him to suppose that the molecule of mercury and of all metals consists of two atoms, like that of hydrogen, and therefore that the compounds of all the metals are of the same type as those of hydrogen. This error even yet persists in the minds of chemists, and has prevented them from discovering amongst the metals the existence of biatomic radicals perfectly analogous to those lately discovered by Wurtz in organic chemistry.

From the historical examination of chemical theories, as well as from physical researches, I draw the conclusion that to bring into harmony all the branches of chemistry we must have recourse to the complete application of the theory of Avogadro and Ampère in order to compare the weights and the numbers of the molecules; and I propose in the sequel to show that the conclusions drawn from it are invariably in accordance with all physical and chemical laws hitherto discovered.

I begin in the fifth lecture by applying the hypothesis of Avogadro and Ampère to determine the weights of molecules even before their composition is known.

On the basis of the hypothesis cited above, the weights of the molecules are proportional to the densities of the substances in the gaseous state. If we wish the densities of vapours to express the weights of the molecules, it is expedient to refer them all to the density of a simple gas taken as unity, rather than to the weight of a mixture of two gases such as air.

Hydrogen being the lightest gas, we may take it as the unit to which we refer the densities of other gaseous bodies, which in such a case express the weights of the molecules compared to the weight of the molecule of hydrogen = 1.

Since I prefer to take as common unit for the weights of the molecules and for their fractions, the weight of a half and not of a whole molecule of hydrogen, I therefore refer the densities of the various gaseous bodies to that of hydrogen = 2. If the densities are referred to air = 1, it is sufficient to multiply by 14.438 to change them to those referred to that of hydrogen = 1; and by 28.87 to refer them to the density of hydrogen = 2.

I write the two series of numbers, expressing these weights in the following manner:—

Names of Substances.	Densities or weights of one volume, the volume of Hydrogen being made = 1, *i.e.*, weights of the molecules referred to the weight of a whole molecule of Hydrogen taken as unity.	Densities referred to that of Hydrogen = 2, *i.e.*, weights of the molecules referred to the weight of a half a molecule of Hydrogen taken as unity.
Hydrogen....................	1	2
Oxygen, ordinary..............	16	32
Oxygen, electrised.............	64	128
Sulphur below 1000°...........	96	192
Sulphur* above 1000°..........	32	64
Chlorine....................	35.5	71
Bromine....................	80	160
Arsenic.....................	150	300
Mercury....................	100	200
Water......................	9	18
Hydrochloric Acid.............	18.25	36.50†
Acetic Acid..................	30	60

* This determination was made by Bineau, but I believe it requires confirmation.

† The numbers expressing the densities are approximate: we arrive at a closer approximation by comparing them with those derived from chemical data, and bringing the two into harmony.

Whoever wishes to refer the densities to hydrogen = 1 and the weights of the molecules to the weight of half a molecule of hydrogen, can say that the weights of the molecules are all represented by the weight of two volumes.

I myself, however, for simplicity of exposition, prefer to refer the densities to that of hydrogen = 2, and so the weights of the molecules are all represented by the weight of one volume.

From the few examples contained in the table, I show that the same substance in its different allotropic states can have different molecular weights, without concealing the fact that the experimental data on which this conclusion is founded still require confirmation.

I assume that the study of the various compounds has been begun by determining the weights of the molecules, *i.e.*, their densities in the gaseous state, without enquiring if they are simple or compound.

I then come to the examination of the composition of these molecules. If the substance is undecomposable, we are forced to admit that its molecule is entirely made up by the weight of one and the same kind of matter. If the body is composite, its elementary analysis is made, and thus we discover the constant relations between the weights of its components: then the weight of the molecule is divided into parts proportional to the numbers expressing the relative weights of the components, and thus we obtain the quantities of these components contained in the molecule of the compound, referred to the same unit as that to which we refer the weights of all the molecules. By this method I have constructed the following table:—[table given on p. 413]

All the numbers contained in the preceding table are comparable amongst themselves, being referred to the same unit. And to fix this well in the minds of my pupils, I have recourse to a very simple artifice: I say to them, namely, "Suppose it to be shown that the half molecule of hydrogen weighs a millionth of a milligram, then all the numbers of the preceding table become concrete numbers, expressing in millionths of a milligram the concrete weights of the molecules and of their components: the same thing would follow if the common unit had any other concrete value," and so I lead them to gain a clear conception of the comparability of these numbers, whatever be the concrete value of the common unit.

Once this artifice has served its purpose, I hasten to destroy it by explaining how it is not possible in reality to know the concrete value of this unit; but the clear ideas remain in the minds of my pupils whatever may be their degree of mathematical knowledge. I proceed pretty much as engineers do when they destroy the wooden scaffolding which has served them to construct their bridges, as soon as these can support themselves. But I fear that you will say, "Is it worth the trouble and the waste of time and ink to tell me of this very common artifice?" I am, however, constrained to tell you that I have paused to do so because I have become attached to this pedagogic expedient, having had such great success with it amongst my pupils, and thus I recommend it to all those who, like myself, must teach chemistry to youths not well accustomed to the comparison of quantities.

Once my students have become familiar with the importance of the numbers as they are exhibited in the preceding table, it is easy to lead them to discover the law which results from their comparison. "Compare," I say to them, "the various quantities of the same element contained in the molecule of the free substance and in those of all its different compounds, and you will not be able to escape the following law: *The different quantities of the same element contained in different molecules are all*

Name of Substance.	Weight of one volume, *i.e.*, weight of the molecule referred to the weight of half a molecule of Hydrogen = 1.	Component weights of one volume, *i.e.*, component weights of the molecule, all referred to the weight of half a molecule of Hydrogen = 1.		
Hydrogen...............	2	2 Hydrogen		
Oxygen, ordinary........	32	32 Oxygen		
" electrised.......	128	128 Oxygen		
Sulphur below 1000°......	192	192 Sulphur		
Sulphur above 1000° (?)..	64	64 Sulphur		
Phosphorus.............	124	124 Phosphorus		
Chlorine...............	71	71 Chlorine		
Bromine...............	160	160 Bromine		
Iodine.................	254	254 Iodine		
Nitrogen...............	28	28 Nitrogen		
Arsenic................	300	300 Arsenic		
Mercury...............	200	200 Mercury		
Hydrochloric Acid........	36.5	35.5 Chlorine	1 Hydrogen	
Hydrobromic Acid.......	81	80 Bromine	1 "	
Hydriodic Acid.........	128	127 Iodine	1 "	
Water.................	18	16 Oxygen	2 "	
Ammonia..............	17	14 Nitrogen	3 "	
Arseniuretted Hyd.......	78	75 Arsenic	3 "	
Phosphuretted Hyd......	35	32 Phosphorus	3 "	
Calomel................	235.5	35.5 Chlorine	200 Mercury	
Corrosive Sublimate......	271	71 "	200 "	
Arsenic Trichloride.......	181.5	106.5 "	75 Arsenic	
Protochloride of Phosphorus............	138.5	106.5 "	32 Phosphorus	
Perchloride of Iron.......	325	213 "	112 Iron	
Protoxide of Nitrogen....	44	16 Oxygen	28 Nitrogen	
Binoxide of Nitrogen.....	30	16 "	14 "	
Carbonic Oxide..........	28	16 "	12 Carbon	
Carbonic Acid...........	44	32 "	12 "	
Ethylene...............	28	4 Hydrogen	24 "	
Propylene..............	42	6 "	36 "	
Acetic Acid, hydrated....	60	{ 4 " { 32 Oxygen { 24 Carbon		
" anhydrous....	102	{ 6 Hydrogen { 48 Oxygen { 48 Carbon		
Alcohol................	46	{ 6 Hydrogen { 16 Oxygen { 24 Carbon		
Ether..................	74	{ 10 Hydrogen { 16 Oxygen { 48 Carbon		

whole multiples of one and the same quantity, which, always being entire, has the right to be called an atom."

Thus:—

One molecule	of free hydrogen	contains	2 of hydrogen	=	2 × 1
"	of hydrochloric acid	"	1 "	=	1 × 1
"	of hydrobromic acid	"	1 "	=	1 × 1
"	of hydriodic acid	"	1 "	=	1 × 1
"	of hydrocyanic acid	"	1 "	=	1 × 1
"	of water	"	2 "	=	2 × 1
"	of sulphuretted hydrogen	"	2 "	=	2 × 1
"	of formic acid	"	2 "	=	2 × 1
"	of ammonia	"	3 "	=	3 × 1
"	of gaseous phosphuretted hydrogen	"	3 "	=	3 × 1
"	of acetic acid	"	4 "	=	4 × 1
"	of ethylene	"	4 "	=	4 × 1
"	of alcohol	"	6 "	=	6 × 1
"	of ether	"	10 "	=	10 × 1

Thus all the various weights of hydrogen contained in the different molecules are integral multiples of the weight contained in the molecule of hydrochloric acid, which justifies our having taken it as common unit of the weights of the atoms and of the molecules. The atom of hydrogen is contained twice in the molecule of free hydrogen.

In the same way it is shown that the various quantities of chlorine existing in different molecules are all whole multiples of the quantity contained in the molecule of hydrochloric acid, that is, of 35.5; and that the quantities of oxygen existing in the different molecules are all whole multiples of the quantity contained in the molecule of water, that is, of 16, which quantity is half of that contained in the molecule of free oxygen, and an eighth part of that contained in the molecule of electrised oxygen [ozone].

Thus:—

One molecule	of free oxygen	contains	32	of oxygen	= 2 × 16
"	of ozone	"	128	"	= 8 × 16
"	of water	"	16	"	= 1 × 16
"	of ether	"	16	"	= 1 × 16
"	of acetic acid etc. etc.	"	32	"	= 2 × 16
One molecule	of free chlorine	contains	71	of chlorine	= 2 × 35.5
"	of hydrochloric acid	"	35.5	"	= 1 × 35.5
"	of corrosive sublimate	"	71	"	= 2 × 35.5
"	of chloride of arsenic	"	106.5	"	= 3 × 35.5
"	of chloride of tin etc. etc.	"	142	"	= 4 × 35.5

In a similar way may be found the smallest quantity of each element which enters as a whole into the molecules which contain it, and to which may be given with reason the name of atom. In order, then, to find the atomic weight of each element, it is necessary first of all to know the weights of all or of the greater part of the molecules in which it is contained and their composition.

If it should appear to any one that this method of finding the weights of the molecules is too hypothetical, then let him compare the composition of equal volumes of substances in the gaseous state under the same conditions. He will not be able to escape the following law: *The various quantities of the same element contained in equal volumes either of the free element or of its compounds are all whole multiples of one and the same quantity;* that is, each element has a special numerical value by means of which and with the help of integral coefficients the composition by weight of equal volumes of the different substances in which it is contained may be expressed. Now, since all chemical reactions take place between equal volumes, or integral multiples of them, it is possible to express all chemical reactions by means of the same numerical values and integral coefficients. The law enunciated in the form just indicated is a direct deduction from the facts: but who is not led to assume from this same law that the weights of equal volumes represent the molecular weights, although other proofs are wanting? I thus prefer to substitute in the expression of the law the word molecule instead of volume. This is advantageous for teaching, because, when the vapour densities cannot be determined, recourse is had to other means for deducing the weights of the molecule of compounds. The whole substance of my course consists in this: to prove the exactness of these latter methods by showing that they lead to the same results as the vapour density when both kinds of method can be adopted at the same time for determining molecular weights.

The law above enunciated, called by me the law of atoms, contains in itself that of multiple proportions and that of simple relations between the volumes; which I can demonstrate amply in my lecture. After this I easily succeed in explaining how, expressing by symbols the different atomic weights of the various elements, it is possible to express by means of formulae the composition of their molecules and of those of their compounds, and I pause a little to make my pupils familiar with the passage from gaseous volume to molecule, the first directly expressing the fact and the second interpreting it. Above all, I study to implant in their minds thoroughly the difference between molecule and atom. It is possible indeed to know the atomic weight of an element without knowing its molecular weight; this is seen in the case of carbon. A great number of the compounds of the substance being volatile, the weights of the molecules and their composition may be compared, and it is seen that the quantities of carbon which they contain are all integral multiples of 12, which quantity is thus the atom of carbon and expressed by the symbol C; but since we cannot determine the vapour density of free carbon we have no means of knowing the weight of its molecule, and thus we cannot know how many times the atom is contained in it. Analogy does not in any way help us, because we observe that the molecules of the most closely analogous substances (such as sulphur and oxygen), and even the molecules of the same substance in its allotropic states, are composed of different numbers of atoms. We have no means of predicting the vapour density of carbon; the only thing that we can say is that it will be either 12 or an integral multiple of 12 (in my system of numbers). The number which is given in different treatises on chemistry as the theoretical density of carbon is quite arbitrary, and a useless datum in chemical calculations; it is useless for calculating and verifying the weights of the molecules of the various compounds of carbon, because the weight of the molecule of free carbon may be ignored if we know the weights of the molecules of all its compounds; it is useless for determining the weight of the atom of carbon, because this is deduced by comparing the composition of a certain number of molecules containing carbon, and the knowledge of the weight of the molecule of this last would scarcely add a datum more to those which are already sufficient for the solution of the problem. Any one will easily convince himself of this by placing in the following manner the numbers expressing the molecular weights derived from the densities and the weights of the compounds contained in them:—

Name of Compounds of Carbon.	Weights of the molecules referred to the atom of Hydrogen.	Weights of the components of the molecules referred to the weight of the atom of Hydrogen taken as unity.		Formulae, making H = 1 C = 12 O = 16 S = 32
Carbonic Oxide..............	28	12 Carbon	16 Oxygen	CO
Carbonic Acid..............	44	12 "	32 "	CO^2
Sulphide of Carbon...........	76	12 "	64 Sulphur	CS^2
Marsh Gas..................	16	12 "	4 Hydrogen	CH^4
Ethylene..................	28	24 "	4 "	C^2H^4
Propylene..................	42	36 "	6 "	C^3H^6
Ether.......	74	$\left\{ \begin{array}{l} 48 \text{ " } \quad 10 \text{ " } \\ \phantom{48 \text{ " } \quad} 16 \text{ Oxygen} \end{array} \right\}$		$C^4H^{10}O$
etc.	etc.	etc.		etc.

In the list of molecules containing carbon there might be placed also that of free carbon if the weight of it were known; but this would not have any greater utility than what we would derive by writing in the list one more compound of carbon; that is, it would do nothing but verify once more that the quantity of carbon contained in any molecule, whether of the element itself or of its compounds, is 12 or $n \times 12 = C^n$, n being an integral number.

I then discuss whether it is better to express the composition of the molecules of compounds as a function of the molecules of the components, or if, on the other hand, it is better, as I commenced by doing, to express the composition of both in terms of those constant quantities which always enter by whole numbers in both, that is, by means of the atoms. Thus, for example, is it better to indicate in the formula that one molecule of hydrochloric acid contains the weight of half a molecule of hydrogen and half a molecule of chlorine, or that it contains an atom of one and an atom of the other, pointing out at the same time that the molecules of both of these substances consist of two atoms?

Should we adopt the formulae made with symbols indicating the molecules of the elements, then many coefficients of these symbols would be fractional, and the formula of a compound would indicate directly the ratio of the volumes occupied by the components and by the compounds in the gaseous state. This was proposed by Dumas in his classical memoir, *Sur quelques points de la Théorie atomique* (*Annales de Chimie et de Physique*, tom. 33, 1826).

To discuss the question proposed, I give to the molecules of the elements symbols of a different kind from those employed to represent the atoms, and in this way I compare the formulae made with the two kinds of symbols. . . .

Friedrich August Kekulé

(*1829–1896*)

THE final step in the development of modern structural formulas for organic compounds was taken by Kekulé. Like most of the chemists of his time, Kekulé had great difficulty in deciding whether to use the old equivalent weights (with $C = 6$) or the atomic weights (with $C = 12$) which had been proposed by Gerhardt in 1843. At last, in 1858, he settled on the use of atomic weights, which he designated by the barred atoms of Berzelius. From the type theory he took the marsh gas type, $\bar{C}H_4$, and, perhaps unconsciously, from Frankland's work the idea of the "combining power of the elements." From these concepts he developed the idea of affinity units, which we would call *valence bonds*. He recognized that in terms of this theory, carbon was a "tetratomic" element. Once he had grasped this idea, which now appears basically simple, he was able to reduce all the vast number of aliphatic compounds to order. An important deduction from his theory was that carbon atoms could link with each other. The way was opened for eliminating the varied and confusing formulas which different chemists had been using almost at will. The development and application of Kekulé's ideas are shown in the first selection.[1]

THE CONSTITUTION AND THE METAMORPHOSES OF CHEMICAL COMPOUNDS AND THE CHEMICAL NATURE OF CARBON

Constitution of Radicals. Nature of Carbon.

It has often been pointed out that radicals are not groups of atoms closely bound together but only atoms located near each other, which in certain reactions do not separate, while in others they break apart. It depends on the nature of the atoms which are located together and on the nature of the reacting substance whether or not an atom group plays the part of a so-called "radical" directly; whether it is a more or less stable radical. In general, it can be said that the greater the difference in the nature of the individual atoms, the more easily will an atom group, a radical, break apart.

It will not be necessary to extend these considerations further: I will give only one example to show how this association of atoms can occur. The radical of sulfuric acid SO_2 contains three atoms, each of which is diatomic, thus representing two affinity units. By joining together, one affinity unit of one atom combines with one of the other. Of the six affinity units, four are thus used to hold the three atoms themselves together: two remain over, and the group appears to be diatomic; it unites, e.g., with two atoms of a monatomic element:

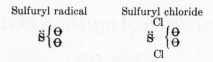

If the sulfuryl chloride acts on water, two HCl split off, the residue remains combined, and the resulting product can be considered as two molecules of H_2O in which two atoms of H are replaced by the group SO_2.*

---

[1] *Annalen der Chemie*, **106**: 129–159 (1858); the selection given is taken from pages 151 to 157 of this paper. This and the paper from which the following selection is taken have been reprinted in Ostwald's *Klassiker*, No. 145, "Über die Konstitution und die Metamorphosen der chemischen Verbindungen und über die chemische Natur des Kohlenstoffs. Untersuchungen über aromatische Verbindungen. Herausgegeben von A. Ladenburg," Leipzig, 1904.

* It can easily be seen that the group SO, which under certain conditions plays the part of a radical, must also be diatomic. The sulfurous acid (as a hydrate), which according to one view contains the same radical as sulfuric acid and belongs to the intermediate type $H_2 + H_2O$, is, according to another, one of the compounds of the

In a similar way the manner in which the atoms are associated can be shown for all radicals, including those which contain carbon. To do this, it is only necessary to form a picture of the nature of carbon.

If only the simplest compounds of carbon are considered (marsh gas, methyl chloride, carbon tetrachloride, chloroform, carbonic acid, phosgene gas, carbon disulfide, prussic acid, etc.), it is striking that the amount of carbon which the chemist has known as the least possible, as the *atom*, always combines with four atoms of a monatomic, or two atoms of a diatomic, element; that generally, the sum of the chemical unities of the elements which are bound to one atom of carbon is equal to 4. This leads to the view that carbon is *tetratomic* (or tetrabasic).[2]

Accordingly, carbon stands with the three groups of elements mentioned earlier as the only representative yet known of the tetratomic group (the compounds of boron and silicon are still too little known). Its simplest combinations with elements of the three other groups are

$$IV + 4I \qquad\qquad IV + 2II$$
$$\qquad IV + (II + 2I) \qquad\qquad IV + (III + I)$$

or, in examples,

C̶H_4 C̶O̶Cl_2 C̶O̶$_2$ CNH
C̶Cl_4 C̶S_2
C̶H_3Cl
C̶HCl_3

For substances which contain more atoms of carbon, it must be assumed that at least part of the atoms are held just by the affinity of carbon and that the carbon atoms themselves are joined together, so that naturally a part of the affinity of one for the other will bind an equally great part of the affinity of the other.

The simplest, and therefore the most obvious, case of such linking together of two carbon atoms is this, that one affinity unit of one atom is bound to one of the other. Of the 2×4 affinity units of the two carbon atoms, two are thus used to hold both atoms themselves together; there still remain six extra which can be bound by the atoms of other elements. In other words, one group of two atoms of carbon $=$ C̶$_2$ will be hexatomic, it will form compounds with six atoms of a monatomic element, or in general, with so many atoms that the sum of their chemical unities is 6 (*e.g.*, ethyl hydride, ethyl chloride, elayl chloride, $1\frac{1}{2}$ carbon tetrachloride, acetonitrile, cyanogen, aldehyde, acetyl chloride, glycol, etc.).

If we put more than two carbon atoms together in the same way, then

---

radical S̶O̶, which belongs to the type $2H_2$O̶. Both expressions are certainly synonymous.

[2] If carbon is introduced among the types as a *tetratomic radical*, proportionally simple formulas are obtained for some of the well-known compounds. It would lead too far to go further into this.

for each further one added, the basicity of the carbon group will be raised by two units. The number of hydrogen atoms (chemical units) which is bound with n atoms of carbon joined together in this way, *e.g.*, will be expressed by

$$n(4 - 2) + 2 = 2n + 2$$

For n = 5, the basicity is thus = 12 (amyl hydride, amyl chloride, amylene chloride, valeronitrile, valeraldehyde, valeryl oxide, angelic acid, pyrotartaric acid anhydride, etc.). Until now it has been assumed that all the atoms linked on the carbon are held by the affinity of carbon. However, it is equally possible to think that in the polyatomic elements (O, N, etc.) only a part of their affinity, only one of the two units of oxygen for example, or only one of the three units of nitrogen, is bound to the carbon, so that thus, of the two affinity units of oxygen, one, and of the three affinity units of nitrogen, two, are still left over and can be bound to other elements. These other elements are thus only indirectly bound to carbon, which is expressed by the type method of writing formulas,

$$\left.\begin{matrix} C_2H_5 \\ H \end{matrix}\right\}O \qquad \left.\begin{matrix} C_2H_5 \\ H \\ H \end{matrix}\right\}N \qquad \left.\begin{matrix} C_2H_5O \\ C_2H_5 \end{matrix}\right\}O \qquad \left.\begin{matrix} C_2H_5 \\ C_2H_5 \\ C_2H_5 \end{matrix}\right\}N$$

In the same way different carbon groups are held together through the oxygen or the nitrogen.

When such compounds are actually considered in regard to those atoms which are linked thus to the carbon group, then the carbon group appears to be a radical, and it is said that the radical replaces one atom of H of the type, because instead of its one atom of H the affinity of O or N would be saturated in its place.

When comparisons are made between compounds which have an equal number of carbon atoms in the molecule and which can be changed into each other by simple transformations (*e.g.*, alcohol, ethyl chloride, aldehyde, acetic acid, glycolic acid, oxalic acid, etc.) the view is reached that the carbon atoms are arranged in the same way and only the atoms held to the carbon skeleton are changed.

When the homologous bodies are then considered, the view is reached that in them the carbon atoms (regardless of how many are held in a molecule) are arranged together in the same way, according to the same laws of symmetry. In deeper decompositions, in which the carbon skeleton itself is attacked and broken into fragments, each fragment shows the same arrangement of carbon atoms, so that each fragment of the compound is homologous with the starting substance or with a substance which can be obtained from the homologous body by a simple transformation (*e.g.*, replacement of hydrogen by oxygen).

In a great many organic compounds such a "simplest" arrangement of carbon atoms can be assumed. Others contain so many carbon atoms in the molecule that for them a denser arrangement of carbons must be assumed.[3]

Benzene, for example, and all its derivatives, like the hydrocarbons homologous with it, shows such a high carbon content as to differentiate these bodies characteristically from all the substances resulting from the transformation of ethyl.

Naphthalene contains still more carbon. It must be assumed that in it carbon is arranged in a still denser form, that is, the individual atoms are still more closely bound to one another.

When these carbon-rich hydrocarbons, benzene and its homologues and naphthalene, are compared with the hydrocarbons of the alcohol group (elayl and its homologues), with which they show analogies in many respects, they show

Ethylene	Propylene	Butylene	Amylene
C_2H_4	C_3H_6	C_4H_8	C_5H_{10}
	Benzene	Toluene	Xylene
	C_6H_6	C_7H_8	C_8H_{10}
		Naphthalene	
		$C_{10}H_8$	

Comparing the hydrocarbons of the second row with those of the first, it is found that with an equal hydrogen content, they contain three more carbons. Between naphthalene and toluene the same relation occurs. It thus seems as if here the same sort of denser arrangement of carbon atoms is repeated and as if there were three classes of carbon-containing compounds differentiated from each other by the type of arrangement of carbon atoms.

The aliphatic structures were clearly explained by Kekulé's theory of 1858, but the nature of the aromatic compounds remained unsettled. The best explanation Kekulé could find in 1858 was that they were more "densely" arranged than the aliphatic substances. His mind continued to work with the problem, however, and in 1865 he published the famous paper in which he proposed his ring structure for benzene. The following selection is taken from this paper.[4]

STUDIES ON AROMATIC COMPOUNDS

The theory of the atomicity of the elements, and especially the knowledge of carbon as a tetratomic element, has made possible in recent years

---

[3] It is easy to be convinced that the formulas of these compounds can be constructed through the "next simplest" arrangement of carbon atoms.

[4] *Annalen der Chemie,* **137**: 129–196 (1865); the selection is taken from pages 130 to 135.

in a very satisfactory way the explanation of the atomistic constitution of a great many carbon compounds, particularly those which I have called *fatty bodies*. Until now, so far as I know, no one has attempted to apply these views to the aromatic compounds. When I developed my views on the tetratomic nature of carbon seven years ago, I indicated in a note that I had already formed an opinion on this subject, but I had not considered it suitable to develop the idea further. Most chemists who have since written on theoretical questions have left this subject untouched; some stated directly that the composition of aromatic compounds could not be explained by the theory of atomicity; others assumed the existence of a hexatomic group formed by six carbon atoms, but they did not try to find the method of combination of these carbon atoms, nor to give an account of the conditions under which this group could bind six monatomic atoms. . . .

In order to give an account of the atomistic constitution of aromatic compounds, it is necessary to take into consideration the following facts:

1. All aromatic compounds, even the simplest, are proportionally richer in carbon than the analogous compounds in the class of the fatty bodies.

2. Among the aromatic compounds, just as in the fatty bodies, there are numerous homologous substances, *i.e.*, those whose differences of composition can be expressed by n CH_2.

3. The simplest aromatic compound contains at least six atoms of carbon.

4. All alteration products of aromatic substances show a certain family similarity, they belong collectively to the group of "aromatic compounds." In more deeply acting reactions, it is true, one part of carbon is often eliminated, but the chief product contains at least six atoms of carbon (benzene, quinone, chloranil, carbolic acid, hydroxyphenic acid, picric acid, etc.). The decomposition stops with the formation of these products if complete destruction of the organic group does not occur.

These facts obviously lead to the conclusion that in all aromatic substances there is contained one and the same atom group, or, if you wish, a common nucleus which consists of six carbon atoms. Within this nucleus the carbon atoms are certainly in close combination or in more compact arrangement. To this nucleus, then, more carbon atoms can add and, indeed, in the same way and according to the same laws as in the case of the fatty bodies.

It is next necessary to give an account of the atomic constitution of this nucleus. Now this can be done very easily by the following hypothesis, which, on the now generally accepted view that carbon is tetratomic, explains in such a simple manner that further development is scarcely necessary.

If many carbon atoms can unite with one another, then it can also happen that *one* affinity unit of one atom can bind *one* affinity unit of the neighboring atom. As I have shown earlier, this explains homology and in general the constitution of the fatty bodies.

It can now be further assumed that many carbon atoms are thus linked together, that they are always bound through two affinity units; it can also be assumed that the union occurs *alternately* through first *one* and then *two* affinity units. The first and the last of these views could be expressed by somewhat the following periods:

1/1, 1/1, 1/1, 1/1 etc.

1/1, 2/2, 1/1, 2/2 etc.

The first law of symmetry of union of the carbon atoms explains the constitution of the fatty bodies, as already mentioned; the second leads to an explanation of the constitution of aromatic substances, or at least of the nucleus which is common to all these substances.

If it is accepted that *six* carbon atoms are linked together according to this law of symmetry, a group is obtained which, if it is considered as an *open chain*, still contains *eight* nonsaturated affinity units (Table II, Fig. 1). If another assumption is made, that the two carbon atoms which end the chain are linked together by one affinity unit, then there is obtained a *closed chain*[5] (a symmetrical ring) which still contains *six* free affinity units (Table II, Fig. 2).[6]

From this *closed chain* now follow all the substances which are usually called *aromatic compounds*. The *open chain* occurs in quinone, in chloranil, and in the few substances which stand in close relation to both. I leave these bodies here without further consideration; they are proportionately easy to explain. It can be seen that they stand in close relation with the

---

[5] In the group of fatty bodies, the hydrocarbons of the ethylene series can be considered as closed chains. It should be clear that ethylene is the starting member of this series and that the hydrocarbon CH_2 (methylene) does not exit, for it cannot be believed that two affinities which belong to the same carbon atom should be able to link themselves together.

[6] In order to make the views developed here more understandable than can be done by words alone, I have gathered "graphic formulas" for many of the substances mentioned here in Table II. The ideas which can be expressed by these formulas are now so widely known that I need not discuss them again in detail. I have used the same type of graphic formulas that I used in 1859 when for the first time I developed further my views on the atomistic constitution of molecules. This form has been accepted with alterations scarcely worth noting by Wurtz (Leçons de philosophie chimique); it seems to me it offers certain advantages over the recent modifications of Loschmidt and of Crum-Brown. For an understanding of the table, I need only mention that I have represented the closed chain C_6A_6 as a straight line, thus open, with the dashes denoting the terminal affinities which are to be understood as affinity units linking the opposite ends. The dots of formulas 1, 2 and 31, 32 mean still unsaturated affinity units.

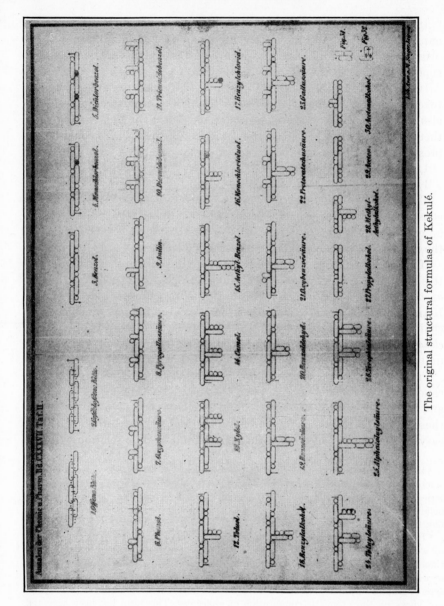

The original structural formulas of Kekulé.

aromatic substances, but they still cannot truly be counted with the group of aromatic substances.

In all aromatic substances there can be assumed to be a common nucleus; it is the closed chain C_6A_6 (where A means an unsaturated affinity or affinity unit).

The six affinity units of this nucleus can be saturated by six monatomic elements. They can also all, or at least in part, be saturated by an affinity of a polyatomic element, but this latter must then be joined to other atoms, and so one or more *side chains* are produced, which can be further lengthened by linking themselves with other elements.

A saturation of two affinity units of the nucleus by an atom of a diatomic element or a saturation of three affinity units by an atom of a triatomic element is not possible in theory. Compounds of the molecular formula C_6H_4O, C_6H_4S, C_6H_3N are thus unthinkable; if bodies of these compositions exist, and if the theory is correct, the formulas of the first two must be doubled, that of the third tripled.[7]

Wilhelm Körner

(*1839–1925*)

THE theory of Kekulé had cleared up the major difficulty in understanding the structure of aromatic compounds, but there were many consequences of the theory which demanded further work. Chief among these was that of the isomers of benzene. Before the structures of complex organic compounds could be understood, it was necessary to know positively the structures of the simple compounds into which they were broken down. This work was done by Körner, who had been a pupil of Kekulé. He showed on theoretical grounds that each of the three possible disubstituted isomers of benzene could give rise to a different number of trisubstituted derivatives. Experimental determinations then showed beyond a doubt the structure of any of the simple aromatic isomers. It should be noted that Körner's use of the terms *ortho*, *meta*, and *para* does not conform to the usage of the

[7] I remember, however, the compound C_6H_4O which Limpricht obtained along with phenol by dry distillation of salicyclic anhydride. The molecular formula of this substance is obviously

$$C_{12}H_8O_2 = \left. \begin{matrix} C_6H_4 \\ C_6H_4 \end{matrix} \right\} OO$$

Its formation is explained by the equation

$$2\ C_{14}H_{10}O_5 = C_{12}H_8O_2 + 2\ C_6H_6O + 2CO_2 + 2\ CO$$

present day. He had arbitrarily assigned these terms before he knew the structures of the isomers.

The following selection is taken from Körner's paper of 1874, "Studies on the Isomerism of So-called Aromatic Compounds with Six Atoms of Carbon."[1]

Assuming the equivalence of the six positions of hydrogen in benzene to be proved, it is enough to prepare any complete series of trisubstituted derivatives and among these three compounds to study and report their relation to each other, thus obtaining an unqualified solution to the problem. In fact, by preparing the three possible tribromobenzenes, always starting with the dibromobenzenes; by determining how many of the trisubstituted compounds are obtained and from which of the disubstituted compounds they come, or vice versa; by determining for each of the disubstituted compounds how many trisubstituted compounds can give it, we will have solved the structures of the di- and trisubstituted bromobenzenes as well as of related substances, directly and decisively. This can be shown in the following way:

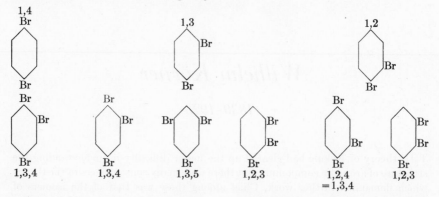

In a similar way, *six* different modifications of dibromoaniline are possible and consequently also six nitrodibromobenzenes, which can be expressed by the following scheme, with reference to the three possible dibromobenzenes:

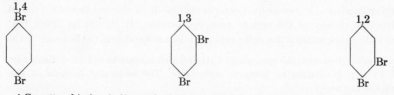

[1] *Gazzetta chimica italiana,* **4:** 305–446 (1874); the selection is taken from pages 311 to 313. The paper has been translated in Ostwald's *Klassiker,* No. 174, "Über die Bestimmung des chemischen Ortes bei den aromatischen Substanzen. Vier Abhandlungen von Wilhelm Koerner. Herausgegeben von G. Bruni und B. L. Vanzetti," Leipzig, 1910.

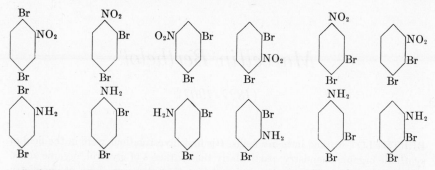

It follows directly that that form of dibromobenzene which is capable of furnishing *all three* modifications of tribromobenzene, or *three* mononitro derivatives, or, on the other hand, can arise from *three* dibromo-anilines by reverse substitution of the NH_2 residue, *necessarily has the 1,3 position*. The 1,2 modification can give two forms of tribromobenzene and two mononitro derivatives and will result from only two dibromoanilines by substitution of H for the ammoniacal residue.

The 1,4 modification can result *from only one* dibromoaniline by introduction of hydrogen in the place occupied by the ammonia residue and, on the other hand, can give rise to only one tribromobenzene and to only one mononitrodibromobenzene.

I have therefore made a detailed study of the nitro derivatives of dibromobenzene prepared from the three well-known modifications of nitroaniline: on the other hand, I have tried by various methods to obtain dibromoanilines and then change them by replacing the NH_2 group with hydrogen or with bromine into di- or tribromobenzenes, and finally I have obtained the two known and the three unknown forms. I tried this successfully, and the tribromobenzene of Mitscherlich gave all three of the dibromobenzenes, while the new one obtained by me gave only two, and that of Meyer only one, and that the paradibromobenzene. Then it necessarily follows

1. That we must regard the positions of the substituted hydrogens in the tribromobenzene of Mitscherlich as 1,3,4; in mine, 1,2,3; and in that of Meyer, 1,3,5.

2. For the disubstituted products, the substituents of the compounds *which I call paraderivatives* (chiefly ordinary dinitrobenzene and resorcin) occupy the position 1,3; in the meta derivatives (chiefly as in pyrocatechine), 1,2; and in the ortho derivatives (corresponding to hydroquinone), 1,4.

Marcellin Berthelot

(1827–1907)

BERTHELOT worked in many fields. His first investigations were in the field of synthetic organic chemistry, particularly the syntheses of glycerol, organic acids, and hydrocarbons. This work convinced him that the same laws of chemistry govern the organic and inorganic fields. In his text on organic chemistry[1] he gave many examples to illustrate the total synthesis of organic compounds from the elements, and thus he completed the overthrow of the doctrine of "vital force" which had been begun by Wöhler with his synthesis of urea (pages 309–312).

After publication of this book, Berthelot's interest shifted to the subject of reaction velocities, continuing the work of Wilhelmy. With Péan de St. Gilles (1832–1863) he studied the kinetics of esterification[2] and only the fact that he did not consider the reverse reaction probably prevented him from anticipating Guldberg and Waage in the discovery of the law of mass action.

His interest in physical chemistry led him into thermochemistry. He developed the bomb calorimeter and determined the heat of combustion of many compounds. His work, along with that of Julius Thomsen (1826–1909), supplied much of the data which made possible the application of the Hess law (page 331). He introduced the terms *endothermic* and *exothermic*. Berthelot summed up his work in a series of principles which systematized many of the earlier studies. The most controversial of these, the "principle of maximum work," was later shown to be valid only in special cases, but it did much in its day to stimulate the development of thermochemistry.

Berthelot carried out notable investigations in the field of explosives, and his pioneering work in the translations of Greek, Syriac, and Arabic alchemical manuscripts laid the foundation for a critical history of alchemy.

The first selection below, taken from Berthelot's text on organic chemistry,[3] explains his views on the importance of total synthesis. The second selection[4] gives the principles of thermochemistry which he considered fundamental.

Indeed, I have undertaken to proceed in organic chemistry in the manner which has been known in mineral chemistry for nearly a century, that is to say, to build up organic materials by combining their elements solely

---

[1] "Chimie organique fondée sur la synthèse," Paris, 1860, 2 vols. See also: "Les Classiques de la découverte scientifique. La synthèse totale en chimie organique. Mémoires de MM. Wöhler, Gerhardt, M. Berthelot, Le Bel, van't Hoff, Jungfleisch, Ladenburg, Pasteur. Préface et commentaires par M. Marcel Delépine," Paris, 1937.

[2] *Ann. chim. phys.*, **65**: 385 (1862); **66**: 5 (1862); **68**: 225 (1863).

[3] "Chimie organique . . . ," pp. xxvi–xxix.

[4] *Ann. chim. phys.*, [5], **4**: 5–131 (1875); the selection is taken from pages 5 to 6.

with the help of chemical forces. The success of these experiments will henceforth allow the whole science to be presented rigorously, proceeding from the simple to the compound, from the known to the unknown, and without relying on ideas other than those which result from the purely physical and chemical studies of mineral substances. Instead of assuming the origin of organic chemistry in the phenomena of life, it will now be found to have an independent basis; in its turn it can render that aid to physiology which it has long secured.

The new course of organic chemistry is effected by proceeding according to the same ideas on which synthesis in mineral chemistry has been based. In both cases it is enough to follow the reverse course from analysis. We have seen how organic analysis leads to decomposition of natural principles, forming first volatile bodies, chiefly alcohols; from these, analysis passes to the carburets of hydrogen [hydrocarbons], and from the carburets to the elements.

Reversing the terms of this problem, I have taken for a point of departure the simple bodies: carbon, hydrogen, oxygen, nitrogen, and I have reconstituted organic compounds by the combination of these elements, first binary, then ternary, etc.; the first analogous, the others identical with the immediate principles contained in the living beings themselves.

Some developments are here necessary to show the progressive course of these synthetic formations. The substances which are first formed by purely chemical methods are the chief carburets of hydrogen, that is to say, the fundamental binary compounds of organic chemistry. This is one of the ways by which we can proceed to produce all the substances by means of mineral compounds and the elements. We take the oxide of carbon, that is, a purely mineral substance, and solely by a combination of time and ordinary affinities we combine this oxide of carbon with the elements of water: we thus obtain a first organic compound, namely, formic acid. This acid when united with a mineral base gives a formate; finally, by destroying the formate by heat we force the carbon from the oxide of carbon and the hydrogen of water to combine in the nascent state to give rise to carburets of hydrogen. Thus marsh gas, olefiant gas, propylene, etc., are formed. Analogous methods allow us to obtain the chief carburets of hydrogen from the elements; this is the first step in synthesis.

The carburets of hydrogen obtained thus become in their turn the point of departure for the synthesis of alcohols. With marsh gas and oxygen, methyl alcohol is formed; with olefiant gas and the elements of water ordinary alcohol is formed; with propylene and the elements of water, propyl alcohol is formed, etc.

It is by these general methods that I have produced the synthesis of carburets of hydrogen and of alcohols. They are the first products of synthesis and the most difficult to obtain. The carburets of hydrogen and the alcohols are, indeed, perhaps the most characteristic among organic compounds. There are no analogies in mineral chemistry; they constitute the base of our edifice, and they become the point of departure for all other formations. The intervention of slow reactions, those of weak and delicate affinities, suffices to produce them. By relying on the same methods, we can push on further; indeed, as we rise to more complex compounds, the reactions become easier and more varied, and the resources of synthesis increase at each new step. In a word, in the order of organic syntheses, the essential point resides in the formation of the first terms from the elements, that is, in that of the carburets of hydrogen and the alcohols: it is this which wipes out in principle all lines of demarcation between mineral chemistry and organic chemistry.

This formation is the more decisive in that it permits us to connect the new results with the work already done in organic chemistry. Indeed, the chemist today knows how to produce from alcohols and carburets of hydrogen a multitude of other compounds: such are aldehydes, the first term of oxidation, which comprise the great part of oxygenated essential oils; such are organic acids, so widely distributed in plants and animals. By combining these same alcohols and these same carburets of hydrogen with the acids, we obtain compound ethers, a new category of substances characteristic of organic chemistry which are also found in plants. The whole of these results comprise the great part of the ternary compounds. We can go farther. Indeed, the alcohols, the aldehydes, the acids, united with ammonia, give rise in their turn to quarternary substances formed from carbon, hydrogen, oxygen, and nitrogen, that is to say, to bodies designated by the names of amides and of bases.

Thus synthesis extends its conquests from the elements up to the domain of the most complicated substances without our being able to assign any limit to its progress. Indeed, if we envisage in our minds the almost infinite number of organic compounds, from the substances which our art knows how to produce, such as carburets of hydrogen, alcohols, and their derivatives, up to those which still exist only in nature, such as the sugars and the nitrogenous principles of animal origin, we pass from one term to the other by insensible degrees, and we cannot see any absolute barrier or break which we may with any appearance of certitude fear to find unsurpassable. We can then affirm that organic chemistry is henceforth founded on the same base as mineral chemistry. In these two sciences, synthesis as well as analysis results from the play of the same forces, applied to the same elements.

Berthelot sets forth his fundamental principles of thermochemistry in the following.[5]

[5] See footnote 4.

ON THE GENERAL PRINCIPLES OF THERMOCHEMISTRY.

Thermochemistry rests on three fundamental principles, which are the following:

1. *Principle of molecular work.* The quantity of heat liberated in any reaction measures the sum of chemical and physical work accomplished in this reaction.

2. *Principle of the calorific equivalence of chemical transformations.* If a system of simple or compound bodies, taken under determined conditions, undergoes physical or chemical changes capable of bringing it to a new state without the introduction of any mechanical effect outside the system, the quantity of heat liberated or absorbed by the effect of these changes depends solely on the initial and final states of the system; it is the same whatever may be the nature and the sequence of the intermediate states.

I have already given in this report some developments of these two principles and their consequences ([4] **6**: 292 *ff.*); I have especially defined the *heat of atomic combination*, which expresses the real work of the chemical forces and should be related to the *reaction of perfect gases* working at *constant volume.* For lack of such a state of a perfect gas, which it is often impossible to obtain except in theory, I have proposed then to relate the reactions to the *solid state*, which has almost the same theoretical advantages, as shown by the study of specific heats and the law of Dulong and Petit. Several new memoirs will be devoted to explaining these ideas with more details and to proving them by numerous experiments.

3. *Principle of maximum work.* All chemical changes, occurring without the intervention of outside energy tend toward the production of bodies, or of a system of bodies, which liberate more heat.

Vladimir Vasil'evich Markovnikov

(*1838–1904*)

MARKOVNIKOV began his work in organic chemistry just as the structural theory was becoming generally accepted, and many of his early studies were conducted with A. Butlerov (1828–1886), who had been active in establishing the theory. In its earliest phases, however, this theory tended to be a more or less schematic representation. There was little realization of the effect of the atoms in an organic molecule on the reactivity of other atoms or of their effect on the course of reactions in which the molecule was involved. Markovnikov made a systematic study of the addition of halogen acids to double bonds and quickly realized the importance of the reciprocal action of atoms in organic compounds. His ideas were first expressed completely in his doctoral thesis at the University of Kazan in 1869, but they did not become generally known until he published a German summary in 1870. In this is stated the principle which has become known as Markovnikov's rule. It permits prediction, in many cases, of the order of addition of halogen acids to double bonds. Subsequent work has shown that the rule is not completely general, but it remains of great importance, since it is the first explanation of the course of a reaction in terms of the nature of the atoms involved and, as such, is a forerunner of the more recent electronic theories of organic chemistry.

Markovnikov's chief work lay in establishing his rule, but he carried out many investigations in petroleum chemistry which were of considerable importance to the oil industry.

The following selection is taken from the German summary of his doctoral thesis, entitled "The Dependence of Differing Replaceability of the Hydrogen of Radicals in the Isomeric Butyric Acids."[1]

If we wish to find the rule which underlies the separation of the individual groups of elements in the so-called "direct union" of hypochlorous acid with unsaturated hydrocarbons, we must conclude that the facts already known can give no definite answer. We know the combination of ethylene, of propylene, of butylene, and of amylene with hypochlorous acid. The first compound can give no answer owing to the symmetrical structure of ethylene $\begin{matrix} CH_2 \\ CH_2 \end{matrix}$.

Consideration of the combination of propylene and butylene, however, leads to entirely contradictory conclusions. From the formulas

$$\begin{matrix} CH_2Cl \\ CHOH \\ CH_3 \end{matrix} \text{ and } ClC\begin{cases} CH_3 \\ CH_3 \\ CH_2OH \end{cases}$$

we see that the more electronegative hydroxyl unites in the first case with the less hydrogenated carbon atom but behaves in exactly the opposite manner in the formation of butylene chlorohydrin, where it occupies a place on the side of the more hydrogenated carbon. The origin of such differences is evidently to be found in differences of the chemical structure of the two hydrocarbons. In hydrocarbons constituted in an analogous manner we may well find an analogy in manner of addition, and the formation of amylene chlorohydrin can evidently be expressed by the following equation:

$$\begin{matrix} CH_2 \\ CH \\ CH \\ \underbrace{CH_3 \quad CH_3} \end{matrix} + ClOH = \begin{matrix} CH_2Cl \\ CHOH \\ CH \\ \underbrace{CH_3 \quad CH_3} \end{matrix}$$

[1] *Annalen der Chemie*, **153**: 228–259 (1870); the selection is taken from pages 255 to 257.

If, because of the insufficient number of observations, it is impossible as yet to establish a rule for the type of union of the elements of hypochlorous acid with unsaturated hydrocarbons, nevertheless for the hydrogen halides such a rule is available. I cannot here go into a detailed consideration of the different facts which permit us to establish such a rule: *if an unsymmetrically constituted hydrocarbon unites with a hydrohalogen acid, the halogen adds to the less hydrogenated carbon atom, i.e., to the carbon which is more under the influence of other carbons.* We have such a case in the union of propylene:

$$\begin{matrix} CH_2 & & CH_3 \\ CH & + HI = & CHI \\ CH_3 & & CH_3 \end{matrix}$$

of both butylenes:

$$C\begin{cases} CH_3 \\ CH_3 \\ CH_2 \end{cases} + HI = IC\begin{cases} CH_3 \\ CH_3 \\ CH_3 \end{cases} \qquad \begin{matrix} CH_2 & & CH_3 \\ CH & + HI = & CHI \\ C_2H_5 & & C_2H_5 \end{matrix}$$

<table>
<tr><td>butylene</td><td>tertiary
pseudobutyl
iodide</td><td>butylene</td><td>butylene iodo-
hydrate
of de Luynes</td></tr>
</table>

of both amylenes:

$$\begin{matrix} CH_2 & & CH_3 \\ CH & + HCl = & CHCl \\ CH & & CH \\ \underbrace{CH_3 \quad CH_3} & & \underbrace{CH_3 \quad CH_3} \end{matrix} \qquad \begin{matrix} CH_2 & & CH_3 \\ CH & + HI = & CHI \\ CH_2 & & CH_2 \\ C_2H_5 & & C_2H_5 \end{matrix}$$

<table>
<tr><td>β-amylene</td><td>β-amylene
iodohydrate</td><td>α-amylene</td><td>α-amylene
iodohydrate</td></tr>
</table>

Conforming to the general rule of the influence of halides, which I have mentioned earlier, we can expect *that by addition of hydrogen chloride, bromide, or iodide to vinyl chloride, chlorinated propylene, and other analogues, the halide will always add to the carbon atom which is already united to a halide.* This rule, which derives from the law of substitution, is in its turn actually supported by a number of facts.

Julius Lothar Meyer

(1830–1895)

LOTHAR Meyer was active in many fields of chemistry. He designed much new apparatus, determined physical constants, and studied problems of organic chemistry. He proposed the first centric formula for benzene. His text, "Die modernen Theorien der Chemie und ihre Bedeutung für die chemische Statik" (Breslau, 1864), was influential in inducing chemists to accept the new atomic weights. Meyer had been strongly influenced by the ideas of Cannizzaro while writing this book. In it he first presented his ideas on the relation of the properties of elements and their atomic weights. Although he recognized this relationship clearly, he at first devoted most of his attention to the regular differences between the atomic weights of related elements. His ideas underwent further development, however, and by 1868 he had prepared a table which in many respects resembled the present periodic table. He did not publish this work until after the appearance of Mendeleev's first paper on the subject in 1869 (pages 438–442). His table was very similar to that of Mendeleev, but it contained some improvements and was, perhaps, influential in causing some of the revisions made by Mendeleev in the second version of his table, published in 1870. In general, Meyer was more impressed by the periodicity of the physical properties of the elements, while Mendeleev saw more clearly the chemical consequences of the periodic law. The following selection is taken from the paper of 1870, in which Meyer first fully expressed his ideas.[1]

THE NATURE OF THE CHEMICAL ELEMENTS AS A FUNCTION OF THEIR ATOMIC WEIGHTS.

The regularities which exist between the numerical values of the atomic weights are not only sought by different authors between very different elements but are also presented very differently. Since we no longer base our consideration of these on the so-called "equivalents" of Gmelin but use the atomic weights determined by the rules of Avogadro and of Dulong and Petit, the presentation of these regularities has been considerably simplified. Even in 1864, I found regularities which brought into one and the same scheme families of chemical elements which until then had been considered different. By the correct determination of different atomic weights, it has since become possible to arrange in the same scheme the elements discovered up to now which are well enough known. Recently

[1] *Annalen der Chemie, Supplementband,* **7**: 354–364 (1870); reprinted in Ostwald's *Klassiker*, No. 68, "Lothar Meyer und D. Mendelejeff, Abhandlungen über das naturliche System der chemischen Elemente (1864–1869 und 1869–1871). Herausgegeben von Kanl Seubert," Leipzig, 1895.

Mendeleev has shown that such an arrangement is obtained if the atomic weights of all the elements, without any arbitrary selection, are simply arranged in a single series according to the size of their numerical values; this series is divided into sections, and these are added together in unaltered succession. The following table is essentially identical with that given by Mendeleev.

The table contains all the elements whose atomic weights have been determined up to now either by the gas densities of their compounds or by their heat capacities, arranged according to increasing atomic weight,

I.	II.	III.	IV.	V.	VI.	VII.	VIII.	IX
	B = 11,0	Al = 27,3		—		? In = 113,4		Tl = 20?,7
	C = 11,97	Si = 28		—		Sn = 117,8		Pb = 206,4
			Ti = 48		Zr = 89,7			
	N = 14,01	P = 30,9		As = 74,9		Sb = 122,1		Bi = 207,5
			V = 51,2		Nb = 93,7		Ta = 182,2	
	O = 15,96	S = 31,98		Se = 78		Te = 128?		—
			Cr = 52,4		Mo = 95,6		W = 183,5	
	F = 19,1	Cl = 35,38		Br = 79,75		J = 126,5		—
			Mn = 54,8		Ru = 103,5		Os = 198,6?	
			Fe = 55,9		Rh = 104,1		Ir = 196,7	
			Co = Ni = 58,6		Pd = 106,2		Pt = 196,7	
Li = 7,01	Na = 22,99	K = 39,04		Rb = 85,2		Cs = 132,7		—
			Cu = 63,3		Ag = 107,66		Au = 196,2	
?Be = 9,3	Mg = 23,9	Ca = 39,9		Sr = 87,0		Ba = 136,8		—
			Zn = 64,9		Cd = 111,6		Hg = 199,8	

Periodic table according to Lothar Meyer, 1870.

with the single exception of hydrogen, which appears to be anomalous, and including also Be and In, whose probable atomic weights are derived from their equivalent weights; in all, 56 elements. Besides H, it lacks only Y, Eb, (Tb?), Ce, La, Di, Th, U, Jg (Jargonium),[2] none of whose atomic weights are known, and even some of whose equivalent weights are unknown. Probably these elements later will, at least in part, fill the blanks which are still found in the table. Other blanks will perhaps be filled by elements to be discovered later; possibly also through future discoveries one or another element will be removed from its place and replaced by a more suitable one.

While the elements follow through the nine vertical rows from first to last according to the size of their molecular weights, the horizontal rows

[2] [In the *Chemical News*, **20:** 7 (1869), H. C. Sorby claimed on the basis of spectroscopic evidence to have isolated a new element, jargonium, from the mineral jargon, from Ceylon. In the *Chemical News*, **21:** 73 (1870), he withdrew the claim. The spectral lines upon which he had relied were due to slightly impure zirconium.]

contain the natural families. To obtain this arrangement, some few of the elements whose atomic weights have been found to be nearly equal and which have probably not been very carefully determined must be rearranged somewhat, tellurium before iodine, osmium before iridium and platinum, and these before gold. Whether this reversal of the series corresponds to the properly determined atomic weights must be shown by later researches. Here I will add only one observation to those which Mendeleev made in his table, that the elements standing in vertical rows IV, VI, and VIII are often isomorphically related to those of the next preceding horizontal row; thus, Ti and Zr with Si, V with P, Cr and Mo with S, Mn with Cl, Ag with Na, Zn with Mg, etc. As to the question of atoms, which so far have not been broken down, the table makes plain an especially important conclusion. If we assume that the atoms are aggregates of one and the same material and differ only in their different masses, then we can consider the properties of the elements as depending on the size of their atomic weights; they appear as direct functions of the atomic weight. The table gives us the conception that the properties of the elements are in great part *periodic* functions of the atomic weight. The same or similar properties reappear if the atomic weight has a certain size, then after 16 units, then about 46, and finally 88 to 92 units. This is true in all cases, whatever the element from which we may start. As striking and attractive as this observation is, however, it leaves us completely in the dark as to the change in properties within the periods at whose ends the properties which were present at the beginning repeat themselves. If, for example, we start from Li, we find that after an increase of nearly 16 units, essentially these properties are found in Na, and again after 16 units, in K. On the way there, however, we encounter in a most varied series first the elements Be, B, C, N, O, F, and then again, Mg, Al, Si, P, S, Cl, apparently without any means of transition; only the saturation capacity of the atoms rises and falls regularly and equally in both intervals.

Monat.	Diat.	Triat.	Tetrat.	Triat.	Diat.	Monat.
Li	Be	B	C	N	O	F
Na	Mg	Al	Si	P	S	Cl

But if we wish to describe the nature of the elements as depending on the atomic weight, then we must follow step-wise the change of each property from element to element. To obtain a starting point for this is the purpose of the following considerations.

One of the properties which changes quite regularly with the atomic weight is the atomic volume of the elements. Table 3 gives a graphic picture of its changes, depending on changes in the atomic weight. On the abscissa, the curve is proportional to the atomic weights; the ordinates relate to the atomic volume of the elements in the solid state (except for

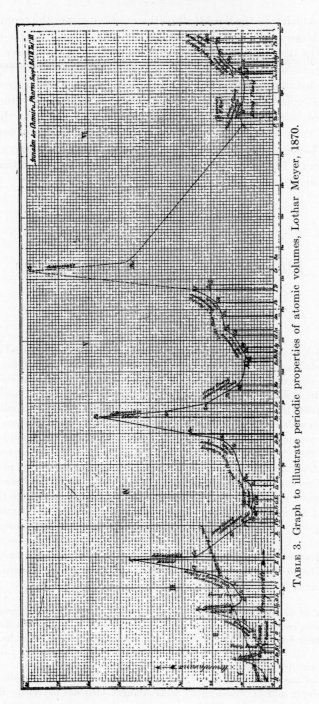

TABLE 3. Graph to illustrate periodic properties of atomic volumes, Lothar Meyer, 1870.

chlorine, which is in the liquid); thus the quotients from the atomic weight and the density are plotted proportionally. The atomic weight of hydrogen and the density of water are taken as units. The successive points of the ordinates are joined by a continuous curve in order to make more clearly evident the changes which the atomic volume undergoes with increasing atomic weight. Where the knowledge of the atomic volume of one or more elements is lacking, the curve is a dotted line, and the atomic values of these elements are given in italics instead of heavy type.

It can be seen from the course of the curve that the atomic volume of the elements, like their chemical properties, is a periodic function of their atomic weight.

Dmitriĭ Ivanovich Mendeleev

(1834–1907)

MENDELEEV was responsible for much important work in physical chemistry and in metrology and for important theories of the nature of solutions and the origin of petroleum, but his chief claim to fame has always been his statement of the periodic law and its consequences. His announcement of the law appeared slightly earlier than that of Lothar Meyer, and it is probable that similar factors were responsible for the independent formulation of the law by these two men. Both had attended the Congress of Karlsruhe in 1860 and had there been influenced by the ideas of Cannizzaro. The clarification of the concept of atomic weight which came as a result of his paper was essential before the periodic law could be discovered. Both Mendeleev and Meyer soon afterward wrote textbooks which required a systematization of ideas that no doubt led directly to the law. In the case of Mendeleev, the book was his famous "Principles of Chemistry" (St. Petersburg 1868–1870), which appeared in eight Russian editions, three English, and several in French and German. It was one of the most original works of the science. Mendeleev announced the periodic law at a meeting of the newly formed Russian Chemical Society in March, 1869, and the paper was published in the first volume of its Journal.[1]

---

[1] *Journal of the Russian Chemical Society*, **1**: 60–77 (1869). The first version of the periodic table, contained in this paper, was reprinted almost at once as a short note in the *Zeitschrift für Chemie*, **12**, 405 (1869). The original Russian paper has been reprinted in "D. I. Mendeleev. Collected Works," Leningrad, 1934, 3 vols. (vol. 2, pp. 3–16); and it is from this that the selection given here has been taken.

The paper has been given in German translation in Ostwald's *Klassiker*, No. 68, "Lothar Meyer und D. Mendelejeff, Abhandlungen über das natürliche System der

THE RELATION BETWEEN THE PROPERTIES AND ATOMIC WEIGHTS OF THE ELEMENTS.

. . . In undertaking to prepare a textbook called "Principles of Chemistry," I wished to establish some sort of system of simple bodies in which their distribution is not guided by chance, as might be thought instinctively, but by some sort of definite and exact principle. We previously saw that there was an almost complete absence of numerical relations for establishing a system of simple bodies, but in the end any system based on numbers which can be determined exactly will deserve preference over other systems which do not have numerical support, since the former leave little room for arbitrary choices. The numerical data for simple bodies are limited at the present time. If for some of them the physical properties are determined with certainty, yet this applies only to a very small number of the elementary bodies. For example, such properties as optical, or even electrical or magnetic, ones, cannot in the end serve as a support for a system because one and the same body can show different values for these properties, depending on the state in which they occur. In this regard, it is enough to recall graphite and diamond, ordinary and red phosphorus, and oxygen and ozone. Not only do we not know the density in the vapor state for most of them, by which to determine the weight of the particles of the simple bodies, but this density is subject to alteration exactly like those polymeric alterations which have been noted for complex bodies. Oxygen and sulfur show this effect positively, but the relations between nitrogen, phosphorus, and arsenic offer further confirmation because these similar elements have particle weights of N_2, P_4, and As_4, unequal in the number of atoms among themselves. A number of the properties of the simple bodies must change with these polymeric changes. Thus we cannot be sure that for any element, even for platinum, there may not occur another state, and the location of an element in a system based on its physical properties would then be changed. Besides this, anyone understands that no matter how the properties of a simple body may change in the free state, *something* remains constant, and when the elements form compounds, this *something* has a material value and establishes the characteristics of the compounds which include the given element. In this respect, we know only one constant peculiar to an element, namely, the atomic weight. The size of the atomic weight, by the very essence of the matter, is a number which is not related to the state of division of the simple body but to the material part which is common to the simple body and all its compounds. The atomic weight belongs not to coal or the diamond, but to carbon. The property which Gerhardt and

---

chemischen Elemente (1864–1869 und 1869–1871). Herausgegeben von Karl Seubert," Leipzig, 1895.

Cannizzaro determined as the atomic weight of the elements is based on such a firm and certain assumption that for most bodies, especially for those simple bodies whose heat capacity in the free state has been determined, there remains no doubt of the atomic weight, such as existed some years ago, when the atomic weights were so often confused with the equivalents and determined on the basis of varied and often contradictory ideas.

This is the reason I have chosen to base the system on the size of the atomic weights of the elements.

The first attempt which I made in this way was the following: I selected the bodies with the lowest atomic weights and arranged them in the order of the size of their atomic weights. This showed that there existed a period in the properties of the simple bodies, and even in terms of their atomicity the elements followed each other in the order of arithmetic succession of the size of their atoms:

Li = 7; Be = 9.4; B = 11;   C = 12; N = 14; O = 16; F = 19
Na = 23; Mg = 24; Al = 27.4; Si = 28; P = 31; S = 32; Cl = 35.3
 K = 39; Ca = 40; .... Ti = 50; V = 51 ....

In the arrangement of elements with atoms greater than 100, we meet an entirely analogous continuous order:

Ag = 108; Cd = 112; Ur = 116; Sn = 118; Sb = 122; Te = 128; I = 127.

It has been shown that Li, Na, K, and Ag are related to each other, as are C, Si, Ti, Sn, or as are N, P, V, Sb, etc. This at once raises the question whether the properties of the elements are expressed by their atomic weights and whether a system can be based on them. An attempt at such a system follows.

In the assumed system, the atomic weight of the element, unique to it, serves as a basis for determining the place of the element. Comparison of the groups of simple bodies known up to now according to the weights of their atoms leads to the conclusion that the distribution of the elements according to their atomic weights does not disturb the natural similarities which exist between the elements but, on the contrary, shows them directly. . . .

All the comparisons which I have made in this direction lead me to conclude that *the size of the atomic weight determines the nature of the elements,* just as the weight of the molecules determines the properties and many of the reactions of complex bodies. If this conclusion is confirmed by further applications of this approach to the study of the elements, then we are near an epoch in understanding the existing differences and the reasons for the similarity of elementary bodies.

I think that the law established by me does not run counter to the general direction of natural science, and that until now it has not been demonstrated, although already there have been hints of it. Henceforth, it seems to me, there will be a new interest in determining atomic weights, in discovering new elementary bodies, and in finding new analogies between them.

I now present one of many possible systems of elements based on their atomic weights. It serves only as an attempt to express those results which can be obtained in this way. I myself see that this attempt is not final, but it seems to me that it clearly expresses the applicability of my assumptions to all combinations of elements whose atoms are known with certainty. In this I have also wished to establish a general system of the elements. Here is this attempt:

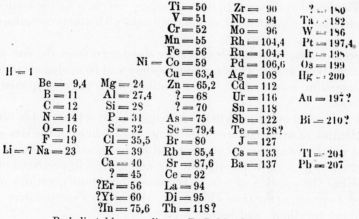

Periodic table according to D. I. Mendeleev, 1869.

. . . In conclusion, I consider it advisable to recapitulate the results of the above work.

1. Elements arranged according to the size of their atomic weights show clear *periodic* properties.

2. Elements which are similar in chemical function either have atomic weights which lie close together (like Pt, Ir, Os) or show a uniform increase in atomic weight (like K, Rb, Cs). The uniformity of such an increase in the different groups is taken from previous work. In such comparisons, however, the workers did not make use of the conclusions of Gerhardt, Regnault, Cannizzaro, and others who established the true value of the atomic weights of the elements.

3. Comparisons of the elements or their groups in terms of size of their atomic weights establish their so-called "atomicity" and, to some extent,

differences in chemical character, a fact which is clearly evident in the group Li, Be, B, C, N, O, F, and is repeated in the other groups.

4. The simple bodies which are most widely distributed in nature have small atomic weights, and all the elements which have small atomic weights are characterized by the specificity of their properties. They are therefore the typical elements. Hydrogen, as the lightest element, is in justice chosen as typical of itself.

5. The *size* of the atomic weight determines the character of the element, just as the size of the molecule determines the properties of the complex body, and so, when we study compounds, we should consider not only the properties and amounts of the elements, not only the reactions, but also the weight of the atoms. Thus, for example, compounds of S and Te, Cl and I, etc., although showing resemblances, also very clearly show differences.

6. We should still expect to discover many *unknown* simple bodies; for example, those similar to Al and Si, elements with atomic weights of 65 to 75.

7. Some *analogies* of the elements are discovered from the size of the weights of their atoms. Thus uranium is shown to be analogous to boron and aluminum, a fact which is also justified when their compounds are compared.

The purpose of my paper will be entirely attained if I succeed in turning the attention of investigators to the same relationships in the size of the atomic weights of nonsimilar elements, which have, as far as I know, been almost entirely neglected until now. Assuming that in problems of this nature lies the solution of one of the most important questions of our science, I myself, as my time will permit, will turn to a comparative study of lithium, beryllium, and boron.

The remarkable ability which Mendeleev showed in the application of his theory distinguishes him from all the other workers in this field. He was particularly interested in the chemical consequences of the theory and was thus led to make predictions of the properties of certain as yet undiscovered elements. Within a short time after the prediction of these properties for the elements which he called *eka-aluminum, eka-boron,* and *eka-silicon* (1871), the elements *gallium* (1874), *scandium* (1879), and *germanium* (1885) were discovered and were shown to agree in properties remarkably well with his predictions. This confirmation of the ideas of Mendeleev established the validity of the periodic law. The following selection, taken from his paper, "A Natural System of the Elements and Its Use in predicting the Properties of Undiscovered Elements,"[2] illustrates the detail with which his predictions were made.

[2] *Journal of the Russian Chemical Society,* **3**: 25–56 (1871); "Collected Works," vol. 2, pp. 140–163. A German version of this paper appeared in *Annalen der Chemie, Supplementband,* **8**: 133–229 (1872).

And now, in order to clarify the matter further, I wish to draw some conclusions as to the chemical and physical properties of those elements which have not been placed in the system and which are still undiscovered but whose discovery is very probable. I think that until now we have not had any chance to foresee the absence of these or other elements, because we have had no order for their arrangement, and even less have we had occasion to predict the properties of such elements. An established system is limited by its order of known or discovered elements. With the periodic and atomic relations now shown to exist between all the atoms and the properties of their elements, we see the possibility not only of noting the absence of some of them but even of determining, and with great assurance and certainty, the properties of these as yet unknown elements; it is possible to predict their atomic weight, density in the free state or in the form of oxides, acidity or basicity, degree of oxidation, and ability to be reduced and to form double salts and to describe the properties of the metalloorganic compounds and chlorides of the given element; it is even possible also to describe the properties of some compounds of these unknown elements in still greater detail. Although at the present time it is not possible to say when one of these bodies which I have predicted will be discovered, yet the opportunity exists for finally convincing myself and other chemists of the truth of those hypotheses which lie at the base of the system I have drawn up. Personally, for me these assumptions have become so strong that, as in the case of indium, there is justification for the ideas which are based on the periodic law which lies at the base of all this study.

Among the ordinary elements, the *lack* of a number of *analogues of boron and aluminum* is very striking, that is, in group III, and it is certain that we lack an element of this group immediately following aluminum; this must be found in the even, or second, series, immediately after potassium and calcium. Since the atomic weights of these latter are near 40, and since then in this row the element of group IV, titanium, Ti = 50, follows, then the atomic weight of the missing element should be nearly 45. Since this element belongs to an even series, it should have more basic properties than the lower elements of group III, boron or aluminum, that is, its oxide, R_2O_3, should be a stronger base. An indication of this is that the oxide of titanium, TiO_2, with the properties of a very weak acid, also shows many signs of being clearly basic. On the basis of these properties, the oxide of the metal should still be weak, like the weakly basic properties of titanium dioxide; compared to aluminum, this oxide should have a more strongly basic character, and therefore, probably, it should not decompose water, and it should combine with acids and alkalis to form simple salts; ammonia will not dissolve it, but perhaps the hydrate will dissolve weakly in potassium hydroxide, although the latter is doubtful, because the element belongs to the even series and to a group of elements whose oxides contain a small amount of oxygen. I have decided to give this element the preliminary name of *ekaboron*, deriving the name from this, that it follows boron as the first element of the even group, and the syllable *eka* comes from the Sanskrit word meaning "one." Eb = 45. Ekaboron should be a metal with an atomic volume of about 15, because in the elements of the second series, and in all the even series, the atomic volume falls quickly as we go from the first group to the following ones. Actually, the volume of potassium is nearly 50, calcium nearly 25, titanium and vanadium nearly 9, and chromium, molybdenum, and iron nearly 7; thus the specific gravity of the metal should be close to 3.0, since its atomic weight = 45. The metal will be nonvolatile, because all the metals in the even series of all the groups (except group I) are nonvolatile; hence it can hardly be discovered by the ordinary method of spectrum analysis. It should not decompose water at ordinary temperature, but at somewhat raised temperatures it should decompose it, as do many other metals of this series which form basic oxides. Finally, it will dissolve in acids. Its chloride $EbCl_3$ (perhaps Eb_2Cl_6), should be a volatile substance but a salt, since it corresponds to a basic oxide. Water will act on it as it does on the chlorides of calcium and magnesium, that is, ekaboron chloride will be a hygroscopic body and will be able to evolve hydrogen chloride without having the character of a hydrochloride. Since the volume of calcium chloride = 49 and that of titanium chloride = 109, the volume of ekaboron chloride should be close to 78, and therefore its specific gravity will probably be about 2.0 Ekaboron oxide, Eb_2O_3, should be a nonvolatile substance and probably should not fuse; it should be insoluble in water, because even calcium oxide is very slightly soluble in water, but it will probably dissolve in acid. Its specific volume should be about 39, because in the series potassium oxide has a volume of 35, CaO = 18, TiO = 20, and CrO_3 = 36; that is, considered on the basis of a content of one atom of oxygen, the volume quickly falls to the right, thus, for potassium = 35, for calcium = 18, for titanium = 10, for chromium = 12, and therefore the volume for ekaboron oxide containing one atom of oxygen should be nearly 13, and so the formula Eb_2O_3 should correspond to a volume of about 39, and therefore anhydrous ekaboron oxide will have a specific gravity close to 3.5. Since it is a sufficiently strong base, this oxide should show little tendency to form alums, although it will probably give alum-forming compounds, that is, double salts with potassium sulfate. Finally, ekaboron will not form metalloorganic compounds, since it is one of the metals of an even series. Judging by the data now known for the elements which accompany cerium, none of them belong in the place which is assigned to ekaboron, so that this metal is certainly not one of the members of the cerium complex which is now known.

Jacobus Henricus van't Hoff

(1852–1911)

FEW chemists have contributed papers to the theory of both organic and physical chemistry. Such, however, was the achievement of J. H. van't Hoff. His early work was in the field of organic chemistry, at a time when the studies of Pasteur had laid the foundations of stereochemistry but before its principles were well understood. With remarkable ability to visualize three-dimensional structures, van't Hoff saw that the explanation for the occurrence of optical isomers lay in the nature of the groups tetrahedrally arranged around a central carbon atom. His first publication on this subject, which appeared in September, 1874, preceded that of Le Bel on the same subject by only two months. The two men had worked out the theory entirely independently. In addition, however, van't Hoff explained the cause of the isomerism of maleic and fumaric acids by geometrical isomerism. Thus his work, together with that of Le Bel, extended the two-dimensional structures of Kekulé into three dimensions and explained facts which could only be understood by such an enlarged view.

Van't Hoff's theory was first published at Utrecht in the form of a pamphlet in Dutch, but it was quickly translated into French.[1]

A SUGGESTION LOOKING TO THE EXTENSION INTO SPACE
OF THE STRUCTURAL FORMULAS AT PRESENT USED IN CHEMISTRY.
AND A NOTE UPON THE RELATION BETWEEN THE OPTICAL ACTIVITY
AND THE CHEMICAL CONSTITUTION OF ORGANIC COMPOUNDS.

I desire to introduce some remarks which may lead to discussion and hope to avail myself of the discussion to give my ideas more definiteness and breadth. Since the starting point for the following communication is found in the chemistry of the carbon compounds, I shall for the present do nothing more than state the points having reference to it.

It appears more and more that the present constitutional formulas are incapable of explaining certain cases of isomerism; the reason for this is

---

[1] *Archives néerlandaises des sciences exactes et naturelles*, **9**: 445–454 (1874); reprinted in "Les Classiques de la découverte scientifique. La synthèse totale en chimie organique. Mémoires de MM. Wöhler, Gerhardt, M. Berthelot, Le Bel, van't Hoff, Jungfleisch, Ladenburg, Pasteur. Préface et commentaires par M. Marcel Delépine," Paris, 1937.

It has been translated into English in "Foundations of Stereochemistry. Memoirs by Pasteur, van't Hoff, Le Bel, and Wislicenus," translated and edited by George M. Richardson, New York, 1901, pp. 37–46. The following selection is taken from this translation.

perhaps the fact that we need a more definite statement about the actual positions of the atoms.

If we suppose that the atoms lie in a plane, as for example with isobutyl alcohol (Figure I) where the four affinities are represented by four lines in this plane occupying two directions perpendicular to one another, then methane (CH_4) (to start with the simplest case) will give the following isomeric modifications (the different hydrogen atoms being replaced one after the other by univalent groups R′ R″ etc.):

One for $CH_3(R')$ and for $CH(R')_3$

Two for CH_2R_2' (Figures II and III), for

$CH_2R'R''$, and for CHR'_2R''

Three for $CHR'R''R'''$ and for $CR'R''R'''R''''$

(Figures IV, V, and VI); numbers that are clearly greater than the numbers actually known thus far.

The theory is brought into accord with the facts if we consider the affinities of the carbon atom directed toward the corners of a tetrahedron of which the carbon atom itself occupies the center.

The number of isomers is then reduced and will be as follows:

One for CH_3R', CH_2R_2', $CH_2R'R''$, CHR_3',

and $CHR_2'R''$ but

Two for $CHR'R''R'''$ or more general, for

$CR'R''R'''R''''$.

If one imagines himself in the line R′R‴ in Figures VII and VIII with head toward R′ and looking toward the line R″R‴ then R″ may be on the right (Figure VII) or on the left (Figure VIII) of the observer; in other words: *When the four affinities of the carbon atom are satisfied by four univalent groups differing among themselves, two and not more than two different tetrahedrons are obtained, one of which is the reflected image of the other, they cannot be superposed; that is, we have here to deal with two structural formulas isomeric in space.* According to this hypothesis the combination $CR'R''R'''R''''$ presents a condition not presented by the combinations $CR_2' R''R'''$, $CR_3'R''$ or CR_4', a condition not expressed by the ordinary mode of representation. According to the present mode there would be between $CR'R''R'''R''''$ and $CR_2'R''R'''$ a difference quite as great as between $CR_2'R''R'''$ and $CR_3'R''$, or between $CR_3'R''$ and CR_4'.

Submitting the first result of this hypothesis to the control of facts, I believe that it has been thoroughly established that some combinations which contain a carbon atom combined with four different univalent groups (such carbon atoms will henceforth be called asymmetric carbon atoms) present some anomalies in relation to isomerism and other charac-

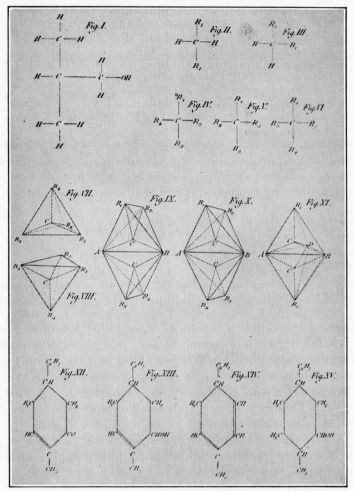

Figures to illustrate the stereochemical ideas of van't Hoff.

teristics which are not indicated by the constitutional formulas thus far used.

FIRST PART

I. Relation Between the Asymmetric Carbon and the Property of Optical Activity:

(a) *All of the compounds of carbon which in solution rotate the plane of polarized light possess an asymmetric carbon atom.*

In order to convince oneself of the justice of these remarks it is necessary to run through the following list of optically active compounds in the formula of which the asymmetric carbon is indicated by **C**:

Ethylidene lactic acid, $CH_3C.H.OH.COOH$.
Aspartic acid, $COOH$ $C.H.NH_2.(CH_2COOH)$.
Asparagine, $COOH$ $C.H.NH_2.(CH_2CONH_2)$.
Malic acid, $COOH$ $C.OH.H.(CH_2COOH)$.
Glutaric acid [Itamalic acid] CH_2OH $C.H.COOH.(CH_2COOH)$.
Tartaric acid, $COOH$ $C.H.OHC.H.OH.COOH$.
Dextrose, Laevulose, Galactose, Maltose.
Sorbin, Eucalyn, etc. $CH_2OH.C.H.OH.(C_4H_7O_4)$
Mannite, Quercite, Pinite: $(C_4H_9O_4).C.H.OH.CH_2OH$.

Cane sugar, milk sugar, Melezitose, Melitose, Parasaccharose, and Trehalose; Starch, Inuline, Glycogen, Dextrine, and Arabin all contain the asymmetric carbon atom that was present in the previous compounds inasmuch as they are compound ethers of the previous compounds.

Camphor, according to Kekulé (Figure XII).
Borneol, according to the same (Figure XIII).
Camphoric acid, according to the same.
    $COOH$ $CH(C_8H_{14}O.)$.
Terpinolene which apparently has the structure shown in Figure XIV
    and Menthol which perhaps has the structure shown in Figure XV.

Concerning the active alkaloids, albumens, etc., too little is as yet known of their structure to permit of any conclusion being reached in regard to the relation between their structures and the rotatory power.

The sole definite exception to this rule that I have been able to find is the active propyl alcohol of Chancell, but, according to a private communication of Henniger, this relatively small rotatory power is due to the presence of an impurity.

(b) *The derivatives of optically active compounds lose their rotatory power when the asymmetry of all the carbon atoms disappears; in the contrary case they do not usually lose this power.*

A few examples will be sufficient here:

Inactive malonic, fumaric, and maleïc acids from the active malic acid; inactive succinic and tartronic acids from the active tartaric acid; inactive cymene from active camphor, etc.

In the contrary case there are,
Active malic acid from active tartaric acid;
Active tartaric acid from active lactose;
Active glucose from active glucosides;
Active nitro mannite from active mannite;
Active camphoric acid and Borneol from active camphor;
Active salts and esters from active acids, etc.

(c) *If one makes a list of compounds which contain an asymmetric carbon atom it is then seen that in many cases the converse of (a) is not true, that is, not every compound with such an atom has an influence upon polarized light.*

This may be ascribed to three causes:

1. The compounds consist of an inactive mixture of two isomers with equal but opposite optical power, which owing to their close agreement in all other properties can be separated with great difficulty, and which have not up to the present been separated.

2. The study of the rotatory power has been imperfect, either on account of the slight solubility of the compounds or on account of the slight specific rotatory power of many compounds, as for example, in the case of mannite.

3. The asymmetric carbon atom may not in itself be sufficient to cause optical activity, the latter may not depend solely upon the mutual diversity of the groups which are in combination with the carbon atom, but may also be dependent upon their character.

However the case may be the facts noted indicate a probable relation between constitution and active power which may be made use of in the following cases when more convincing arguments fail:

1. A compound which rotates the plane of polarized light probably possesses an asymmetric carbon atom; which gives a means of choosing between possible structures in the case of compounds where the structure is not completely determined.

For example, active amyl alcohol with an asymmetric carbon atom can have only the formula

$$\begin{matrix} CH_3 \\ C_2H_5 \end{matrix} CHCH_2OH$$

a formula which has also been suggested by Erlenmeyer but upon altogether different grounds.

2. A compound which up to the present has shown no physical isomers acting upon polarized light in all probability contains no asymmetric carbon atom; this fact also may be of service in choosing between possible structural formulas; as for example, citric acid, which on account of its transformation into aconitic acid and tricarballylic acids must have one of the two formulas:

$$\begin{matrix} C.H.OH.COOH \\ | \\ CH.COOH \\ | \\ CH_2COOH \end{matrix} \quad \text{or} \quad \begin{matrix} CH_2COOH \\ | \\ C.OH.COOH \\ | \\ CH_2COOH \end{matrix}$$

its inactivity gives preference to the second formula; the first, however, contains an asymmetric carbon atom for which reason I hope to be able to produce the acid named by following the method of Frankland and Duppa from oxalic acid and iodo acetic acid esters by the aid of zinc.

3. Finally the limits of the rotatory power can be stated with some measure of probability, that is to say, the simplest combinations which will show active power can be indicated; for example, the simplest active monatomic alcohol will be:

$$CH_3C.H.OH.CH_2CH_3.$$

The simplest active monobasic acid:

$$CH_3C.H.COOH.CH_2CH_3.$$

The simplest active diatomic alcohol:

$$CH_3CHOH\ CH_2OH.$$

The simplest active saturated hydrocarbon:

$$\begin{matrix} CH_3 \\ C_2H_5 \end{matrix} CHC_3H_7.$$

The simplest active aromatic hydrocarbon:

$$\begin{matrix} CH_3 \\ C_2H_5 \end{matrix} CHC_6H_5\ etc.$$

At the same time it is probable that some series will be excluded from active power, as for example:

The normal hydrocarbons $CH_3(CH_2)_nCH_3$
The normal alcohols $CH_3(CH_2)_nCH_2OH$
The normal acids $CH_3(CH_2)_nCOOH$ etc.

It is more noteworthy that in consequence of the assumptions made, the compound CHBrClI can probably be split up into two isomers which will act upon polarized light. . . .

SECOND PART

Thus far we have considered the influence of the hypothesis upon compounds in which the carbon atoms are united by a single affinity only, (leaving out some aromatic bodies); there remains now to be considered:

The influence of the new hypothesis upon compounds containing doubly linked carbon atoms. Double linking is represented by two tetrahedrons with one edge in common (Figure IX) in which A and B represent the union of the two carbon atoms, and R'R''R'''R'''' represent the univalent groups which saturate the remaining free affinities of the carbon atoms.

If R'R''R'''R'''' all represent the same group, then but one form is conceivable, and the same is true if R' and R'' or R''' and R'''' are identical, *but if R' differs from R'' and at the same time R''' differs from R'''', which does not preclude R' and R''', R'' and R'''' from being equal, then two figures become possible shown in Figures IX and X, which differ from one another in regard to the positions of R' and R'' with respect to R''' and R''''. The dissimilarity of these figures, which are limited to two, indicates a case of isomerism not shown by the ordinary formulas.*

Turning to the facts, I believe that I have met with such cases among organic compounds.

1. Maleïc and fumaric acids, all explanations of the isomerism between these have made shipwreck, (I count here also the assumption of a bivalent carbon atom since this can exist alone in the case of carbon monoxide and the carbylamines, for evident reasons, without doubling of the molecule); as a matter of fact these acids realize the conditions outlined above: *Two doubly linked carbon atoms each carrying two unlike univalent groups, H and COOH.*

2. Brom and isobrom maleïc acid, the explanation of the isomerism here is entirely the same as before, one has only to replace an H in the fumaric and maleïc acid by a Br.

3. Citra-, ita- and mesaconic acids. With the adoption of

$$CH_3CHCOOHCH_2COOH$$

for pyrotartaric acid there remain for the acids mentioned only the formulas

$$CH_2\!\!=\!\!C.COOH.CH_2COOH$$
$$CH_3C\ COOH\!\!=\!\!CHCOOH$$

and if the latter does not contain two isomers (probably ita- and citraconic acids) in accordance with my hypothesis, no plausible explanation can be given.

4. Solid and liquid crotonic acids. The constitution of the solid crotonic acid according to Kekulé is without doubt

$$CH_3CH\!\!=\!\!CHCOOH,$$

for the liquid crotonic acid there remains therefore (thus it is held) only the formula

$$CH_2\!\!=\!\!CHCH_2COOH$$

to explain their lack of identity.

But if we take into consideration the following facts with regard to this acid:

(a) Fused with KOH it gives, according to M. Hemilian, acetic acid only.

(b) Oxidizing agents, according to the same authority, convert it into acetic and oxalic acids, and indirectly from oxalic acid into carbonic acid.

(c) At 170–180°, also according to Hemilian, it goes over into the solid crotonic acid. Thus there is nothing in favor of the formula $CH_2\!\!=\!\!CHCH_2$

COOH and everything in favor of the isomer $CH_3CH\!\!=\!\!CHCOOH$, exactly like fumaric and maleïc acids. The formula $CH_3CH\!\!=\!\!CHCOOH$ really satisfies the conditions exacted by my hypothesis for the possibility of two isomers: two doubly linked carbon atoms, the free affinities of each of which are saturated by two unlike univalent groups, in this case H and CH_3, H and COOH.

Geuther's chlorcrotonic acid and chlorisocrotonic acid, the isomerism of which has hitherto been expressed by the formulas

$$CH_2\!\!=\!\!CClCH_2COOH$$

and

$$CH_3CCl\!\!=\!\!CHCOOH$$

according to Froelich give with nascent hydrogen the acids treated under (4) whence the constitution of both becomes

$$CH_3CCl\!\!=\!\!CHCOOH$$

and this case of isomerism strengthens my hypothesis.

THIRD PART

There remain now to be treated carbon atoms which are united by a triple union as in acetylene; this combination is represented by two tetrahedrons with three summits in common or with one of their faces in common (Figure XI). ACB is the triple union, R′ and R″ are the univalent groups which saturate the two remaining affinities of the carbon atoms. The new hypothesis does not in this case lead to any discordance with the views previously held.

In closing, I wish to remark that

1. The new hypothesis leaves nothing unexplained that is clearly set forth by the previous conceptions.

2. Certain properties and isomers not explained by the usual theories receive some light from this point of view.

3. Finally my remarks about active compounds in solution, that is, active molecules, are related to the views of Rammelsberg upon active crystals.

Extending the observations of Herschell and Pasteur, Rammelsberg maintains that the property of acting upon the plane of polarization in the solid state (that is the active condition of crystals with inactive molecules as well as the inactive condition of crystals with active molecules) coincides with the appearance of two crystal forms, one of which is the reflected image of the other.

It is evident that we have here to deal with an arrangement of the molecules in the active crystal altogether similar to the arrangement of the groups of atoms in the active molecule according to my hypothesis; an arrangement in which neither the crystal mentioned by Rammelsberg nor the active molecules, represented in a general way by Figures VII and VIII have a plane of symmetry.

The process of osmosis was first described in 1784 by the Abbé Nollet, but reliable quantitative experiments in this field were not carried out until the work of the botanist, Wilhelm Friedrich Philipp Pfeffer (1845–1920), in 1877. By this time, van't Hoff's interest had shifted from the stereochemical studies which had at first occupied his attention, and he was engaged in studies of chemical equilibrium. When he learned of the work of Pfeffer, he realized that here was a new tool with which to study phenomena which occurred in solution. Quantitative treatment of the relations involved soon showed him that in dilute solutions, even nongaseous solutes obeyed the laws which had been established for gases. The laws of Boyle, Gay-Lussac, and even Avogadro could be extended to dilute solutions. This opened the way for an explanation of the findings of Raoult and led to a series of far-reaching conclusions upon which modern theories of solution are founded. The original papers in which van't Hoff developed his theory of dilute solutions appeared in relatively obscure journals,[2] but the publication which was the most influential appeared in German in 1887.[3]

THE ROLE OF OSMOTIC PRESSURE IN THE ANALOGY BETWEEN SOLUTIONS AND GASES.

In an investigation, whose essential aim was a knowledge of the laws of chemical equilibrium in solutions, it gradually became apparent that there is a deep-seated analogy—indeed, almost an identity—between solutions and gases, so far as their physical relations are concerned; provided that with solutions we deal with the so-called osmotic pressure, where with gases we are concerned with the ordinary elastic pressure. This analogy will be made as clear as possible in the following paper, the physical properties being considered first:

1.—OSMOTIC PRESSURE. KIND OF ANALOGY WHICH ARISES THROUGH THIS CONCEPTION.

In considering the quantity, with which we shall chiefly have to deal in what follows, at first from the theoretical point of view, let us think of a

[2] *Archives néerlandaises des sciences exactes et naturelles*, **20**: 239–302 (1885); *Köngl. Svenska Vetenskaps-Akademiens Handlingar*, **21**, No. 17: 3–58 (1886). The latter paper has been translated in Ostwald's *Klassiker*, No. 110, "Die Gesetze des chemischen Gleichgewichtes für den verdünnten, gasförmigen oder gelösten Zustand, von J. H. van't Hoff. Herausgegeben von Georg Bredig," Leipzig, 1900.

[3] *Zeitschrift für physikalische Chemie*, **1**: 481–508 (1887). This paper has been translated in "The Modern Theory of Solution. Memoirs by Pfeffer, van't Hoff, Arrhenius, and Raoult. Translated and edited by Harry C. Jones," New York, 1899, pp. 13–42. The selection given here is taken from pages 13 to 15 and 21 to 25 of this translation. Also translated in *Alembic Club Reprints*, No. 19, "The Foundations of the Theory of Dilute Solutions. Papers on Osmotic Pressure by J. H. van't Hoff and on Electrolytic Dissociation by Svante Arrhenius, 1887," Edinburgh, 1929.

vessel, A, completely filled, for example, with an aqueous solution of sugar, the vessel being placed in water, B. If, now, the perfectly solid wall of the vessel is permeable to water, but impermeable to the dissolved sugar, the attraction of the water by the solution will, as is well known, cause the water to enter A, but this action will soon reach its limit due to the pressure produced by the water which enters (in minimal quantity). Equilibrium exists under these conditions, and the pressure exerted on the wall of the vessel we will designate in the following pages as osmotic pressure.

It is evident that this condition of equilibrium can be established in A also at the outset, that is, without previous entrance of water, by providing the vessel B with a piston which exerts a pressure equal to the osmotic pressure. We can then see that by increasing or diminishing the pressure on the piston it is possible to produce arbitrary changes in the concentration of the solution, through movement of water in the one or the other direction through the walls of the vessel.

Let this osmotic pressure be described from an experimental standpoint by one of Pfeffer's experiments. An unglazed porcelain cell was used, which was provided with a membrane permeable to water, but not to sugar. This was obtained as follows: The cell, thoroughly moistened, so as to drive out the air, and filled with a solution of potassium ferrocyanide, was placed in a solution of copper sulphate. The potassium and copper salts came in contact, after a time, by diffusion, in the interior of the porous wall, and formed there a membrane having the desired property. Such a vessel was then filled with a one-per-cent. solution of sugar, and, after being closed by a cork with manometer attached, was immersed in water. The osmotic pressure gradually makes its appearance through the entrance of some water, and after equilibrium is established it is read on the manometer. Thus, the one-per-cent. solution of sugar in question, which was diluted only an insignificant amount by the water which entered, showed at 6.8°, a pressure of 50.5 millimetres of mercury, therefore about $\frac{1}{15}$ of an atmosphere.

The porous membranes here described will, under the name "semipermeable membranes," find extensive application in what follows, even though in some cases the practical application is, perhaps, still unrealized. They furnish a means of dealing with solutions, which bears the closest resemblance to that used with gases. This evidently arises from the fact that the elastic presure, characteristic of the latter condition, is now introduced also for solutions as osmotic pressure. At the same time let stress be laid upon the fact that we are not dealing here with an artificially forced analogy, but with one which is deeply seated in the nature of the case. The mechanism by which, according to our present conceptions, the elastic pressure of gases is produced is essentially the same as that which gives rise to osmotic pressure in solutions. It depends, in the first case, upon the impact of the gas molecules against the wall of the vessel; in the latter, upon the impact of the molecules of the dissolved substance against the semipermeable membrane, since the molecules of the solvent, being present upon both sides of the membrane through which they pass, do not enter into consideration.

The great practical advantage for the study of solutions, which follows from the analogy upon which stress has been laid, and which leads at once to quantitative results, is that the application of the second law of thermodynamics to solutions has now become extremely easy, since reversible processes, to which, as is well known, this law applies, can now be performed with the greatest simplicity. It has been already mentioned above that a cylinder, provided with semipermeable walls and piston, when immersed in the solvent, allows any desired change in concentration to be produced in the solution beneath the piston by exerting a proper pressure upon the piston, just as a gas is compressed and can then expand; only that, in the first case the solvent, in these changes in volume, moves through the wall of the cylinder. Such processes can, in both cases, preserve the condition of reversibility with the same degree of ease, provided that the pressure of the piston is equal to the counter-pressure, i.e., with solutions, to the osmotic pressure.

We will now make use of this practical advantage, especially for the investigation of the laws which hold for "ideal solutions," that is, for solutions which are diluted to such an extent that they are comparable with "ideal gases," and in which, therefore, the reciprocal action of the dissolved molecules can be neglected, as also the space occupied by these molecules, in comparison with the volume of the solution itself.

Van't Hoff next shows by theoretical and experimental methods that dilute solutions obey the laws of Boyle and Gay-Lussac. He then proceeds to his most original and important discovery, the fact that they also obey Avogadro's law.

4.—AVOGADRO'S LAW FOR DILUTE SOLUTIONS.

While up to the present, essentially only those changes have been dealt with which the osmotic pressure in solutions undergoes due to changes in concentration and temperature, and while the agreement with the corresponding laws which hold for gases manifested itself, we must now deal with the direct comparison of the two analogous quantities, elastic pressure and osmotic pressure of one and the same substance. It is evident that this applies to gases which have also been investigated in solution; and, as a matter of fact, it will be proved that, in case the law of Henry is satisfied, the osmotic pressure in solution is exactly equal to the elastic pressure as gas, at least at the same temperature and concentration.

For the purpose of demonstration, we will perform a reversible cycle at constant temperature, by means of semipermeable walls, and then employ the second law of thermodynamics, which, in this case, as is known, leads to an extremely simple result, that no heat is transformed into work, or work into heat, and consequently the sum of all the work done must be equal to zero.

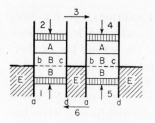

The reversible cycle is performed by two similarly arranged double cylinders, with pistons, like the one already described. One cylinder is partly filled with a gas (A), say oxygen, in contact with a solution of oxygen (B), saturated under the conditions of the experiment, for example, an aqueous solution. The wall bc allows only oxygen, but no water to pass through; the wall ab, on the contrary, allows water but not oxygen to pass, and is in contact on the outside with the liquid (E) in question. A reversible transformation can be made with such a cylinder; which amounts to this, that by raising the two pistons (1) and (2) oxygen is evolved from its aqueous solution as gas, while water is removed through ab. This transformation can take place so that the concentrations of gas and solution remain the same. The only difference between the two cylinders is in the concentrations which are present in them. These we will express in the following manner:

The unit of weight of the substance in question fills, in the left vessel, as gas and as solution, the volumes v and V respectively, in the right of $v + dv$ and $V + dV$; then in order that Henry's law be satisfied, the following relation must obtain:

$$v : V = (v + dv) : (V + dV)$$

therefore:

$$v : V = dv : dV.$$

Let now the pressure and osmotic pressure of gas and solution, in case unit weight is present in unit volume, be respectively P and p (values which hereafter will be shown to be equal), the pressure in gas and solution is, then, from Boyle's law, respectively P/v and p/V.

If we now raise the pistons (1) and (2), and thus liberate a unit weight of gas from the solution, we increase, then, this gas volume v by dv, in order that it may have the concentration of the gas in the left vessel; if the gas just set free is forced into solution by lowering pistons (4) and (5), and thus the volume of the solution $V + dV$ diminished by dV in the cylinder with semipermeable walls, the cycle is then completed.

Six amounts of work are to be taken into consideration, whose sum, from what is stated above, must be equal to zero. We will designate these by numbers, whose meaning is self-evident. We have, then:

$$(1) + (2) + (3) + (4) + (5) + (6) = 0.$$

But (2) and (4) are of equal value and opposite sign, since we are dealing with volume changes v and $v + dv$, in the opposite sense, which takes place at pressures which are inversely proportional to the volumes. For the same reasons the sum of (1) and (5) is zero; then, from the above relation:

$$(3) + (6) = 0.$$

The work done by the gas (3), in case it undergoes an increase in volume dv at a pressure P/v, is:

$$(3) = P/v \, dv,$$

while the work done by the solution (6), in case it undergoes a diminution in volume dV at an osmotic pressure p/V is:

$$(6) = p/V \, dV.$$

We obtain then:

$$P/v \, dv = p/V \, dV;$$

and since $v:V = dv:dV$, P and p must be equal, which was to be proved.

The conclusion here reached, which will be repeatedly confirmed in what follows, is, in turn, a new support to the law of Gay-Lussac applied to solutions. In case gaseous pressure and osmotic pressure are equal at the same temperature, changes in temperature must have also an equal influence on both. But, on the other hand, the relation found permits of an important extension of the law of Avogadro, which now finds application also to all solutions, if only osmotic pressure is considered instead of elastic pressure. At equal osmotic pressure and equal temperature, equal volumes of the most widely different solutions contain an equal number of molecules, and, indeed, the same number which, at the same pressure and temperature, is contained in an equal volume of a gas.

5.—General Expression of the Laws of Boyle, Gay-Lussac, and Avogadro, for Solutions and Gases.

The well-known formula which expresses for gases the two laws of Boyle and Gay-Lussac:

$$PV = RT,$$

is now, where the laws referred to are also applicable to liquids, valid also for solutions, if we are dealing with the osmotic pressure. This holds even with the same limitation which is also to be considered with gases, that

the dilution shall be sufficiently great to allow one to disregard the reciprocal action of, and the space taken by, the dissolved particles.

If we wish to include in the above expression, also, the third, the law of
Avogadro, this can be done in an exceedingly simple manner, following
the suggestion of Horstmann, considering always kilogram-molecules of
the substance in question; thus, 2 k. hydrogen, 44 k. carbon dioxide, etc.
Then R in the above equation has the same value for all gases, since at the
same temperature and pressure the quantities mentioned occupy also
the same volume. If this value is calculated, and the volume taken in
Mr^3, the pressure in $K°$ per Mr^2, and if, for example, hydrogen at 0° and
atmospheric pressure is chosen:

$$P = 10333, \ V = \frac{2}{0.08956}, \ T = 273, \ R = 845.05.$$

The combined expression of the laws of Boyle, Gay-Lussac, and Avogadro is, then:

$$PV = 845T,$$

and in this form it refers not only to gases, but to all solutions, P being
then always taken as osmotic pressure.

In order that the formula last obtained may be hereafter easily applied,
we give it finally a simpler form, by observing that the number of calories,
which is equal to a kilogram-metre, therefore to the equivalent of work
$(A = \frac{1}{423})$, stands in a very simple relation to R, indeed, AR $= 2$ (more
exactly, about one-thousandth less).

Therefore, the following form can be chosen:

$$APV = 2T,$$

which has the great practical advantage that the work done, of which we
shall often speak hereafter, finds a very simple expression, in case it is calculated in calories.

Joseph Achille Le Bel

(1847–1930)

ALMOST simultaneously with van't Hoff but independently of him, Le Bel presented the explanation for the puzzling facts of optical isomerism which could not be understood as long as organic structures were formulated only in two dimensions. Le Bel's discussion was more abstract and general than van't Hoff's. Taken together, the two papers firmly established the stereochemical viewpoint, which was very fruitfully extended by Wislicenus (1835–1902) and which was applied to numerous special cases, such as steric hindrance, by V. Meyer and the strain theory of Baeyer. The paper of Le Bel appeared in November, 1874, two months after that of van't Hoff.[1]

ON THE RELATIONS WHICH EXIST BETWEEN THE ATOMIC FORMULAS OF ORGANIC COMPOUNDS AND THE ROTATORY POWER OF THEIR SOLUTIONS.

Up to the present time we do not possess any certain rule which enables us to foresee whether or not the solution of a substance has rotatory power. We know only that the derivatives of an active substance are in general also active; nevertheless we often see the rotatory power suddenly disappear in the most immediate derivatives, while in other cases, it persists in very remote derivatives. By considerations, purely geometrical, I have been able to formulate a rule of a quite general character.

Before giving the reasoning which has led me to this law I shall give the facts upon which it rests, and then shall conclude with a discussion of the confirmation of the law offered by the present state of our chemical knowledge.

The labors of Pasteur and others have completely established the correlation which exists between molecular asymmetry and rotatory power. If the asymmetry exists only in the crystalline molecule, the crystal alone will be active; if, on the contrary, it belongs to the chemical molecule, the solution will show rotatory power, and often the crystal also if the struc-

---

[1] *Bull. soc. chim.*, **22**: 337–347 (1874); "Les Classiques de la découverte scientifique. La synthèse totale en chimie organique. Mémoires de MM. Wöhler, Gerhardt, M. Berthelot, Le Bel, van't Hoff, Jungfleisch, Ladenburg, Pasteur. Préface et commentaires par M. Marcel Delépine," Paris, 1937.

The paper has been translated into English in "The Foundations of Stereochemistry Memoirs by Pasteur, van't Hoff, Le Bel, and Wislicenus," translated and edited by George M. Richardson, New York, 1901, pp. 49–59. The following selection is taken from this translation.

ture of the crystal allows us to perceive it, as in the case of the sulphate of strychnine and the alum of amyl amine.

There are, moreover, mathematical demonstrations of the necessary existence of this correlation, which we may consider a perfectly ascertained fact.

In the reasoning which follows, we shall ignore the asymmetries which might arise from the arrangement in space possessed by the atoms and univalent radicals; but shall consider them as spheres or material points, which will be equal if the atoms or radicals are equal, and different if they are different. This restriction is justified by the fact that, up to the present time, it has been possible to account for all the cases of isomerism observed without recourse to such arrangement and the discussion at the end of the paper will show that the appearance of the rotatory power can be equally well foreseen without the aid of the hypothesis of which we have just spoken.

First general principle.   Let us consider a molecule of a chemical compound having the formula MA_4; M being a simple or complex radical combined with four univalent atoms A, capable of being replaced by substitution. Let us replace three of them by simple or complex univalent radicals differing from one another and from M; the body obtained will be asymmetric.

Indeed, the group of radicals R, R′, R″, A when considered as material points differing among themselves form a structure which is enantimorphous with its reflected image, and the residue, M, cannot re-establish the symmetry. In general then, it may be stated that if a body is derived from the original type MA_4 by the substitution of three different atoms or radicals for A, its molecules will be asymmetric, and it will have rotatory power.

But there are two exceptional cases, distinct in character.

(1) If the molecular type has a plane of symmetry containing the four atoms A, the substitution of these by radicals (which we must consider as not capable of changing their position) can in no way alter the symmetry with respect to this plane, and in such cases the whole series of substitution products will be inactive.

(2) The last radical substituted for A may be composed of the same atoms that compose all the rest of the group into which it enters, and these two equal groups may have a neutralizing effect upon polarized light, or they may increase the activity; when the former is the case the body will be inactive. Now this arrangement may present itself in a derivative of an active asymmetric body where there is but slight difference in constitution, and later we shall see a remarkable instance of this.

Second general principle.   If, in our fundamental type we substitute but two radicals, R, R′, it is possible to have symmetry or asymmetry according to the constitution of the original type MA_4. If this molecule originally had a plane of symmetry passing through the two atoms A which have been replaced by R and R′, this plane will remain a plane of symmetry after the substitution; the body obtained will then be inactive. Our knowledge of the constitution of certain simple types will enable us to assert that certain bodies derived from them by two substitutions will be inactive.

Again, if it happens not only that a single substitution furnished but one derivative, but also that two and even three substitutions give only one and the same chemical isomer, we are obliged to admit that the four atoms A occupy the angles of a regular tetrahedron, whose planes of symmetry are identical with those of the whole molecule MA_4; in this case also no bisubstitution product can have rotatory power. . . .

Theorem. When an asymmetric body is formed in a reaction where there are present originally only unsymmetric bodies, the two isomers of inverse symmetry will be formed in equal quantities.

We know that the general principle of the calculation of probabilities consists in this:

When any phenomenon whatever can take place in two ways only, and there is no reason why it should take place in one of the ways in preference to the other, if the phenomenon has taken place m times in one manner and m′ times in the other manner, the ratio m/m' approaches unity as the sum $m + m'$ approaches infinity.

When an asymmetric body has been formed by substitution from a symmetric one, the asymmetry has been introduced by one of the substitutions which has taken place; let us consider this point carefully. The radical or the atom, the substitution of which introduced the asymmetry had formerly a homolog which was symmetrical to it by its connection with a point or a plane of symmetry; these radicals being in similar dynamic and geometrical considerations, if m and m′ represent the number of times that each one of them is substituted, m'/m ought to approach unity as the number of these substitutions grows beyond a measurable unit.

Now if the substitution of these similar radicals produces a dextro-body, then the other will produce the laevo-body, both will in consequence be formed in equal proportions.

It is the same for asymmetric bodies formed by addition; indeed the body which destroys the symmetry of a symmetrical molecule by adding itself to it, would be able to occupy an identical place situated on the other side of the point or plane of symmetry; the preceding reasoning therefore can be applied equally well to this case.

This is not necessarily true of asymmetric bodies formed in the presence of other active bodies, or traversed by circularly polarized light, or, in short, when submitted to any cause whatever which favors the formation of one of the asymmetric isomers. Such conditions are exceptional; and generally in the case of bodies prepared synthetically those which are active will escape the observation of the chemist unless he endeavors to separate the mixed isomeric products, the combined action of which upon polarized light is neutral.

We have a striking example of this in tartaric acid, for neither the dextro- nor the laevo-tartaric acid has ever been obtained directly by synthesis, but the inactive racemic acid which is a combination of equal parts of the dextro and laevo acids, is always obtained.

Victor Meyer

(1848–1897)

IT HAD been noted from time to time that certain organic reactions took an unusual, but well-defined, course, as compared to the expected behavior under a set of standardized conditions. It seemed probable that the cause of these anomalies was the presence of nonreacting groups which interfered with reacting radicals by virtue of a physical blockage. Although others had noticed this type of interference, the chief author of the theory of steric hindrance was Victor Meyer. In 1894 he began a series of experiments on the effect of introducing substituents into one or both of the positions ortho to a carboxyl group as this altered the rate and amount of esterification. These studies were continued until his death in 1897. The following selections are taken from two of his earlier papers on steric hindrance which appeared in 1894.[1]

Some time ago I had occasion to prepare the methyl ester of mesitylene carboxylic acid, and I wished to prepare it from the acid by the customary procedure with methyl alcohol and hydrochloric acid gas. To my surprise, I recovered very little ester, and the largest part of the acid was unchanged. A quantitative determination revealed that only about 9 per cent ester was formed, while benzoic acid under similar conditions produced a yield of 92 per cent.

I believed then that the accumulation of methyl groups was the basis of this singular phenomenon and had H. Gümbel begin a research upon tetramethyl benzoic acid, which, however, was easily and fully esterified.

[1] *Ber.*, **27**: 510–512; 1580–1592 (1894). The latter paper was written with J. J. Sudborough.

In order to arrive at an explanation for this phenomenon, a number of aromatic acids were esterified under exactly the same conditions. . . . Research subsequently showed that the number of methyl groups exerted no influence on esterifiability . . . and that in reality each trisubstituted benzoic acid which possesses its substituents in a symmetrical (1,3,5) arrangement can be esterified only in greatly reduced measure by hydrochloric acid gas and methyl alcohol, while its isomers and all its analogues, on the contrary, form esters with no difficulty. . . .

Our next problem was to discover the basis for the curious behavior which acids of the structure

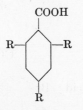

(R = CH₃, NO₂, Br, etc.)

display.

They are, collectively, not esterifiable. The reason for this can lie in the presence 1) of all three substituents; 2) of a part of the three substituents; 3) of both unreplaced hydrogen atoms.

In order to solve this problem, it is necessary to investigate the acids which result from the further substitution of the symmetrical trisubstituted acids, for instance, tetra- and pentasubstituted acids of the formulas

as well as both benzoic acids substituted thus:

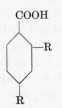

which can be prepared from the trisubstituted symmetrical acids by removal of one of the substituents.

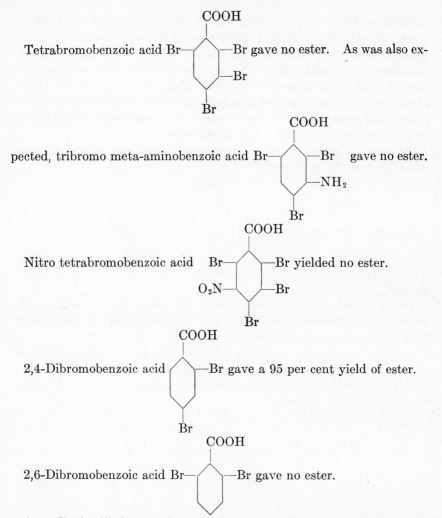

Tetrabromobenzoic acid Br—⟨ ⟩—Br gave no ester.   As was also ex-

pected, tribromo meta-aminobenzoic acid Br—⟨ ⟩—Br   gave no ester.

Nitro tetrabromobenzoic acid   Br—⟨ ⟩—Br yielded no ester.

2,4-Dibromobenzoic acid ⟨ ⟩—Br gave a 95 per cent yield of ester.

2,6-Dibromobenzoic acid Br—⟨ ⟩—Br gave no ester.

Accordingly, all the questions which we posed above are experimentally answered. The result is unequivocal: as soon as the two hydrogen atoms ortho to the carboxyl are replaced by radicals such as Br, NO_2, CH_3, and so forth, an acid unesterifiable by means of alcohol and hydrochloric acid results. It depends only upon the radicals neighboring the carboxyl, together. The presence of the third substituent, as well as the two hydrogen atoms, in the symmetrical trisubstituted acids is unimportant.

The next question to be answered then was, are these acids totally unesterifiable, or does only the specified method produce no ester from them?

The answer was easily obtained by treatment of silver salts with methyl iodide. By this means acids unesterifiable with hydrochloric acid, mesitylene carboxylic acid, and tetrabromobenzoic acid gave almost quantitative yields of their methyl esters.

From these results, we venture to risk—with all reservations for the present—a hypothesis to illuminate the phenomenon demonstrated. *The cause of the phenomenon* seems to be *stereochemical.* Apparently *the groups neighboring the carboxyl, because of their volume, make the entrance of the alkyl groups requisite to ester formation difficult* to such a degree that the formation of esters by a reaction of the alcohol-hydrochloric acid type, which itself proceeds slowly, is wholly absent. None the less, it is quite understandable that formation of esters by means of the silver salts is not hindered. Salt formation cannot be compared with ester formation in respect to ease and smoothness of formation; it takes place instantaneously, as, for example, the ready precipitation of silver salts proves. The silver atom attached to the carboxyl by salt formation acquires under any circumstance the room necessary for its entrance and accordingly produces space for the replacing alkyl group. Hence the acids not esterifiable by alcohol and hydrochloric acid can be converted into esters by means of the silver salts and methyl iodide with the same facility as other acids.

Adolf Baeyer

(*1835–1917*)

ONE of the great masters of organic chemistry in the late nineteenth century was Adolf Baeyer. He was responsible for numerous important syntheses, including that of indigo. In much of his work he was concerned with studies of acetylene and other unsaturated derivatives, including many ring compounds. In the course of these studies he was led to his *strain theory*, which extended the stereochemical ideas of van't Hoff, Le Bel, and Victor Meyer. It furnished an explanation for the stability of five- and six-membered rings. The theory was first announced in a paper on polyacetylene compounds which appeared in 1885.[1]

I. Theory of ring closure and the double bond.

Ring closure is obviously the phenomenon which can give most information about the spatial arrangement of atoms. If a chain of five and six members can easily be closed and one with fewer or more members can be

---

[1] *Ber.*, **18**: 2269–2281 (1885); the selection given here is taken from pages 2277 to 2279.

closed with difficulty or not at all, there must be a definite spatial basis for this fact. Any theory of the spatial arrangement of carbon compounds will naturally have to start from ring closure.

The general statements of the nature of carbon atoms which have previously been established run as follows:

1 The carbon atom is generally tetravalent.

2. The four valences are equivalent to one another. Example: there is only one monosubstitution product of methane.

3. The four valences are equally divided in space and correspond to the corners of a regular tetrahedron inscribed in a sphere.

4. The atoms or groups bound to the four valences cannot exchange places with one another by themselves. Example: there are two tetrasubstitution products, abcd, of methane. Le Bel-van't Hoff law.

5. Carbon atoms can unite with one another by 1, 2, or 3 valences.

6. The compounds form open or ringlike closed chains.

To these almost universally accepted statements I might now add

7. The four valences of the carbon atom act in directions which unite the mid-point of the sphere with the corners of the tetrahedron and which make an angle of 109° 28′ with each other.

The direction of these attractions can undergo a diversion which causes a strain which increases with the size of the diversion.

The meaning of this statement can easily be explained if we start from the Kekulé spherical model and assume that the wires, like elastic springs are movable in all directions. If, now, the explanation that the direction of attraction always coincides with the direction of the wires is also assumed, a true picture is obtained of the hypothesis outlined in the seventh statement.

If, now, as can be shown clearly only by the use of a model, an attempt is made to join a greater number of carbon atoms without force, that is, in the direction of the tetrahedral axes, or the wires of the models, the result is either a zigzag line or a ring of five atoms, which is entirely comprehensible, since the angles of a regular pentagon, 108°, differ only slightly from the angle 109° 28′ which the axes of attraction make with one another. When a larger or smaller ring is formed, the wires must be bent, i.e., there occurs a strain, in the sense of the seventh statement.

How well this view agrees with the facts is made clear by a consideration of rings formed from many methylene groups.

The simplest methylene ring is ethylene, which can be considered as a dimethylene. To obtain the double bond which occurs, there must be, according to the seventh statement and the hypothesis that both axes undergo an equal diversion, such a wide bending of the axes that they are parallel, i.e., each axis must be diverted about ½ of 109° 44′ from their resting position. In trimethylene, which can be considered an equilateral triangle, the angle which the axes must make with one another amounts to 60°, the diversion of each of them is then $\frac{1}{2}(109° \; 28' - 60°) = 24° \; 44'$; in tetramethylene it amounts to $\frac{1}{2}(109° \; 28' - 90°) = 9° \; 44'$; in pentamethylene, which corresponds to the angle of a regular pentagon of 108°, $\frac{1}{2}(109° \; 28' - 108°) = 0° \; 44'$; in hexamethylene, corresponding to the angle of a regular hexagon of 120°, $\frac{1}{2}(109° \; 28' - 120°) = -5° \; 16'$, *i.e.*, the axes must be bent about 5° apart. The following examples will make these relations clearer:

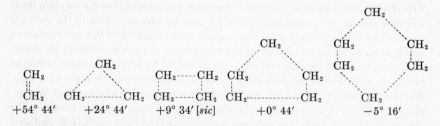

| $+54° \; 44'$ | $+24° \; 44'$ | $+9° \; 34' \; [sic]$ | $+0° \; 44'$ | $-5° \; 16'$ |

Dimethylene is in fact the loosest ring, broken by hydrogen bromide, bromine, and even iodine. Trimethylene is split only by hydrogen bromide, not by bromine. Tetramethylene and hexamethylene, finally, are split with great difficulty or not at all. It may be added that as a point of fact six-membered rings have been very frequently found up to now, while five-membered rings occur very rarely and in complicated compounds. However, this objection has no great weight, because the six-membered ring is found almost entirely in the form of a hydrogen-poorer compound, benzene, and it may well be possible that pentamethylene itself, under the same conditions, is a little more easily formed and a little more stable than hexamethylene. I intentionally disregard the consideration of thiophene, lactones, etc., in this discussion, because there the presence of other elements must be considered.

Cato Maximilian Guldberg (1836–1902)

Peter Waage (1833–1900)

THE fact that the mass of reacting compounds has an effect on the reaction itself was first clearly recognized by Berthollet, but his incorrect idea of the variable composition of compounds prevented proper understanding of the significance of his ideas on mass. As knowledge of the importance of reaction velocity increased (Wilhelmy) and effects at equilibrium were studied, it finally became possible to formulate a mathematical expression for the effects produced by mass on a reaction. In the years 1864 to 1867, two Norwegian scientists, Guldberg and Waage, proposed the law of mass action.[1] The work did not become so widely known as the authors had hoped, and other workers, including Ostwald and van't Hoff, deduced expressions for special cases of the law, in ignorance of the work of Guldberg and Waage. In 1879, therefore, the two men published a paper[2] in which they restated their previous work, showed how other investigators had confirmed it, and presented new experimental evidence of its correctness. The following selection gives their basic formulation of the law.

In the year 1867, we presented a study under the title of "Etudes sur les affinités chimiques" in which we were concerned chiefly with chemical mass action. We expressed the view that the result of a chemical process depends not only on the substances which enter into the new compound but also on all other substances which are present in the process. The latter we called *foreign substances*, in so far as they exert a noticeable influence, even though they do not themselves undergo any chemical change during the process. The solvent is considered one of these foreign substances.

The chemical forces which come into effect between the substances are dependent on temperature, pressure, the aggregate condition, and the mass ratios.

We differentiate two chief groups of chemical forces: the true affinity forces which bring about the formation of new chemical compounds, and

---

[1] The theory was first published in Norwegian in the *Forhandlinger i Videnskabs-Selskabet i Christiana*, **1864**: 35–40, 111–120; and then as a French pamphlet, "Etudes sur les affinités chimiques," Christiania, 1867. These papers have been reprinted in Ostwald's *Klassiker*, No. 104, "Untersuchungen über die chemischen Affinitäten. Abhandlungen an den Jahren 1864, 1867, 1879 von C. M. Guldberg und P. Waage. Uebersetz und herausgegeben von R. Abegg," Leipzig, 1899.

[2] *J. prakt. Chem.*, [2], **19**: 69–114 (1879); the selection given is taken from pages 69 to 73. This paper is included in Ostwald's *Klassiker*, No. 104.

the secondary forces whose action can be refered back to the foreign substances.

The chemical processes which are most suitable for the study of the chemical forces in them are, in our view, those in which an equilibrium state exists between the forces, or, in other words, processes in which the chemical reaction goes equally in two opposite directions. As examples, we will mention

1. A metal is oxidized by water vapor, and the metal oxide under the same conditions is reduced by hydrogen.

2. Dissociation of a body AB, in which both parts A and B and the original substance AB are present at the same time.

3. Two dissolved substances give rise to a double decomposition: thus alcohol and acetic acid go partly into ester and water, and reversibly, ester and water go partly into alcohol and acetic acid.

4. A soluble and an insoluble salt partly exchange their acids; thus potassium sulfate and barium carbonate go partly into potassium carbonate and barium sulfate, and reversibly, potassium carbonate and barium sulfate change partly into potassium sulfate and barium carbonate.

These last classes of chemical compounds were those which we chiefly made the subject of our experimental studies.

From our own experimental studies combined with already known material, we deduced the law for chemical mass action which we stated as follows:

If two substances A and B change into two new substances A' and B', the chemical strength with which A and B are held together is measured by the mass of new substances A' and B' formed in unit time.

The mass with which a definite substance enters the unit volume of the body in which the chemical process proceeds we have called the *active mass* of the substance.

Actually, we mean by the active mass only the mass of the substance within the sphere of action; under otherwise equal conditions, however, the action sphere can be represented by the unit volume.

The chemical force with which two substances A and B act on each other is equal to the product of their active masses multiplied by the affinity coefficient (see "Etudes sur les affinités chimiques," page 6).

By the affinity coefficient is understood a coefficient which depends on the chemical nature of both substances and on the temperature. If the active masses of A and B are called p and q, and k is the affinity coefficient, then the chemical forces acting between A and B are expressed by kpq; this expression accordingly represents the mass of A and B which is transformed into A' and B' in unit time.

If in a chemical process A and B are changed to A' and B', and reversibly, A' and B' are changed to A and B, then an equilibrium occurs if the chemical force acting between A and B equals the chemical force acting between A' and B'.

If the active masses of A' and B' are expressed by p' and q' and their affinity coefficient by k', the chemical force which acts between A' and B' is expressed by $k'p'q'$. This expression represents, as above, the masses of A' and B' which are changed to A and B in unit time.

The condition of equilibrium will thus be expressed by the equation

$$kpq = k'p'q'$$

The above equation comprises in the shortest form the law of mass action and the condition of equilibrium, assuming that the secondary forces are not considered (see "Etudes," paragraph 5).

In our work cited above we have verified the law of mass action, and for this, among others, we have especially used the following two types of chemical processes:

1. The action of alkali carbonates on barium sulfate, and the action of alkali sulfates on barium carbonate.

2. Ester formation, see Berthelot and Saint Giles, *Ann. chim. phys.*, 1862.

In 1869, J. Thomsen in Copenhagen (see *Pogg. Ann.*, Bd. 138) presented a thermochemical study of the affinity relations between acids and bases in aqueous solution, and the results of this study also establish our law of mass action.

Also, W. Ostwald in Dorpat in 1876 sought to determine the affinity relations between acids and bases with the aid of volume changes (see this Journal [2], **16,** 385), thus furnishing a further confirmation of the results of Thomsen. Ostwald, too, from his studies has deduced a property of the affinity coefficient which can be expressed as follows: the affinity coefficient is the product of two coefficients, one of which relates to substance A and the other to substance B.

In 1877 Horstmann proposed a theory of the combustion of mixtures of carbon monoxide and hydrogen (*Ann. Chem. Pharm.*, 190). Actually, however, this theory is nothing but our law of mass action. If we replace p in the above equation by the amount of hydrogen, q by the amount of carbon dioxide, p' by the amount of water, and q' by the amount of carbon monoxide (all at the conclusion of the combustion), then Horstmann finds in his study that the ratio of $k:k'$ depends on temperature. In the same year (1877), van't Hoff further (*Ber. Berl. chem. Ges.*, 10) expressed ester formation by a formula which agrees completely with our equation. As mentioned above, we had already made this calculation in our work which appeared in 1867.

Since in these ways the law of mass action appears to be valid for insoluble, soluble, and gaseous substances, we are forced to the assumption that it must be considered a general law which is valid for all chemical processes. In the following part we will try to prove this assumption still more positively, partly by developing the physical meaning of the law still further and partly by indicating its applicability to a series of very different chemical processes.

François-Marie Raoult

(1830–1901)

THE fact that dissolved substances lower the freezing points of their solvents had been observed as early as 1788 by Blagden, and the similar effect on vapor pressure was discovered by von Babo in 1847, but the early investigators used solutions of ionizing substances, and the unsuspected effect of the dissociation prevented the discovery of any regular laws governing these effects. Then in 1882, F.-M. Raoult published his results on the effects of nondissociating organic solutes, from which he deduced a general law controlling the lowering of freezing points. Four years later he extended this work to show the effect of solutes on vapor pressure. Having established the effect of nondissociating compounds, he was in a position to show that salts produced an effect which, though anomalous, could nevertheless be explained by the supposition that a dissolved molecule broke up into other molecules. This work was of great value in supplying a new method for determining molecular weights, since the depression of freezing point and vapor pressure (as well as the related rise in boiling point later discovered) are proportional to the molecular concentrations of the solutions; it was of equal value in supporting the ideas of van't Hoff on osmotic pressure (pages 435–458). With the announcement of the dissociation theory of Arrhenius, the anomalies were explained and the full significance of the generalizations of Raoult was recognized.

Raoult published the formulations of his laws in the *Comptes rendus* for 1882 and 1887. The selections which follow are taken from these two papers.

GENERAL LAW OF THE FREEZING OF SOLUTIONS.[1]

If A is the lowering of the freezing point due to the presence of 1 gram of a substance dissolved in 100 grams of solvent; M the molecular weight of the dissolved substance, supposedly anhydrous, calculated according to the *atomic* formula $H = 1$, $O = 16$ . . . ; T its molecular lowering of the freezing point (that is, the lowering of the freezing point caused by

[1] *Compt. rend.*, **95**: 1030–1033 (1882).

one molecule dissolved in 100 gram of liquid), then, if the solutions are dilute,

$$MA = T$$

My previous studies have shown that, in the same liquid, the molecular lowering, T, is a nearly constant number for very numerous groups of compounds of the same type. Since then I have made new experiments using as solvents the following compounds whose freezing points can always be determined with extreme precision.

	Freezing Point, Degrees		Freezing Point, Degrees
Water..................	0.00	Ethylene dibromide......	7.92
Benzene...............	4.96	Formic acid.............	8.52
Nitrobenzene...........	5.28	Acetic acid.............	16.75

All these liquids except water contract when solidifying.

Lack of space prevents me from giving details here of the extremely numerous experiments made with these solvents. I will limit myself to giving a summary. Nevertheless, it is possible to judge of the number and variety of dissolved compounds as well as the degree of concordance of the results from the table of 60 analogous experiments made on solutions of organic compounds in water and in benzene published in the *Comptes rendus* of the Academy (June 5 and 24, 1882). My new studies confirm the former and permit the formulation of the *law of freezing of solvents* in a general and complete manner. . . .

Conclusions. These experiments, in which more than two hundred compounds have been dissolved in *six* different liquids, are very numerous and agree in establishing the following:

All bodies, on dissolving in a definite liquid compound which can solidify, lower the freezing point.

In all liquids, the molecular lowering of the freezing point due to the different compounds approaches two values, invariable for each liquid, of which one is double the other. The larger is more often found and constitutes the normal molecular lowering. The lesser corresponds to the case where the molecules of the dissolved body are joined two to two.

The normal molecular lowering of the freezing point varies with the nature of the solvent: it is 37 for water, 28 for formic acid, 39 for acetic acid, 49 for benzene, 70.5 for nitrobenzene, and 117 for ethylene dibromide. If each of these numbers is divided by the molecular weight of the solvent to which it relates (which is equivalent to reducing the results to the case where one molecule of dissolved body will be contained in 100 molecules of the solvent), the quotients differ little from each other, except for water. Thus

Water................ 37:18 = 2.050   Benzene............ 49:78 = 0.628
Formic acid........... 28:46 = 0.608   Nitrobenzene....... 70.5:123 = 0.600
Acetic acid............ 39:60 = 0.650   Ethylene dibromide.. 117:188 = 0.623

To make water agree with the general rule, it is enough to admit that the physical molecules which compose it are formed from three chemical molecules joined together, at least near the freezing point. Then, indeed, this solvent gives 37:18 × [*sic*] 3 = 0.685, a number which does not differ much from 0.622 degrees, the mean of the five others. The following law can then be formulated:

One molecule of any compound dissolved in 100 molecules of any liquid of a different nature lowers the freezing point of this liquid by a nearly constant quantity, close to 0.62 degrees.

This statement is altogether general if we admit that the physical molecules which act here can be formed of two, and exceptionally, three, chemical molecules.

GENERAL LAW OF THE VAPOR PRESSURE OF SOLVENTS.[2]

The molecular reduction of the vapor pressure K of a solution, that is to say, the relative reduction of pressure produced by 1 molecule of a substance held in 100 grams of a volatile liquid, can be calculated by means of the following formula:

$$K = \frac{f - f'}{fP} \times M$$

in which f is the vapor pressure of the pure solvent, f′ the vapor pressure of the solution, M the molecular weight of the dissolved substance, P the weight of this substance in solution in 100 grams of the solvent; if it is admitted that the relative reduction of pressure $\frac{f - f'}{f}$ is proportional to the concentration. As this proportionality is rarely rigorous, even when the solutions are very dilute, I have been obliged in these comparative studies to use solutions which always have nearly the same molecular concentrations and contain four to five molecules of substance held per 100 molecules of volatile solvent. A greater dilution would not allow sufficiently exact measurements. All the experiments were performed by the barometric method and conducted like those I have run in ether solutions. The tubes were plunged in a water bath limited by parallel glasses, constantly agitated, and heated at will.

In each case the temperature was so chosen that the vapor pressure of the pure solvent was about 400 millimeters of mercury. The measurements were made from fifteen to forty-five minutes after agitation of the contents of each tube, the temperature being constant.

[2] *Compt. rend.*, **104**: 1430–1433 (1887).

I have used 12 different volatile liquids as solvents, namely, water, phosphorous chloride, the sulfide of carbon, the bichloride of carbon (CCl_4), chloroform, amylene, benzene, methyl iodide, ethyl bromide, ordinary ether, acetone, methyl alcohol.

In water I have dissolved the following organic materials: cane sugar, glucose, tartaric acid, citric acid, urea. All these substances have produced sensibly the same molecular reduction in vapor pressure: K = 0.185. I have, for the present, left the mineral substances to one side; actually, the effect of these substances has been determined by enough conclusive experiments performed by Wüllner, by myself, and recently by M. Tammann.

In solvents other than water, I have dissolved materials as little volatile as possible, chosen among the following: oil of turpentine, naphthalene, anthracene, sesquichloride of carbon (C_2Cl_6), methyl salicylate, ethyl benzoate, antimonous chloride, mercury ethyl, benzoic, valeric, and trichloroacetic acids, thymol, nitrobenzene, and aniline. The error due to the vapor pressure of these compounds can often be rendered negligible. The vapor pressure of the dissolved substances is, in fact, considerably reduced by their mixture with a great excess of the solvent; and in order that it should not exercise a sensible influence on the results, it is enough that it should not surpass 5 or 6 millimeters at the experimental temperature.

The molecular reductions in vapor pressure caused by these different bodies in the same solvent are constantly grouped around two values, of which one, which I call *normal*, is double the other. The normal reduction is always produced by simple and chlorinated hydrocarbons and by ethers; the anomalous reduction is almost always produced by acids. There are found, however, solvents in which all the dissolved bodies produce the same molecular reduction of pressure; such are, for example, ether and acetone.

Among the volatile solvents examined there are two, water and benzene, in which I have studied carefully the lowering of freezing point. The comparison of the results obtained shows that *for all solutions made in the same solvent there is a nearly constant relation between the molecular lowering of freezing point and the molecular reduction of vapor pressure.* In water this ratio is equal to 100; in benzene it is equal to 60, nearly 1/20.

If we divide the molecular reduction of vapor pressure K produced in a determined volatile liquid by the molecular weight M' of the liquid, the quotient obtained K/M' represents the relative reduction of pressure which will be produced by 1 molecule of substance held in 100 molecules of volatile solvent. In making this calculation for the *normal* values of K produced in the various solvents by the organic materials and nonsaline metallic compounds, I have obtained these results:

Solvent	Molecular weight of solvent M′	Normal molecular reduction of pressure K	Reduction of pressure produced by 1 mol. in 100 mols. K/M′
Water.....................	18	0.185	0.0102
Phosphorus chloride..........	137.5	1.49	0.0108
Sulfide of carbon.............	76	0.80	0.0105
Bichloride of carbon(CCl₄).....	154	1.62	0.0105
Chloroform.................	119.5	1.30	0.0109
Amylene....................	70	0.74	0.0106
Benzene....................	78	0.83	0.0106
Methyl iodide...............	142	1.49	0.0105
Ethyl bromide...............	109	1.18	0.0109
Ether......................	74	0.71	0.0096
Acetone....................	58	0.59	0.0101
Methyl alcohol..............	32	0.33	0.0103

The values of K and M′ assigned in the table vary in the ratio from 1 to 9; in spite of this, the values of K/M′ vary very little and remain always near the mean 0.0105. We can then say,

1 molecule of nonsaline substance (held in the solvent) dissolved in 100 molecules of any volatile liquid decreases the vapor pressure of this liquid by a nearly constant fraction, nearly 0.0105.

This law is entirely analogous to that which I announced in 1882 relating to the lowering of the freezing point of solvents. The anomalies which it presents are explained for the most part by admitting that, in certain liquids, the dissolved molecules can be formed from two chemical molecules.

Josiah Willard Gibbs

(1839–1903)

THAT constancy of composition was evidence of chemical combination was generally assumed throughout most of the nineteenth century. Gases in solutions were regarded as physical mixtures, since they could be removed by boiling; with halogen hydrides, however, a different approach was used, for an acid of constant composition was obtained on distillation whatever concentration of the same acid was used originally, *e.g.*, hydrochloric acid (20.2 per cent). This was soon shown to be true only at atmospheric pressure, for the concentration of the distilled acid was seen to vary with the variation in pressure. The characterization of the composition of a material was, therefore, recognized to be true only over a certain range of conditions. A generalized summary of this subject was made by Josiah Willard Gibbs between 1875 and 1878 in the discussion of equilibrium in heterogeneous systems and is now known as the *phase rule*. Gibbs derived his phase rule from thermodynamic considerations. The paper which contained his principle was published in two parts in an obscure journal *Transactions of the Connecticut Academy*, and was entitled "On the Equilibrium of Heterogeneous Substances."[1] An abstract of the paper appeared in 1878,[2] and unpublished fragments of a supplement to the "Equilibrium of Heterogeneous Substances" are printed in his collected works. It was neglected for almost ten years, due to its complicated mathematical analysis, until Bakhuis Roozeboom recognized its value in classifying chemical equilibria.[3] The principles of the rule soon found wide application to the study of chemical equilibria. The phase rule is presented in a section of the first part of the paper, "On Coexistent Phases of Matter."

In considering the different homogeneous bodies which can be formed out of any set of component substances, it will be convenient to have a term which shall refer solely to the composition and thermodynamic state of any such body without regard to its quantity or form. We may call such bodies as differ in composition or state different *phases* of the matter considered, regarding all bodies which differ only in quantity and form as different examples of the same phase. Phases which can exist together, the dividing surfaces being plane, in an equilibrium which does not depend upon passive resistances to change, we shall call *coexistent*.

If a homogeneous body has n independently variable components, the phase of the body is evidently capable of $n + 1$ independent variations. A system of r coexistent phases, each of which has the same n independently variable components is capable of $n + 2 - r$ variations of phase. For the temperature, the pressure, and the potentials for the actual components have the same values in the different phases, and the variations of these quantities are by (97)[4] subject to as many conditions as there are

[1] *Trans. Conn. Acad.*, **3**: 108–248 (Oct. 1875–May 1876); **3**: 353–524 (May 1877–July 1878); reprinted in "Scientific Papers of J. Willard Gibbs," London, 1906, 2 vols. The selection given here is taken from volume 1, pages 96 to 100, of this work. Also included in "The Collected Works of J. Willard Gibbs, PhD., LL.D., . . ." New Haven, 1928, reprinted 1948.

A German translation was made by W. Ostwald, "Thermodynamische Studien . . . ," Leipzig, 1892.

A French translation was prepared by H. Le Chatelier, "Équilibre des systèmes chimiques . . . ," Paris, 1899.

[2] "On the Equilibrium of Heterogeneous Substances. Abstract of the Preceding Paper by the Author," *Amer. Jour. Sci.*, [3], **16**: 441–458 (1878).

[3] "Die heterogenen Gleichgewichte vom Standpeinste der Phasenlehre," Braunschweigh, 1901–1904.

[4] (97) $\quad -vdp + \eta dt + m_1 d\mu_1 + m_2 d\mu_2 \cdots + m_n d\mu_n = 0$

different phases. Therefore the number of independent variations in the values of these quantities, i.e., the number of independent variations of phase of the system, will be $n + 2 - r$.

Or, when the r bodies considered have not the same independently variable components, if we still denote by n the number of independently variable components of the r bodies taken as a whole, the number of independent variations of phase of which the system is capable will still be $n + 2 - r$. In this case, it will be necessary to consider the potentials for more than n component substances. Let the number of these potentials be $n + h$. We shall have by (97), as before, r relations between the variations of the temperature, of the pressure, and of these $n + h$ potentials, and we shall also have by (43)[5] and (51)[6] h relations between these potentials, of the same form as the relations which subsist between the units of the different component substances.

Hence, if $r = n + 2$, no variation in the phases (remaining coexistent) is possible. It does not seem probable that r can ever exceed $n + 2$. An example of $n = 1$ and $r = 3$ is seen in the coexistent solid, liquid, and gaseous forms of any substance of invariable composition. It seems not improbable that in the case of sulphur and some other simple substances there is more than one triad of coexistent phases; but it is entirely improbable that there are four coexistent phases of any simple substance. An example of $n = 2$ and $r = 4$ is seen in a solution of a salt in water in contact with vapor of water and two different kinds of crystals of the salt.

CONCERNING $n + 1$ COEXISTENT PHASES.

We will now seek the differential equation which expresses the relation between the variations of the temperature and the pressure in a system of $n + 1$ coexistent phases (n denoting, as before, the number of independently variable components in the system taken as a whole).

In this case we have $n + 1$ equations of the general form of (97) (one for each of the coexistent phases), in which we may distinguish the quantities n, v, m_1, m_2, etc., relating to the different phases by accents. But t and p will each have the same value throughout, and the same is true of μ_1, μ_2, etc., so far as each of these occurs in the different equations. If the total number of these potentials is $n + h$, there will be h independent relations between them, corresponding to the h independent relations between the units of the component substances to which the potentials relate, by means of which we may eliminate the variations of h of the potentials from the equations of the form of (97) in which they occur.

---

[5] (43) $a_1 M_1 + a_2 M_2 \cdots + a_n M_n = 0,$
 $b_1 M_1 + b_2 M_2 \cdots + b_n M_n = 0,$ $\Big\}$ r equations
 etc.

[6] (51) $\mu \delta m_1 \geqq M_1 \delta m_1, \ \mu_2 \delta m_2 \geqq M_2 \delta m_2, \ \mu_n \delta m_n = M_n \delta m_n$

Let one of these equations be

$$v'dp = \eta'dt + m_a'd\mu_a + m_b'd\mu_b + \text{etc.,} \tag{124}$$

and by the proposed elimination let it become

$$v'dp = \eta'dt + A_1'd\mu_1 + A_2'd\mu_2 \cdots + A_n'd\mu_n. \tag{125}$$

It will be observed that μ_a for example, in (124) denotes the potential in the mass considered for a substance S_a which may or may not be identical with any of the substances S_1, S_2, etc., to which the potentials in (125) relate. Now as the equations between the potentials by means of which the elimination is performed are similar to those which subsist between the units of the corresponding substances (compare equations (38),[7] (43), and (51)), if we denote these units by $\mathfrak{S}_a$, $\mathfrak{S}_b$, etc., $\mathfrak{S}_1$, $\mathfrak{S}_2$, etc., we must also have

$$m_a'\mathfrak{S}_a + m_b'\mathfrak{S}_b + \text{etc.} = A_1'\mathfrak{S}_1 + A_2'\mathfrak{S}_2 \ldots A_n'\mathfrak{S}_n. \tag{126}$$

But the first member of this equation denotes (in kind and quantity) the matter in the body to which equations (124) and (125) relate. As the same must be true of the second member, we may regard this same body as composed of the quantity A_1' of the substance S_1, with the quantity A_2' of the substance S_2, etc. We will therefore, in accordance with our general usage, write m_1', m_2', etc. for A_1', A_2', etc., in (125), which will then become

$$v'dp = \eta'dt + m_1'd\mu_1 + m_2'd\mu_2 \ldots + m_n'd\mu_n \tag{127}$$

But we must remember that the components to which the m_1', m_2', etc., of this equation relate are not necessarily independently variable, as are the components to which the similar expressions in (97) and (124) relate. The rest of the $n + 1$ equations may be reduced to a similar form, viz.,

$$v''dp = \eta''dt + m_1''d\mu_1 + m_2''d\mu_2 \ldots + m_n''d\mu_n \tag{128}$$

By elimination of $d\mu_1$, $d\mu_2$, $\ldots$ $d\mu_n$ from these equations we obtain

$$\begin{vmatrix} v'm_1'm_2' & \cdots & m_n' \\ v''m_1''m_2'' & \cdots & m_n'' \\ v'''m_1'''m_2''' & \cdots & m_n''' \\ \cdot & \cdot & \cdot \\ \cdot & \cdot & \cdot \end{vmatrix} dp = \begin{vmatrix} \eta'm_1'm_2' & \cdots & m_n' \\ \eta''m_1''m_2'' & \cdots & m_n'' \\ \eta'''m_1'''m_2''' & \cdots & m_n''' \\ \cdot & \cdot & \cdot \\ \cdot & \cdot & \cdot \end{vmatrix} dt \tag{129}$$

[7] (38)

$$\left.\begin{array}{l} a_1\mathfrak{S}_1 + a_2\mathfrak{S}_2 \cdots a_n\mathfrak{S}_n = 0 \\ b_1\mathfrak{S}_1 + b_2\mathfrak{S}_2 \cdots b_n\mathfrak{S}_n = 0 \\ \text{etc.} \end{array}\right\} r \text{ equations}$$

In this equation we make v', v'', etc., equal to unity. Then m_1', m_2', m_1'', etc., will denote the separate densities of the components in the different phases, and η', η'', etc., the densities of entropy.

When $n = 1$

$$(m''v' - m'v'')dp = (m''\eta' - m'\eta'')dt, \qquad (130)$$

or, if we make $m' = 1$ and $m'' = 1$, we have the usual formula

$$\frac{dp}{dt} = \frac{\eta' - \eta''}{v' - v''} = \frac{Q}{t(v'' - v')}, \qquad (131)$$

in which Q denotes the heat absorbed by a unit of the substance in passing from one state to the other without change of temperature or pressure.

CONCERNING CASES IN WHICH THE NUMBER OF COEXISTENT PHASES IS LESS THAN $n + 1$.

When $n > 1$, if the quantities of all the components S_1, S_2, ... S_n are proportional in two coexistent phases, the two equations of the form of (127) and (128) relating to these phases will be sufficient for the elimination of the variations of all the potentials. In fact, the condition of the coexistence of the two phases together with the condition of the equality of the $n - 1$ ratios of m_1', m_2', ... m_n' with the $n - 1$ ratios of m_1'', m_2'', ... m_n'' is sufficient to determine p as a function of t if the fundamental equation is known for each of the phases. The differential equation in this case may be expressed in the form of (130), m' and m'' denoting either the quantities of any one of the components or the total quantities of matter in the bodies to which they relate. Equation (131) will also hold true in this case if the total quantity of matter in each of the bodies is unity. But this case differs from the preceding in that the matter which absorbs the heat Q in passing from one state to another, and to which the other letters in the formula relate, although the same in quantity, is not in general the same in kind at different temperatures and pressures. Yet the case will often occur that one of the phases is essentially invariable in composition, especially when it is a crystalline body, and in this case the matter to which the letters in (131) relate will not vary with the temperature and pressure.

When $n = 2$, two coexistent phases are capable, when the temperature is constant, of a single variation in phase. But as (130) will hold true in this case when $m_1':m_2'::m_1'':m_2''$, it follows that for constant temperature the pressure is in general a maximum or a minimum when the composition of the two phases is identical. In like manner, the temperature of the two coexistent phases is in general a maximum or a minimum, for constant pressure, when the composition of the two phases is identical. Hence, the series of simultaneous values of t and p for which the composition of two coexistent phases is identical separates those simultaneous values of t and p for which no coexistent phases are possible from those for which there are two pair of coexistent phases. This may be applied to a liquid having two independently variable components in connection with the vapor which it yields, or in connection with any solid which may be formed in it.

When $n = 3$, we have for three coexistent phases three equations of the form of (127), from which we may obtain the following,

$$
\begin{vmatrix} v'm_1'm_2' \\ v''m_1''m_2'' \\ v'''m_1'''m_2''' \end{vmatrix} dp = \begin{vmatrix} \eta'm_1'm_2' \\ \eta''m_1''m_2'' \\ \eta'''m_1'''m_2''' \end{vmatrix} dt + \begin{vmatrix} m_1'm_2'm_3' \\ m_1''m_2''m_3'' \\ m_1'''m_2'''m_3''' \end{vmatrix} d\mu_3 \qquad (132)
$$

Now the value of the last of these determinants will be zero, when the composition of one of the three phases is such as can be produced by combining the other two. Hence, the pressure of three coexistent phases will in general be a maximum or minimum for constant temperature, and the temperature a maximum or minimum for constant pressure, when the above condition in regard to the composition of the coexistent phases is satisfied. The series of simultaneous values of t and p for which the condition is satisfied separates those simultaneous values of t and p for which three coexistent phases are not possible, from those for which there are two triads of coexistent phases. These propositions may be extended to higher values of n, and illustrated by the boiling temperatures and pressures of saturated solutions of $n - 2$ different solids in solvents having two independently variable components. . . .

Henri Louis Le Chatelier

(1850–1936)

STUDIES of equilibrium systems became rather common toward the end of the nineteenth century. The generalization of the law of mass action by Guldberg and Waage and the work of van't Hoff on reaction velocities greatly stimulated this trend. In 1884, Le Chatelier considered the case of equilibria under the influence of external forces. He proposed the principle which has since been known by his name, that when an external force exists, the reversible reaction will proceed in the direction which tends to diminish the force acting upon it. The principle has received its most spectacular application in the course of working out the ammonia synthesis. The principle was first fully stated in the *Comptes rendus* of the Academy of Sciences.[1]

[1] *Compt. rend.*, **99**: 786–789 (1884).

A GENERAL STATEMENT OF THE LAWS OF CHEMICAL EQUILIBRIUM.

In a recent work on chemical equilibrium, M. van't Hoff has shown that the majority of his experimental laws can be summarized in the following statement:

All equilibria between two different states of matter (systems) are displaced by a lowering of temperature toward that of the two systems whose formation develops the heat.

It has seemed to me that this law could be generalized still more by extending what it says of the temperature to condensation, and, moreover, it can be given an identical form to that of the laws of all equilibria which produce mechanical work by their displacement, and which depend consequently on the theorem of Carnot. The statement which I propose to make includes *reversible* chemical phenomena in the class of *reciprocal* phenomena to which M. Lippmann has recently added reversible electrical phenomena.

Every system in stable chemical equilibrium submitted to the influence of an exterior force which tends to cause variation either in its temperature or its condensation (pressure, concentration, number of molecules in the unit of volume) in its totality or only in some one of its parts can undergo only those interior modifications which, if they occur alone, would produce a change of temperature, or of condensation, of a sign contrary to that resulting from the exterior force.

These modifications are generally progressive and partial.

They are sudden and complete when they can be produced without changing the individual condensation of various homogeneous parts which constitute the system in equilibrium, while changing the condensation of the system as a whole.

They are zero when their production cannot produce changes analogous to those due to the exterior force.

Finally, if these modifications are possible, nevertheless they are not essential. In the case where they do not occur, and where the system remains unaltered, the equilibrium, from being stable, becomes unstable and can then undergo only modifications which tend to bring it nearer the condition of stability.

Some examples of equilibria, for the most part well known, will show the generality of the applications of this law which includes equally phenomena of fusion, vaporization, and solution, which cannot in any way be distinguished from chemical phenomena, properly called.

1. *Heating the total system produces the endothermic modification*, such as *fusion and volatilization* of the whole body; *polymerization* of C_2N, etc.; reversible *dimorphic transformation* of AgI; NH_4O, NO_5; dissociation of CO_2; CaO, CO_2; Bi_2O_3, $3NO_5$, $4HO$; reversible endothermic *combination*

of CS_2 and very probably also of NO_5, etc.; endothermic *solution* of most salts; endothermic *crystallization* of some salts: NaO, SO_3; CaO, HO, well known to have a solubility decreasing with temperature.

2. *Partial heating of a system produces modifications which tend to cool the part heated altogether,* such as the *propagation of heat* by conduction, the production of *thermoelectric* currents, the *change of concentration* by diffusion, the *transfer of metal* from one point to another of a strip placed in a solution of one of its salts.

3. *The increase in condensation of a whole system maintained at constant temperature produces modifications which tend to reduce the condensation of the system,* such as the *fusion* of ice, the *solidification* of paraffin, the *dimorphic transformation* of AgI, the *combination* of the dissociation products of CO_2.

4. *The increase of condensation of part of a system produces modifications tending to diminish the condensation of the part which is altered,* such as *condensation* of water vapor, *combination* of CaO + CO_2 at red heat, *diffusion* of unequally concentrated solutions, *transfer of metal* on a strip placed in a solution of one of its salts of variable concentration, *lowering of the melting point* of an alloy or a mixture of salts during its progressive solidification.

5. *The modifications of equilibrium are usually progressive:* for example, in the dissociation of CO_2, and in general in all systems whose elements are not simply juxtaposed, but of which some form homogeneous mixtures between themselves.

6. *The modifications of equilibrium are total when they can be produced without altering the condensation of any of the parts of the system, while changing the total condensation of the whole system.* Such is the *condensation* of water vapor, the *fusion* of ice, the *dimorphic transformation* of AgI, the *dissociation* of CaO, CO_2 and of solid CuO, the *solution* of salts. These systems for an infinitely small change of condensation of one of their parts pass from an extreme limit of their equilibrium state to the extreme opposite limit.

7. *The modifications of equilibrium are zero when they cannot produce an effect analogous to that due to the exterior force.* Dissociation is independent of *pressure* for mixtures which combine without change of volume, hydriodic acid, for example. The limit of equilibrium is independent of *temperature* when their transformations do not liberate heat, which is the case in esterification.

8. *Finally, all modifications of equilibrium are only possible, but are not necessarily produced,* as is shown in *superfusion, superheating, supersaturation,* the rapid cooling of dissociated carbonic acid. The unstable systems thus obtained can only be modified to bring nearer the conditions of stable equilibrium. The transformation of these unstable equilibria is

generally effected with a liberation of heat, conforming to the *principle of maximum work* because, as M. van't Hoff has remarked, ordinary temperature differs little from absolute zero, for which stable equilibrium corresponds to liberation of all the heat contained in the body.

Svante Arrhenius

(1859–1927)

DURING the years 1853 to 1859, Hittorf had shown that the current in electrolysis seemed to be carried by the ions of a salt, each moving with a different speed toward an electrode. In 1874, Kohlrausch demonstrated that the equivalent conductivity divided by the concentration (in equivalents per cubic centimeter) of a very dilute solution of a salt is the same as the sum of both terms. When these facts were taken in conjunction with the discoveries of Raoult, everything necessary for the formulation of the theory of electrolytic dissociation was known. The final statement of the theory was presented by Svante Arrhenius in a memoir submitted to the Swedish Academy of Sciences in 1883, entitled "Researches on the Galvanic Conductibility of Electrolytes" and published in two parts by the Academy in the following year.[1]

The full statement of the theory of electrolytic dissociation was published in 1887. Van't Hoff presented his work on osmotic pressure (pages 453–458) at about the same time, and this supplemented the ideas of Arrhenius. The theory of electrolytic dissociation was not widely accepted at first, but owing to the efforts of men such as Ostwald, it was soon adopted, and with it was initiated a new period in experimental and theoretical chemistry.[2]

ON THE DISSOCIATION OF SUBSTANCES DISSOLVED IN WATER

In a paper submitted to the Swedish Academy of Sciences, on the 14th of October, 1885, van't Hoff proved experimentally, as well as theoreti-

[1] *Bihang der Stockholmer Akademie*, **8**: Nos. 13 and 14 (1884). Both these papers are available in Ostwald's *Klassiker*, No. 160, "Svante Arrhenius, Untersuchungen über die galvanische Leitfähigkeit der Electrolyte. Uebersetzt von A. Hamburger und herausgegeben von O. Sakur," Leipzig, 1907.

[2] The German version, which was the most influential publication, appeared in *Z. physik. Chem.*, **1**: 631–648 (1887).

English translations are available in: *Alembic Club Reprints*, No. 19, "The Foundations of the Theory of Dilute Solutions. Papers on Osmotic Pressure by J. H. van't Hoff and on Electrolytic Dissociation by Svante Arrhenius, 1887," Edinburgh, 1929; "The Modern Theory of Solution. Memoirs by Pfeffer, van't Hoff, Arrhenius, and Raoult. Translated and edited by Harry C. Jones," New York, 1899, pp. 47–66. The following selection is taken from this translation, pages 47 to 59.

cally, the following unusually significant generalization of Avogadro's law:

"The pressure which a gas exerts at a given temperature, if a definite number of molecules is contained in a definite volume, is equal to the osmotic pressure which is produced by most substances under the same conditions, if they are dissolved in any given liquid."

Van't Hoff has proved this law in a manner which scarcely leaves any doubt as to its absolute correctness. But a difficulty which still remains to be overcome, is that the law in question holds only for "most substances"; a very considerable number of the aqueous solutions investigated furnishing exceptions, and in the sense that they exert a much greater osmotic pressure than would be required from the law referred to.

If a gas shows such a deviation from the law of Avogadro, it is explained by assuming that the gas is in a state of dissociation. The conduct of chlorine, bromine, and iodine at higher temperatures is a very well-known example. We regard these substances under such conditions as broken down into simple atoms.

The same expedient may, of course, be made use of to explain the exceptions to van't Hoff's law; but it has not been put forward up to the present, probably on account of the newness of the subject, the many exceptions known, and the vigorous objections which would be raised from the chemical side, to such an explanation. The purpose of the following lines is to show that such an assumption, of the dissociation of certain substances dissolved in water, is strongly supported by the conclusions drawn from the electrical properties of the same substances, and that also the objections to it from the chemical side are diminished on more careful examination.

In order to explain the electrical phenomena we must assume with Clausius that some of the molecules of an electrolyte are dissociated into their ions, which move independently of one another. But since the "osmotic pressure" which a substance dissolved in a liquid exerts against the walls of the confining vessel, must be regarded, in accordance with the modern kinetic view, as produced by the impacts of the smallest parts of this substance, as they move, against the walls of the vessel, we must, therefore, assume in accordance with this view, that a molecule dissociated in the manner given above, exercises as great a pressure against the walls of the vessel as its ions would do in the free condition. If, then, we could calculate what fraction of the molecules of an electrolyte is dissociated into ions, we should be able to calculate the osmotic pressure from van't Hoff's law.

In a former communication "On the Electrical Conductivity of Electrolytes," I have designated those molecules whose ions are independent of one another in their movements, as active; the remaining molecules, whose ions are firmly combined with one another, as inactive. I have also maintained it as probable that in extreme dilution all the inactive molecules of an electrolyte are transformed into active. This assumption I will make the basis of the calculations now to be carried out. I have designated the relation between the number of active molecules and the sum of the active and inactive molecules, as the activity coefficient. The activity coefficient of an electrolyte at infinite dilution is therefore taken as *unity*. For smaller dilution it is less than *one*, and from the principles established in my work already cited, it can be regarded as equal to the ratio of the actual molecular conductivity of the solution to the maximum limiting value which the molecular conductivity of the same solution approaches with increasing dilution. This obtains for solutions which are not too concentrated (i.e., for solutions in which disturbing conditions, such as internal friction, etc., can be disregarded).

If this activity coefficient (α) is known, we can calculate as follows the values of the coefficient i tabulated by van't Hoff. i is the relation between the osmotic pressure actually exerted by a substance and the osmotic pressure which it would exert if it consisted only of inactive (undissociated) molecules. i is evidently equal to the sum of the number of inactive molecules, plus the number of ions, divided by the sum of the inactive and active molecules. If, then, m represents the number of inactive, and n the number of active molecules, and k the number of ions into which every active molecule dissociates (e.g., $k = 2$ for KCl, i.e., K and Cl; $k = 3$ for $BaCl_2$ and K_2SO_4, i.e., Ba, Cl, Cl, and K, K, SO_4), then we have

$$i = \frac{m + kn}{m + n}$$

But since the activity coefficient (α) can, evidently, be written $\dfrac{n}{m + n}$:

[1] $$i = 1 + (k - 1)\alpha.$$

Part of the figures given below (those in the last column) were calculated from this formula.

On the other hand, i can be calculated as follows from the results of Raoult's experiments on the freezing-point of solutions, making use of the principles stated by van't Hoff. The lowering (t) of the freezing-point of water (in degrees Celsius), produced by dissolving a gram-molecule of the given substance in one litre of water, is divided by 18.5. The values of i thus calculated, $i = t/18.5$, are recorded in next to the last column. All the figures given below are calculated on the assumption that one gram of the substance to be investigated was dissolved in one litre of water (as was done in the experiments of Raoult).

In the following table the name and chemical formula of the substance investigated are given in the first two columns, the value of the activity coefficient in the third (Lodge's dissociation ratio), and in the last two the values of i calculated by the two methods: $1 = t/18.5$ and $i = 1 + (k - 1)\alpha$.

The substances investigated are grouped together under four chief divisions: 1, non-conductors; 2, bases; 3, acids; and 4, salts.

Arrhenius then gives a table of the values for i calculated by both methods for ninety substances. In all cases, the values lie close to the number of ions liberated by the compound in question.

An especially marked parallelism appears,[3] beyond doubt, on comparing the figures in the last two columns. This shows, *a posteriori*, that in all probability the assumptions on which I have based the calculation of these figures are, in the main, correct. These assumptions were:

1. That van't Hoff's law holds not only for *most*, but for *all substances*, even for those which have hitherto been regarded as exceptions (electrolytes in aqueous solution).

2. That every electrolyte (in aqueous solution), consists partly of active (in electrical and chemical relation), and partly of inactive molecules, the latter passing into active molecules on increasing the dilution, so that in infinitely dilute solutions only active molecules exist.

The objections which can probably be raised from the chemical side are essentially the same which have been brought forward against the hypothesis of Clausius, and which I have earlier sought to show, were completely untenable. A repetition of these objections would, then, be almost superfluous. I will call attention to only one point. Although the dissolved substance exercises an osmotic pressure against the wall of the vessel, just as if it were partly dissociated into its ions, yet the dissociation with which we are here dealing is not exactly the same as that which exists when, e.g., an ammonium salt is decomposed at a higher temperature. The products of dissociation in the first case (the ions) are charged with very large quantities of electricity of opposite kind, whence certain conditions appear (the incompressibility of electricity) from which it follows that the ions cannot be separated from one another to any great extent, without a large expenditure of energy. On the contrary, in ordinary dissociation where no such conditions exist, the products of dissociation can, in general, be separated from one another.

The above two assumptions are of the very widest significance, not only in their theoretical relation, of which more hereafter, but also, to the highest degree, in a practical sense. If it could, for instance, be shown that the law of van't Hoff is generally applicable—which I have tried to show

[3] In reference to some salts which are distinctly exceptions, compare below [page 487].

is highly probable—the chemist would have at his disposal an extraordinarily convenient means of determining the molecular weight of every substance soluble in a liquid.[4]

At the same time, I wish to call attention to the fact that the above equation (1) shows a connection between the two values of i and α, which play the chief roles in the two chemical theories developed very recently by van't Hoff and myself.

I have tacitly assumed in the calculation of i, carried out above, that the inactive molecules exist in solution as simple molecules and not united into larger molecular complexes. The result of this calculation (i.e., the figures in the last column), compared with the results of direct observation (the figures in next to the last column), shows that, in general, this supposition is perfectly justified. If this were not true, the figures in next to the last column would, of course, prove to be smaller than in the last. An exception, where the latter undoubtedly takes place, is found in the group of sulphates of the magnesium series ($MgSO_4$, $FeSO_4$, $CuSO_4$, $ZnSO_4$, and $CdSO_4$), also in cadmium iodide. We can assume, to explain this, that the inactive molecules of these salts are, in part, combined with one another. Hittorf, as is well known, was led to this assumption for cadmium iodide, through the large change in the migration number. And if we examine his tables more closely we will find, also, an unusually large change of this number for the three of the above named sulphates ($MgSO_4$, $CuSO_4$, and $ZnSO_4$) which he investigated. It is then very probable that this explanation holds for the salts referred to. But we must assume that double molecules exist only to a very slight extent in the other salts. It still remains, however, to indicate briefly the reasons which have led earlier authors to the assumption of the general existence of complex molecules in solution.

Since, in general, substances in the gaseous state consist of simple molecules (from Avogadro's law), and since a slight increase in the density of gases often occurs near the point of condensation, indicating a union of the molecules, we are inclined to see in the change of the state of aggregation, such combinations taking place to a much greater extent. That is, we assume that the liquid molecules in general are not simple. I will not combat the correctness of this conclusion here. But a great difference arises if this liquid is dissolved in another (e.g., HCl in water). For if we assume that by dilution the molecules which were inactive at the beginning become active, the ions being separated to a certain extent from one another, which of course requires a large expenditure of energy, it is not difficult to assume, also, that the molecular complexes break down, for the most part, on mixing with water, which in any case does not require

[4] This means has already been employed. Compare Raoult, *Ann. chim. phys.* [6], **8**: 317 (1886); Paternò and Nasini, *Ber.*, **1886**: 2527.

very much work. The consumption of heat on diluting solutions has been interpreted as a proof of the existence of molecular complexes. But, as stated, this can also be ascribed to the conversion of inactive into active molecules. Further, some chemists, to support the idea of constant valence, would assume molecular complexes, in which the unsaturated bonds could become saturated. But the doctrine of constant valence is so much disputed that we are scarcely justified in basing any conclusions upon it. The conclusions thus arrived at, that, e.g., potassium chloride would have the formula $(KCl)_3$, L. Meyer sought to support by the fact that potassium chloride is much less volatile than mercuric chloride, although the former has a much smaller molecular weight than the latter. Independent of the theoretical weakness of such an argument, this con-clusion could, of course, hold only for the pure substances, not for solu-tions. Several other reasons have been brought forward by L. Meyer for the existence of molecular complexes, e.g., the fact that sodium chloride diffuses more slowly than hydrochloric acid, but this is probably to be referred to the greater friction (according to electrical determinations), of sodium against water, than of hydrogen. But it suffices to cite L. Meyer's own words: "Although all of these different points of departure for ascertaining molecular weights in the liquid condition are still so in-complete and uncertain, nevertheless they permit us to hope that it will be possible in the future to ascertain the size of molecules." But the law of van't Hoff gives entirely reliable points of departure, and these show that in almost all cases the number of molecular complexes in solutions can be disregarded, while they confirm the existence of such in some few cases, and, indeed, in those in which there were formerly reasons for assuming the existence of such complexes. Let us, then, not deny the possibility that such molecular complexes also exist in solutions of other salts—and especially in concentrated solutions; but in solutions of such dilution as was investigated by Raoult, they are, in general, present in such small quantity that they can be disregarded without appreciable error in the above calculations.

Most of the properties of dilute solutions of salts are of a so-called addi-tive nature. In other words, these properties (expressed in figures) can be regarded as a sum of the properties of the parts of the solution (of the solvent, and of the parts of the molecules, which are, indeed, the ions). As an example, the conductivity of a solution of a salt can be regarded as the sum of the conductivities of the solvent (which in most cases is zero), of the positive ion, and of the negative ion. In most cases this is controlled by comparing two salts of one acid (e.g., potassium and sodium chlorides) with two corresponding salts of the same metals with another acid (e.g., potassium and sodium nitrates). Then the property of the first salt (KCl) *minus* the property of the second (NaCl), is equal to the property of the third (KNO_3), *minus* the property of the fourth ($NaNO_3$). This holds in most cases for several properties, such as conductivity, lowering of freezing-point, refraction equivalent, heat of neutralization, etc., which we will treat briefly later on. It finds its explanation in the nearly complete dissociation of most salts into their ions, which was shown above to be true. If a salt (in aqueous solution) is completely broken down into its ions, most of the properties of this salt can, of course, be expressed as the sum of the properties of the ions, since the ions are independent of one another in most cases, and since every ion has, therefore, a characteristic property, independent of the nature of the opposite ion with which it occurs. The solutions which we, in fact, investigate are never completely dissociated, so that the above statement does not hold rigidly. But if we consider such salts as are 80 to 90 per cent. dissociated (salts of the strong bases with the strong acids, almost without exception), we will, in general, not make very large errors if we calculate the properties on the assumption that the salts are completely broken down into their ions. From the above table this evidently holds also for the strong bases and acids: $Ba(OH)_2$, $Sr(OH)_2$, $Ca(OH)_2$, LiOH, NaOH, KOH, TlOH, and HCl, HBr, HI, HNO_3, $HClO_3$, and $HClO_4$.

But there is another group of substances which, for the most part, have played a subordinate role in the investigations up to the present, and which are far from completely dissociated, even in dilute solutions. Examples taken from the above table are the salts $HgCl_2$ (and other salts of mercury), CdI_2, $CdSO_4$, $FeSO_4$, $MgSO_4$, $ZnSO_4$, $CuSO_4$, and $Cu(C_2H_3O_2)_2$; the weak bases and acids, as NH_3, and the different amines, H_3PO_4, H_2S, $B(OH)_3$, HCN, formic, acetic, butyric, tartaric, malic, and lactic acids. The properties of these substances will not, in general, be of the same (additive) nature as those of the former class, a fact which is completely confirmed, as we will show later. There are, of course, a number of substances lying between these two groups, as is also shown by the above table. Let attention be here called to the fact that several investigators have been led to the assumption of a certain kind of complete dissociation of salts into their ions, by considering that the properties of substances of the first group, which have been investigated far more frequently than those of the second, are almost always of an additive nature. But since no reason could be discovered from the chemical side why salt molecules should break down (into their ions) in a perfectly definite manner, and, moreover, since chemists, for certain reasons not to be more fully considered here, have fought as long as possible against the existence of so-called unsaturated radicals (under which head the ions must be placed), and since, in addition, it cannot be denied that the grounds for such an assumption were somewhat uncertain, the assumption of complete dissociation has not met with any hearty approval up to the present. The above table shows also, that the aversion of the chemist to the idea advanced, of complete dissociation, has not been without a certain justification, since at the dilutions actually employed, the dissociation is never complete, and even for a large number of electrolytes, (the second group) is relatively inconsiderable.

Wilhelm Friedrich Ostwald

(1853–1932)

PROBABLY the greatest contribution of Wilhelm Ostwald was the establishment of physical chemistry as an independent branch of chemistry. This he did through his "Lehrbuch der allgemeinen Chemie," 1885, his founding with van't Hoff of the *Zeitschrift für physikalische Chemie* in 1887, and his numerous investigations of topics which lay in this field. He gave great support to the dissociation theory of Arrhenius and showed by his *dilution law* that the law of mass action applied to dilute solutions of weak electrolytes. The dilution law was first expressed in a preliminary note published in 1888[1] though the supporting experimental details were not presented until the following year.[2] The following selection gives the first (1888) statement of this law.

The researches of van't Hoff, Planck, and Arrhenius on dilute solutions have in recent times led to the recognition of a complete analogy of these with gases. One of the most valuable advances of these studies is that the compounds usually spoken of as held together by the strongest affinities, such as, for example, potassium chloride, hydrogen chloride, or potassium hydroxide, must actually be regarded in dilute solutions as very largely dissociated.

Since this result is derived according to the laws of thermodynamics on the basis of a hypothesis which is at least very plausible, if not positive, it does not leave much to say against it, so much does it satisfy the usual views. But before deciding on such a change in viewpoint, we have the duty to apply the strongest tests possible for its verification.

One such test is to deduce the broadest possible consequences of the theory, to compare them with practice. The following lines attempt to develop such consequences, and this preliminary communication reports the results of the test.

If the electrolytes are dissociated in water solution and therefore obey

[1] *Z. physik. Chem.*, **2**: 36–37 (1888).
[2] *Ibid.*, **3**: 170, 241 (1889).

laws which are analogous to the gas laws, then the dissociation laws which have been learned for gases will also find use for solutions. In the simplest case, where a molecule decomposes into two, the theory now leads to the following formula which is valid for gases (Ostwald, *Allg. Chem.*, **2**, 732):

$$R \log \frac{p}{p_1 p_2} = \frac{\rho}{T} + \text{const.,}$$

which for a constant temperature and the case where no decomposition products are left over accords with the law

$$p/p_1{}^2 = C$$

where p is the pressure of the undecomposed part, p_1 of the decomposed part, and C is a constant.

Now, according to the work mentioned above, it is permissible to place the pressure in solution proportional to the actual masses u and u_1 of the substance and inversely proportional to the volume; the equation then becomes $p : p_1 = \dfrac{u}{v} : \dfrac{u_1}{v}$, and so $\dfrac{u}{u_1} v = C$. Further, the masses u and u_1 can be calculated from the electrical conductivity, as Arrhenius has shown. If we call the molecular conductivity of an electrolyte of volume v, μ_v, and the limit of conductivity of infinite dilution μ_∞, then $u : u_1 = \mu_\infty - \mu_v : \mu_v$, since the conductivity μ_v is proportional to the dissociated mass of electrolyte u_1. From this follows the dilution law, valid for all binary electrolytes:

$$\frac{\mu_\infty - \mu_v}{\mu_v{}^2} v = \text{const.}$$

The test of this conclusion can be performed with great assurance in the acids and bases, for which numerous measurements of electrical conductivity exist. Since I will publish future communications on this subject, I will content myself now with pointing out that the results of my calculations speak favorably for the theory. The formula expresses not only an altogether general law, which I have earlier found empirically for the influence of dilution on acids and bases, as well as over a hundred substances but it leads also to numerical results which in part agree completely, in part show a variation whose size is of the same order of magnitude as has been established in gases.

Ostwald gave to the theory of catalysis its modern form. Berzelius had opened the way to this development (pages 265–268), and Ostwald carried the work through. His catalytic theory stressed the effect of the catalyst on the reaction velocity and thus brought the subject into the field of chemical kinetics. Ostwald chose to state his theory of catalysis in the course of an abstract which he prepared for an article by F. Stohmann on the heats of combustion of foodstuffs. It ap-

peared in the Abstract section of the *Zeitschrift für physikalische Chemie* in 1894.[3]
He disagreed with Stohmann's definition of catalysis and so devoted most of the
abstract to a discussion of his own ideas. The abstract is presented as follows.

After a historical introduction the author brings together the essential
values for the heat of combustion of the most important ingredients of
nutrients as determined by him and his students. Some general considerations of this are discussed in which the author points out in a praiseworthy
manner the great significance of catalytic phenomena for physiology.
After a summary of the views of different investigators on this problem,
he formulates his own, in which he defines *catalysis* in the following way:

"Catalysis is a condition of movement of the atoms in a molecule of a
labile body which follows the entrance of the energy emitted from one
body into another and leads to the formation of more stable bodies with
loss of energy."

The abstractor has several objections to make to this definition. First,
the assumption of a "condition of movement of the atoms in a molecule"
is hypothetical and therefore not suitable for purposes of definition. Also,
that is plainly not a loss of energy. What is more, in describing characteristic conditions of catalysis, a loss of free energy can follow under conditions even of absolute energy uptake.

If the abstractor were to formulate for himself the problem of characterizing the phenomenon of catalysis in a general way, he would consider
the following expression as probably most suitable: Catalysis is the acceleration of a chemical reaction, which proceeds slowly, by the presence of a
foreign substance. It would then be necessary to give the following
explanations.

There are numerous substances or combinations of substances which in
themselves are not stable but undergo slow change and only seem stable
to us because their changes occur so slowly that during the usual short
period of observation they do not strike us. Such substances or systems
often attain an increased reaction rate if certain foreign substances, that
is, substances which are not in themselves necessary for the reaction, are
added. This acceleration occurs without alteration of the general energy
relations, since after the end of the reaction the foreign body can again be
separated from the field of the reaction, so that the energy used up by the
addition can once more be obtained by the separation, or the reverse.
However, these processes, like all natural ones, must always occur in such
a direction that the free energy of the entire system is decreased.

It is therefore misleading to consider catalytic action as a force which
produces something which would not occur without the substance which
acts catalytically; still less can it be assumed that the latter performs

[3] *Ibid.*, **15**: 705–706 (1894).

work. It will perhaps contribute to an understanding of the problem if I especially mention that time is not involved in the idea of chemical energy; thus if the chemical energy relations are such that a definite process must occur, then it is only the initial and final states, as well as the whole series of intermediate given states which must be passed through, which must occur, but in no way is the time during which the reaction takes place of concern. Time is here dependent on conditions which lie outside the two chief laws of energetics. The only form of energy which contains time in its definition is kinetic energy, which is proportional to the mass and the square of the velocity. All cases in which such energies take a fixed part are therefore completely determined in time if the conditions are given; but all cases in which the vibrational energy does not play this role are independent of time, that is, they can occur without violating the laws of energy in any given time. Catalytic processes are empirically found to be of the type in which this last property is observed; the existence of catalytic processes is to me therefore a positive proof that chemical processes cannot have a kinetic nature.

W. O.

Hermann Walther Nernst

(1864–1941)

ALTHOUGH much of the important work of Nernst, including his third law of thermodynamics, was done in the twentieth century, he made a number of significant discoveries in the early part of his life. His major interests in the field of physical chemistry involved solutions, and he extended the work of van't Hoff, Arrhenius, and Ostwald in several directions. It was from the ideas of these men that he derived his theory of the solution pressure of ions, by which the production of an electromotive force in galvanic cells could be explained. This theory was published in 1889 in a paper on the electromotive activity of ions[1] and forms the first of the two selections given below.

In the same year, Nernst explained the precipitation of salts from saturated solutions by addition of a common ion and thus announced the principle of the solubility product.[2] The account of this derivation forms the second of the two selections.

[1] *Z. physik. chem.*, **4**: 129–181 (1889); the selection given is taken from pages 150 to 154.

[2] *Ibid.*, **4**: 372–383 (1889); the selection is taken from pages 375 to 377 and 379.

6. ON THE PROCESS OF SOLUTION OF SOLID BODIES.

The fact that when solid or liquid bodies evaporate, their molecules are forced into a space in which they occur under a definite pressure, the partial pressure of the gas resulting from this process, made it possible to attribute to the evaporating bodies the power of expansion; the pressure under which the gaseous evaporation product is found when equilibrium conditions are attained was called the *vapor pressure* of these bodies.

If, now, in terms of the van't Hoff theory we assume that the molecules of a body in solution are also under a definite pressure, then we must likewise attribute an expansion power to a dissolved substance in contact with the solvent, because here also its molecules are forced into a space in which they are under a certain pressure; obviously, such bodies will go into solution until the osmotic partial pressure of the molecules which results from the process becomes equal to the "solution pressure" of the body.

Accordingly, we have, in evaporation and solution, processes which can be regarded as entirely analogous, as they have been many times; although without knowledge of the osmotic pressure, a sound basis is lacking.

These considerations are so simple and almost self-evident that they lead directly to some far-reaching and noteworthy conclusions which permit a test of the van't Hoff theory from an entirely new standpoint; here, however, they will be considered only for their importance for our immediate purpose.

As we can obviously find for each gas either a solid or a liquid body whose vapor or dissociation pressure agrees with the pressure of this gas, developed either by evaporation or decomposition, so for each molecule occurring in solution or indeed in a freely movable state, that is, for each ion, we must assume the existence of a substance from whose solution molecules of this kind will result. This approaches and perhaps offers the possibility of maintaining the idea just expressed, that of attributing to the metals the power to go into solution as ions. According to this, each metal possesses in water an individual solution pressure whose magnitude can be called P.

We will now consider what happens if we dip a metal with an electrolytic solution pressure P into a solution of a salt formed from this metal in which the ion of the metal exists under a pressure p. First, if $P > p$, then immediately on contact, driven by this excess pressure, a number of positively charged metallic ions go into solution. Since a certain positive amount of electricity is transported by the latter from the metal into solution, the liquid acquires a positive charge and the positive ions contained in it are arranged in a pattern on its surface; and naturally, a corresponding amount of negative electricity will be free in the metal, which also is arranged on the surface. It can be seen directly that at the place of contact between metal and electrolyte, both electricities must accumulate in the form of a double layer, whose existence had been made known some time ago in another way by Herr v. Helmholtz.

This double layer now gives rise to a component of force which is directed perpendicular to the contact surface of metal and solution and seeks to drive the metallic ion from the electrolyte to the metal, thus working in opposition to the electrolytic solution pressure.

The equilibrium condition will obviously be such that both these forces are present; as a final result we get the appearance of an electromotive force between metal and electrolyte which causes a galvanic current in the direction from metal to liquid if by any sort of an apparatus its occurrence is possible.

If $P < p$ the reverse process naturally occurs; metallic ions are driven from the electrolyte and precipitate on the metal until the electrostatic-force component of the positive charge of the metal and the minus charge of the liquid, resulting here, and the osmotic-pressure excess reach an equilibrium. With this there again appears an electromotive force between metal and electrolyte which here, however, under suitable conditions, will cause a galvanic current in the opposite direction. In both cases, corresponding to the unusually great electrostatic capacity of the ions, the mass of metal which goes into solution or precipitates is very small.

Finally, if $P = p$, there also occurs at the first instant of contact of metal and electrolyte an equilibrium; no potential difference occurs on this between the two. If we formulate these conditions mathematically, we obtain in a new way at once the equations (6) and (7).

$$(6) \qquad E = p_0 \ln \frac{P}{p} \qquad (7) \quad E = 0.860T \ln \frac{P}{p} \times 10^{-4} \text{ volt}$$

Since P in the nature of things must always have a positive value, it follows that for $p = 0$, that is, in pure water, all metals are infinitely strongly charged negatively; this result stands in closest relation to the recent results of Herr v. Helmholtz, according to which for a concentration cell, one of whose poles is bathed by pure water, an infinitely strong electromotive force is given which seeks to cause a flowing galvanic current in the cell from one pole to the other. This condition, which forces us to a physically impossible infinite potential difference, naturally means that metals and pure water cannot exist together; this agrees very well with the above argument in which we attribute to all metals the ability to go into solution to form traces of ions.

The analogous method of thinking which we have just established for "electrodes of the first class" is naturally applicable also for "electrodes reversible with respect to anions"; instead of the metal, the electronegative ion enters here, and accordingly we have, for example, in the mercury electrode covered with calomel, a dissociation pressure relative to the chloride ion, that is, we must ascribe to it "an electronegative solution pressure." In this way we again get equation (8).

$$(8) \qquad E' = p_0 \, ln \, \frac{P}{p'} = 0.860T \, ln \, \frac{P}{p'} \times 10^{-4} \, \text{volt}$$

Naturally, p', the electronegative solution pressure, always here also has a positive value for pressure; these electrodes may suitably be called "electrodes of the second class."

The method given here for explaining the experimentally established facts of formation of a potential difference between metals and electrolytes is perhaps not so very different from the earlier theories of the origin of the current in a galvanic battery as at first glance appears; but it leads farther than the methods used before inasmuch as it gives simple, formal relations for the questionable potential difference. Whether, for the explanation of this, we attribute to the metals a specific attraction of electricity, as Herr v. Helmholtz does, or, as Herr G. Wiedemann does, we explain the facts by an attractive force between the metals and ions of the electrolyte as actually occurring, or, as I have done here, assume that metals tend to drive their ions into solution through forces analogous to the usual vapor pressure, the explanation is perhaps not so important, if only we admit, as has been done before, that a transport of electricity occurs by contact of metal and electrolyte, producing an equilibrium condition, and that this transport of electricity is inseparably bound up with a transport of material particles. Which sort of forces cause this can to a certain extent be left doubtful for a time; it is much more important first to calculate the work production connected with them. In this matter, I think we are justified in considering it more closely, just as with osmotic pressure we introduce ideas and calculations on the basis of phenomena established by almost certain facts, and here we need not concern ourselves with the question of whether the origin lies in some attractive force between solvent and dissolved body or in the reciprocal relations between the molecules of dissolved bodies. Similarly also, we may venture to use the idea of "electrolytic solution pressure," even if the physical meaning is still somewhat uncertain. I will conclude the discussion of the nature of the forces which drive the ions from the metal into solution with other questions, namely, how does osmotic pressure occur, in what form does the ion remain bound, and finally how the latter is related to its solution. These are not essential and we must content ourselves with showing that the introduction of the electrolytic solution pressure leads to formal relationships which are in agreement with the facts. This will be shown in many ways in the following chapters.

The principle of the solubility product is presented in the citation below.[3]

THE RECIPROCAL EFFECT OF THE SOLUBILITY OF SALTS.

. . . 4. We will consider for simplicity a binary electrolyte which is not very soluble in water, as, for example, potassium chlorate. The saturated solution of this substance contains about half a gram-molecule per liter at room temperature and for the most part occurs in the state of free ions K and ClO_3. If then we add either K or ClO_3 ions to this solution, the solubility of potassium chlorate must decrease, and therefore solid salt precipitates. Now we cannot add K or ClO_3 ions alone to the solution, because of their electrical charge, but only along with a negative or positive ion. This we do when we mix a strongly dissociated potassium salt or chlorate with the solution. The negative radical of the first or the positive of the second is without influence, since, as we saw above, indifferent substances do not alter the dissociation tension.

5. I actually observed that when I added some drops of a very concentrated KOH or KCl solution to 10 cubic centimeters of saturated potassium chlorate, in the first case (where the content of the solution could be made much stronger because of the great solubility of KOH) there was an immediate strong separation of $KClO_3$, and in the second case, a separation after a few minutes; the process here is that the concentration and therefore the osmotic partial pressure of K ion is increased by the addition; the solution pressure of the solid salt $KClO_3$ no longer has the power to hold this increased pressure in equilibrium, the K ion will be forced out of the solution and will precipitate itself on the solid salt, naturally in combination with its equivalent amount of ClO_3 ion, as a solid, because in a solution the opposite ion must always act in an amount electrically equivalent.

The same thing occurs when instead of K ions, ClO_3 ions are added to the solution, and indeed by the addition of a very concentrated $NaClO_3$ solution. Here also a clear crystallization of $KClO_3$ occurred as soon as expected. This experiment was fully analogous to the one in which Horstmann used ammonium carbaminate; in place of the vapor tension we have here the solution tension, in place of the gaseous decomposition product, the ions which occur in solution.

I made an analogous experiment with silver acetate, which at room temperature dissolves to a content of about 0.06 normal, and here also I easily recognized qualitatively the effects demanded by the theory; with addition of either silver nitrate or sodium acetate solid, crystalline AgAc

[3] See footnote 2 p. 493.

separated. I have followed this case quantitatively in order to test the correctness of the formula which I develop later.

6. The reciprocal effects of solubility of salts have been, up to now, the subject of repeated intensive investigations, without the advancing of any simple law to date. Thus, recently Engel stated that thanks to these intensive investigations no general rule can be established for the action which a chemical compound exerts on the saturated solution of another. We have seen that this may very well be possible, and have therefore proceeded to a proportionally simpler case. The fact that such a rule has remained hidden until now is explained by the fact that up to the present the work has been almost exclusively with easily soluble salts and with correspondingly very concentrated solutions. Since a pressure prevails in these which equals hundreds of atmospheres, the gas laws lose their validity, and therefore naturally simple relations fail. The qualitative character of the phenomenon that the solubility of a salt decreases steadily with the addition of another with a common ion would always be admitted under these conditions, were it not that another complication frequently enters. In the above and in the following considerations it is always assumed that the molecular condition of the solid salt in contact with the saturated solution will not be altered by addition of another salt; if there should be some change in crystal form or crystal water content, or if something should crystallize with the added salt, then, in general, this new solid body would have a new solution pressure, for the conditions of which our considerations will permit us no conclusions, but which could be calculated by the introduction of a new constant in the equation. If such a further complication enters, the experimenter can easily distinguish it in the particular case. . . .

8. The formula for use in the above cases is derived directly from the dissociation theory; if we assume that the electrolyte is completely dissociated into its ions, then according to the law of mass action the product of the active masses must be constant and indeed must be equal to the square of the solubility m_0 of the salt without any other additions. If we designate by m the solubility of the salt after addition and by x the added amount (in gram-molecules per liter), then

$$(1) \quad m(m + x) = m_0^2$$

Emil Fischer

(1852–1919)

COMPLEX substances of biochemical importance were slow to yield to the methods of organic chemistry, but in the hands of Emil Fischer the first great advances in this field were made. His early discovery of phenyl hydrazine (1875) gave him a reagent with which to begin the study of simple sugars, and by patient work, among the earliest to be based on the stereochemical ideas of van't Hoff, he gradually unraveled the fundamental structure of these substances. His determination of the configurations of the various monosaccharides is a classic application of purely organic methods for structure determination. In his later work, Fischer elucidated the structures of the purines (1882 to 1901) and the polypeptides (1900 to 1906), thus opening the way to an understanding of the structure of proteins. The following selections are taken from the famous paper in which the structure of glucose is established, "Ueber die Configuration des Traubenzucker und seiner Isomeren."[1] They illustrate the methods of reasoning used by Fischer in reaching his highly important conclusions.

All the previous observations in the sugar group are in such close agreement with the theory of the asymmetric carbon atom that we may venture to use it as a basis for the classification of these substances. The theory allows 16 isomers of the structure of grape sugar to be predicted. This number is reduced to 10 for its derivatives whose molecules are symmetric.

The following table, which is taken from page 11 of the booklet of van't Hoff-Hermann, "Die Lagerung der Atome im Raum," contains the 16 different forms for the sugar, of which numbers 11 to 16 become identical with 5 to 10 in the hexavalent alcohols and the dibasic acids.

				11	12	13	14	15	16
				+	+	+	+	+	−
				+	+	+	−	−	+
+	+	−	−	+	−	−	+	−	−
+	−	+	−	−	+	−	−	−	−
+	−	+	−						
+	+	−	−	−	+	−	−	−	−
				+	−	−	+	−	−
1	**2**	**3**	**4**	+	+	+	−	−	+
				+	+	+	+	+	−
				5	**6**	**7**	**8**	**9**	**10**

[1] *Ber.*, **24**: 1836–1845, 2683–2687 (1891); the selections given are taken from pages 1836 to 1840 and 2683 to 2386.

In order to choose the form which belongs to grape sugar on the basis of facts, it is first necessary to consider the saccharic acids. Of these, both optically active forms are known; moreover, the d-saccharic acid results on the one hand from grape sugar (d-glucose) and on the other hand from the stereoisomeric d-gulose.

From this it follows that both saccharic acids must come under the numbers 5 to 10; only then can they result from these two stereoisomeric sugars.

But under these six numbers are two optically inactive systems (7 and 8) which consequently drop out.

Finally, numbers 6 and 10 can be excluded by the following considerations. Glucose and mannose are distinguished from each other only by the different arrangement on the asymmetric carbon atom which in the following formula is indicated by *

$$\overset{*}{CH_2OH{-}CH.OH{-}CH.OH{-}CH.OH{-}CH.OH{-}COH}$$

The same applies also to gluconic and mannonic acids, or sorbitol and mannitol, or finally, to saccharic acid and mannosaccharic acid.

I will place together the facts which concordantly lead to this conclusion

1. Mannose and glucose give the same osazone.

2. Arabinose adds hydrocyanic acid to give at the same time l-mannonic and l-gluconic acids.

3. Fructose is converted by sodium amalgam into a mixture of mannitol and sorbitol.

4. Mannonic acid and gluconic acid can be mutually converted into each other by heating them with quinoline.

5. All attempts to separate gluconic and mannonic acids into two components have remained fruitless.

But now, if saccharic acid, or, what is the same thing, sorbitol, possesses the configuration

$$+ - + + \quad (No. 6)$$

or

$$- + - - \quad (No. 10)$$

then mannosaccharic acid or mannitol must have one of the two configurations

$$- - + + \quad (No. 7)$$

or

$$- + - + \quad (No. 8)$$

But these are the optically inactive systems which again are excluded by the activity of mannitol and mannosaccharic acid.

Consequently there remain for d- and l-saccharic acid only the two configurations

$$- + + + \quad (No. 5)$$

and

$$+ - - - \text{(No. 9)}$$

Since it is equally valid to call either one $+$ or $-$, I will arbitrarily assign to the d-saccharic acid the formula

$$\underset{-}{COOH}—\underset{+}{CH.OH}—\underset{+}{CH.OH}—\underset{+}{CH.OH}—\underset{}{CH.OH}—COOH$$

and to the l compound the opposite signs.

Two aldoses correspond to d-saccharic acid,

$$\underset{-}{COH}.\underset{+}{CH(OH)}.\underset{+}{CH(OH)}.\underset{+}{CH(OH)}.CH(OH).CH_2OH$$

or

$$\underset{+}{COH}.\underset{+}{CH(OH)}.\underset{+}{CH(OH)}.\underset{-}{CH(OH)}.CH(OH).CH_2OH.$$

To distinguish which of these formulas belongs to grape sugar and which to d-gulose it is necessary to consider the arabinose and xylose. It is true they belong to the l-series; but this is immaterial for the conclusion.

Arabinose can be changed into l-glucose, while from xylose under the same conditions, l-gulose results.

For l-glucose and l-gulose there once more remains the choice between the formulas

$$\overset{*}{COH}.\underset{+}{CH(OH)}.\underset{-}{CH(OH)}.\underset{-}{CH(OH)}.\underset{-}{CH(OH)}CH_2OH$$

or

$$\overset{*}{COH}.\underset{-}{CH(OH)}.\underset{-}{CH(OH)}.\underset{-}{CH(OH)}.\underset{+}{CH(OH)}.CH_2OH$$

If we remove from both the asymmetric carbon atom marked with the *, which is the first result of the synthesis, there remain for arabinose and xylose the following formulas:

$$COH.\underset{-}{CH(OH)}.\underset{-}{CH(OH)}.\underset{-}{CH(OH)}.CH_2OH$$

and

$$COH.\underset{-}{CH(OH)}.\underset{-}{CH(OH)}.\underset{+}{CH(OH)}.CH_2OH$$

For the pentoses (of the structure of arabinose and xylose) the theory now permits us to predict eight isomers; but the number is reduced to four if the molecule is symmetric. There are thus only four pentavalent alcohols $CH_2OH.(CH.OH)_3.CH_2OH$, or four different trihydroxyglutaric acids.[2]

[2] In the van't Hoff-Herrmann booklet, page 10, this case is discussed only briefly, and the number of isomers is established as three. However, Herr van't Hoff had the kindness to send me a private communication that a mistake had occurred here, and his theory actually required four isomers, two active and two inactive.

Two of these are optically active and opposites. For the two acids there are the formulas

$$\underset{+}{COOH.CH(OH)}.\underset{}{CH(OH)}.\underset{+}{CH(OH)}.COOH$$

and

$$\underset{+}{COOH.CH(OH)}.\underset{}{CH(OH)}.\underset{}{CH(OH)}.COOH;$$

The middle carbon atom here has lost its asymmetry.

The two other formulas,

$$\underset{+}{COOH.CH(OH)}.\underset{+}{CH(OH)}.\underset{-}{CH(OH)}.COOH$$

and

$$\underset{+}{COOH.CH(OH)}.\underset{-}{CH(OH)}.\underset{-}{CH(OH)}.COOH$$

are, on the other hand, identical with their mirror images and must therefore be optically inactive. Possibly such isomers are so similar that they cannot be separated, since the optical test is automatically excluded.

Thus the possibility is offered of distinguishing between the above formulas for arabinose and xylose; since it suffices to test optically the pentavalent alcohols or dibasic acids corresponding to the two sugars.

The attempt has given an unambiguous result.

The arabitol prepared by Kiliani from arabinose, as mentioned earlier, on addition of borax turns polarized light to the left. The same is true for the trihydroxyglutaric acid also obtained by Kiliani from arabinose, as will be shown later.

On the other hand, the xylitol obtained from xylose remains inactive in the presence of borax, and the dibasic acid resulting from the sugar, to be described later, behaves in exactly the same way.

Since the hydroxyacids in general possess a very strong rotation, we are justified in assuming with greater assurance from these results that the derivatives of xylose which we have discussed are in fact optically inactive substances. It follows from this that arabinose has the first of the above two formulas,

$$\underset{-}{COH.CH(OH)}.\underset{}{CH(OH)}.\underset{-}{CH(OH)}.CH_2OH$$

and xylose the second,

$$\underset{-}{COH.CH(OH)}.\underset{-}{CH(OH)}.\underset{+}{CH(OH)}.CH_2OH$$

For the compounds of the hexose group, as is easily evident, the following configurations result:

Aldoses	COH.CH(OH).CH(OH).CH(OH).CH(OH).CH₂OH			
d-glucose	−	+	+	+
l-glucose	+	−	−	−
d-gulose	+	+	+	−
l-gulose	−	−	−	+
d-mannose	+	+	+	+
l-mannose	−	−	−	−

For galactose there still remains the choice between four configurations, as comparison with the formulas of mucic and allomucic acids indicates.

Ketoses	CH₂OH.CO.CH(OH).CH(OH).CH(OH).CH₂OH		
d-fructose	+	+	+
l-fructose	−	−	−

. . . In the first communication, I developed for grape sugar the formula

$$CH_2(OH).CH(OH).CH(OH).CH(OH).CH(OH).COH$$
$$\quad\quad\ \ +\quad\quad\quad +\quad\quad\quad +\quad\quad\quad -$$

The + and − signs for spatial arrangement which were introduced by van't Hoff and were retained in unaltered form by me can, however, in such complicated molecules easily result in a mistaken understanding. To prevent this, I consider a detailed interpretation of the formulas to be necessary, and for this purpose I call the four asymmetrical carbon atoms by the numbers 1 to 4:

$$CH_2(OH).\overset{1}{C}H(OH).\overset{2}{C}H(OH).\overset{3}{C}H(OH).\overset{4}{C}H(OH).COH$$

In the general considerations of van't Hoff, which lie at the basis of my special deductions, carbon atom 1 compares only with 4, and similarly, carbon atom 2 only with 3. In grape sugar, therefore, the arrangement of hydrogen and hydroxyl on carbon atom 1 is the opposite of 4; further, this arrangement on 2 and 3 is the same. But now compare carbon atom 1 also with the two middle atoms. I did this when I related grape sugar to xylose and arabinose. This showed that the arrangement of hydrogen and hydroxyl on carbon atom 1 was the same as on 3.

It would now be possible to believe from superficial considerations that the same must also be true for carbon atoms 1 and 2. Actually, however, exactly the opposite occurs.

With the help of models, it is easy to see that on carbon atom 2 the sign changes, whether it is compared with 1 or 3.

Since, then, the above expression for the configuration of grape sugar is ambiguous, it seemed to me necessary to elucidate it through the following pictures.

Using the very simple Friedländer rubber models, the molecules of *d*-tartaric acid, *l*-tartaric acid, and inactive tartaric acids are constructed, and these are laid in such a way on the plane of the paper that the four carbon atoms lie in a straight line, and the hydrogen and hydroxyl which are under discussion stand above the plane of the paper. The following formulas are then obtained by projection:

```
        COOH                    COOH                    COOH
       H—Ċ—OH                 HO—Ċ—H                  H—Ċ—OH
      HO—Ċ—H                  H—Ċ—OH                  H—Ċ—OH
        ĊOOH                    ĊOOH                    ĊOOH
              d- and l-                           Inactive tartaric
             tartaric acid                              acid
```

Proceeding in the same way with the models for d- and l-saccharic acids, these two projections result:

```
          I                       II
        COOH                    COOH
       H—Ċ—OH                 HO—Ċ—H
      HO—Ċ—H                  H—Ċ—OH
       H—Ċ—OH                 HO—Ċ—H
     *H—Ċ—OH                 HO—Ċ—H
        ĊOOH                    ĊOOH
```

Once more I arbitrarily chose the form I for d-saccharic acid, and in it, it naturally remains undecided whether on the carbon atom marked with the * the order of the hydroxyl and hydrogen is clockwise or the reverse. Then grape sugar and its isomers give the following forms:

```
     COH            COH            COH            COH
    H—Ċ—OH        HO—Ċ—H         HO—Ċ—H         H—Ċ—OH
   HO—Ċ—H         H—Ċ—OH        HO—Ċ—H         H—Ċ—OH
    H—Ċ—OH        HO—Ċ—H         H—Ċ—OH        HO—Ċ—H
    H—Ċ—OH        HO—Ċ—H         H—Ċ—OH        HO—Ċ—H
    ĊH₂OH          ĊH₂OH          ĊH₂OH          ĊH₂OH
  Grape sugar     l-glucose      d-mannose       l-mannose
     COH            COH            CH₂OH          CH₂OH
   HO—Ċ—H         H—Ċ—OH          ĊO             ĊO
   HO—Ċ—H         H—Ċ—OH        HO—Ċ—H         H—Ċ—OH
    H—Ċ—OH        HO—Ċ—H         H—Ċ—OH        HO—Ċ—H
   HO—Ċ—H         H—Ċ—OH         H—Ċ—OH        HO—Ċ—H
    ĊH₂OH          ĊH₂OH          ĊH₂OH          ĊH₂OH
    d-gulose       l-gulose      d-fructose     l-fructose
```

Finally, from the dulcite series, I give the formulas for both inactive dibasic acids which are most probable for mucic and allomucic acids

```
      COOH                          COOH
        |                             |
   H—C—OH                        H—C—OH
        |                             |
  HO—C—H                         H—C—OH
        |                             |
  HO—C—H                         H—C—OH
        |                             |
   H—C—OH                        H—C—OH
        |                             |
      COOH                          COOH
```

By the help of projections, the models of these molecules can easily be reconstructed.

Further, these methods of notation, without anything else, can be carried over either to the pentoses or to the heptoses, octoses, etc., in which the ambiguity of the old signs + and − constantly increases.

Thus the following projections are obtained for the two previously known pentoses and the trihydroxyglutaric acids resulting from them, corresponding to the earlier explanations:

```
     COH              COH              COOH             COOH
       |                |                |                |
  H—C—OH           H—C—OH           H—C—OH           H—C—OH
       |                |                |                |
 HO—C—H           HO—C—H           HO—C—H           HO—C—H
       |                |                |                |
 HO—C—H            H—C—OH           HO—C—H            H—C—OH
       |                |                |                |
   CH₂OH            CH₂OH             COOH             COOH
  Arabinose         Xylose        Active acid      Inactive acid
                                 from arabinose     from xylose
```

The advantages of the new formulas are shown especially by the consideration of some reactions which lead to an increase or a decrease of asymmetric carbon atoms.

An example that will serve is the oxidation of fruit sugar.

According to the observation of Kiliani, on treatment with nitric acid this gives, along with glycolic acid, the inactive tartaric acid. The formation of the latter fits very simply into the above formula:

```
    CH₂OH
      |
      CO
  ............
      |
 HO—C—H                              COOH
      |                                |
  H—C—OH                           H—C—OH
      |                                |
  H—C—OH                           H—C—OH
      |                                |
    CH₂OH                            COOH
  d-fructose                       Inactive
                                 tartaric acid
```

The results are not sufficiently certain for the changes of other sugars, or the related acids, into tartaric acid or its isomers. Therefore I myself will take up this study.

Eduard Buchner

(1860–1917)

THE process of fermentation had been familiar from earliest times, though it was not understood. As soon as chemistry began to be studied scientifically, attention was directed to the problem. Berzelius, the master of generalization, recognized that processes of this type were related to the phenomenon of catalysis (pages 265 –268). By the time that Pasteur worked on the problem, it was generally assumed that living cells were necessary for fermentation. Thus there still persisted a remnant of the vitalistic theory which had been partly overthrown by the Wöhler synthesis of urea (pages 309–312) and the total organic syntheses of Berthelot (pages 428–430). In 1878, Kühne suggested that the name *enzyme* be applied to the "unorganized ferments" which occurred outside the cell (such as ptyalin from saliva), while cellular ferments continued to be referred to as *organized*. The experiments of Buchner finally abolished this distinction and completed the destruction of the vitalistic theory by showing that yeast extracts entirely free from living cells could ferment sugar to alcohol. The way was opened for the study of enzymes by purely chemical methods, and the great advances of the twentieth century in this field stem directly from the pioneer work of Buchner. The description of his experiments appeared in 1897 in a paper "Alkoholische Gärung ohne Hefezellen."[1]

A separation of the fermentative action of living yeast cells has not previously been successful; in the following, a procedure is described which solves this problem.

One thousand grams of brewers' yeast, purified for the preparation of pressed yeast but still not treated with potato starch, is carefully mixed and then rubbed with an equal weight of quartz sand and 250 grams of kieselguhr, until the mass becomes moist and plastic. The paste is then treated with 100 grams of water and, wrapped in a press cloth, is placed gradually under a pressure of 400 to 500 atmospheres: 300 cubic centimeters of press juice result. The residual cake is again rubbed, sieved, and treated with 100 grams of water; treated once more in the hydraulic press

[1] *Ber.*, **30**: 117–124 (1897); the selection is taken from pages 117 to 121.

with the same pressure, it gives another 150 cubic centimeters of press juice. From 1 kilo of yeast there is thus obtained 500 cubic centimeters of press juice which contains about 300 cubic centimeters of substances which are cell contents. To remove traces of cloudiness, the press juice is finally shaken with 4 grams of kieselguhr and filtered through a paper filter with repeated refiltrations of the first filtrate.

The press juice thus obtained is a clear, slightly opalescent, yellow liquid with a pleasant yeastlike odor. The specific gravity was once found to be 1.0416 (17°C.). When this is heated, a strong separation of coagulum occurs, so that the liquid almost completely solidifies: the formation of insoluble flakes begins at about 35 to 40 degrees; even before this, bubbles of gas, evidently carbonic acid, were seen rising, for the liquid itself is saturated with this gas.[2] The press juice contains over 10 per cent dry substance. In an earlier, less well-prepared press juice there were 6.7 per cent dry substance, 1.15 per cent ash, and according to nitrogen content, 3.7 per cent protein substances.

The most interesting property of the press juice lies in this, that it can cause fermentation of a carbohydrate. By mixing it with an equal volume of a concentrated raw-sugar solution, there occurs after one-quarter to one hour a regular evolution of carbon dioxide which lasts for a day. Grape, fruit, and malt sugar behave in the same way, but no appearance of fermentation occurs in mixtures of the press juice with saturated milk sugar or mannite solutions, just as these bodies are also not fermented by living brewers' yeast cells. Mixtures of press juice and sugar solution which have been fermenting for several days, when set in the icebox, usually grow turbid without the appearance of microscopic organisms, but at 700 times magnification they show a rather considerable number of protein curds, whose separation apparently depends upon the acids resulting from the fermentation. Saturation of the mixture of press juice and saccharose solution with chloroform does not hinder the fermentation but leads to an early slight precipitation of proteins. Filtration of the press juice through a sterilized Berkefeldt kieselguhr filter, which safely holds back all yeast cells, has just as slight an effect on the strength of fermentation; the mixture of the entirely clear filtrate with sterilized raw-sugar solution at the temperature of the icebox undergoes fermentation, somewhat delayed, after about a day. If a parchment-paper bag is filled with press juice in a 37 per cent raw-sugar solution, the surface of the bag after some hours is covered with numerous small gas bubbles; naturally, lively gas evolution was observed inside the bag, also due to diffusion of the sugar solution inward. Further studies must determine whether the bearer of the fermenting action can actually diffuse through the parchment paper, as it

---

[2] Plant physiologists must decide whether this carbonic acid has some connection with oxidation processes related to respiration.

seems. The fermenting power of the press juice is usually lost with time: five days in ice water in a half-filled flask of preserved press juice leads to inactivity toward saccharose. However, it is noteworthy that when treated with raw-sugar solution, this fermentatively active press juice retains its fermenting power at least two weeks in the icebox. A favorable action must be assumed from this for the action of the carbonic acid formed in the reaction in holding off the oxygen of the air; but the easily assimilable sugar could also contribute to obtaining the agent.

Too few studies have yet been made to enable a conclusion to be drawn as to the nature of the active substance in the press juice. When the press juice is warmed to 40 to 50 degrees, carbon dioxide evolution first occurs, then general separation of coagulated protein. After an hour this was filtered, with numerous refilterings. The clear filtrate still had weak fermenting power toward raw sugar in one study, but in a second, none; the active substance therefore appears either to lose its action at this surprisingly low temperature or to coagulate and precipitate. Further, 20 cubic centimeters of the press juice was put into triple its volume of absolute alcohol and the precipitate sucked off and dried over sulfuric acid in a vacuum; 2 grams of dry substance resulted, and upon digestion of this with 10 cubic centimeters of water, only the smallest part again dissolved. The filtrate from this had no fermenting action on raw sugar. This experiment must be repeated; especially, the isolation of the active substance by ammonium sulfate will be attempted.

Up to now, the following conclusions have been drawn for the theory of fermentation. First, it is recognized that to conduct the fermentation process, such a complicated apparatus as the yeast cell presents is not required. It is considered that the bearer of the fermenting action of the press juice is much more probably a dissolved substance, doubtless a protein; this will be called *zymase*.

The view that a protein especially formed from the yeast cell causes fermentation was expressed as long ago as 1858 by M. Traube as the enzyme or ferment theory, and it was later specially defended by F. Hoppe-Seyler. The separation of such an enzyme from yeast cells, however, had not so far been successful.

It still remains questionable also whether the zymase can be considered an addition to the enzymes already longer known. As. C. v. Nägeli has already mentioned, there are important differences between fermenting action and the action of ordinary enymes. The latter are solely hydrolytic and can be imitated by the simplest chemical media. A. v. Baeyer has recently increased our understanding of the chemical processes in alcoholic fermentation when he related them to relatively simple principles, but the decomposition of sugar to alcohol and carbon dioxide still is one of the more complicated reactions; the breakdown of carbon compounds in this manner has not been accomplished by any other method. There is also an important difference in the heat of the reaction.[3]

Invertin can be extracted with water from yeast cells killed by dry heat (heated one hour at 150 degrees), and by precipitation with alcohol it can easily be isolated as a water-soluble powder. The substance active in fermentation cannot be obtained in a similar way. It is no longer present as a rule in yeast cells heated so high; alcoholic precipitation of the product of an attempt such as the above leads only to a water-insoluble modification. It can hardly be doubted, therefore, that zymase belongs to the true proteins and stands closer to the living protoplasm of the yeast cell than does invertin.

The French bacteriologist, Miguel, has similar views as to urase which is separated from bacteria and shows the so-called "urea fermentation"; he calls this protoplasm which acts directly outside the cell walls, lacking the protection of these, and which differs from that of the cell contents essentially only in this.[4]

The experiments of E. Fischer and P. Lindner on the action of the yeast *Monilia candida* on raw sugar also belong here. This yeast ferments saccharose; but neither Ch. E. Hansen nor the authors mentioned could extract from fresh or dried yeast with water an enzyme like invertin which could cause the splitting into grape and fruit sugars. The study went entirely otherwise when Fischer and Lindner used fresh Monilia yeast in which, by careful grinding with glass powder, a part of the cells were first opened. The inverting action was now unrecognizable. "The inverting agent seemed here truly not to be a water-stable, soluble enzyme but seemed to be a part of the living protoplasm."

The fermentation of sugars by zymase can occur within the yeast cells,[5] but apparently the yeast cells separate this protein out into the sugar solution, where it causes fermentation.[6] The occurences in alcoholic fermentation are, then, perhaps to be considered a physiological act only as far as the separation of the zymase by the living yeast cells. Nägeli and Löw have shown that the nutrient solution from yeast cells, which is originally

[3] A. Brouffard, *Compt. rend.*, **121**: 357, has recently again determined the amount of heat developed during alcoholic fermentation by yeast.

[4] It must be noted here that the so-called "urea fermentation," the decomposition of urea into ammonia and carbon dioxide, is chemically very different from the usual fermentation process and therefore in general cannot be considered much like alcoholic fermentation. It is a simple hydrolysis, obtained with water even at 120 degrees.

[5] The diosmotic properties make this seem possible.

[6] This also seems to clarify the study of J. de Rey-Pailhade (*Compt. rend.*, **118**: 201), who prepared a weak alcoholic extract (22 per cent) from fresh brewers' yeast with the addition of some grape sugar. After being freed from microorganisms by filtering through a sterile Arsonval candle, this extract, which contained sugar, spontaneously developed carbonic acid in the absence of oxygen.

weakly alkaline (from K_3PO_4), later becomes neutral at 30 degrees, and even after fifteen hours, a considerable amount of protein coagulable by heating has diffused out. Actually, it appears, as the above study shows, that zymase can pass through parchment paper.

Friedrich Karl Johannes Thiele

(1865–1918)

THE work of Markovnikov opened the way to a consideration of the effects of the structure of organic compounds on the addition of halogens and similar substances to double bonds. This work was extended by Johannes Thiele, with particular attention to conjugated systems, in which addition reactions appeared to follow special rules. The theory of partial valences by which Thiele explained his results helped also to account for the peculiar properties of aromatic compounds. More important, it was a forerunner of the later theories of the effect of the electron structure of organic compounds on their reactions. The theory was first advanced in a paper on the theory of unsaturated and aromatic compounds.[1]

I now assume that in bodies to which a double bond is assigned, actually two affinities of each of the participating atoms are used for binding themselves, but that—owing to the additive power of the double bond—the strength of the affinity is not fully used, and on each atom there is still an affinity residue, or a *partial valence*, an assumption which can also be based on thermal grounds.

In formulas this can be expressed

$$C{=}C \qquad C{=}O \qquad C{=}N \qquad N{=}N \qquad \text{etc.,}$$

where the sign ... signifies the partial valence. In the partial valence I see the origin of the additive power.

The system of alternate double bonds C=C—C=C adds hydrogen (and, as I shall show, also bromine) at the ends, so that either CH—C= C—CH or BrC—C=C—CBr results (reduction of doubly unsaturated acids). Thus the additive power of the middle carbon atoms is lost. The scheme C=C—C=C does not express this. Since the middle carbon atoms do not add, they have *no* more partial valences; the partial valences must

---

[1] *Annalen der Chemie*, **306**: 87–142 (1899); the selection given is taken from pages 89 to 90.

have been neutralized, which can be expressed by the scheme

$$C{=}C{-}C{=}C$$

Thus a new double bond results which bears no partial valences and therefore can be called an *inactive* double bond. Such a neutralization can perhaps be thus explained: the atoms of a double bond, located together, are charged positively and negatively—

$$\overset{+}{C}{=}\overset{-}{C}$$

The alternate double bonds will then neutralize the inner charges:

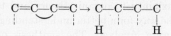

Thus an arrangement is obtained similar to that used to explain the constitution of magnets with the help of "molecular magnets."

Such a system of alternate double bonds with neutralized inner partial valences can be called *conjugated*.

If additions enter at the ends of the system, affinity forces become free on the middle carbon atoms, so that the inactive double bonds obtain partial valences and go over to ordinary active ones:

$$C{=}C{-}C{=}C \rightarrow \underset{H}{C}{-}C{=}C{-}\underset{H}{C}$$

This view, which is the central point of my theory, can also be applied to other systems of alternate double bonds, such as $O{=}C{-}C{=}C$ and $O{=}C{-}C{=}O$, and with its help a whole series of phenomena of unsaturated compounds can be explained. Especially can it be shown that exactly those properties of benzene which until now stood in the way of general acceptance of the benzene formula of Kekulé are necessary conclusions of this formula, that the fine nuances which differentiate naphthalene from benzene, as well as the properties of hydronaphthalenes deduced from Erlenmeyer's formula, and the ketone formula of quinone, have their peculiarities smoothly explained, etc.

Moses Gomberg

(1866–1947)

THE theory of valence as originally proposed by Frankland permitted the recognition of variable valences among the elements. Study of inorganic compounds would very quickly have established that variable valence actually occurred, but almost immediately after the work of Frankland, Kekulé proposed his structural theory (pages 418–421), and the attention of most chemists was turned to establishing structural formulas for all the known organic compounds. Kekulé assumed that valence was constant, and he made the idea of the tetravalence of carbon a foundation stone of his theory. This, of course, at once ruled out the possibility of the independent existence of organic radicals, the presence of which had been accepted in the earlier history of organic chemistry. At the same time it imparted a rigidity to the theory of organic chemistry which tended to reduce it to a mere formal exercise.

In succeeding years, chemists were forced to admit the existence of divalent carbon, but the discovery by Gomberg in 1899 of a compound which dissociated into a free radical containing trivalent carbon opened new vistas to organic chemists. It restored flexibility to organic theory and to the valence theory in general, and it opened the way for a better understanding of reaction mechanisms in which free radicals were involved. The synthesis of triphenyl methyl was described in a paper entitled "An Instance of Trivalent Carbon: Triphenyl Methyl."[1]

Some time ago I published a method of preparing tetraphenyl methane. The yield was rather small and I was obliged to study the solubilities, composition, molecular weight, and the nitro derivative on about 0.5 gram of the hydrocarbon. The stereochemical interest attached to this compound has induced me to take up the subject once more, in the hope of obtaining larger yields. I have, therefore, gone over most of the methods which have been tried by others for the preparation of tetraphenyl methane. My results, while differing in detail from those published by others, agree in the main—the hydrocarbon could not be obtained by the usual reactions. One of the main proofs advanced by me for the constitution of tetraphenyl methane was that it furnished a tetranitro derivative which gave no colored salts with alcoholic potash, while most of the less phenylated methanes do respond to this test. To prove whether this reaction could be safely relied upon, I decided to prepare hexaphenyl ethane

[1] *J. Am. Chem. Soc.*, **22**: 757–771 (1900); the selection given is taken from pages 757 to 759, 760, and 768 to 770.

$(C_6H_5)_3C$—$C(C_6H_5)_3$. This hydrocarbon should by nitration give a hexanitro body with no hydrogen attached to the ethane carbon atoms. Consequently, it also should give no colored salts with sodium ethylate or alcoholic potash.

Accordingly, triphenylbrommethane in benzene was treated with metallic sodium, but without success. The chloro compound gave no better results. Molecular silver was substituted for sodium. After several hours' boiling a white crystalline body began to separate, and on filtering the hot benzene solution a considerable amount of the same substance separated on cooling. It was recrystallized from benzene, gave a constant melting point, 185°C., and contained no halogen. In its high melting point and in its only slight solubility in the usual organic solvents it resembled closely tetraphenyl methane, and this new body was taken for hexaphenyl ethane. An elementary analysis gave, however, the following results:

	Calculated for $(C_6H_5)_6C_2$	Found
Carbon.............	93.83	87.93
Hydrogen...........	6.17	6.04

The low per cent. of carbon found was rather surprising. It was explained on the assumption that this was, perhaps, an instance of a hydrocarbon which is not easily burnt. The next combustion was, therefore, carried on in an atmosphere of oxygen from the very beginning. The substance was mixed in the tube with copper oxide; a very high heat was applied towards the end of the combustion. The results were as follows:

Carbon............. 87.74
Hydrogen.......... 6.46

An entirely new lot of the material was then prepared. Ten grams of triphenylchlormethane and 10 grams of silver gave, after several hours' boiling, 4 grams of the same hydrocarbon. This was recrystallized twice from benzene and twice from chloroform. It was perfectly free from halogen, was snow-white, and melted at 185–186°C. The combustion was again made in an atmosphere of oxygen, lead chromate being used instead of copper oxide.

Carbon............. 87.77
Hydrogen.......... 6.23

The next analysis was made in a bayonet tube, the tube being filled with fine copper oxide for about four-fifths of its length, to insure combustion of any methane gas which would perhaps otherwise escape. The combustion was carried on slowly, and a very high heat was used toward the end.

Carbon.............. 88.23
Hydrogen.......... 6.34

Several new lots of the same substance were made both from the triphenylbrommethane and triphenylchlormethane, and purified by successive recrystallization from benzene, chloroform, acetic ether, and carbon disulphide. They all gave the same results, entirely concordant with each other. Combustions were then made in a porcelain tube, applying the direct heat of the furnace; also by the moist method with chromic acid in concentrated sulphuric acid, but with no better result. I therefore came to the conclusion that the body under consideration was not a simple hydrocarbon, but an oxygen derivative.

Here experiments are described to prove that the oxygen did not come from the silver but from the air, and that zinc is the best metal to use in the preparation.

The successful preparation of the unsaturated hydrocarbon requires the *absolute* exclusion of oxygen from the apparatus. Corks are to be avoided, and even rubber stoppers, exposed to the action of benzene vapor, become after a while porous. I have constructed for this work an apparatus by means of which the reaction can be carried on for several weeks and months, if necessary. The zinc, benzene, and triphenylchlormethane are first digested for any length of time desired at ordinary temperature; the solution is then filtered into a distilling flask and the zinc washed with fresh portions of benzene. The combined liquids are distilled under diminished pressure at 30°C., and the solid crystalline residue containing the unsaturated hydrocarbon can be examined as to its solubility in different solvents, or treated in any manner desired. The apparatus is so arranged that all these steps are carried on in an atmosphere of dry carbon dioxide. Only ground glass joints are used. The description of the apparatus is reserved for a future paper.

The reactions of the oxygen compound are described in detail.

V. TRIPHENYL METHYL $(C_6H_5)_3{\equiv}C$.

The experimental evidence presented above forces me to the conclusion that we have to deal here with a free radical, triphenyl methyl, $(C_6H_5)_3{\equiv}C$. On this assumption alone do the results described above become intelligible and receive an adequate explanation. The action of zinc results, as it seems to me, in the mere abstraction of the halogen, leaving the free radical,

$$(C_6H_5)_3C.Cl + zn = (C_6H_5)_3C + znCl.$$

The radical so formed is apparently stable, for it can be kept both in solution and in the dry crystalline state for weeks. The radical refuses to unite with another one of its kind, and thus forms a distinct exception to all similar reactions. It might be said that, perhaps, it does polymerize to hexaphenyl ethane $(C_6H_5)_3C$—$C(C_6H_5)_3$, but this hydrocarbon is so unstable that mere exposure to air is sufficient to break it down. Such an assumption seems to me less tenable than that of a free radical. Hexaphenyl ethane must, according to all our present notions of valence, be a saturated compound. Yet the hydrocarbon under consideration is decidedly unsaturated. We know of no better positive test for unsaturation in hydrocarbons than the absorption of halogens. Perhaps chlorine and bromine would in this case attack and decompose hexaphenyl ethane, if that be the hydrocarbon; but certainly, a dilute solution of iodine, at 0°C., would scarcely do that. It seems to me rather that hexaphenyl ethane, once formed, would prove quite a stable compound. This may be justly inferred from analogous reactions where a fourth heavy radical has been successfully introduced into the methane—as is the case with triphenyl thiophyl methane, $(C_6H_5)_3.C.C_4H_4S$, tetraphenyl methane, $(C_6H_5)_3C.-C_6H_5$, triphenyl acetic acid, etc. It is a phenomenon parallel to that expressed by V. Meyer's esterification law of diortho substituted aromatic acids: It is very difficult to introduce an alkyl into the carboxyl of such acids by the *usual method* of esterification, but once introduced, it is just as difficult to remove it again.

On the assumption of the existence of triphenyl methyl itself, as such, all the reactions of the unsaturated body become clear. Oxygen adds itself, a whole molecule, and gives the peroxide

$$(C_6H_5)_3{\equiv}C \quad O \quad (C_6H_5)_3{\equiv}C{-}O$$
$$+ \; \| \; = \quad\quad | $$
$$(C_6H_5)_3{\equiv}C \quad O \quad (C_6H_5)_3{\equiv}C{-}O$$

. . . The existence of triphenyl methyl implies, of course, the existence of *trivalent carbon*, at least in this particular instance. The conception of such a trivalent carbon in this instance is entirely distinct from that which is ascribed to it by some in benzene, or even in ethylene, where there are always *two* adjoining carbon atoms acting as trivalent. The unsaturation in such cases has always been indicated by a "double linking." In triphenyl methyl there is *only one carbon atom* that is unsaturated. The existence of such a body means that when three valences of carbon are taken up by three phenyl groups, it is difficult, or perhaps even impossible, to introduce as a fourth group such a complicated radical as $(C_6H_5)_3C$—. Only simpler groups, chlorine, bromine, iodine, oxygen, etc., may still combine with such a carbon atom. Whether this be due to the negative character of the three phenyl groups, or whether it is caused by the fact that these groups take up so much space around the carbon atom as to hinder the introduction of another complicated group, is a question of an entirely different nature and need not be discussed here.

Alfred Werner

(1866–1919)

DURING most of the nineteenth century, chemists centered their attention on the structure of organic compounds. As the century drew to a close, physical chemistry began to attract more and more interest. Inorganic chemistry, which had held the main place as the century began, was almost entirely neglected. One of the few contributors in this field as the twentieth century began was Alfred Werner, but his work was of the greatest significance. He brought an order and understanding to the mass of apparently unrelated facts concerning the complex inorganic compounds which was comparable to the order brought to organic chemistry by the Kekulé theory. His extension of the idea of stereochemistry to inorganic compounds permitted an explanation of the puzzling phenomenon of isomerism among them and enabled him to predict cases of optical isomerism which he confirmed by experiment. His concept of the coordination number prepared the way for later theories which resulted in the electron concept of valence. Although he did not finally summarize his ideas until the publication of his famous "Neuere Anschauungen auf den Gebiete der anorganischen Chemie" in 1905, his essential ideas were expressed as early as 1893 in a paper entitled "Beitrag zur Konstitution anorganischer Verbindungen."[1] The following selection is taken from pages 297 to 302 of this paper.

VI. IDEAS ON THE CONSTITUTION AND CONFIGURATION OF THE RADICALS MR_6.

If we must assume that in the hydrates, the metal ammonium salts, etc., the radicals are formed by the grouping of six water molecules, six ammonia molecules, and six monovalent groups around the metal atom, then we may ask in what spatial arrangement we can picture the whole molecular complex.

If we think of the metal atom as the center of the whole system, then we can most simply place the six molecules bound to it at the corners of an octahedron.

This raises the question of what conclusions follow from this assumption and whether these conclusions are in fact supported.

Thus we can think first of a molecule $\left(M \dfrac{(NH_3)_5}{X} \right)$ with ammonia molecules in five corners of the octahedron and an acid residue in the sixth.

If we substitute in this a second ammonia molecule by an acid residue, we can do it in two different ways.

[1] *Z. anorg. Chemie*, **3**: 267–330 (1893).

Either we can replace the ammonia radical lying axial to the acid radical, or we can replace one of the four ammonia molecules at the equal corners of the octahedron from it, as the following figures show.

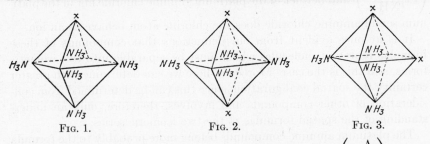

FIG. 1. FIG. 2. FIG. 3.

We must thus obtain two isomeric molecule complexes $\left(M_{X_2}^{A_4} \right)$.

The molecular complex $\left(M_{X_2}^{A_4} \right)$ occurs, however, in the already mentioned praseo salts of the general formula $\left(Co_{(NH_3)_4}^{X_2} \right) X$.

The praseo salts must thus appear in two isomeric modifications.

This conclusion finds confirmation in the facts. As we know from the beautiful work of Jörgensen, there are two isomers of the series $\left(Co_{X_2}^{A_4} \right) X$ in which each A_2 represents an ethylene diamine molecule. These isomeric series behave chemically completely alike; of the three acid residues, only one behaves ionically. However, the two series are distinguished in a very characteristic manner by their color. One is green, the so-called "praseo salts," the other is violet and is called a *violeo* salt.

This interesting isomerism is a first confirmation of the conclusions drawn from the octahedron.

Jörgensen, as is known, has attempted to explain the isomerism of the compounds $\left(Co_{A_4}^{X_2} \right) X$, which by his formula is

$$Co \begin{array}{c} X \\ \diagup \\ {} \\ \diagdown \\ NH_3{-}NH_3{-}NH_3{-}NH_3{-}X \end{array} {-}X$$

, by differences in valence of the cobalt.

It would carry us too far here to enter into a discussion of the developments of Jörgensen; we need only mention that difference in valence is a somewhat less clear concept because valence itself does not present a very clear concept.

The isomerism of the complex $\left(M_{X_2}^{A_4} \right)$ based on our octahedral formula finds further confirmation in the behavior of certain platinum compounds.

As was mentioned earlier, there are two isomeric series, the platinum ammine salts and the platinum semidiammine salts, of the same formula $\left(\text{Pt}\dfrac{X_4}{(NH_3)_2}\right)$, and neither in the platinum ammine chloride nor in the platinum semidiammine chloride does the chlorine atom behave as an ion.

It is at once evident from our deductions that compounds of these formulas represent molecules which must be separable into two isomeric forms, and this is the case. Moreover, here we can determine with greater certainty the spatial configuration, since this can be determined from consideration of other compounds and involves, therefore, only an understanding of the spatial formulas of the two isomeric series.

The platinum ammine compounds belong more probably to the formula with the diagonal position of the ammonia groups, while the platinum semidiammine compounds have the ammonia groups in angular positions to one another.

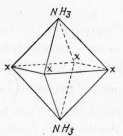

FIG. 4. Platinum ammine compounds.

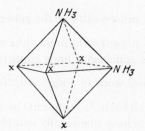

FIG. 5. Platinum semidiammine compounds.

The stereochemistry of carbon and nitrogen compounds is thus ranged beside a stereochemistry of cobalt and platinum compounds!

We will carry our conclusions a step farther. We will consider a molecule of the formula $\left(M\dfrac{(NH_3)_5}{H_2O}\right)X_3$ (roseo salt). The five ammonia molecules and the water molecule occur at the corners of the octahedron, as the following figure shows.

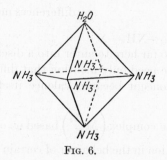

FIG. 6.

The three negative complexes X_3 we consider to be outside a sphere described around the octahedron, and we are dealing with the equilibrium position in one of the chief planes of the system $\left(M \frac{(NH_3)_5}{H_2O} \right)$, that is, one which can be determined by a metal atom and four corners of the octahedron.

With such planes, the octahedral molecule $\left(M \frac{(NH_3)_5}{H_2O} \right)$ still possesses two differences which can be made clear by the following diagrams:

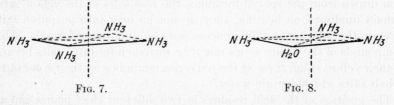

FIG. 7.   FIG. 8.

Thus, according to the three acid radicals, there may be four ammonia molecules in the same plane with the metal atom, or three ammonia atoms and one water molecule, leading to two isomeric modifications of the compound $M \left(\frac{(NH_3)_5}{H_2O} \right) X_3$.

These conclusions from the octahedral formula also find their confirmation in fact. The roseo salts of cobalt $\left(Co \frac{(NH_3)_5}{H_2O} \right) X_3$ exist in two isomeric series; the compounds of the first series are red, those of the second series yellow, and their properties are in full agreement with the characteristic spatial formulas which have been developed.

The one, the salts of the red series, are those in which the three acid residues lie in the same plane with the three ammonia molecules and the water molecule.

The assumption that water and the acid residues lie in the same plane explains why an acid residue, on displacing the water molecule, can approach the metal atom and at the same time lose its character as an ion; further, it explains the easy reverse change into the original compound by the pushing in of the water between metal and acid residue, as is the case when the red roseo salt $\left(Co \frac{(NH_3)_5}{H_2O} \right) X_3$ goes over with extreme cease into the purpureo salt $\left(Co \frac{(NH_3)_5}{X} \right) X_2$, and the purpureo salt forms the red roseo compound reversibly.

The compounds of the yellow series must correspond to that formula in which the three acid residues lie in a plane with the cobalt atom and four ammonia molecules. In these compounds the binding positions of the acid residues can only occur through the binding positions of the ammonia molecules.

From the properties of the salts of the luteo series $(Co(NH_3)_6)X_3$ in which the above condition must also apply, we know that with cobalt a direct substitution of the ammonia molecules by the acid residues does not occur on heating. From this it would be expected that this also would not be the case in the yellow roseo salts. On the other hand, a displacement of the water molecule by an acid residue is not probable because their binding positions do not lie together. Corresponding to this conclusion drawn from the spatial formulas, the rose salts of the yellow series remain unaltered on heating; they do not go over into purpureo salts. Even in the color we find differences corresponding to the formula. While compounds of the yellow series might be mistaken for luteo salts because of their yellow color, those of the red series remind us by their color of the cobalt salts which contain water.

The position of the acid residues in two different chief planes can apparently be explained by the existence of two different octahedral axes, NH_3—Co—NH_3 and NH_3—Co—H_2O, which can both act as the chief axis of the system $\left(Co\dfrac{(NH_3)_5}{H_2O}\right)$. Moreover, since we have two different states of the positive radical, $\left(Co\dfrac{(NH_3)_5}{H_2O}\right)$, it is clear that the salts of these radicals with dibasic acids can be divided into three different modifications corresponding to the formulas $SO_4\begin{smallmatrix}1\\1\end{smallmatrix}$; $SO_4\begin{smallmatrix}1\\2\end{smallmatrix}$; $SO_4\begin{smallmatrix}2\\2\end{smallmatrix}$ if we indicate one state of the radical by 1 and the other by 2. Correspondingly, the roseo cobalt sulfate, and only the sulfate, occurs in three isomeric modifications, of which one corresponds to the red series, another to the yellow series, while the third in its properties takes the middle position between the other two, and the corresponding salts of a monobasic acid cannot be prepared from it.

Thus, these experimental facts are in agreement with the octahedral formula and furnish good support for it.

Marie Curie

(1867-1934)

THE end of the nineteenth century saw the formulation of a new physicochemical principle, radioactivity. Henri Becquerel (1852–1908) discovered radioactive phenomena in 1896, while investigating the fluorescence produced by the irradiation of uranium salts by X rays, reported only a year before by Wilhelm Konrad Roentgen (1847–1923).[1] Becquerel found that the fluorescence and phosphorescence of uranium salts occurred without any previous exposure to radiation. He concluded that this, as well as the property of affecting photographic plates and the acquisition of conductivity of air exposed to uranium salts, was a fundamental property of the uranium. The discovery of radioactivity from uranium was described by Becquerel in a memoir in the *Comptes rendus*.[2] The name *radioactivity* was afterward given to this phenomena by Marie Curie. She had become interested in Becquerel's work and decided to investigate it further. After the examination of many salts, measuring the effect with a Curie electrometer and piezo quartz,[3] she investigated the properties of some minerals. The activity of pitchblende, a uranium ore, was found to be so great that she suspected the existence of some new element. Pierre Curie (1859–1906), who had followed his wife's work with interest, left his study on crystals to help isolate the unknown element. After many fractionations, the existence of two new elements became a certainty. The first, polonium, was announced in July, 1898, in a joint paper, "Sur une substance nouvelle radioactive contenue dans la pechblende."[4] The discovery of radium was reported in December.[5] As the work progressed it became apparent, because of its increasing magnitude, that it should be divided. It was agreed that Pierre would investigate the radioactive properties of the new compounds while Marie would continue the purification of the salts with the isolation of the radioactive elements as the ultimate goal. It is in the doctoral thesis of Marie Curie, "Recherches sur les substances radioactives," presented to the Faculté des Sciences de Paris on June 25, 1903, that her fundamental investigations are best

[1] "Ueber eine neue Art von Strahlen," *Sitzungsberichte der Würzburger Physikalischen-Medicinischen Gesellschaft,*" **137**: (Dec. 1895). See W. F. Magie, "A Source Book in Physics," New York, 1935, pp. 600–610.

[2] "Sur les radiations émises par phosphorescence," *Compt. rend.*, **122**: 420 (1896). See Magie, *op. cit.* pp. 610–613.

[3] The discovery of piezoelectricity was due to Pierre Curie, who worked in collaboration with his brother Jacques. It was described in a series of papers that appeared in the *Comptes rendus*, the first in 1880. See Magie, *op.cit.*, pp. 547–549.

[4] *Compt. rend.*, **127**: 175 (1898). See Magie, *op. cit.*, pp. 613–616.

[5] "Sur une nouvelle substance fortement radioactive contenue dans la pechblende," Marie Curie with P. Curie and G. Bémont, *Compt. rend.*, **127**: 1215 (1898). See Magie, *loc. cit.*

summarized, a document termed by some one of the most important ever presented for a doctor's degree. The thesis was first published in 1903, with English, Russian, and German translations appearing shortly thereafter.[6] It is from the 1904 London edition that the following is taken.

CHAPTER II.

METHOD OF RESEARCH.

The results of the investigation of radio-active minerals, announced in the preceding chapter, led M. Curie and myself to endeavour to extract a new radio-active body from pitchblende. Our method of procedure could only be based on radio-activity, as we know of no other property of the hypothetical substance. The following is the method pursued for a research based on radio-activity:—The radio-activity of a compound is determined, and a chemical decomposition of this compound is effected; the radio-activity of all· the products obtained is determined, having regard to the proportion in which the radio-active substance is distributed among them. In this way, an indication is obtained, which may to a certain extent be compared to that which spectrum analysis furnishes. In order to obtain comparable figures, the activity of the substances must be determined in the solid form well dried.

POLONIUM, RADIUM, ACTINIUM.

The analysis of pitchblende with the help of the method just explained, led us to the discovery in this mineral of two strongly radio-active substances, chemically dissimilar:—Polonium, discovered by ourselves, and radium, which we discovered in conjunction with M. Bémont.

Polonium from the analytical point of view, is analogous to bismuth, and separates out with the latter. By one of the following methods of fractionating, bismuth products are obtained increasingly rich in polonium:—

1. Sublimation of the sulphides *in vacuo;* the active sulphide is much more volatile than bismuth sulphide.

2. Precipitation of solutions of the nitrate by water; the precipitate of the basic nitrate is much more active than the salt which remains in solution.

[6] It was first printed in the *Ann. chim. phys.*, **30**: 99–144, 145–203, 289–326 (1903), and was reprinted in the form usually adopted for such theses, in probably not more than a hundred copies: "Thèses présentées à la Faculté des Sciences de Paris pour obtenir le grade de Docteur ès Sciences Physiques, par Mme Sklodowska Curie," Paris, 1903. In 1904 the demand for a general edition led to the publication of a second French edition.

The English translation first appeared in the *Chem. News*, **88**: 85, 97, 134, 145, 159, 169, 175, 187, 199, 211, 223, 235, 247, 259, 271 (1903). It was issued in 1903 and 1904 (London) as "Radio-Active Substances."

3. Precipitation by sulphuretted hydrogen of a hydrochloric acid solution, strongly acid; the precipitated sulphides are considerably more active than the salt which remains in solution.

Radium is a substance which accompanies the barium obtained from pitchblende; it resembles barium in its reactions, and is separated from it by difference of solubility of the chlorides in water, in dilute alcohol, or in water acidified with hydrochloric acid. We effect the separation of the chlorides of barium and radium by subjecting the mixture to fractional crystallisation, radium chloride being less soluble than that of barium.

A third strongly radio-active body has been identified in pitchblende by M. Debierne, who gave it the name of *actinium*. Actinium accompanies certain members of the iron group contained in pitchblende; it appears in particular allied to thorium, from which it has not yet been found possible to separate it. The extraction of actinium from pitchblende is a very difficult operation, the separations being as a rule incomplete.

All three of the new radio-active bodies occur in quite infinitesimal amount in pitchblende. In order to obtain them in a more concentrated condition, we were obliged to treat several tons of residue of the ore of uranium. The rough treatment was carried out in the factory; and this was followed by processes of purification and concentration. We thus succeeded in extracting from thousands of kilogrms. of crude material a few decigrammes of products which were exceedingly active as compared with the ore from which they were obtained. It is obvious that this process is long, arduous, and costly. . . .

EXTRACTION OF THE NEW RADIO-ACTIVE SUBSTANCES.

The first stage of the operation consists in extracting barium with radium from the ores of uranium, also bismuth with polonium and the rare earths containing actinium from the same. These three primary products having been obtained, the next step is in each case to endeavour to isolate the new radio-active body. This second part of the treatment consists of a process of fractionation. The difficulty of finding a very perfect means of separating closely allied elements is well known; methods of fractionation are therefore quite suitable. Besides this, when a mere trace of one element is mixed with another element, no method of complete separation could be applied to the mixture, even allowing that such a method was known; in fact, one would run the risk of losing the trace of the material to be separated.

The particular object of my work has been the isolation of radium and polonium. After working for several years, I have so far only succeeded in obtaining the former.

Pitchblende is an expensive ore, and we have given up the treatment of it in large quantities. In Europe the extraction of this ore is carried out in the mine of Joachimsthal, in Bohemia. The crushed ore is roasted with carbonate of soda, and the resulting material washed, first with warm water and then with dilute sulphuric acid. The solution contains the uranium, which gives pitchblende its value. The insoluble residue is rejected. This residue contains radio-active substances; its activity is four and a half times that of metallic uranium. The Austrian Government, to whom the mine belongs, presented us with a ton of this residue for our research, and authorised the mine to give us several tons more of the material.

It was not very easy to apply the methods of the laboratory to the preliminary treatment of the residue in the factory. M. Debierne investigated this question, and organised the treatment in the factory. The most important point of his method is the conversion of the sulphates into carbonate by boiling the material with a concentrated solution of sodium carbonate. This method avoids the necessity of fusing with sodium carbonate.

The residue chiefly contains the sulphates of lead and calcium, silica, alumina, and iron oxide. In addition nearly all the metals are found in greater or smaller amount (copper, bismuth, zinc, cobalt, manganese, nickel, vanadium, antimony, thallium, rare earths, niobium, tantalum, arsenic, barium, &c.). Radium is found in this mixture as sulphate, and is the least soluble sulphate in it. In order to dissolve it, it is necessary to remove the sulphuric acid as far as possible. To do this, the residue is first treated with a boiling concentrated soda solution. The sulphuric acid combined with the lead, aluminium, and calcium passes, for the most part, into solution as sulphate of sodium, which is removed by repeatedly washing with water. The alkaline solution removes at the same time lead, silicon, and aluminium. The insoluble portion is attacked by ordinary hydrochloric acid. This operation completely disintegrates the material, and dissolves most of it. Polonium and actinium may be obtained from this solution; the former is precipitated by sulphuretted hydrogen, the latter is found in the hydrates precipitated by ammonia in the solution separated from the sulphides and oxidised. Radium remains in the insoluble portion. This portion is washed with water, and then treated with a boiling concentrated solution of carbonate of soda. This operation completes the transformation of the sulphates of barium and radium into carbonates. The material is then thoroughly washed with water, and then treated with dilute hydrochloric acid, quite free from sulphuric acid. The solution contains radium as well as polonium and actinium. It is filtered and precipitated with sulphuric acid. In this way the crude sulphates of barium containing radium and calcium, of lead, and of iron, and of a trace of actinium are obtained. The solution still contains a little actinium and polonium, which may be separated out as in the case of the first hydro-chloric acid solution.

From one ton of residue 10 to 20 kilogrms. of crude sulphates are ob-tained, the activity of which is from thirty to sixty times as great as that of metallic uranium. They must now be purified. For this purpose they are boiled with sodium carbonate and transformed into the chlorides. The solution is treated with sulphuretted hydrogen, which gives a small quan-tity of active sulphides containing polonium. The solution is filtered, oxi-dised by means of chlorine, and precipitated with pure ammonia. The precipitated hydrates and oxides are very active, and the activity is due to actinium. The filtered solution is precipitated with sodium carbonate. The precipitated carbonates of the alkaline earths are washed and converted into chlorides. These chlorides are evaporated to dryness, and washed with pure concentrated hydrochloric acid. Calcium chloride dissolves almost entirely, whilst the chloride of barium and radium remains in-soluble. Thus, from one ton of the original material about 8 kilogrms. of barium and radium chloride are obtained, of which the activity is about sixty times that of metallic uranium. The chloride is now ready for fractionation.

POLONIUM.

As I said above, by passing sulphuretted hydrogen through the various hydrochloric acid solutions obtained during the course of the process, active sulphides are precipitated, of which the activity is due to polonium. These sulphides chiefly contain bismuth, a little copper and lead; the latter metal occurs in relatively small amount, because it has been to a great extent removed by the soda solution, and because its chloride is only slightly soluble. Antimony and arsenic are found among the oxides only in the minutest quantity, their oxides having been dissolved by the soda. In order to obtain the very active sulphides, the following process was em-ployed:—The solutions made strongly acid with hydrochloric acid were precipitated with sulphuretted hydrogen; the sulphides thus precipitated are very active, and are employed for the preparation of polonium; there remain in the solution substances not completely precipitated in presence of excess of hydrochloric acid (bismuth, lead, antimony). To complete the precipitation, the solution is diluted with water, and treated again with sulphuretted hydrogen, which gives a second precipitate of sulphides, much less active than the first, and which have generally been rejected. For the further purification of the sulphides, they are washed with ammo-nium sulphide, which removes the last remaining traces of antimony and arsenic. They are then washed with water and ammonium nitrate, and treated with dilute nitric acid. Complete solution never occurs; there is always an insoluble residue, more or less considerable, which can be treated afresh if it is judged expedient. The solution is reduced to a small volume and precipitated either by ammonia or by excess of water. In both cases the lead and the copper remain in solution; in the second case, a little bismuth, scarcely active at all, remains also in solution.

The precipitate of oxides or basic nitrates is subjected to fractionation in the following manner:—The precipitate is dissolved in nitric acid, and water is added to the solution until a sufficient quantity of precipitate is formed; it must be borne in mind that sometimes the precipitate does not at once appear. The precipitate is separated from the supernatant liquid, and re-dissolved in nitric acid, after which both the liquids thus obtained are re-precipitated with water, and treated as before. The different fractions are combined according to their activity, and concentration is carried out as far as possible. In this way is obtained a very small quantity of a substance of which the activity is very high, but which, nevertheless, has so far only shown bismuth lines in the spectroscope.

There is, unfortunately, little chance of obtaining the isolation of polonium by this means. The method of fractionation just described presents many difficulties, and the case is similar with other wet processes of fractionation. Whatever be the method employed, compounds are readily formed which are absolutely insoluble in dilute or concentrated acids. These compounds can only be re-dissolved by reducing them to the metallic state, e.g., by fusion with potassium cyanide. Considering the number of operations necessary, this circumstance constitutes an enormous difficulty in the progress of the fractionation. This obstacle is the greater because polonium, once extracted from the pitchblende, diminishes in activity. This diminution of activity is slow, for a specimen of bismuth nitrate containing polonium only lost half its activity in eleven months.

No such difficulty occurs with radium. The radio-activity remains throughout an accurate gauge of the concentration; the concentration itself presents no difficulty, and the progress of the work from the start can be constantly checked by spectral analysis.

When the phenomena of induced radio-activity, which will be discussed later on, were made known, it seemed obvious that polonium, which only shows the bismuth lines and whose activity diminishes with time, was not a new element, but bismuth made active by the vicinity of radium in the pitchblende. I am not sure that this opinion is correct. In the course of my prolonged work on polonium, I have noted chemical effects, which I have never observed either with ordinary bismuth or with bismuth made active by radium. These chemical effects are, in the first place, the extremely ready formation of insoluble compounds, of which I have spoken above (especially basic nitrates), and, in the second place, the colour and appearance of the precipitates obtained by adding water to the nitric acid solution of bismuth containing polonium. These precipitates are sometimes white, but more generally of a more or less vivid yellow, verging on red.

The absence of lines other than those of bismuth does not necessarily prove that the substance only contains bismuth, because bodies exist whose spectrum reaction is scarcely visible.

It would be necessary to prepare a small quantity of bismuth containing polonium in as concentrated a condition as possible, and to examine it chemically, in the first place determining the atomic weight of the metal. It has not yet been possible to carry out this research on account of the difficulties of a chemical nature already mentioned.

If polonium were proved to be a new element, it would be no less true that it cannot exist indefinitely in a strongly radio-active condition, at least when extracted from the ore. There are therefore two aspects of the question:—First, whether the activity of polonium is entirely induced by the proximity of substances themselves radio-active, in which case polonium would possess the faculty of acquiring atomic activity permanently, a faculty which does not appear to belong to any substance whatever; second, whether the activity of polonium is an inherent property, which is spontaneously destroyed under certain conditions, and persists under certain other conditions, such as those which exist in the ore. The phenomenon of atomic activity induced by contact is still so little understood, that we lack the ground on which to formulate any opinion on the matter. . . .

PREPARATION OF THE PURE CHLORIDE OF RADIUM.

The method by which I extracted pure radium chloride from barium chloride containing radium consists in first subjecting the mixture of the chlorides to fractional crystallisation in pure water, then in water to which hydrochloric acid has been added. The difference in solubility of the two chlorides is thus made use of, that of radium being less soluble than that of barium.

At the beginning of the fractionation, pure distilled water is used. The chloride is dissolved, and the solution raised to boiling-point, and allowed to crystallise by cooling in a covered capsule. Beautiful crystals form at the bottom, and the supernatant, saturated solution is easily decanted. If part of this solution be evaporated to dryness, the chloride obtained is found to be about five times less active than that which has crystallised out. The chloride is thus divided into two portions, A and B—portion A being more active than portion B. The operation is now repeated with each of the chlorides A and B, and in each case two new portions are obtained. When the crystallisation is finished, the less active fraction of chloride A is added to the more active fraction of chloride B, these two having approximately the same activity. Thus there are now three portions to undergo afresh the same treatment.

The number of portions is not allowed to increase indefinitely. The activity of the most soluble portion diminishes as the number increases. When its activity becomes inconsiderable, it is withdrawn from the fractionation. When the desired number of fractions has been obtained, fractionation of the least soluble portion is stopped (the richest in radium), and it is withdrawn from the remainder.

A fixed number of fractions is used in the process. After each series of operations, the saturated solution arising from one fraction is added to the crystals arising from the following fraction; but if after one of the series the most soluble fraction has been withdrawn, then, after the following series, a new fraction is made from the most soluble portion, and the crystals of the most active portion are withdrawn. By the successive alternation of these two processes, an extremely regular system of fractionation is obtained, in which the number of fractions and the activity of each remains constant, each being about five times as active as the subsequent one, and in which, on the one hand, an almost inactive product is removed, whilst, on the other, is obtained a chloride rich in radium. The amount of material contained in these fractions gradually diminishes, becoming less as the activity increases.

At first six fractions were used, and the activity of the chloride obtained at the end was only 0.1 that of uranium.

When most of the inactive matter has been removed, and the fractions have become small, one fraction is removed from the one end, and another is added to the other end consisting of the active chloride previously removed. A chloride richer in radium than the preceding is thus obtained. This system is continued until the crystals obtained are pure radium chloride. If the fractionation has been thoroughly carried out, scarcely any trace of the intermediate products remain.

At an advanced stage of the fractionation, when the quantity of material in each fraction is small, the separation by crystallisation is less efficacious, the cooling being too rapid and the volume of the solution to be decanted too small. It is then advisable to add water containing a known quantity of hydrochloric acid; this quantity may be increased as the fractionation proceeds.

The advantage gained thus consists in increasing the quantity of the solution, the solubility of the chlorides being less in water acidified with hydrochloric acid than in pure water. By using water containing much acid, excellent separations are effected, and it is only necessary to work with three or four fractions.

The crystals, which form in very acid solution, are elongated needles, those of barium chloride having exactly the same appearance as those of radium chloride. Both show double refraction. Crystals of barium chloride containing radium are colourless, but when the proportion of radium becomes greater, they have a yellow colouration after some hours, verging on orange, and sometimes a beautiful pink. This colour disappears in solution. Crystals of pure radium chloride are not coloured, so that the colouration appears to be due to the mixture of radium and barium. The maximum colouration is obtained for a certain degree of radium present, and this fact serves to check the progress of the fractionation.

I have sometimes noticed the formation of a deposit composed of crystals of which one part remained uncoloured, whilst the other was coloured, and it seems possible that the colourless crystals might be sorted out.

The fractional precipitation of an aqueous solution of barium chloride by alcohol also leads to the isolation of radium chloride, which is the first to precipitate. This method, which I first employed, was finally abandoned for the one just described, which proceeds with more regularity. I have, however, occasionally made use of precipitation by alcohol to purify radium chloride which contains traces of barium chloride. The latter remains in the slightly aqueous alcoholic solution, and can thus be removed.

M. Giesel, who, since the publication of our first researches, has been preparing radio-active bodies, recommends the separation of barium and radium by fractional crystallisation in water from a mixture of the bromides. I can testify that this method is advantageous, especially in the first stages of the fractionation.

DETERMINATION OF THE ATOMIC WEIGHT OF RADIUM.

In the course of my work I determined at intervals the atomic weight of the metal contained in specimens of barium chloride containing radium. With each newly obtained product I carried the concentration as far as possible, so as to have from 0.1 grm. to 0.5 grm. of material containing most of the activity of the mixture. From this small quantity I precipitated with alcohol or with hydrochloric acid some milligrms. of chloride for spectral analysis. Thanks to his excellent method, Demarçay only required this small quantity of material to obtain the photograph of the spark spectrum. I made an atomic weight determination with the product remaining.

I employed the classic method of weighing as silver chloride the chlorine contained in a known weight of the anhydrous chloride. As control experiment, I determined the atomic weight of barium by the same method, under the same conditions, and with the same quantity of material, first 0.5 grm. and then 0.1 grm. The figures obtained were always between 137 and 138. I thus saw that the method gives satisfactory results, even with a very small quantity of material.

The first two determinations were made with chlorides, of which one was 230 times and the other 600 times as active as uranium. These two experiments gave the same figure as the experiment with the pure barium chloride. There was therefore no hope of finding a difference except by using a much more active product. The following experiment was made with a chloride, the activity of which was about 3500 times as great as that of uranium; and this experiment enabled me, for the first time, to observe a small but distinct difference; I found, as the mean atomic weight of the metal contained in this chloride, the number 140, which showed that the atomic weight of radium must be higher than that of barium. By using more and more active products, and obtaining spectra of radium of increasing intensity, I found that the figures obtained rose in proportion. . . .

From its chemical properties, radium is an element of the group of alkaline earths, being the member next above barium.

From its atomic weight also, radium takes its place in Mendeleeff's table after barium with the alkaline earth metals, in the row which already contains uranium and thorium.

CHARACTERISTICS OF THE RADIUM SALTS.

The salts of radium, chloride, nitrate, carbonate, and sulphate, resemble those of barium, when freshly prepared, but they gradually become coloured.

All the radium salts are luminous in the dark.

In their chemical properties, the salts of radium are absolutely analogous to the corresponding salts of barium. However, radium chloride is less soluble than barium chloride; the solubility of the nitrates in water is approximately the same.

The salts of radium are the source of a spontaneous and continuous evolution of heat. . . .

CONCLUSIONS.

I will define, in conclusion, the part I have personally taken in the researches upon radio-active bodies.

I have investigated the radio-activity of uranium compounds. I have examined other bodies for the existence of radio-activity, and found the property to be possessed by thorium compounds. I have made clear the atomic character of the radio-activity of the compounds of uranium and thorium.

I have conducted a research upon radio-active substances other than uranium and thorium. To this end I investigated a large number of substances by an accurate electrometric method, and I discovered that certain minerals possess activity which is not to be accounted for by their content of uranium and thorium.

From this I concluded that these minerals must contain a radio-active body different from uranium and thorium, and more strongly radio-active than the latter metals.

In conjunction with M. Curie, and subsequently MM. Curie and Bémont, I was able to extract from pitchblende two strongly radio-active bodies—polonium and radium.

I have been continuously engaged upon the chemical examination and preparation of these substances. I effected the fractionations necessary to the concentration of radium and I succeeded in isolating pure radium chloride. Concurrently with this work, I made several atomic weight determinations with a very small quantity of material, and was finally able to determine the atomic weight of radium with a very fair degree of accuracy. The work has proved *that radium is a new chemical element.* Thus the new method of investigating new chemical elements, established by M. Curie and myself, based upon radio-activity, is fully justified.

I have investigated the law of absorption of polonium rays, and of the absorbable rays of radium, and have demonstrated that this law of absorption is peculiar and different from the known laws of other radiations.

I have investigated the variation of activity of radium salts, the effect of solution and of heating, and the renewal of activity with time, after solution or after heating.

In conjunction with M. Curie, I have examined different effects produced by the new radio-active substances (electric, photographic, fluorescent, luminous colourations, &c.).

In conjunction with M. Curie, I have established the fact that radium gives rise to rays charged with negative electricity.

Our researches upon the new radio-active bodies have given rise to a scientific movement, and have been the starting-point of numerous researches in connection with new radio-active substances, and with the investigation of the radiation of the known radio-active bodies.

Bibliography of Biographies

AGRICOLA, GEORG

Darmstaedter, E., "Georg Agricola, 1494–1555; Leben und Werk," München, 1926.
Darmstaedter, E., in G. Bugge, "Das Buch der grossen Chemiker," Berlin, 1929. Vol. I, pp. 99–106.

ARRHENIUS, SVANTE

Palmaer, W., in G. Bugge, "Das Buch der grossen Chemiker," Berlin, 1930. Vol. 2, pp. 443–462.
Riesenfeld, E., *Ber.*, **63A:** 1–40 (1930).
Walker, J., *J. Chem. Soc.*, **1928:** 1380–1401.

AVOGADRO, LORENZO ROMANO AMADEO CARLO

Guareschi, I., "Amadeo Avogadro und die Molekulartheorie," Leipzig, 1903. (Kahlbaum's Monographien aus der Geschichte der Chemie—7 hft.)
Meldrum, A., "Avogadro and Dalton," Aberdeen, 1904.

BAEYER, ADOLF

Henrich, F., *J. Chem. Education*, **7:** 1231–1248 (1930).
Partington, J. R., *Nature*, **136:** 669–670 (1935).
Perkin, W. H., *Nature*, **100:** 188–190 (1917).
Perkin, W. H., *J. Chem. Soc.*, **123:** 1520–1546 (1923).
Richter, F., *Ber.*, **68A:** 175–180 (1935).
Willstätter, R., in G. Bugge, "Das Buch der grossen Chemiker," Berlin, 1930. Vol. 2, pp. 321–335.

BECHER, JOHANN JOACHIM

Cohen, E., *Chem. Weekblad*, **37:** 91 (1940).
"Encyclopaedia Britannica," Chicago, 1950. Vol. 3, pp. 285–286.

BERGMAN, TORBERN

Crell, L., *Crell's Ann.*, [1], **7:** 74–96 (1787).
Ferguson, E. G., *J. Chem. Education*, **17:** 555–562 (1940).

BERTHELOT, MARCELLIN

Armstrong, H. E., *Nature*, **120:** 659–663 (1927).
Ashdown, A. A., *J. Chem. Education*, **4:** 1217–1232 (1927).
Boutaric, A. M. A., "Marcellin Berthelot (1827–1907)," Paris, 1927.
Dixon, H. B., *J. Chem. Soc.*, **99:** 2353–2371 (1911).
Färber, E., in G. Bugge, "Das Buch der grossen Chemiker," Berlin, 1930. Vol. 2, pp. 190–199.
Graebe, C., *Ber.*, **41:** 4805–4872 (1908).
Jungfleisch, E., *Bull. soc. chim. France*, [4], **13:** I–CCLX (1913).
Lavasseur, E., "Marcellin Berthelot (1827–1907)," Paris, 1907.
Sabatier, P., *J. Chem. Education*, **3:** 1099–1102 (1926).
Snyder, C., "The Rise of Synthetic Chemistry and Its Founder," New York, 1903.

Berthollet, Claude Louis

Färber, E., in G. Bugge, "Das Buch der grossen Chemiker," Berlin, 1929. Vol. 1, pp. 342–349.
Lemay, P., and R. E. Oesper, *J. Chem. Education,* **23**: 158–165, 230–236 (1946).
Patterson, T., *Chemistry and Industry,* **22**: 99–102 (1944).

Berzelius, Jöns Jacob

"Jacob Berzelius—1779–1848—Reiseerinnerungen aus Deutschland," Berlin, 1948.
Prandtl, W., "Humphry Davy. Jöns Jacob Berzelius," Stuttgart, 1948.
Söderbaum, H. G., in G. Bugge, "Das Buch der grossen Chemiker," Berlin, 1929. Vol. 1, pp. 428–449.
Söderbaum, H. G., "Jöns Jacob Berzelius, Autobiographical Notes," translated by O. Larsell, Baltimore, 1934.
Walden, P., *Z. angew. Chem.,* **43**: 325–329, 351–354, 366–370 (1930).
Wöhler, F., *Ber.,* **8**: 838–852 (1875); *Am. Chemist,* **6**: 131–136 (1875).

Biringuccio, Vannuccio

Johannsen, O., in G. Bugge, "Das Buch der grossen Chemiker," Berlin, 1929. Vol. 1, pp. 70–84.

Black, Joseph

Dobbin, L., *J. Chem. Education,* **12**: 225–226 (1935).
McKie, D., *Annals of Science,* **1**: 101–110 (1936).
Neave, E. W. J., *Isis,* **25**: 372–390 (1936).
Ramsey, W., "Life and Letters of Joseph Black," London, 1918.
Speter, M., in G. Bugge, "Das Buch der grossen Chemiker," Berlin, 1929. Vol. 1, pp. 240–252.

Boerhaave, Hermann

Atkinson, E., *J. Chem. Education,* **19**: 103–108 (1942).
Johnson, S., "Life of Hermann Boerhaave," London, 1834.
Speter, M., in G. Bugge, "Das Buch der grossen Chemiker," Berlin, 1929. Vol. 1, pp. 204–220.

Boyle, Robert

Birch, T., "The Life of the Honourable Robert Boyle," London, 1744.
Boulton, A., "The Theological Works of the Honourable Robert Boyle, Esq.," London, 1715. 3 vols., including a biography.
Färber, E., in G. Bugge, "Das Buch der grossen Chemiker," Berlin, 1929. Vol. 1, pp. 173–191.
Fulton, J., *Isis,* **18**: 77–102 (1932).
Masson, F., "Robert Boyle: A Biography," London, 1914.
McKie, D., *Sci. Progress,* **31**: 55–67 (1936).
More, T. L., "The Life and Works of the Honorable Robert Boyle," New York, 1944.
Sarton, G., *Chymia,* **3**: 155–189 (1950).

Buchner, Eduard

Gordon, N., *J. Chem. Education,* **6**: 1849–1850 (1929).
Harries, C., *Ber.,* **50**: 1843–1876 (1917).

ol. 1,

1895.
ribu-
the

vols.
Life

930.
l. 1,

2,

ne Sammlung von humoristischen Geschichte aus dem Leben von
1," Heidelberg, 1904.
, **41**: 4875–4910 (1908).
Bugge, "Das Buch der grossen Chemiker," Berlin, 1930. Vol. 2,

. *Chem. Education*, **4**: 431–439 (1927); **18**: 253–260 (1941).
Elektrochem., **7**: 608–618 (1900).
Chymia, **3**: 223–241 (1950).
Chem. Soc., **77**: 513–554 (1900).

NISLAO

ll. soc. chim. France, [4], **7**: I–XIII (1910).
J. Chem. Education, **3**: 1361–1367 (1926).
J. Chem. Education, **4**: 836–844 (1927).
J. Chem. Soc., **101**: 1677–1693 (1926).
d M. Speter, in G. Bugge, "Das Buch der grossen Chemiker," Berlin,
, pp. 173–189.

RY

., in G. Bugge, "Das Buch der grossen Chemiker," Berlin, 1929. Vol.
62.
The Life of the Honble. Henry Cavendish including abstracts of his
rtant papers and a critical inquiry into the claims of all alleged dis-
the composition of water," London, 1851.

HEL EUGÈNE

, A., *J. Am. Chem. Soc.*, **11**: 71–79 (1889).
amp, "Michel-Eugène Chevreul, vie intime, 1786–1889," Paris, 1930.
W., *Ber.*, **22**: 1163–1169 (1889).
nd R. E. Oesper, *J. Chem. Education*, **25**: 62–70 (1948).
, *Archeion*, **14**: 6–11 (1932).
Bull. Hist. Medicine, **8**: 419–445 (1940).
E., and L. O. Amberg, *J. Am. Pharm. Assoc.*, **29**: 89–96 (1940).

"Madame Curie. A Biography," translated by Vincent Sheean, Garden
Y., 1938.
"The Radium Woman, the Life of Marie Curie," London, 1940.
H. S., *J. Chem. Education*, **24**: 278–282 (1947).
S., *J. Chem. Soc.*, **1935**: 654–663.

IN

, E. M., "John Dalton, Some Unpublished Letters of Personal and Scien-
erest," Manchester, 1944.
I. F., *J. Chem. Education*, **4**: 22–37 (1927).
. C., "Memoirs of the Life and Scientific Researches of John Dalton,"
, 1854.
, A., *J. Chem. Education*, **3**: 485–491 (1926).
H., "John Dalton," London, 1874.
n, J. P., "John Dalton," New York, 1906.

Neville-Polley, L. J., "John Dalton," London, 1920.
Ostwald, W., in G. Bugge, "Das Buch der grossen Chemiker," Berlin, 1929. V
   pp. 378–385.
Roscoe, H. E., "John Dalton and the Rise of Modern Chemistry," New York,
Roscoe, H. E., "A New View of the Origin of Dalton's Atomic Theory; a Cont
   tion to Chemical History, together with Letters and Documents concernin
   Life and Labours of John Dalton," London, 1896.

DAVY, HUMPHRY

Davy, J., "Memoirs of the Life of Sir Humphry Davy, Bart," London, 1836. 2
Davy, J., "Fragmentary Remains, Literary and Scientific, with a Sketch of His
   and Selections from His Correspondence," London, 1858.
Gregory, J. C., "The Scientific Achievements of Sir Humphry Davy," London, 1
Ostwald, W., in G. Bugge, "Das Buch der grossen Chemiker," Berlin, 1929. Vc
   pp. 405–416.
Paris, J. A., "The Life of Humphry Davy," London, 1831. 2 vols.
Prandtl, W., "Humphry Davy. Jöns Jacob Berzelius," Stuttgart, 1948.
Thorpe, T. E., "Humphry Davy, Poet and Philosopher," London, 1896.

DEVILLE, HENRI ÉTIENNE SAINTE-CLAIRE

Gay, J., "Henri Sainte-Claire Deville—sa vie et ses travaux," Paris, 1889.
Oesper, R. E., and P. Lemay, *Chymia*, **3**: 205–221 (1950).
Pasteur, L., *Compt. rend.*, **93**: 6–9 (1881).

DÖBEREINER, JOHANN WOLFGANG

Henrich, F., *Z. angew. Chem.*, **36**: 482–484 (1923).
Schiff, J., "Briefwechsel zwischen Goethe und Johann Wolfgang Döbereiner (18
   1830)," Weimar, 1914.
Theis, E., *Z. angew. Chem.*, **50**: 46–50 (1937).

DULONG, PIERRE LOUIS

Lemay, P., and R. E. Oesper, *Chymia*, **1**: 171–190 (1948).

DUMAS, JEAN BAPTISTE ANDRÉ

Henrich, F., in G. Bugge, "Das Buch der grossen Chemiker," Berlin, 1930. Vol.
   pp. 53–68.
Hofmann, A. W., *Ber.*, **17**: 947–949 (1884).
Le Blanc, F., *Bull. soc. chim. France*, [2], **42**: 549–559 (1884).
Perkin, W., *J. Chem. Soc.*, **47**: 310–323 (1885).
Urbain, G., *Bull. soc. chim. France*, [5], **1**: 1425–1447 (1934).

FARADAY, MICHAEL

Appleyard, R., "A Tribute to Michael Faraday," New York, 1931.
Ashcroft, E. W., "Faraday," London, 1931.
Bence-Jones, H., "The Life and Letters of Faraday," London, 1870. 2 vols.
Cramp, W., "Michael Faraday and Some of His Contemporaries," London, 193
Crowther, J. A., "The Life and Discoveries of Michael Faraday," London, 191
Gladstone, J. H., "Michael Faraday," London, 1872.
Hadfield, R. A., "Faraday and His Metallurgical Researches," London, 1931.
Jerrold, W., "Michael Faraday; Man of Science," London, 1891.
Martin, T., "Faraday," London, 1934.

Martin, T., "Faraday's Diary, Being the Various Philosophical Notes of Experimental Investigation made by Michael Faraday . . . ," London, 1932–1936. 7 vols. and index.

Newell, L. C., *J. Chem. Education*, **8**: 1493–1522 (1931).

Ostwald, W., in G. Bugge, "Das Buch der grossen Chemiker," Berlin, 1929. Vol. 1, pp. 417–427.

Randall, W. L., "Michael Faraday (1791–1867)," Boston, 1925.

Thompson, S. P., "Michael Faraday, His Life and Work," London, 1898.

Tyndall, J., "Faraday as a Discoverer," London, 1868.

FISCHER, EMIL

Bergmann, M., in G. Bugge "Das Buch der grossen Chemiker," Berlin, 1930. Vol. 2, pp. 408–420.

Darmstaedter, L., and R. E. Oesper, *J. Chem. Education*, **5**: 37–42 (1928).

Fischer, E., "Aus meinem Leben," Berlin, 1922.

Forster, M. O., *J. Chem. Soc.*, **117**: 1157–1201 (1920).

Hösch, K., *Ber.*, **54**: special number, 480 pp. (1921).

Hudson, C. S., *J. Chem. Education*, **19**: 353–357 (1941).

Jacobson, P., *Chem. Ztg.*, **43**: 565–569 (1919).

FRANKLAND, EDWARD

McLeod, H., *J. Chem. Soc.*, **87**: 574–590 (1905).

"Sketches from the Life of Edward Frankland; born January 18, 1825, died August 9, 1899," edited by his daughter, London, 1902.

Wislicenus, J., *Ber.*, **33**: 3847–3874 (1900).

GAY-LUSSAC, JOSEPH LOUIS

Arago, F., *Smithsonian Report*, **1876**: 138–172.

Bloch, M., in G. Bugge, "Das Buch der grossen Chemiker," Berlin, 1929. Vol. 1, pp. 386–404

GEOFFROY, ÉTIENNE-FRANÇOIS

Speter, M., in G. Bugge, "Das Buch der grossen Chemiker," Berlin, 1929. Vol. 1, pp. 221–227.

GERHARDT, CHARLES

Bloch, M., in G. Bugge, "Das Buch der grossen Chemiker," Berlin, 1930. Vol. 2, pp. 92–114.

Gerhardt, C., Jr., "Correspondence de Charles Gerhardt," Paris, 1924.

Grimaux, E., and C. Gerhardt, Jr., "Charles Gerhardt, sa vie, son oeuvre, sa correspondence," Paris, 1900.

Riegel, E. R., *J. Chem. Education*, **3**: 1105–1109 (1926).

Tiffenau, M., *Compt. rend.*, **215**: 214–216 (1942).

GIBBS, JOSIAH WILLARD

Donnan, F., *J. Franklin Inst.*, **199**: 457–484 (1925).

Johnston, J., *J. Chem. Education*, **5**: 507–514 (1928).

Kraus, C. A., *Science*, **89**: 275–282 (1939).

Rukeyser, M., "Willard Gibbs," New York, 1942.

Wilson, E. B., *Sci. Monthly*, **32**: 211–227 (1931).

GLAUBER, JOHANN RUDOLPH

Armstrong, E. V., and C. K. Deischer, *J. Chem. Education*, **19**: 3–8 (1942).
Darmstaedter, L., *Chem. Ztg.*, **50**: 585–586 (1926).
Walden, P., in G. Bugge, "Das Buch der grossen Chemiker," Berlin, 1929. Vol. 1, pp. 151–172.

GOMBERG, MOSES

Schoepfle, C. S., and W. E. Bachmann, *J. Am. Chem. Soc.*, **69**: 2921–2925 (1947).
White, A. H., *Ind. Eng. Chem.*, **23**: 116–117 (1931).

GRAHAM, THOMAS

Gortner, R. A., *J. Chem. Education*, **11**: 279–283 (1934).
Hofmann, A. W., *Ber.*, **2**: 753–780 (1869).
Hofmann, A. W., *Proc. Roy. Soc.*, **18**: xvii–xxvi (1870).
Smith, R. A., "The Life and Work of Thomas Graham," Glasgow, 1884.
Speter, M., in G. Bugge, "Das Buch der grossen Chemiker," Berlin, 1930. Vol. 2, pp. 69–77.

GULDBERG, CATO MAXIMILIAN

Abegg, R., in Ostwald's *Klassiker*, No. 104, "Untersuchungen über die chemischen Affinitäten," Leipzig, 1899. Pp. 172–174.

HESS, GERMAIN HENRI

Leicester, H. M., *J. Chem. Education*, **28**: 581–583 (1951).
Ostwald, W., "Lehrbuch der allgemeinen Chemie," Leipzig, 1887. Vol. 2, pp. 9–13 (This is a survey of the work of Hess only, not of his life.)
Yakovlev, V., "Brockhaus-Efron, Encyclopedic Dictionary," St. Petersburg, 1892. Vol. 8, pp. 583–584. (In Russian.)

HITTORF, JOHANN WILHELM

Anonymous, *J. Chem. Soc.*, **107**: 582–586 (1915).
Goldschmidt, H., *Z. angew. Chem.*, **27**: 657–658 (1914).

HOFMANN, AUGUST WILHELM VON

Lepsius, B., *Ber.*, **51**: 1–54 (1918).
Lepsius, B., in G. Bugge, "Das Buch der grossen Chemiker," Berlin, 1930. Vol. 2, pp. 136–153.
Playfair, L., F. Abel, W. Perkin, and H. Armstrong, *J. Chem. Soc.*, **69**: 575–732 (1896).
Volhard, J., "August Wilhelm von Hofmann. Ein Lebensbild," Berlin, 1902.
Witt, O., *Chem. Industrie*, **15**: 181–184 (1892).

HOOKE, ROBERT

Andrade, E. N. da C., *Nature*, **136**: 358–361 (1935).
De Milt, C., *J. Chem. Education*, **16**: 503–510 (1939).
Robinson, H. W., and W. Adams, "The Diary of Robert Hooke," London, 1935.

INGENHOUSZ, JAN

Read, H. S., "Jan Ingenhousz, Plant Physiologist," *Chronica Botanica*, vol. 11, Nos. 5/6, Waltham, Mass., 1949.

KEKULÉ, FRIEDRICH AUGUST

Anschütz, R., "August Kekulé, Leben und Wirken," Berlin, 1929. 2 vols.
Darmstaedter, L., and R. E. Oesper, *J. Chem. Education*, **4**: 697–702 (1927).
Japp, F. R., *J. Chem. Soc.*, **73**: 97–138 (1898).
Landolt, H., *Ber.*, **29**: 1971–1976 (1896).
Richardson, G., *J. Am. Chem. Soc.*, **18**: 1107–1109 (1896).
Rimbach, E., *Ber.*, **36**: 4613–4640 (1903).
Schultz, G., *Ber.*, **23**: 1265–1312 (1890).
Winderlich, R., in G. Bugge, "Das Buch der grossen Chemiker," Berlin, 1930. Vol. 2, pp. 200–216.

KOLBE, HERMANN

Hofmann, A. W., *Ber.*, **17**: 2809–2812 (1884).
Lockemann, G., in G. Bugge, "Das Buch der grossen Chemiker," Berlin, 1930. Vol. 2, pp. 124–135.
Meyer, E., *J. prakt. Chem.*, [n.s.], **30**: 417–466 (1884).
Perkin, W., *J. Chem. Soc.*, **47**: 323–327 (1885).

KOPP, HERMANN

Bessmertny, B., *Archeion*, **14**: 62–68 (1932).
Lippmann, E. O. von, *Archeion*, **14**: 1–5 (1932).
Ruska, J., *J. Chem. Education*, **14**: 3–12 (1937).
Thorpe, E., *J. Chem. Soc.*, **63**: 779–815 (1893).

KÖRNER, WILHELM

Anschütz, R., *Ber.*, **59**: 75–111 (1926).
Cohen, J. B., *J. Chem. Soc.*, **127**: 2975–2982 (1925).

LAURENT, AUGUSTE

Bloch, M., in G. Bugge, "Das Buch der grossen Chemiker," Berlin, 1930. Vol. 2, pp. 92–114.
Nicklès, J., *Am. J. Science*, **66**: 103–104 (1853).
Tiffeneau, M., "Correspondence de C. Gerhardt, Laurent et Gerhardt," Paris, 1918.

LAVOISIER, ANTOINE LAURENT

Berthelot, M., "La revolution chimique; Lavoisier," Paris, 1890.
Cochrane, J. A., "Lavoisier," London, 1931.
Daumas, M., "Lavoisier," Paris, 1941.
Foster, M. L., "Life of Lavoisier; Antoine-Laurent Lavoisier, His Life and Works," Northampton, 1926.
French, S. J., "Torch and Crucible, the Life and Death of Antoine Lavoisier," Princeton, 1941.
Grimaux, E., "Lavoisier, 1743–1794, d'après sa correspondence, ses manuscrits, ses papiers de famille et d'autres documents inédits," Paris, 1888.
Hartley, H., *Proc. Roy. Soc.* (London), **134B**: 348–377 (1947).
McKie, D., "Antoine Lavoisier, the Father of Modern Chemistry," Philadelphia, 1935.
Metzger, H., *Archeion*, **14**: 31–50 (1932).
Mieli, A., *Archeion*, **14**: 51–56 (1932).
Speter, M., in G. Bugge, "Das Buch der grossen Chemiker," Berlin, 1929. Vol. 1, pp. 304–333.

Le Bel, Joseph Achille

Pope, W. J., *J. Chem. Soc.*, **1930**: 2789–2791.
Wedekind, E., *Z. angew. Chem.*, **43**: 985–986 (1930).

Le Chatelier, Henri Louis

Bodenstein, M., *Ber.*, **72A**: 122–127 (1939).
Desch, C. H., *J. Chem. Soc.*, **1938**: 139–150.
Oesper, R. E., *J. Chem. Education*, **8**: 442–461 (1931).
Pope, W. J., *Nature*, **138**: 711–712 (1936).
Silverman, A., *J. Chem. Education*, **14**: 555–560 (1937).

Lemery, Nicolas

Leroux, M., *Isis*, **7**: 430–432 (1925).

Libavius, Andreas

Darmstaedter, E., in G. Bugge, "Das Buch der grossen Chemiker," Berlin, 1929. Vol. 1, pp. 107–124.

Liebig, Justus von

Berl, E., *J. Chem. Education*, **15**: 553–562 (1938).
Blunck, R., "Justus von Liebig," Berlin, 1938.
Hofmann, A. W., *J. Chem. Soc.*, **28**: 1065–1140 (1875).
Hofmann, A. W., "The Life Work of Liebig in Experimental and Philosophic Chemistry," London, 1876.
Knapp, G. F., *Ber.*, **36**: 1315–1330 (1903).
Knapp, G. F., "Justus von Liebig nach dem Leben gezeichnet," Munchen, 1903.
Oesper, R. E., *J. Chem. Education*, **4**: 1461–1476 (1927).
Schierz, E. R., *J. Chem. Education*, **8**: 223–231 (1931).
Shenstone, W. A., "Justus von Liebig, His Life and Work, 1802–73," New York, 1895.
Volhard, J., "Justus v. Liebig," Leipzig, 1909.
Winderlich, R., in G. Bugge, "Das Buch der grossen Chemiker," Berlin, 1930, Vol. 2, pp. 1–30.

Markovnikov, Vladimir Vasil'evich

Decker, H., *Ber.*, **38**: 4249–4259 (1905).
Leicester, H. M., *J. Chem. Education*, **18**: 53–57 (1941).
Mills, E. J., *J. Chem. Soc.*, **87**: 597–600 (1905).

Mendeleev, Dmitrii Ivanovich

Leicester, H. M., *Chymia*, **1**: 67–74 (1948).
Tilden, W. A., *J. Chem. Soc.*, **95**: 2077–2105 (1908).
Walden, P., *Chem. Ztg.*, **31**: 167–172 (1907).
Walden, P., *Ber.*, **41**: 4719–4800 (1908).
Walden, P., in G. Bugge, "Das Buch der grossen Chemiker," Berlin, 1930. Vol. 2, pp. 241–250.
Winicov, W., *J. Chem. Education*, **14**: 372–375 (1937).

Meyer, Julius Lothar

Bedson, P. P., *J. Chem. Soc.*, **69**: 1403–1439 (1896).
Long, J. H., *J. Am. Chem. Soc.*, **17**: 664–666 (1895).

Seubert, K., *Ber.*, **28R:** 1109–1146 (1895).
Walden, P., in G. Bugge, "Das Buch der grossen Chemiker," Berlin, 1930. Vol. 2, pp. 230–241.

MEYER, VICTOR

Goldschmidt, H., "Zur Erinnerung an Victor Meyer," Heidelberg, 1897.
Henrich, F., in G. Bugge, "Das Buch der grossen Chemiker," Berlin, 1930. Vol. 2, pp. 374–390.
Horowitz, B., *J. Franklin Inst.*, **182:** 363–394 (1916).
Meyer, R., *Ber.*, **41:** 4505–4718 (1908).
Meyer, R., "Victor Meyer. Leben und Werken," Leipzig, 1917.
Thorpe, T., *J. Chem. Soc.*, **77:** 169–206 (1900).
Witt, O., *Chem. Industrie*, **20:** 325–326 (1897).

MITSCHERLICH, EILHARD

Bugge, G., in G. Bugge, "Das Buch der grossen Chemiker," Berlin, 1929. Vol. 1, pp. 450–457.
Mitscherlich, A., "Gesammelte Schriften von Eilhard Mitscherlich," Berlin, 1896.
Williamson, A., *J. Chem. Soc.*, **17:** 440–442 (1864).

MORVEAU, LOUIS BERNARD GUYTON DE

Bouchard, G., "Guyton-Morveau, chimiste et conventionnel (1737–1816)," Paris, 1938.
Speter, M., *Chem. Ztg.*, **54:** 1005–1007 (1930).

NERNST, HERMANN WALTHER

Eggert, J., *Naturwissenschaften*, **31:** 412–415 (1943).
Eggert, J., *Z. physik. chem. Unterricht*, **56:** 43–50 (1943).
Einstein, A., *Sci. Monthly*, **54:** 195–196 (1942).

OSTWALD, WILHELM FRIEDRICH

Bancroft, W. D., *J. Chem. Education*, **10:** 539–542, 609–613 (1933).
Donnan, F. G., *J. Chem. Soc.*, **1933:** 316–332.
Findlay, A., *Nature*, **129:** 750–751 (1932).
Harrow, B., *J. Chem. Education*, **7:** 2697–2700 (1930).
Hillpern, E. P., *Chymia*, **2:** 57–64 (1949).
Nernst, E., *Z. Elektrochem.*, **38:** 337–341 (1932).
Ostwald, W., "Lebenslinien eine Selbstbiographie," Berlin, 1926.
Walden, P., *Ber.*, **65A:** 101–141 (1932).
Walden, P., "Wilhelm Ostwald," Leipzig, 1933.

PARACELSUS (THEOPHRASTUS BOMBASTUS VON HOHENHEIM)

Davis, T. L., *J. Chem. Education*, **5:** 671–681 (1928).
Hartmann, F., "The Life of Phillippus Theophrastus Bombast of Hohenheim, Known by the Name of Paracelsus," London, 1887.
Mook, F., "Theophrastus Paracelsus," Wurzburg, 1876.
Spunda, F., "Paracelsus," Leipzig, 1925.
Stillman, J. M., "Theophrastus Bombastus von Hohenheim Called Paracelsus, His Personality and Influence as Physician, Chemist, and Reformer," Chicago, 1920.
Stoddard, A. M., "The Life of Paracelsus, Theophrastus von Hohenheim, 1493–1541," London, 1911.

Strunz, F., in G. Bugge, "Das Buch der grossen Chemiker," Berlin, 1929. Vol. 1, pp. 85–98.
Strunz, F., *Archeion*, **14**: 76–87, 183–197 (1932).
Swainson, W. P., "Theophrastus Paracelsus, Medieval Chemist," London, 1919.
Telepnef, B., "Paracelsus, a Genius amidst a Troubled World," St. Gallen, 1945.
Titley, A. F., *Ambix*, **1**: 166–183 (1938).
Walker, F., *J. Chem. Education*, **8**: 885–895 (1931).

PASTEUR, LOUIS

Benz, F., "Pasteur, Knight of the Laboratory," New York, 1938.
Bertrand, G., *J. Chem. Education*, **11**: 614–617 (1934).
Compton, P., "The Genius of Louis Pasteur," New York, 1932.
Descour, L., "Pasteur and His Work," translated by A. F. and B. H. Wedd, London, 1922.
Dubos, R. J., "Louis Pasteur, Free Lance of Science," Boston, 1950.
Duclaux, E., "Pasteur, the History of a Mind," Philadelphia, 1920.
Fischer, E., *Ber.*, **28**: 2336–2343 (1895).
Frankland, P., *J. Chem. Soc.*, **71**: 683–743 (1897).
Frankland, P., "Pasteur," New York, 1898.
Holmes, S. S., "Louis Pasteur," New York, 1924.
Koch, R., in G. Bugge,"Das Buch der grossen Chemiker," Berlin, 1930. Vol. 2, pp. 154–172.
Moseley, H. W., *J. Chem. Education*, **5**: 50–56 (1928).
Paget, S., "Pasteur and after Pasteur," London, 1914.
Vallery-Radot, R., "Louis Pasteur, His Life and Labours," translated by Lady C. Hamilton, London, 1885.
Vallery-Radot, R., "The Life of Pasteur," translated by R. S. Devonshire, Garden City, N.Y., 1923; reissue, 1937.

PRIESTLEY, JOSEPH

Bolton, H. C., "Scientific Correspondence of Joseph Priestley . . . together with Copious Biographical, Bibliographical and Explanatory Notes," Philadelphia, 1892.
Browne, C. A., *J. Chem. Education*, **4**: 159–171, 184–199 (1927).
Caven, R. M., "Joseph Priestley, 1733–1804," London, 1933.
Dixon, R. A. M., *J. Chem. Education*, **10**: 149–150 (1933).
Fulton, J. F., and C. H. Peters, "Works of Joseph Priestley, 1733–1804, Preliminary Short Title List," New Haven, 1937.
Hartley, H., *J. Chem. Soc.*, **1933**: 915–920.
Hartog, P. J., *J. Chem. Soc.*, **1933**: 896–902.
Holt, A., "A Life of Joseph Priestley," London, 1931.
Lockemann, G., in G. Bugge, "Das Buch der grossen Chemiker," Berlin, 1929, Vol. 1, pp. 263–273.
Matignon, C., *Bull. soc. chim. France*, [4], **53**: 1313–1331 (1933).
Meldrum, A. N., *J. Chem. Soc.*, **1933**: 902–915.
Newell, L. C., *J. Chem. Education*, **10**: 151–159 (1933).
Peacock, D. H., "Joseph Priestley," New York, 1919.
"Memoirs of Dr. Joseph Priestley, to the Year 1795, Written by Himself; with a Continuation, to the Time of His Decease, by His Son, Joseph Priestley; and Observations on His Writings, by Thomas Cooper, President Judge of the 4th

District of Pennsylvania, and the Rev. William Christie," Northumberland, 1806. 2 vols.

Rutt, J. T., "Life and Correspondence of Joseph Priestley," London, 1831–1832. 2 vols.

Smith, E. F., "Priestley in America, 1794–1804," Philadelphia, 1920.

Thorpe, T. E., "Joseph Priestley," London, 1906.

Walker, W., *Isis*, **21**: 81–97 (1934).

Ware, H., "A Memoir of the Life of Joseph Priestley, Introductory to Views of Christian Truth, Piety, and Morality Selected from the Writings of Joseph Priestley," Cambridge, 1834.

PROUST, JOSEPH LOUIS

Färber, E., *Z. angew. Chem.*, **34**: 245–246 (1921).

Färber, E., in G. Bugge, "Das Buch der grossen Chemiker," Berlin, 1929. Vol. 1, pp. 350–355.

PROUT, WILLIAM

Glasstone, S., *J. Chem. Education*, **24**: 478–481 (1947).

RAOULT, FRANÇOIS-MARIE

Getman, F., *J. Chem. Education*, **13**: 153–155 (1936).

van't Hoff, J. H., *J. Chem. Soc.*, **81**: 969–981 (1902).

RICHTER, JEREMIAS BENJAMIN

Darmstaedter, L., and R. E. Oesper, *J. Chem. Education*, **5**: 785–790 (1928).

Loewig, K. J., "Jeremias Benjamin Richter, der Entdecker der chemischen Proportionen," Breslau, 1874.

Ostwald, W., in G. Bugge, "Das Buch der grossen Chemiker," Berlin, 1929. Vol. 1, pp. 369–377.

Schwarzkopf, P. *Chem. Ztg.*, **31**: 471–475 (1907).

ROUELLE, GUILLAUME-FRANÇOIS

Cap, P., "G. F. Rouelle," Paris, 1842.

Michaud, "Biographie Universelle, Nouvelle Edition." Vol. 36, pp. 585–588.

SCHEELE, CARL WILHELM

Flückiger, F. A., "Zur Erinnerung an Scheele, ein Jahrhundert nach seinem Ableben," Halle, 1886.

Lockemann, G., in G. Bugge, Das Buch der grossen Chemiker," Berlin, 1929, Vol. 1, pp. 274–290.

Urdang, G., "Pictorial Life History of the Apothecary Chemist Carl Wilhelm Scheele," Madison, Wis., 1942.

Zekert, O., "C. W. Scheele; sein Leben und seine Werke," Mittenwald, 1931–1933. 3 vols.

STAHL, GEORG ERNST

Koch, R., in G. Bugge, "Das Buch der grossen Chemiker," Berlin, 1929. Vol. 1, pp. 192–203.

THIELE, FRIEDRICH KARL JOHANNES

Straus, F., *Ber.*, **60A**: 75–132 (1927).

VALENTINE, BASIL (JOHANN THÖLDE)

Fritz, F. E., in G. Bugge, "Das Buch der grossen Chemiker," Berlin, 1929. Vol. 1, pp. 125–141.

VAN HELMONT, JAN BAPTIST

Davis, T. L., *J. Chem. Education*, **5**: 671–681 (1928).
Partington, J. R., *Annals of Science*, **1**: 359–384 (1936).
Redgrove, H. S., "Joannes Baptista van Helmont, Alchemist, Physician, and Philosopher," London, 1922.
Strunz, F., "Johann Baptista van Helmont," Wien, 1907.
Strunz, F., in G. Bugge, "Das Buch der grossen Chemiker," Berlin, 1929. Vol. 1, pp. 142–150.
van Klooster, H. S., *J. Chem. Education*, **24**: 319 (1947).

VAN'T HOFF, JACOBUS HENRICUS

Bruni, G., *Smithsonian Report*, **1913**: 767–789.
Cohen, E., "Jacobus Hendricus van't Hoff," Leipzig, 1899.
Cohen, E., "J. H. van't Hoff, sein Leben und Werken," Leipzig, 1912.
Cohen, E., in G. Bugge, "Das Buch der grossen Chemiker," Berlin, 1930. Vol. 2, pp. 391–407.
Faulk, C. W., *J. Chem. Education*, **11**: 355–359 (1934).
Jorrissen, W. P., "J. H. van't Hoff's Amsterdamer Periode 1877–1895," Helder, 1912.
Ostwald, W., *Ber.*, **44**: 2219–2252 (1911).
Walker, J., *J. Chem. Soc.*, **103**: 1127–1143 (1913).

VOLTA, ALESSANDRO

Bilancioni, G., *Archeion*, **8**: 351–363 (1927).
Cantoni, G., "La Mente di Alessandro Volta," Pavia, 1878.
Duschnitz, B., *Z. Elektrochem.*, **35**: 822–825 (1929).
Mieli, A., "Alessandro Volta," Roma, 1927.
"Nel 1° centenario della morte di A. Volta. Discorsi e note," Milano, 1927.

WAAGE, PETER

Abegg, R., in Ostwald's *Klassiker*, No. 104, "Untersuchungen über die chemischen Affinitäten," Leipzig, 1899. Pp. 174–178.
Anonymous, *J. Chem. Soc.*, **77**: 591–592 (1900).

WERNER, ALFRED

Anonymous, *J. Chem. Education*, **7**: 1732–1735 (1930).
Berl, E., *J. Chem. Education*, **19**: 153–154 (1942).
Karrer, P., *Helv. Chim. Acta.*, **3**: 196–232 (1920).
Morgan, G. T., *J. Chem. Soc.*, **117**: 1639–1648 (1920).
Pfeiffer, P., *J. Chem. Education*, **5**: 1090–1098 (1928).

WILHELMY, LUDWIG FERDINAND

Quincke, G., in Ostwald's *Klassiker*, No. 29, "Uber das Gesetz nach welchem die Einwirkung der Sauren auf den Rohrzucker stattfindet von Ludwig Wilhelmy," Leipzig, 1891. Pp. 45–47.

WILLIAMSON, ALEXANDER WILLIAM

Foster, G. C., *J. Chem. Soc.*, **87**: 605–618 (1905).

WÖHLER, FRIEDRICH

Hofmann, A. W., *Ber.*, **15**: 3127–3290 (1882).
Lepsius, B., *Ber.*, **65A**: 89–94 (1932).
Smith, E. F., *J. Chem. Education*, **5**: 1554–1557 (1928).
Valentin, J., "Friedrich Wöhler," Stuttgart, 1949.
van Klooster, H. S., *J. Chem. Education*, **21**: 158–170 (1944).
Warren, W. H., *J. Chem. Education*, **5**: 1539–1553 (1928).
Winderlich, R, in G. Bugge, "Das Buch der grossen Chemiker," Berlin, 1930. Vol. 2, pp. 31–52.

WOLLASTON, WILLIAM HYDE

Ferguson, E. G., *J. Chem. Education*, **18**: 3–7 (1941).

WURTZ, CHARLES ADOLPHE

Bugge, G., in G. Bugge, "Das Buch der grossen Chemiker," Berlin, 1930. Vol. 2, pp. 115–123.
Friedel, C., *Bull. soc. chim. France*, [2], **43**: I–LXXX (1885).
Friedel, C., "Notice sur la vie et les travaux de Charles Adolphe Wurtz," Paris, 1885.
Hofmann, A. W., *Ber.*, **17**: 1207–1211 (1884).
Hofmann, A. W., "Adolphe Wurtz Ein Lebensbild," Braunschweig, 1888.
Perkin, W., *J. Chem. Soc.*, **47**: 328–329 (1885).
Urbain, G., *Bull. soc. chim. France*, [5], **1**: 1425–1447 (1934).

Name Index

Page numbers in **boldface** type refer to citation material

A

Abegg, R., 468, 538, 544
Abel, F., 538
Adams, W., 538
Adet, 181
Agricola, G., ix, 1, 4, **10-16,** 21, 31, 533
Albertus Magnus, 3
Amberg, L. O., 535
Ammonius, 13
Ampère, A. M., 231, 232, 365, 407–410
Andrade, E. N. da C., 538
Anschütz, R., 539
Appleyard, R., 536
Arago, F., 276, 277, 296, 537
Aristotle, 1–3, 24
Armstrong, E. V., ix, 538
Armstrong, H. E., 533, 538
Arrhenius, S., 401, 453, 471, **483–490,** 491, 493, 533
Ashcroft, E. W., 536
Ashdown, A. A., 533
Atkinson, E., 534
Avicenna, 16
Avogadro, L. R. A. C., 215, **231–238,** 258, 275, 276, 292, 293, 406–410, 434, 453, 455, 457, 458, 484, 487, 533

B

Babo, C. H. L. von, 471
Bachmann, W. E., 538
Bacon, F., 64
Bacon, R., 3
Baeyer, A., 459, **465–467,** 508, 533
Bailey, C., 208
Baker, H., 47, 48, 126
Balard, A. J., 102, 243, 382
Bancroft, W. D., 541
Banks, J., 142, 238, 239
Barry, F., viii
Bartow, V., ix
Bauer, G. (*see* Agricola)
Baumé, A., 181, 192

Becher, J. J., **55–58,** 63, 77, 154, 533
Becquerel, H., 521
Bedson, P. P., 540
Beilstein, F. K., 345
Bemmelen, van, 333
Bémont, G., 521, 522, 531
Bence-Jones, H., 536
Benz, 541
Bérard, 297
Bergman, T., **92–101,** 153, 192–194, 197, 205, 392, 406, 533
Bergmann, M., 537
Berl, E., 540, 544
Berthelot, D., 231
Berthelot, M., 309, 410, **428–431,** 445, 459, 470, 506, 533, 539
Berthollet, A., 296
Berthollet, C. L., 92, 102, 109, 179, 181, 186, 190, **192–201,** 202, 205, 206, 208, 216, 238, 243, 250, 254, 294–296, 396, 468, 534
Bertrand, G., 541
Berzelius, J. J., viii, 206, 212, 238, **258–268,** 269, 272, 273, 276, 306, 308, 309, 311, 312, 316, 318, 320, 327, 329, 333, 336, 350, 351, 365, 369, 379, 384, 385, 388, 400, 402, 406, 408–410, 417, 491, 506, 534, 536
Bessmertny, B., 539
Bewly, 124
Bilancioni, G., 544
Billinger, R. D., ix
Bineau, 411
Biot, J. B., 276, 277, 296, 374, 376, 377
Birch, T., 33, 534
Biringuccio, V., ix, 1, **4–10,** 28, 534
Black, J., **80–91,** 134, 142, 154, 189, 534
Blagden, 471
Bloch, M., 537, 539
Blunck, R., 540
Bodenstein, M., 354, 540
Boerhaave, H., **63–67,** 170, 534
Bolton, H. C., 542
Bonnet, C., 126, 127

547